oz
W
GUIDE

1998

FOURTEENTH EDITION

Reviews of previous editions of Oz *Clarke's Wine Guide*

'…cram-full of the straightforward, practical info you really need to know. In other words, "Where from? How good? How much?"' *Manchester Evening News*

'Oz relentlessly pulls the cork on the old-fashioned wine snobs. This no-nonsense guide gives the amateur wine enthusiast the confidence to explore wine…in an informal yet informed way.' *Daily Mirror*

'Packed with insider information and opinion, and worth every penny.' Derek Cooper

'…the guide gets better with every vintage. Clarke writes with enthusiasm virtually steaming off the page. Here is someone who loves wine.' *The Guardian*

'If you haven't bought a copy, there is little hope for you.' *The Sunday Telegraph*

'An enthusiastic, opinionated and entertaining survey of the world's wines and a price guide to wines on the shelves of Britain.' *The Sunday Times*

'…typically up-to-date, irreverent but informative.' *The Independent*

'Scholarly, funny and thought-provoking.' Robert Parker

OZ CLARKE'S
WINE
GUIDE

1998
FOURTEENTH EDITION

'WEBSTER'S'
THE COMPLETE WINE
BUYER'S HANDBOOK

WEBSTERS
LITTLE, BROWN
LONDON

Oz Clarke's Wine Guide *is an annual* publication. **Please use the questionnaire at the back of the book to send us suggestions for the 1999 edition.**

Wine Editor Margaret Rand
Editor Bill Evans
Price Guides Editor Lorna Bateson
Assistant Price Guides Editor Julie Ross
Editorial Assistants Paul Bones, Andrew Brown, Sarah Carley, Chris Drennan, Sophie Howard, Emma Richards, Scott Wells
Art Editor Christopher Howson
Database Consultant Alexandra Boyle
Indexer Naomi Good
Editorial Director Claire Harcup
Project Art Director Nigel O'Gorman

Advertising Sales
Logie Bradshaw Media Limited,
Strathallan House, Fernville Lane,
Midland Road, Hemel Hempstead,
Herts HP2 4LS
tel 0144 2233331, fax 0144 2231131

Created and designed by
Websters International Publishers Limited,
Axe and Bottle Court, 70 Newcomen Street,
London SE1 1YT
in association with
Little, Brown and Company (UK),
Brettenham House, Lancaster Place,
London WC2E 7EN

Oz Clarke's Wine Guide 1998 Edition
© Websters International Publishers

ISBN 0-316-64148-0

Printed and bound in the UK by
Clays Ltd, St Ives plc

CONTENTS

INTRODUCTION

I have seen the future and the future is – red! What, as in 'red wine'? Surely we drink twice as much white wine as red. Don't we? And isn't red a man's drink – and a rather middle-aged man's drink at that? Doesn't sound quite right for the biggest growth market in wine – those drinkers who are both young and female.

Well, that's what I would have said if I hadn't been chatting to the people who control about three-quarters of the wine we drink in this country – the buyers for the supermarkets and the high-street chains. And they all confirm, with a mixture of trepidation and excitement, that the future is red.

I mean, just look at what's happened to our buying habits. Two years ago, only 30 per cent of the wine Sainsbury's sold was red. Now it is half the total. The other high-street stores and supermarkets report exactly the same massive shift. Last autumn Safeway relaunched their range – and had run out of all their top reds before Christmas. So they revised their forecast of red sales upwards, amongst other things placing the largest single order that the two Australian giants Hardy and Southcorp had ever received. By the spring, they'd run out again, and had to hike up their red forecasts one more time. By the time you read this they'll be selling twice as much red wine as they were a couple of years ago.

BLANC CHECK

It's all the fault of Chardonnay. Before the 1980s, white wine drinkers here generally had a rather gloomy choice to make between Muscadet and Mâcon Blanc, white Bordeaux or Soave. But then the first bottles of Aussie Chardonnay hit our shops – sunshine in a bottle, all fruit flavours and lashings of oak; Ferrari flavours at a Ford Fiesta price. The wine drinker's life was never the same again: Chardonnay became the wine we all drank, on all occasions, with food, or without.

And once the Australians had shown the way, the rest of the world dived in, planting thousands upon thousands of acres of Chardonnay vines to try to satisfy the thirsty world. Every major wine-producing country decided that the future was golden with a little streak of green: that the future was Chardonnay.

But alarm bells were ringing long ago for the more far-sighted wine experts. After Chardonnay, what? The search for the second wave of white was on. Sauvignon Blanc had already created a niche for itself as a sharper, greener alternative to Chardonnay, but there are loads of other grapes, and they have been enthusiastically promoted over the last few years. So now we have an unparalleled choice of white wine in this country: Riesling from Germany, Australia, France, New Zealand; Sémillon from France, Australia and South Africa; honeyed Marsanne and Roussanne from France and Australia; Chenin – oaked or unoaked – from all over the southern hemisphere; Viura, Verdejo, Vermentino, Viognier in all its perfumed glory. We've got a bewildering choice of whites to follow on from Chardonnay. Pity we're passing them up and reaching for the red. But why?

Okay, I've always thought that people who get genuinely interested in wine are likely to gravitate towards red because of the far wider range of taste and stylistic experiences, and far greater possibilities for aging the wines. But I have pushed as hard as anyone for drinkers to try the new whites, perhaps failing to catch sight of a crucial fact that was shown up by our tastings to find this year's Best Buys: formula wine-making.

More and more whites from all over the world are being made to a provide a standard measure of soft ripe fruit of a vaguely peachy sort, a streak of lemony acidity to whet the palate and a sprinkling of spicy oak and richness – in other words, they're direct if more subtle successors to those first Aussie Chardonnays. Obviously there will always be wonderful, individual whites, but increasingly whites are lumped together, bought to a price point and general style rather than with any real passion and enthusiasm. And the consumers are not fooled. Wine enthusiasts are inquisitive souls, and they're not going to be satisfied by white wines that are in danger of tumbling into the status of a commodity.

IN THE RED?

Yet, if everyone has been frantically expanding their white vineyards, won't we run short of red? Well, yes and no. One of the most distressing phenomena of the '90s is illustrated by the quip that, if you want to find out what the next great wine fashion will be, check which grape variety the growers are ripping up fastest. It was only when ancient Shiraz and Grenache vines were being torn up and replaced by Chardonnay in Australia's Barossa Valley that a doughty band of producers started making superb sumptuous reds that caught our imaginations so strongly that we threw money at them for our share. A doubling, a tripling of the amounts the local growers were paid preserved priceless areas of ancient vines. It was the same in California with ancient Zinfandel and Mourvèdre vines, in southern Italy with irreplaceable old Primitivo and Negroamaro vines and even in South Africa, where the indigenous Pinotage grape suddenly gave the Cape the red wine standard bearer it had lacked – just as growers were rooting out their old Pinotage vines in favour of Cabernet and Chardonnay. The price of Pinotage grapes has quadrupled in the last four years, and, of course, the uprooting programme has been replaced by – yes – a replanting programme. And all these obscure objects of desire had one thing in common – they made wines with *loads* of flavour. And it is *loads* of flavour upon which the rush to red is based.

For such last-chance-saloon rescue acts, British drinkers can take a lot of the credit. And since none of these varieties was remotely fashionable until we took up the cudgels on their behalf, another reassuring trend is evident: this shift to red is spread far more widely than the surge to white that characterized the '80s and early '90s. Then, we got stuck in a Chardonnay warp, but the newly popular red varieties are so distinct that they can all establish themselves in their own right without pausing to pay homage to the flavours of Cabernet Sauvignon and Merlot.

At the extreme, let's take the three most despised and derided grape varieties from the South of France – Carignan, Alicante Bouschet and Aramon. When you get southern France's star winemaker, Aimé Guibert of Mas de Daumas Gassac, producing a wonderful herb-scented, sweet-textured Aramon; when you get Segu Ollé creating a delightful spice and pepper red from 40-year-old Carignan vines in Chile's Maule Valley; or Chile's Concha y Toro winery finding a patch of ancient Alicante Bouschet vines and making a tar-dark red resplendent in black plum and treacle richness – then every red vine in the world is a valid target for a committed winemaker to get to work on. There is no such thing as a non-legitimate red variety anymore.

GOLDEN HANDSHAKE

This red wine surge is excellent news for the world of wine: it will preserve old vineyard areas and old varieties, encourage traditionalists and iconoclasts alike, and provide us with a spectrum of pleasure and excitement that means the red revolution will run and run.

So, thank you, Chardonnay, for leading the way, but just for now, I have seen the future and the future is bright, glowing, mouth-filling, heart-warming red.

HOW TO USE THIS BOOK

There's no right way to use this book, other than to help you to buy quality wines at competitive prices. That's what every page is geared towards.

We kick off with some specific wine recommendations. The Best Buys are the pick of the crop from the UK's top merchants; the Supermarket Selection has been chosen from a huge array of own-brand wines to help you take advantage of low prices and ready availability. Then we've let the supermarket wine-buyers have their turn, dreaming up their Ideal Cellars alongside my own.

After that the choice is yours – from over 10,000 wines from all around the world. If you know what you want, turn straight to the Price Guides. These are the pages on which we have collated the current retail prices of the thousands of wines we hold on our computer database. Just a glance at the price of the same wine from one merchant to another can show why this information is so valuable – the difference can be dramatic.

In addition, many wines are in limited distribution: it's therefore of crucial importance to find out where the wines are stocked, and whether they'll sell by mail order. And that's where the Merchant Directory comes in: it gives you the lowdown on over 100 of the UK's top wine merchants. The merchants included in this year's guides have been chosen on the basis of the quality and interest of their lists, and we've picked out some notable wines from each of them. If you want to find local suppliers, merchants are listed by region in the Who's Where directory on page 448; if you want to find a specialist in a particular country's wines, you'll find a list at the beginning of each country's Price Guides.

But buying wine can feel like a lucky dip when you are faced with shelves or lists full of unfamiliar names. The chapters on the wine-producing countries of the world will help you to develop a nose for the wines that suit your palate. They provide a quick introduction and a guide to the grapes, wines styles, regions and producer names, plus a review of recent vintages – in other words, a complete run-down of what's on the bottle label.

To get the most out of the Price Guides in the book, please remember that they are not meant to replace up-to-date merchants' lists. What they *do*, however, is give you a unique opportunity to compare prices; to develop a sense of what you can expect to pay for any given wine; to spot a bargain; to work out what you can afford – *and to find it.* This book is an invaluable reference whenever you are ordering or buying wine.

It is our aim to make sure this *Guide* improves every year: for this edition we have introduced the Supermarket Selection, extended the Merchant Directory and listed exact prices for all the wines in the Price Guides. We hope you find the *Guide* easy and rewarding to use. Please let us know what you think by returning the tear-out questionnaire at the back of the book. That way we can produce an even better *Guide* next year – and you could win a case of wine from a top merchant.

SYMBOLS AND ABBREVIATIONS

In the Price Guides, the letters in brackets are abbreviations for the names of the stockists for each of the wines listed. The key to these abbreviations is on page 10 and full details of these and other merchants appear in the Merchant Directory on pages 413–47.

★–★★★★★ These star ratings appear in the Producers Who's Who sections, and apply to the quality of wine currently being made by a producer, ranging from sound to world class. A star in brackets (★) indicates that the producer can attain that quality but does not always do so. We rate wines, not reputations.

£ This symbol is used in the Bordeaux chapter to denote producers that are particularly good value – though that's not the same as saying that they're cheap.

EC and **IB** See Bordeaux Price Guides.

HOW THE PRICE GUIDES WORK

We hope you find the Price Guides fairly self explanatory, but to make full use of them you should be aware of the following:

● All prices listed are *per bottle inclusive of VAT*, unless otherwise stated. The prices we list are those which applied in the late spring/early summer of 1997. When comparing prices remember that some wine merchants sell only by the case. In this instance, we have arrived at a bottle price by dividing by 12 the VAT-inclusive price of a single case. Where merchants who sell by the case will sell cases of mixed bottles, we have used the bottle price that would apply in a mixed case.

● Wines are listed in price bands – under £5, £5 to £5.99, and so on – and by vintage. Price bands run from the lowest to the highest. Vintages run from the most recent to the oldest. Within these two categories the wines are listed in alphabetical order.

● Within the price bands, stockists are listed using the abbreviations over the page after each entry in ascending order of price. The same wine may fall into more than one price band, but before you get too agitated about variations in price, remember that wine warehouses, for example, often come out much cheaper than individual merchants because you have to buy by the case, they do not deliver, they do not have smart high street premises to maintain, and

so on. Equally, there's no getting away from the fact that the price of a given wine sometimes varies wildly for no good reason.

● When clubs have both member and non-member prices we have used the *non-member* prices.

BORDEAUX PRICE GUIDES

The red Bordeaux Price Guides are a special case. All châteaux are listed alphabetically regardless of class, with prices for each château given in order of vintage from the most recent to the oldest. There are no price bands in this section.

There are some dramatic price variations here – some are to do with keen pricing and the reverse; more often it will be because claret is now (for better or for worse) an investment medium and is therefore highly responsive to market pressures. A merchant buying wine en primeur in Bordeaux on Monday *afternoon* may pay 25 per cent more than the going rate that morning. Replacement stocks over the years will vary in cost, and currency movements will also be a factor.

EC and **IB** (*ex-cellars* and *in bond*) A wine quoted EC is offered on an en primeur basis (in Bordeaux or at the châteaux); one quoted IB is offered in bond (in the UK). All EC and IB prices are **per case**.

The EC price simply includes the price of the wine in the bottle and excludes shipping, duties and taxes such as VAT. The EC price is usually payable when the wine is offered in the summer following the vintage. Other costs (including VAT on both invoices) become payable when the wine is shipped.

The *crus classés* and better *bourgeois* are shipped two years later, the *petits châteaux* and the lesser *bourgeois* after a year. You should check beforehand the exact terms of sale with your merchant who will give you a projection of the final 'duty paid delivered' price at current rates of shipping, duty and VAT.

MERCHANT NAME CODES

These are the merchants whose prices are featured in the Price Guides. The abbreviations are listed in brackets along with the price per bottle for each of the wines they stock. You will find full details of the services they offer in the Merchant Directory on pages 413–47.

AD	Adnams	LON	Longford Wines
AME	Amey's Wines	MAJ	Majestic
AS	Ashley Scott	MAR	Marks & Spencer
ASD	ASDA	MV	Morris & Verdin
AUR	Stéphane Auriol Wines	NA	Nadder Wines Ltd
AUS	Australian Wine Centre	NEW	New London Wine
AV	Averys of Bristol	NEZ	Le Nez Rouge
BAN	Adam Bancroft	NI	James Nicholson
BEN	Bennetts	NO	The Nobody Inn
BER	Berry Bros. & Rudd	OD	Oddbins
BIB	Bibendum	PEN	Penistone Court Wine Cellars
BO	Booths	PIP	Christopher Piper Wines
BOD	Bordeaux Direct	PLA	Terry Platt
BOT	Bottoms Up	POR	Portland Wine Co
BU	Butlers Wine Cellar	QUE	Quellyn Roberts
BUT	Bute Wines	RAE	Raeburn Fine Wines
BY	Anthony Byrne	REI	Reid Wines (1992) Ltd
CAP	Cape Province Wines	RES	La Réserve
CB	Corney & Barrow	RIP	Howard Ripley
CHA	Châteaux Wines	ROB	Roberson
CO	CWS (Co-op)	ROS	Rose Tree Wine Company
COU	Country Wine Merchant Ltd	RSJ	RSJ Wine Company
CRO	Croque-en-Bouche	SAF	Safeway
DI	Direct Wine	SAI	J Sainsbury
DOM	Domaine Direct	SAT	Satchells
EL	Eldridge, Pope & Co	SO	Somerfield/Gateway
ELL	Ben Ellis Wines	SOM	Sommelier Wine Co
FA	Farr Vintners	STA	Frank Stainton Wines
FIZ	Fine Wines of New Zealand	SUN	Sunday Times Wine Club
FLE	Le Fleming Wines	TAN	Tanners
FOR	Forth Wines Ltd	TES	Tesco
FUL	Fuller's	THR	Thresher
GAL	Gallery Wines	TW	T & W Wines
GAU	Gauntleys	UB	The Ubiquitous Chip
GN	Great Northern Wine Co	UN	Unwins
GOE	Goedhuis & Co	VA	Valvona & Crolla
GRAP	Grape Ideas	VIC	Victoria Wine
GRE	Peter Green & Co	VIG	La Vigneronne
HA	John Harvey & Sons	VIN	Vintage Wines Ltd
HAH	Haynes Hanson & Clark	WAI	Waitrose
HAL	Halves	WAT	Waterloo Wine Co
HAW	Roger Harris Wines	WATT	David J Watt
HIC	Hicks & Don	WHI	Whitesides of Clitheroe
HIG	High Breck Vintners	WIW	Wines of Westhorpe Ltd
HOG	J E Hogg	WR	Wine Rack
JON	S H Jones	WRI	Wright Wine Co
KWI	KwikSave	WS	Wine Society
LAY	Lay & Wheeler	WY	Peter Wylie Fine Wines
LAYT	Laytons	YAP	Yapp Brothers
LEA	Lea & Sandeman	YOU	Noel Young Wines

BEST BUYS

I thought last year's results were good, but this year the sheer pleasure of the tasting, and the challenging, inspired flavours that so many wines exhibited were an absolute delight

Wow! What a tasting. We invited all the wine merchants featured in this *Guide* last year to send in what they considered to be the best-value tasty, characterful wines on their lists – any style, any price. Then we settled down to the happy task of choosing the best of the merchants' best. And Best Buys don't come better than this year's winners.

The results also show that the old order is definitely changing. My top dozen features seven different nations. But France wasn't among them. Nor were Italy or Germany. Yet Canada was, and Portugal, Spain and New Zealand, too. But they all trailed the king of flavour – Australia.

Twenty wines were snapping at the heels of the top dozen and we had a few good fizzes. I've also made bargain selections at the £4 and £5 price points; here, Australia was less impressive and the field was swamped by South America.

Finally, I've picked a separate selection of Old-World Champions – wines which display the best of the more restrained, traditional European flavours.

Wines in each section are ranked in order of merit. Non-vintage Champagnes are marked NV; other non-vintage wines are simply undated.

MY 1998 TOP DOZEN

A thrilling bunch of wines – and not one of them over £10 a bottle. Sure, they're not the most famous wines in the world – that's why they aren't at ridiculous prices. My kind of wine. Yours too

① **1995 Tim Adams The Fergus, Clare Valley (red; Australia), £8.99, Australian Wine Centre**
One of the most irresistibly original reds in the world, with so many gorgeous flavours all swooning about together, they're almost impossible to describe. Here are just a few: Dr Collis Browne's, marron glacé, mint and eucalyptus, thyme and root ginger and the autumn pepperiness of a fresh-peeled conker. Now try it!

② **1994 The Willows Vineyard Shiraz, Barossa Valley (red; Australia), £7.99, Australian Wine Centre**
Massive treacly monster, thick with the richness of toffee, black plums, black cherries and bacon. Like a great doorstep of fresh white bread, half an inch of butter and half a jar of blackcurrant jam.

③ **1996 David Wynn Unwooded Shiraz (red; Australia), £6.99, Adnams**
A deep purple gobful of sweet damson fruit, the smooth soothing texture of cream and the scent of violets tinged with distant bonfire smoke. (*Also available from Sommelier Wine Co.*)

④ **1995 Quinta do Crasto, Douro (red; Portugal), £5.75, Oddbins**
More violets, gloriously scented, and more damson fruit as well in a soft, fragrant wine from the Douro Valley in Portugal that also offers a suggestion of almond trees in flower and a sprinkling of cinnamon spice.

⑤ **Matusalem, González Byass (sherry; Spain), £9.99/half-bottle, Safeway**

Fabulous dark, sultry wine with every brown flavour you can think of lurking in its depths. Sultanas, dates, Christmas pudding and Harrogate toffee, brown treacle and burnt currants at the bottom of a fruit cake.

⑥ **1995 Chateau des Charmes Late Harvest Riesling (sweet white; Canada), £6.95, Grape Ideas**

Well, here's a surprise. A Canadian wine in the top 12?! Yup. They're making brilliant sweet wines now in both Ontario and British Columbia that are rich yet finely balanced with acidity and this one has a delightful flavour of angelica and ripe Williams pears and just a hint of toast. *(Also available from Nadder Wines Ltd.)*

⑦ **1994 Elyse Zinfandel, Napa Valley (red; United States), £9.58, Bibendum**

A tangled mass of bramble and briar, the scent of sloes stewed together with cranberries and poured over a bread-and-butter pudding. Old-fashioned blockbuster.

⑧ **1996 David Wynn Unwooded Chardonnay (white; Australia), £6.99, Adnams**

When the fruit is ripe enough and the winemaker is as good as Adam Wynn, you get a gorgeous unoaked Chardie, full of fresh peach fruit and honey richness, but

with appetizing hints of ginger, green herbs, lemon and salt.

⑨ **1995 Tim Adams Semillon, Clare Valley (white; Australia), £8.99, Australian Wine Club**

Challenging, original flavours from one of Australia's great traditionalists. This is still very young and will age for years yet, but is showing a lanolin-coated blend of leather, toast and cream all holding the fort as the searing lime zest tackles your tonsils. *(Also available from Wine Society and Tesco.)*

⑩ **1996 Chapel Hill Unwooded Chardonnay (white; Australia), £7.99, Australian Wine Club**

Another superb unwooded Chardie from a star winemaker – Pam Dunsford. Fresh but soft fruit like fluffy peach and apple flesh is wrapped in honey yet spruced up with lemon zest and angelica.

⑪ **1996 Palliser Estate Sauvignon Blanc, Martinborough (white; New Zealand), £7.65, Anthony Byrne**

Really leads the way in NZ's 96 vintage with a wine of stinging lime zest acidity, yet juicy exotic passion fruit and pomegranate tropical ripeness.

⑫ **1995 Casablanca Cabernet Sauvignon, Santa Isabel Estate (red; Chile), £6.99, Oddbins**

Gorgeous fruity red, piled full of sweet blackcurrant fruit and mint yet balanced with some serious tannins and acidity.

THE RUNNERS UP

Another pack of excellent wines, all exciting in their own right, and some so cheap you'd think they must have got their pounds and pence mixed up

① **1996 Water Wheel Vineyards Chardonnay (white; Australia), £7.99, Australian Wine Centre**

Here's your big, oaky Aussie Chardonnay – a great rich mouthful of peachy fruit, toast and toffee that will make your head swirl.

② **1996 Villa Maria Private Bin Sauvignon Blanc, Marlborough (white; New Zealand), £6.49, Thresher**

Widely available classic Kiwi Sauvignon with enough passion fruit, coffee beans, green grass and grapefruit zest to make your tastebuds shake. *(Also available from Wine Rack, Bottoms Up, Wine Society, Ben Ellis Wines, Waitrose, Sainsbury's and Booths.)*

③ 1995 Carmen Reserve Merlot, Rapel (red; Chile), £5.99, Grape Ideas

Beautifully crunchy red with a juicy fat texture of blackcurrants and plums, coconut and vanilla that just gobbles up the underlying tannin. *(Also available from Berry Bros. & Rudd and Portland Wine Co.)*

④ 1994 Hollick Wilgha Shiraz-Malbec-Cabernet, Coonawarra (red; Australia), £8.20, Lay & Wheeler

Original blend showing Coonawarra at its best – mulberry, pastry and mum's blackcurrant jam elegantly balanced.

⑤ 1996 Basa (white; Spain), £4.25, Adnams

Unusual but intriguing dry white from Spain, weighty but not heavy, balancing nectarine skins and angelica with green pepper and fresh cut grass.

⑥ 1995 Chilean Cabernet Merlot, Vinicola las Taguas (red), £3.99, ASDA

What quality at £3.99! This is raw-boned red, packed with blackcurrant and coffee bean scent yet seared with tannin.

⑦ 1995 Blanck Tokay Pinot Gris, Patergarten (white; Alsace), £10.50, Lay & Wheeler

Lovely gentle white with the mellow flavours of a warm autumn – honey, and lime, orchard fruit left just too long on the bough and a sense of good earth, lovingly tended over the years.

⑧ 1994 Gigondas, Cuvée de la Tour Sarrazine (red; Rhône), £8.70, Tanners

Excellent burly Rhône red that starts off tasting of wild red cherries but this rapidly transforms into blackberry, sandalwood and a squeeze of bayleaf.

⑨ 1995 Penfolds Clare Valley Chardonnay-Semillon (white; Australia), £5.99, Safeway

An irresistible blend of creamy custard, the flesh of a white peach and a lick of lime juice and leather.

⑩ 1994 St Hallett Blackwell Shiraz, Barossa (red; Australia), £7.99, Australian Wine Centre

Deep, soft, attractive mix of stewed black plums, bacon smoke and cream.

⑪ 1994 Elyse Nero Misto, Napa Valley (red; United States), £8.75, Bibendum

An excellent old-fashioned concoction of California's half-forgotten black grape varieties that gives a soft but chewy wine tasting of black cherries and plums as well as the minerally rasp of ink and herbs.

⑫ 1996 Bonny Doon Clos de Gilroy California Grenache (red; United States), £7.65, Morris & Verdin

Another West-Coast original from the Grenache grape – a lovely sexy glugger oozing red plum and damson juice and the scent of Mediterranean herbs. *(Also available from Reid Wines.)*

⑬ 1996 Wairau River Sauvignon Blanc (white; New Zealand), £7.99, Reid Wines

Aggressive Sauvignon packed with gooseberry fruit and coffee bean scent and the wake-up citrus snap of lemon and lime acid.

⑭ 1995 Les Abeilles Côtes du Rhône, André Roux (red), £6.55, Sunday Times Wine Club

Beautiful Rhône red, full of super-ripe blackberry fruit and the scent of damsons and thyme, and a teasing prickle of black pepper, too.

⑮ **1995 Chablis Vieilles Vignes, Emmanuel Dampt (white; Burgundy), £9.99, Sunday Times Wine Club**

This is what Chablis should taste like but rarely does – a powerful yet restrained mix of honey and nuts and acidity. Streaked with mineral scent and wrapped in a viscous cloak of ripeness.

⑯ **1994 Le Chemin des Mulets, Châteauneuf-du-Pape (red; Rhône), £8.99, Tesco**

Deep, almost cooked style but enough rich scented loganberry fruit and herbs and bay perfume for it to succeed quite triumphantly.

⑰ **1994 Saintsbury Garnet Pinot Noir, Carneros (red; United States), £9.99, Adnams**

Classy Burgundy in everything but name – an elegant, sophisticated kind of wine, marrying gentle strawberry fruit and creamy oak with just a twist of spice and Burgundian undergrowth.

⑱ **1995 Carmen Grande Vidure Cabernet, Maipo (red; Chile), £6.99, Nadder Wines**

Splendid, powerful red with a great wodges of black cherry and black plum fruit held in place by unintrusive tannins.

⑲ **1995 Casablanca Barrel Fermented Chardonnay, Santa Isabel Estate (white; Chile), £6.99, Oddbins**

Rich, almost figgy tropical fruit and toasty oak that could be too much of a good thing, but in fact maintains a neat balance between syrup and acidity.

⑳ **1994 Wakefield Cabernet Sauvignon, Clare Valley (red; Australia), £5.99, Unwins**

Not subtle, but a lovely, self-indulgent goo of blackcurrant, toffee and blades of mint.

GOOD VALUE FIZZ

Not many sparklers featured in our tasting this year; in fact the Supermarket Selection revealed more stars. Even so, these seven will all bring a glint to your eyes

① **1992 Seaview Edwards & Chaffey Pinot Noir-Chardonnay Brut (Australia), £9.99, Safeway**

About as near as you can get to mature Champagne without forking out for the real thing. Full, foaming, classy mix of oatmeal and grilled nuts.

② **NV Drappier Brut Carte d'Or Champagne, £14.99, Thresher**

Well, here is the real thing: mature, classy fizz blending Ovaltine yeastiness and nuts with pleasant apple acidity. *(Also available from Wine Rack, Bottoms Up and Anthony Byrne.)*

③ **Berrys' Australian Quality Sparkling Wine, £10.25, Berry Bros & Rudd**

Not at all like the taste of true Champagne, but a good sparkling wine nonetheless, with mature peach and nectarine fruits and a flick of leather.

④ **Scharffenberger Brut, Mendocino (United States), £9.49, ASDA**

Good full-blown Champagne-method fizz from California with a full, mature nuts and yeast style.

⑤ **Villa Pigna Riserva Extra Brut, Fratelli Rozzi (Italy), £5.99, Tesco**

Pretty good frothy stuff with fresh apple fruit and an almost bready yeast. Good now and will actually age rather well.

⑥ **Richmond Royal Brut (Australia), £5.75, Whitesides of Clitheroe**
Traditional Aussie-style fizz – soft apple fruit and a slap of leather and oatmeal and no hard edges.

⑦ **Vallformosa Cava Brut (Spain), £6.90, Forth Wines**
Fairly aggressive stuff with a strong splash of apple acid leading the charge, but it still makes for a refreshing drink.

FINDS FOR A FIVER

We found a whole slew of wines between four and five quid that were packed with personality. This bunch scored well above average marks and could easily hold their own in more exalted company

① **1996 Baso (red; Spain), £4.25, Adnams**
Creamy red with a positively suckable raspberry fruit pastille flavour balanced by acid and a scent of herbs and angelica.

② **1994 Rowan Brook Reserve Cabernet Sauvignon, Mataquito (red; Chile), £4.99, ASDA**
Brawny and oak-dominated, but the fruit is so ripe and the blackcurrant fragrance so pure that it is set to keep improving.

③ **1993 Bodegas Trapiche Malbec, Mendoza (red; Argentina), £4.99, Grape Ideas**
Lovely gentle spicy red with soft sweet plum fruit and the scent of violets.

④ **1996 Peter Lehmann Semillon, Barossa Valley (white; Australia), £4.99, ASDA**
Softer than usual, but still a fascinating marriage of apricot skins, lime zest and the pungent spice of cinnamon and cloves. *(Also available from Safeway.)*

⑤ **1995 Palo Alto Cabernet Franc, Limarí (red; Chile), £4.99, Averys of Bristol**
Slightly charred quality but blackcurrant fruit and creamy texture still shine through.

⑥ **1996 Deakin Estate Sauvignon Blanc, Victoria (white; Australia), £4.50, Bibendum**
Surprisingly good Sauvignon from an area

usually thought of as too hot for this grape. This has a very nice pear flesh and peach syrup flavour flecked with grass and lemon. *(Also available from Victoria Wine.)*

⑦ **1996 Jacana Bush Vine Chenin Blanc (white; South Africa), £4.99, Fuller's**
Mild apple flesh perfume and a hint of toast in a good soft dry Cape white.

⑧ **1996 Villa Rosa Merlot, Rapel (red; Chile), £4.35, Whitesides of Clitheroe**
Doesn't smell brilliant but in your mouth the deep ripe mulberry syrup, blackcurrant and coffee bean flavour just blasts your reservations away.

⑨ **1995 Domaine de Grangeneuve, Coteaux du Tricastin (red; Rhône), £5.50, Yapp Brothers**
Soft-textured, the fruit just tinged with toffee and seasoned with pepper and thyme.

⑩ **1995 Domaine Maby, Vin de Pays des Coteaux de la Cèze (red), £4.95, Yapp Brothers**
Big assertive red, quite tannic, but the deep ripe fruit and the splattering of bay leaf and thyme across your palate hits the spot.

⑪ **1995 Dom. de l'Ameillaud, Vin de Pays de Vaucluse (red; Rhône), £4.55, Haynes Hanson & Clark**
Intense, almost rasping texture, but I like it because there's lots of stewed cherry and

plumskin fruit, strong bay leaf perfume, and a sensation like the sap rising in the vine.

⑫ **1996 Carta Vieja Merlot, Maule Valley (red; Chile), £3.99, Majestic Wine Warehouses**
I'd prefer this slightly less tannic, but there's a great chunk of blackcurrant and crunchy plum fruit in there, so I guess it works.

⑬ **White Burgundy, £4.99, Sainsbury**
Good, gentle modern Burgundy, clean, dry, slightly neutral fruit attractively balanced by a nutty texture and whiff of perfume.

⑭ **1996 Salisbury Grenache (red; Australia), £4.99, Victoria Wine**
Bright, youthful red full of juicy fruit, cinnamon spice and violet perfume. Not to be taken too seriously.

⑮ **1996 Les Landiers Sauvignon Blanc, Vin de Pays du Jardin de la France (white; Loire), £4.89, Sunday Times Wine Club**
Nice, rather fat white scythed through with green grass and lime zest.

⑯ **1996 West Peak Sauvignon Blanc, Stellenbosch (white; South Africa), £4.49, Portland Wine Co**
Powerful limy white with a slightly hard edge but enough green grass and citrus zest to make it not matter too much.

⑰ **1996 Bodega Norton Cabernet Sauvignon, Mendoza (red; Argentina), £4.99, Oddbins**
Yet another South American red – this time a dark, powerful Cabernet full of brooding black fruit and dishonourable intentions towards a juicy great steak.

TOP TIPS UNDER £4

The majority of wines were £5 to £10, yet there was a bunch of real cheapos too and they didn't disgrace themselves. Here's our top ten at the bottom end – and I can't help it if you think there are too many South American wines, because that's where the value is today

① **1995 Chilean Cabernet Merlot, Vinicola las Taguas (red; Chile), £3.99, ASDA**
See The Runners Up for tasting notes.

② **1996 las Colinas Merlot, Central Valley (red; Chile), £3.99, Thresher**
South America is clearly the place to go to for top quality reds at a really decent price. Full-flavoured meaty Merlot oozing blackcurrant fruit. *(Also available from Wine Rack and Bottoms Up.)*

③ **1996 Balbi Vineyards Malbec, Mendoza (red; Argentina), £3.99, Safeway**
Well, what do you know? South America again – this time it's Argentina that provides a crunchy damson red with a streak of pepper and a beefy floral scent.

④ **1995 Casa Leona Cabernet Sauvignon, Rapel (red; Chile), £3.99, Marks & Spencer**
More South Americans? Now this is getting boring – except what is boring about a string of deep, satisfying blackcurranty reds selling for less than £4?

⑤ **1996 Rylands Grove Chenin Blanc, Stellenbosch (white; South Africa), £3.99, Tesco**
Chenin isn't a fashionable grape, but that doesn't stop it from being good. This barrel fermented example from the Cape is a lovely honeyed wine with peach and melon fruit.

⑥ **1996 Angove's Nanya Estate Malbec/Ruby Cabernet (red; Australia), £3.99, Thresher**

Vibrantly fruity red that is actually quite earthy, but juicy fruit, bacon and a hint of flowers keep the earth firmly in place. *(Also available from Wine Rack and Bottoms Up.)*

⑦ **Noble Oak Merlot, Lyaskovets (red; Bulgaria), £3.99, Tesco**
A massive great Neanderthal mouthful of black treacle, Harrogate toffee and thick stewed blackcurrant.

⑧ **1996 La Bamba Tempranillo, Mendoza (red; Argentina), £3.85, Waitrose**
What a surprise! Back to Argentina, this time using the Spanish Tempranillo grape to produce a delightful easy-going mulberry

red that reeks of pepper and cloves, yet feels like cream.

⑨ **1996 Jacques y François Lurton Malbec (red; Argentina), £3.85, Fuller's**
Argentine Malbec made by a Frenchman into a dark, sturdy red that could use a bit of time but already shows buckets of fruit as well as pepper and green leaf acid.

⑩ **1996 Bright Brothers Argentine Dry Red, £2.99, Fuller's**
Is there no end to Argentine bargains? This time it's an Australian who has produced this bargain beauty with a flavour of Kirsch cherries and the scent of jasmine.

OLD-WORLD CHAMPIONS

Overall, I was depressed at the poor showing of Europe this year – and especially of France. But it's not all gloom: all these traditional wines did well, and I recommend them to everyone who sometimes finds the full-frontal flavours of the New World a bit much

① **1994 Sandrone Barbera d'Alba (red; Italy), £9.50, Tanners**
Well, you don't get much more Old World than this! Wonderful off-the-wall flavours that start out slightly unnerving, but end up in a welter of sandalwood, brown sugar and a stew of cranberries, sloes and redcurrants.

② **1992 Domaine de St Georges, Côtes du Rhône (red), £5.99, Christopher Piper Wines**
Fascinating, oddball Rhône, with rich, mature – almost overmature – fruit that heads off into the hills with a remarkable flavour of vine-ripened tomato and celery salt.

③ **1994 Gigondas, Domaine de Font-Sane (red; Rhône), £8.17, Bibendum**
Splendid, classic Gigondas flavours of mulberry, plums and rosehip made more exciting by a dose of bay leaf and pepper.

④ **1995 Morgon les Versauds, Jacques Perrachon (red; Burgundy), £7.72, Christopher Piper Wines**
That rare beast in modern times – a Beaujolais *cru* that is both delicious and impressive at the same time. The ripe cherry and red plum fruit is again assaulted – in the nicest possible way – by fresh ground pepper and celery salt.

⑤ **1995 Bourgueil, Domaine de la Grive (red; Loire), £6.30, Tanners**
Classic Loire red with that lovely smell of raspberries. The taste is dominated by raspberries too, tamed by a mineral quality that is like pebbles washed clean in a babbling mountain stream.

⑥ **1994 Madiran, Domaine Moreau (red; southern France), £6.00, Tanners**
This is powerhouse red and probably needs to be kept for ten years before it really shows what it can do. As it stands

now it's a sweet-natured brute, with a lot of toasty oak, rich dark fruit and a touch of the stableyard.

⑦ 1995 Syrah, Domaine de la Jonction, Vin de Pays d'Oc (red), £4.47, Corney & Barrow

Exciting and chunky Syrah from the South of France, with loads of rich, juicy damson fruit streaked with coffee bean and grass and wrapped in toasty oak.

⑧ 1995 Domaine de la Janasse, Vin de Pays d'Orange (red), £5.99, Majestic Wine Warehouses

Fascinating stuff – it has a beguiling floral quality, and yet is pumped up with black plum and tar and tannin. It manages to be aggressive and seductive. Must be a lesson in there somewhere.

⑨ 1995 Quinta de Panças Cabernet Sauvignon (red; Portugal), £5.09, Somerfield

Deep, strong, strapping wine. You get a wallop of ripe cooked blackcurrant and a smack of tar and pastry that's easily able to cope with the rumbling tannin in the background.

⑩ 1993 Múrice Rioja Crianza, Viña Ijalba (red; Spain), £6.99, Whitesides of Clitheroe

Now why can't we have more Riojas like this? Not only does it have the traditional coconut vanilla and slightly squashed strawberry taste, but it throws in hazelnuts and a peck of pepper and some very decent sun-dried tomato for a smashing mouthful.

⑪ 1990 Château l'Estage Simon, Haut-Médoc (red; Bordeaux), £9.95, Wine Society

A rare appearance for red Bordeaux in these lists – there were quite a few of them, but they just didn't score well enough. But this is fine, solid, yeoman stuff, full of the thick-thighed ripeness of 1990

but with a core of sweet plum and blackcurrant fruit that will take it through to a worthy maturity – if you want to wait.

⑫ 1995 The Society's Vin d'Alsace, Hugel (white), £5.60, Wine Society

Lovely gentle summer evening white, mixing the paleness of apples with the ripeness of honey and the musky promise of perfumed leather dusted with women's talcum powder.

⑬ 1994 Matarromera Ribera del Duero (red; Spain), £7.40, Le Nez Rouge

Classy red from Spain, displaying deep red fruit with an almost savoury edge wrapped in a warm cloak of coconut and vanilla.

⑭ 1993 Corbières, Château Hélène (red; southern France), £8.45, Waterloo Wine Co

Mature Corbières is a bit of a rarity, but this one is a beaut. Lovely deep black plum fruit, chaffed at by a little charred wood then seasoned with the hillside aromas of wild bay leaf.

⑮ 1996 Sauvignon Blanc/Sauvignon Gris, Château Pierrail (white; Bordeaux), £5.47, Châteaux Wines

Excellent example of what much of Bordeaux could do best – producing really snappy white wines with the whiplash of green grass and lime sweet-talked into obedience by the perfume of apple blossom and the crunchy fruit of a pale white peach.

⑯ 1995 Cépage Counoise, Domaine de Monpertuis, Vin du Pays du Gard (red; southern France), £4.65, Eldridge Pope & Co

This is a really fascinating red from the rare Châteauneuf-du-Pape grape Counoise. It's sturdy yet gentle and fresh acid makes up for lack of tannin and the peppery raspberry fruit is perked up with sprigs of thyme and lovage.

Only one
champagne
was voted
absolutely
fabulous.
And it wasn't
the Bolly.

Bollinger Vintage.

What's this, sweetie?

Bolly and Moët upstaged by a bunch of supermarket bubblies?

Well, yes, actually.

A well-known TV consumer programme conducted a blind taste test.

They asked various lucky people to sample 5 different makes of champagne, and give them marks out of ten.

The most illustrious (and expensive) contender was the Bollinger Vintage at £40 a bottle.

It came equal last with Tesco's Premier Cru Brut.

In third place was Moët & Chandon, while Safeway's grandly named Albert Etienne Brut Vintage 1990 was the runner-up.

The winner by a nose (and a palate) was Sainsbury's Vintage Blanc de Blancs Brut at only £14.95 a bottle.

Which just goes to show, you can't judge champagne by looking at the price tag.

 Moët & Chandon.    Safeway.    Tesco.   Sainsbury's.

SUPERMARKET SELECTION

Supermarkets are always telling us how wonderful their own-label goods are. Fine. Let's test the wines

Supermarkets sell more than half of the wine drunk each year in Britain. But how good is it? Well, over a dozen of the supermarket wines entered for the Best Buys tasting this year made the grade, but there are an awful lot of bottles on those long shelves. So (cue fanfare) we've inaugurated a second tasting to answer the question: does a supermarket's own-brand label say 'Trust me, I'm tasty and good value' or does it say 'I'm cheap, so don't expect to enjoy yourself too much'?

In fact, supermarkets sell two types of 'own-label' wine: truly own-label stuff that simply says what it is – Australian Chardonnay, or Corbières, say – and wines on which they have exclusive distribution deals, where words like 'Specially Selected For' appear discreetly.

So, which do you want: the good news or the bad? Several supermarkets sent us boxes full of all the tired old names of European wine – mostly made too cheaply to stand a chance, and ready to condemn the unadventurous and parsimonious wine-drinker to one disappointment after another. Other companies sent us a mix of exclusivities and own labels that did not rely on traditional names. More likely they relied on popular grape varieties, grown wherever price and quality came together. These are the supermarkets that did best in our tasting; and if you think I'm about to recommend a preponderance of New World wines – you'd be right. The really good news is that we can all get our hands on the best stuff next time we run out of baked beans, loo rolls or cornflakes.

Wines in each section are ranked in order of merit. Non-vintage Champagnes are marked NV; other non-vintage wines are simply undated.

SUPERMARKET SUPERSTARS

These are the dozen outright winners chosen regardless of price. An amazing range of styles came up trumps – though only one white had the necessary character – and the last two wines are just what we hoped for: proof that low prices don't have to mean low quality

① **1995 Rosemount Estate Orange Vineyard Chardonnay (white; Australia), £11.99, Marks & Spencer**
The most expensive table wine in the tasting, so I'm demanding the business – and I get it: classic Chardonnay from a brand new area of Australia with all the cream, toasted cashews and acid freshen-up you could ask for.

② **1995 Carmen Vineyards Cabernet Sauvignon Reserve (red; Chile), £5.99, Marks & Spencer**
Another coup by M&S. A thrilling red made

by one of Chile's most exciting young tyros – loaded with super-ripe blackcurrant fruit, toasty oak and a serious undercurrent of black ink and pepper.

③ **Fino Sherry, Luis Caballero (Spain), £5.99/litre, Waitrose**
If all Fino sherry were this good, we'd all be drinking it. A fascinating mixture of cream, nuts and yeast with a teasing hint of sourness. Come on, you Aussie Chardonnay freaks – give this one a try and open your minds to one of the great Old World originals.

④ **1996 South Eastern Australia Oaked Shiraz (red), £4.69, Safeway**
Hardy is making some of the best reds in Australia at the fairest prices, and Safeway did well to snaffle this succulent, juicy blackberry, plum and toasted nuts beauty.

⑤ **1995 Carmen Vineyards Merlot (red; Chile), £4.99, Marks & Spencer**
Beautiful, viscous red that coats your mouth with plum and blackcurrant juice, and leaves a lingering perfume long after you've swallowed it.

⑥ **NV Blanc de Blancs Champagne, £13.95, Waitrose**
I don't know how they do it, but the people at Waitrose manage to keep the beautiful foaming creamy style of this Champagne year in, year out.

⑦ **Fino Sherry, Luis Caballero (Spain), £4.39, Somerfield**
Another excellent Fino sherry from the same supplier as Waitrose's. This version has just a little more assertiveness and acid – so choose the style you prefer.

⑧ **1994 McLaren Vale Shiraz (red; Australia), £6.99, Tesco**
Smashing, full-throated dark ripe red, hemmed in happily with clove spice and toast, but still managing a lingering perfume after you've swallowed it.

⑨ **Beyers Truter Pinotage (red; South Africa), £4.99, Tesco**
Another rip-roaring red from Tesco – with this weird but wonderful grape from the Cape providing delicious flavours of woodsmoke, cream and damson flesh.

⑩ **1996 South Eastern Australia Oaked Cabernet Sauvignon (red), £5.29, Safeway**
Not quite so beautifully balanced as the Oaked Shiraz (above), but the overpowering spicy oak is dissolving in the deep soft black fruit. It should be beautiful by Christmas.

⑪ **Chilean Cabernet Sauvignon (red), £3.99, Tesco**
What a smashing mouthful of luscious black fruit – wonderfully rich black plum and blackcurrant happily reined in with a mild slap of tannin.

⑫ **1996 Australian Malbec/Ruby Cabernet (red), £3.89, Waitrose**
Another cracker, using less trendy – and therefore less expensive – grape varieties to produce a deep, almost earthy red that just bubbles with dark, ripe fruit.

HIGH STREET HEROES
Two dozen wines hot on the heels of the star performers. Not the pinnacle of own brand, but you'll feel well rewarded after a hard-won trolley battle. Again, these have been picked out regardless of price

① **1996 Averill Estate Kaituna Hills Chardonnay (white; New Zealand), £5.50, Marks & Spencer**
Gentle toffee, crunchy hazelnuts and quite high acid – good, typical Kiwi Chardonnay.

② **1996 Domaine Jeune Cépage Counoise Vin de Pays du Gard (red), £4.49, Marks & Spencer**
Fascinating red from a very rare grape variety – red plums, strawberries and rosehip mixed with allspice and almond paste. Intriguing or what?

③ **1995 McLaren Vale Chardonnay (white; Australia), £5.99, Tesco**
A bit old-fashioned, but none the worse for that – a rich, juicy soup of peaches and melons, with toast and a good hearty slosh of syrup.

④ 1995 White Burgundy – Barrel Aged Chardonnay (white), £4.99, Waitrose

Pretty classy stuff, soft and restrained with a creamy texture and nutty fruit just streaked lightly with lemon acidity.

⑤ 1994 Montagny 1er Cru Les Vignes de la Croix, (white; Burgundy), £6.99, Marks & Spencer

Another classy Burgundy, almost for its texture alone, but with tastes of honey coiled round crunchy Brazil nuts, fruit and lemony acid.

⑥ Amontillado Sherry (Spain), £4.65, Waitrose

It's not often that I recommend Amontillado sherry, but this is good with lots of Brazil-nuttiness and soft raisiny weight.

⑦ 1993 Berberana Rioja Crianza (red; Spain), £4.45, Waitrose

Despite the unwelcome price rises from Rioja in recent years, Berberana shows that you can still provide gentle strawberry fruit coated with coconut cream and not break the bank.

⑧ 1996 Australian Marsanne (white), £5.99, Safeway

Really interesting deep, round white, full of peach and honeysuckle and the whiff of a leather belt that is excellent now but will improve.

⑨ 1996 South Eastern Australia Oaked Chardonnay (white), £4.99, Safeway

More mainstream Aussie grog – lovely easy wine; peaches and cream sprinkled with spice and toast.

⑩ 1995 Chablis, Cuvée Domaine Yves Pautré, (white; Burgundy), £7.99, Safeway

This is modern Chablis with a mild

honeyed feel, restrained acid and a slightly savage creaminess that reminded me of – of all things – a mug of Ovaltine. However, I won't be waiting until bedtime to drink this stuff.

⑪ Australian Chardonnay (white), £4.65, Sainsbury

And here comes another Australian Chardonnay – fairly deep but fresh with lots of pleasantly peachy fruit and toasted nuts flavour.

⑫ Chianti Classico (red; Italy), £4.69, Tesco

And now for something completely different! A fascinating flavour of ripe Rosa plums and juicy wild tomatoes still on the vine.

⑬ 1995 Gewürztraminer (white; Alsace), £5.99, Waitrose

A true taste of Alsace: a beautiful, seductive mouthful of lychee flesh, rose petals and sandalwood.

⑭ Australian Chardonnay (white), £4.65, Somerfield

This time it's a soft-centred Chardonnay, with a flavour of sweet golden peaches and a wisp or two of woodsmoke.

⑮ 1996 Averill Estate Kaituna Hills Sauvignon Blanc (white; New Zealand), £5.50, Marks & Spencer

Powerful no-prisoners-taken gobful of typical New Zealand Sauvignon Blanc, the flavour of it all gooseberries, lemon and summertime earth splashed about with syrup.

⑯ 1996 Domaine Mandeville Viognier, Vin de Pays d'Oc (white), £4.99, Marks & Spencer

Viognier has one of the most memorable flavours of any white grape. This is a graceful, elegantly perfumed white, tasting of the fruit of green melon and pear lightly scented with apricot blossom.

⑰ **1996 South Eastern Australia Chardonnay (white), £4.69, Safeway**
Soft appley Chardonnay with reasonably strong toast and bacon smokiness swishing through it.

⑱ **1995 Oak Aged Pinotage (red; South Africa), £4.99, Safeway**
A bit powerful on the gums, but tons of really juicy damson fruit, a wisp or two of smoke and a good wodge of marshmallow and custard creams.

⑲ **Australian Chardonnay (white), £4.65, Tesco**
These own-label Aussie Chardies just won't lie down. Here's another with a cool melon and peach fruit warmed up with bacony spice.

⑳ **Australian Cabernet Shiraz (red), £4.99, Somerfield**
Loads of chunky plum fruit, but also a streak of greenness that needs the coconut and grilled nuts richness of its good oak barrels to make it work.

㉑ **1996 South African Reserve Selection Chardonnay (white), £4.99, Sainsbury**
Gentle Cape Chardonnay with a light spice jazzing up the mild melon and apple creaminess.

㉒ **Chilean Merlot (red), £4.29, Sainsbury**
Mouthfilling juicy blackcurrant fruit with a touch of toasty oak and a sprinkling of grass cuttings and lovage.

㉓ **Solera Manzanilla Sherry (Spain), £5.25, Waitrose**
Not as exciting as the Fino sherry that made it into my Supermarket Superstars, but a good, dry, if slightly stolid style all the same.

㉔ **Veuve de Medts Champagne Brut 1er Cru, £13.99, Marks & Spencer**
A satisfyingly reliable exclusivity, matching creamy softness with an almost grainy oatmeal depth.

BUBBLING UP

Liquid indigestion is a thing of the past for own-label Champagne, and some exclusivities are reliably impressive. New World bubbles are best for a classy party mouthful – and Spanish Cava can be good cheap fizz

① **NV Blanc de Blancs Champagne, £13.95, Waitrose**
See Supermarket Superstars for tasting notes.

② **NV Veuve de Medts Champagne Brut 1er Cru, £13.99, Marks & Spencer**
See High Street Heroes for notes.

③ **Yarden Blanc de Blancs, Golan Heights Winery (Israel), £9.99, Marks & Spencer**
Wow! I didn't expect this! Deep, creamy, old-fashioned fizz from the disputed Golan Heights.

④ **NV Rosé Champagne, £14.95, Waitrose**
Just a hint of strawberry perfume on a gentle, fresh, foaming wine.

⑤ **Asti Dolce (Italy), £5.49, Safeway**
Lovely bright lemon zest and elderflower stuff. Not that sweet, and wonderfully refreshing.

⑥ **1990 1er Cru Vintage Champagne, Centre Vinicole de la Champagne, £18.99, ASDA**
Rich, mature, almost overripe style, not a very sophisticated Champagne but good stuff nonetheless.

⑦ **Moscato Spumante (Italy), £3.99, CWS Co-op**
Really youthful frothy fizz with a delightful summer picnic flavour of elderflower and rosehip.

⑧ **NV Blanc de Noirs Champagne, £11.99, Waitrose**
Strong, slightly aggressive Champagne that could ideally use a few months more age.

⑨ **NV Champagne Blanc de Noirs Brut, £11.99, Sainsbury**
Gentle, almost bland fizz bar just a hint of red fruit perfume and some bread yeast softness.

⑩ **1994 Seppelt Australian Chardonnay Blanc de Blancs Brut, £7.99, Marks & Spencer**
Creamy, soft seductive sparkler with a slightly unexpected perfume of apples.

⑪ **Australian Brut, £4.99, Safeway**
Dead straight soft, easy-going fizz, tasting of apple flesh and icing sugar.

⑫ **Cava Brut Rosado (Spain), £4.99, Sainsbury**
Uncompromising pepper and apple-peel stuff – but pretty nice after an hour or two in the ice-box.

⑬ **Cava Brut (Spain), £5.29, Safeway**
Cava again – with a real splash of pepper and lemon zest; but it hits the spot if it's chilled enough.

THE ECONOMY DOZEN

If you're spending between £2.99 and £3.99, don't settle for low quality. The best wines in this range are more than bearable: they're characterful, enjoyable mouthfuls at a really keen price – two are in the top dozen

① **Chilean Cabernet Sauvignon (red), £3.99, Tesco**
See Supermarket Superstars for tasting notes.

② **1996 Australian Malbec/Ruby Cabernet (red), £3.89, Waitrose**
See Supermarket Superstars for tasting notes

③ **Chilean Cabernet Sauvignon (red), £3.69, CWS Co-op**
Chile again – this time with a delightful, plump red that mixes yoghurt softness with blackcurrant and plum fruit and just a nip of roughness.

④ **Paarl Cabernet Sauvignon (red; South Africa), £3.99, Tesco**
Gentle, smoky red from South Africa with a good dollop of squashy strawberry fruit to it. Not very typical of Cabernet, but nice stuff all the same.

⑤ **Mariscol Rioja Tinto (red; Spain), £3.99, CWS Co-op**
Good unabashed oaky red, piled full of coarse-chopped coconut, crème fraîche and strawberry jam.

⑥ **1996 Australian Oaked Colombard (white), £3.99, Safeway**
Fragrant, toasty oak perfume on a fresh bright fruit flavour of apple and white peach.

⑦ **Stellenbosch Merlot (red; South Africa), £3.99, Safeway**
More of the South African smoke, plus a rather sappy green streak wrapped round with rich fruit.

⑧ **1995 Côtes du Rhône (red), £3.65, Waitrose**
Very pleasant French red with gentle strawberry pastille fruit and a Mediterranean whiff of bayleaf.

⑨ **1996 Australian Riesling/ Gewürztraminer (white), £3.79, Waitrose**
This blend produces an exotic mix of mangoes and guava slashed through with the zest of a lime.

⑩ **1995 Cabernet Sauvignon, Vin de Pays d'Oc (red), £3.99, Marks & Spencer**
Good powerful blast of blackcurrant fruit and grassy acidity softened out with buttercream.

⑪ **1991 Valdepeñas Reserva Aged in Oak (red; Spain), £3.99, Safeway**
Despite the 1991 vintage, this is still fairly youthful red with a splash of cream softening a quite powerful scent of sandalwood.

⑫ **South African Pinotage (red), £3.89, Sainsbury**
This may seem a bit flat on the nose, but the taste in the mouth is a good enticing mishmash of damsons, bonfire smoke and marshmallow.

BARGAIN BASEMENT

Is there decent wine at £2.99? Well, a little. But avoid famous names like Soave and Bordeaux that ought to cost more. These 10 aren't world-beaters, but all taste pretty good – and they'll leave your tooth enamel intact

① **Moscadel de Valencia, Vicente Gandia (sweet white; Spain), £2.95, ASDA**
These Spanish Muscats are always the best value sweet wines on the market, full of peach and orange-peel fruit, syrupy richness and a smack of throat-warming spirit.

② **San Juan Argentine Country Red, £2.99, Somerfield**
Soft, gently perfumed light red wine. This is the future of plonk.

③ **1992 Leon (red; Spain), £2.99, ASDA**
Just about the best value soft vanilla creamy Spanish red on the shelves. Somehow, Asda keep the quality high and the price low year after year.

④ **Cabernet Sauvignon, SICA des Coteaux Limousins, Vin de Pays d'Oc (red), £2.99, Asda**
Dry, not too rough and has a nice perfume of plums and blueberries.

⑤ **1996 Vin de Pays de Vaucluse (red), £2.99, Safeway**
Slightly raw, with a green rasp like pepper and celery sticks, but there's attractive light strawberry fruit too.

⑥ **South African Dry White, £2.99, Somerfield**
Mild, vaguely perfumed soft white with a flavour of apple and pear flesh.

⑦ **Cahors, Southern France (red), £2.89, ASDA**
Rough and ready slap of plumskins and tobacco and apple peel – but that's what Cahors *should* taste like.

⑧ **St-Chinian, Southern France (red), £2.85, ASDA**
Soft, easy-going red with a nice flicker of bay-leaf scent.

⑨ **Cape Red (South Africa), £2.99, ASDA**
Not bad. Light, smoky red with a welcome flash of raspberry fruit.

⑩ **Bergerac Rouge (red; Southern France), £2.95, ASDA**
A bit tannic, but there's quite good grassy fruit there – and at this price, what do you expect?

WINES OF THE WORLD

UNCORK A NEW TASTE EVERY DAY

Take a look at your nearest Co-op store where you'll find an enviable range of wines, carefully selected from the four corners of the globe, covering new exciting countries like Argentina and Chile as well as the favourite classics. All our wines offer superb quality and value for money. Whatever your choice, you are guaranteed the added peace of mind afforded by our 'Responsible Retailing' pledge and 'Double guarantee, so that if you're not entirely satisfied with your purchase you may return it with its receipt, and we will promptly replace the product and refund your money.

If you have any comment or query about Co-op Brand products or policies please talk to us on:

FREEPHONE 0800 317827

For information and
purchase on selected wines
WWW.CO-OP.CO.UK

We're always thinking of you.

IDEAL CELLARS

Everyone's at it: fantasy football, fantasy shareholding – you can even join a fantasy movie-star stock exchange on the Internet. Well, since 1984 we've been inviting merchants to spend our fantasy money – in £100, £500 and £1000 denominations – on wines they would love to have at home; and, along with my own selections, this has produced an invaluable collection of very real wine advice. This year our guest contributions come from supermarket wine-buyers. All, with the adventurous exception of Liz Robertson at Safeway, have picked mainly from their own lists, so you know where to get hold of their recommendations.

NICK DYMOKE-MARR
ASDA

This is the first time that I have been asked to complete an Ideal Cellar and I had no idea that it would be so difficult to pick a small selection from our range of 350 or so wines. This is an international collection of personal favourites.

£100

Enough money to spend to get a real flavour for the diversity that can be found across four continents.

1996 Van Loveren Spes Bona Chardonnay, Robertson
A crisp and elegant Chardonnay which has been partially barrel fermented. From winemaker Wynand Retief in South Africa's Robertson Valley.

£23.94 for 6

1995 ASDA Chilean Cabernet-Merlot
A big, juicy, upfront red packed with spicy, berryish flavours. Enjoy now or over the next 18 months.

£23.94 for 6

1995 ASDA South Eastern Australia Shiraz-Cabernet
A full-flavoured blend of these two famous grapes from the Yaldara winery in South Australia's Barossa Valley.

£22.74 for 6

1995 Mas Segala Côtes du Roussillon-Villages
Warm and savoury southern French red. A short period of oak aging has given the wine extra depth and roundness.

£23.94 for 6

Total cost: £94.56

£500

This amount of money allows for a selection of wines for current drinking as well as some to keep for the future.

1996 Rowan Brook Chilean Chardonnay Reserve
Barrel fermentation gives the wine richness and elegance.

£53.88 for 12

1995 Cranswick Estate Oak Aged Marsanne, Riverina
This little-known grape produces intense, complex wines which can age gracefully.

£59.88 for 12

1996 Sancerre, Domaine de Sarry
Good Sauvignon Blanc from the central Loire is pretty hard to beat and this one displays all the characteristic flavour of this famous AC.

£83.88 for 12

1996 Peter Lehmann Barossa Valley Semillon
All the fruit for this wine was selected from the old bush vines of up to 40 years of age. The result is an absolute gem! Also has the ability to age for at least five years.

£59.88 for 12

1995 Bordeaux Supérieur, Château l'Église-Vieille
A really hot property in Bordeaux combined with a super vintage. The result is a ripe-flavoured, well-balanced claret which can be enjoyed either young or aged.

£59.88 for 12

1996 Rozzano Villa Pigna
A huge mouthful of wine from the Marches region of central Italy. Produced from 35-year-old Montepulciano vines, it must be just about the best red around to enjoy with a delicious Spaghetti Bolognese.

£59.88 for 12

1996 Jennsberg Pinot Noir, Paarl
Good South African Pinot Noir is rare, but this wine from the Backsberg Estate is full of ripe raspberry flavours and backed up with good acidity and soft tannins.

£53.88 for 12

NV Cranswick Pinot Chardonnay Brut, Riverina
Delicious, rich Aussie fizz which has benefited from a full three years of bottle maturation.

£83.88 for 12

Total cost: £515.04

£1000
Yum, yum! Lots of fun here for both now and the next millennium.

1996 Saint-Véran, Domaine des Deux Roches
Consistently brilliant white Burgundy from this well-known domaine located close to the boundary of Pouilly-Fuissé.

£77.88 for 12

1995 Pouilly-Fumé, Domaine Coulbois
Really complex Fumé typified by a smoky, almost minerally quality. All of Patrick Coulbois' wines age fantastically well.

£93 for 12

1996 Côtes du Rhône Blanc, Château du Trignon
A really interesting unoaked blend of four less-well-known grapes: Grenache Blanc, Clairette, Bourboulenc and Roussanne.

£65.88 for 12

1996 Frascati Superiore, Colli di Catone
A real stunner from the excellent estate of Antonio Pulcini in Frascati. Rich and complex with refreshing acidity.

£47.88 for 12

1996 Viña Porta Chardonnay Reserve
Deliciously full-flavoured and ripe barrel-aged Chardonnay from Chile.

£71.88 for 12

1995 Bordeaux Supérieur, Château de Parenchère
Jean Gazaniol's wines are regarded as some of the best from this AC. Combined with the quality of the 1995 vintage, this should make great drinking well into the next century.

£71.88 for 12

1994 Rowan Brook Chilean Cabernet Sauvignon Reserve 1994
Savoury Cabernet with good oak flavours. Has not been filtered, so it retains maximum flavour and colour. Decant prior to drinking.

£59.88 for 12

1995 Fairview Estate Shiraz, Paarl
Brilliantly juicy and full bodied, from award-winning wine- and cheesemaker, Charles Back.

£59.88 for 12

1994 Chateau Reynella Basket Pressed Cabernet-Merlot, Southern Vales
Ripe and blackcurranty Aussie blend with lovely hints of dark chocolate and coffee.

£95.88 for 12

1993 Campillo Rioja Crianza
Deliciously spicy wine layered with ripe, almost sweetish fruit; proves why Rioja is well loved.
£59.88 for 12

1993 Barolo Angelo Veglio
Spicy and smoky with elegance and finesse. Angelo Veglio is heading towards stardom.
£93 for 12

1990 ASDA Vintage Champagne
When it comes to a party, I have to say that I'm a sucker for good Champagne and this would add extra sparkle to any special celebration. Rich, mature and beautifully balanced.
£227.88 for 12

Total cost: £1024.80

LIZ ROBERTSON
SAFEWAY

£100

I have made this up of a few current personal passions – all very inexpensive and in 6-bottle lots to get in as much variety as possible.

1996 Safeway Matra Mountain Pinot Grigio, Nagyrede
Cool and understated, then grows up and fattens up a year to 18 months after vintage. Suddenly a thoroughly worthy glass with something approaching rich palate power.
£22.14 for 6

1996 Rosenview Cinsaut, Stellenbosch
I'm mad about this flavour. It's a touch decadent, aromatic and slightly warped, very soft, with the sort of talcy texture Merlot can give. One of the few reds that really works with Indian spicing but also good on its own. Must find out how it ages.
£22.74 for 6

1995 Vin de Pays de l'Aude, Richemont Montbrun Old Vine Carignan
Extraordinarily deep and dark, yet has lots of juiciness and hidden spice to it. I'm sure this will last and last, but I don't know how to hang on to it at the price.
£35.94 for 6

1996 Balbi Malbec, Mendoza
Gorgeously juicy and intense. Here is the truth in all the hype about Argentine Malbec – it's wonderful when you find the real stuff! Made in a small out-of-the-way winery by the young winemaker from Calvet in Bordeaux. Never mind watching this space, catch it now.
£23.94 for 6

Total cost: £104.76
(but with Safeway's discount net total £99.52)

£500

This is the hard-working cellar; I've visualized it as mostly short/medium-term interesting drinking with an eyebrow raised over the long term.

1995 Rosemount Show Reserve Chardonnay, Hunter Valley
If Philip Shaw says this is his best, then I'm making sure of my share. Always a wonderful evocation of Chardonnay.
£56.94 for 6

1993 Lindemans Pyrus, Coonawarra
Here is yet another top pro telling us this 1993 is his best yet. There's an element of extra flavour that gives the palate a sort of second wind, letting in a fine floral perfume.
£77.94 for 6

NV Caballo Loco Number One, Lontue
One of the most exciting wines introduced this year. 'Crazy Horse' Valdivieso is promoting it as the Chilean wine to match Australia's Grange. Well, let's give it its chance.
£56.94 for 6

1995 Château Marquis d'Alesme, Becker, Margaux 3ème Cru Classé
Buy while the price still shows the proprietor is trying to attract your attention. Lots of every flavour – brave and beautiful.

£77.94 for 6

1994 Podere Il Bosco Syrah, Fattoria di Manzano
Wonderfully elegant Syrah, classy, finely expressed and delicious right now. A crowd-pleaser certainly, but more interestingly a thorough crowd confuser. Every drop a joy.

£107.70 for 6

Matusalem Oloroso Muy Viejo, González Byass
One of the (so far) utterly reliable joys of our changing world and one of its unrecognized treasures. Great old sherries offer a gamut of flavour quite outside any other wine experience, and they beg to be appreciated as private pleasures, alone, with a book. So this is just for me.

£119.88 for 12 halves

Total cost: £497.34
(Safeway and Lea & Sandeman discounts can reduce the cost)

£1000

There just has to be Burgundy in my cellar after a most memorable tasting visit to the region. I had a set of flavours planted in my tasting memory that will never be erased.

1994 Meursault 1er Cru Charmes, Domaine Charles et Rémi Jobard
Clarity and golden riches, even in a vintage not quite as fat as I might wish for Meursault. But with this fruit definition and persistence, what more can I ask at the price?

£303.12 for 12

1994 Chablis 1er Cru Sechet, Domaine René et Vincent Dauvissat
The perfect match of house style with regional style was made for me here, with the drama of Dauvissat worked into the cool deliberate format of Chablis.

£88.14 for 6

1994 Mercurey Clos Rochette, Domaine Faiveley
This region's wines are challenging – no two ways about it. But they can offer jewel-bright fruit flavours covering diamond-cut acidity and tannins – all adding up to a great column of flavour that will last and last.

£90 for 6

1993 Beaune 1er Cru Montrevenots, Domaine Jean-Marc Boillot
Dreaming of the unutterably pure, sweet, smooth wines of Domaine Tollot-Beaut, I was thrilled to be reminded of the no-less-lovely wines of Jean-Marc Boillot. Freshness and purity of fruit are watchwords here, too.

£111.06 for 6

There must be other countries too, so:

1994 Ridge Geyserville
This Zinfandel is as much of the incomparable Californian Paul Draper as we can afford, but there won't be any disappointments.

£170 for 12

1990 Brunello di Montalcino Riserva, Talenti
Huge and masterful, dark dense fruit in a splendid vintage that may well go on forever.

£150 for 6

1995 Château Carbonnieux, Pessac-Léognan
Whenever I've looked at Bordeaux wines since Christmas, this property has marched up and taken all the limelight for me. I've fallen for the 1995 and '96 reds and whites, but the '95 red really has to take the palm with its smooth and assured ripe elegance.

£135 for 6

Total cost: £1047.32
(Lea & Sandeman and Bibendum can improve on that with discounts)

For those with a nose for quality and value – why pay more?

CHILEAN

Deep
Pacific
Merlot
Cabernet
.....

CHILEAN

White
Pacific
Sauvignon
Chardonnay
.....

AUSTRALIAN

Pelican
Bay
Chardonnay
.....

AUSTRALIAN

Pelican
Bay
Shiraz
Cabernet
.....

FRENCH

Skylark
Hill
Very
Special
Red
.....

FRENCH

Skylark
Hill
Very
Special
White
.....

From a supermarket that is renowned for top brands at low prices you'd expect nothing less when it comes to our wine selection.

KWIK SAVE

KEEPING IT SIMPLE, SAVING YOU MONEY

For your nearest store call FREEPAGES 📞 0800 192 192

STEPHEN CLARKE
TESCO

I've been lucky in life to be able to combine work and pleasure. In two decades of travelling the world of wine I have tasted some great wines, so making this selection has been as challenging as running the country's largest off-licence.

£100

A red and a white with amazing levels of fruit and complexity for the price, and a great everyday white from Australia.

Tesco Beyers Truter South African Pinotage
Beyers packs lots of rich, ripe fruit into this Pinotage; light and quickly forgotten it isn't!
£29.94 for 6

1995 Domaine St-James Viognier, Languedoc-Roussillon
Complex with exotic fruits; but not as one-dimensional as most affordable Chardonnays.
£32.34 for 6

1995 Tesco Clare Valley Riesling
Wonderful soft fruit balanced by just the right acidity. Chilled on a hot day…heaven!
£29.94 for 6

Total cost: £92.22

£500

Four great, medium-priced textbook wines.

1996 Jackson Estate Sauvignon Blanc, Marlborough
Loved this one from the first taste: intense classic Sauvignon notes and considerably cheaper and easier to get hold of than some.
£95.88 for 12

1993 St Hallet Old Block Shiraz, Barossa
This is Aussie Shiraz; gutsy and intense, with more fruit in one bottle than in a case of some reds – and it really stands up to rich foods.
£143.88 for 12

1990 Campillo Gran Reserva Rioja
Faustino's Bodega Campillo wines are getting better and better, and this is Rioja at its best. The oak is in perfect balance with the soft tannins and fruit.
£119.88 for 12

1995 Thelema South African Chardonnay
A rich, delicious Chardonnay from the Cape. Slight citrus tones with just the right amount of oak and a long rich finish. South Africa is really getting its act together and there's still much more to come.
£113.88 for 12

Total cost: £473.52

£1000

I attended the Académie du Champagne in 1988 and got the opportunity to taste all the truly great Champagnes. In my job showing favouritism is risky, but…I have blown nearly £800 on a case of Krug.

NV Krug Grand Cuvée Champagne
One of the world's truly great wines: rich, full and incredibly complex, this would be part of my cellar for pure indulgence.
£797.98 for 12

1993 Wynn's Michael Shiraz
A real headbanger of a Coonawarra red! It's packed with fruit, it has layer after layer of complex finesse and it screams at you out of the glass! Great for keeping, if you can resist.
£149.94 for 6

1995 Zind-Humbrecht Alsace Riesling
All the fruit is there, the acidity is refreshing now and will help keep this wine in great shape for a long time to come. And that almost spicy bouquet makes it unmistakably Alsace at its most splendid.
£59.94 for 6

Total cost: £1007.86

ALLAN CHEESMAN
SAINSBURY

Having contributed my Ideal Cellars for a number of years, I have found it is always a challenge to browse our list of over 500 wines from 23 countries to select them, and inevitably difficult choices have to be made. The quality and value found on the shelves today also makes the selection that much more difficult.

£100

Perhaps the most difficult to choose, with the quality/value relationship really tested, but there are some great New World treats in store here.

1996 Sainsbury's South African Reserve Selection Sauvignon Blanc
Hailing from the Vergelegen Estate in the Cape, this has all the freshness of cooler climate Sauvignon, yet with a hint of tropical fruit in it, too.
£28.50 for 6

Sainsbury's Chilean Chardonnay
Lightly oaked, and with good balance of acidity underscoring the quality from this exciting source of wine.
£25.74 for 6

1994 Bulgarian Cabernet Sauvignon Reserve
Full, rich, almost cedary Cabernet, this wine is a 'banker' to fool many an expert in a blind tasting.
£22.74 for 6

1996 Domaine Saint-Marc Syrah, Vin de Pays d'Oc
Great strides have been made in recent years in the South of France and this is no exception. This is full, meaty Syrah, with bags of fruit. You can taste the influence of Australian wine-making.
£23.94 for 6

Total cost: £100.92

£500

This gives more scope and the opportunity for a bit of experimentation. Also eight cases (96 bottles) makes quite a reasonable wine-rack fill!

Sainsbury's Cava
I believe this is one of the best-value quality sparklers on the market. From Mont Marcal, this wine has good fruit yet a touch of elegance not always found in Cava.
£63.48 for 12

Sainsbury's La Baume Chardonnay
This BRL Hardy-owned estate near Beziers in the South of France produces full, fruity New World style with lots of fruit and just a touch of oak.
£59.88 for 12

1996 Sanctuary New Zealand Sauvignon Blanc
Herbaceous, almost zesty Sauvignon, typical of the Marlborough region of New Zealand. A real classic.
£77.40 for 12

1995 Sainsbury's Alsace Gewürztraminer
I love Alsace wines with their perfumed, floral, spicy fruit – a perfect accompaniment to rich and exotic foods. This is a real stunner.
£67.80 for 12

Sainsbury's Cabernet Rosé de Loire
Dry rosé with excellent fruit, hand-crafted by Jacques Lurton in the Loire Valley. A perfect summer drinking wine but ideal, too, with oriental foods.
£47.88 for 12

1995 Santa Rita '120' Pinot Noir
Not an easy grape variety to find, but this Chilean example incorporates all the red berry fruit and balance that one can find in more established areas.
£53.40 for 12

1996 Sainsbury's South African Reserve Selection Cabernet-Merlot
Deep coloured, with good varietal character retained in the blend, this is claret from the southern hemisphere! Another wine from the Vergelegen Estate.
£59.88 for 12

1995 Château de la Tour, Bordeaux
Lighter style but from the excellent 1995 vintage, this Right Bank wine has balance with good tannin and fruit: good luncheon claret.
£65.40 for 12

Total cost: £495.12

£1000

This is always a treat, enabling a bit of indulgence while also being able to really stock the cellar – in fact, £1000 spent on my list would give 11 cases (132 bottles) and a tremendous variety of choice.

NV Sainsbury's Blanc de Noirs Champagne
The consistent, award-winning Champagne from our stable. Excellent!
£143.88 for 12

1996 Santa Rita Chardonnay Reserve
Full bodied, yet with good oak, fruit balance and acidity too. Certainly New World in style, but with elegance, too.
£71.40 for 12

1996 Sainsbury's Classic Selection Chablis
From the House of Brocard, this typical Chablis has the varietal notes of Chardonnay with a touch of added backbone. This is classic stuff.
£89.40 for 12

1995 'Gentil', Hugel
My penchant for Alsace again from this renowned house. Delicate, with good fruit and a hint of spice. Ideal summer drinking.
£67.80 for 12

1990 Sainsbury's Classic Selection Rioja
This Riserva wine from the house of La Rioja Alta is a real stunner with good balance – fruit, oak, but still a hint of tannin.
£89.40 for 12

1994 Nuits-St-Georges, Domaine Bertagna
Getting to the real stuff here! This German-owned domaine has invested heavily and the result is a classic Burgundian Pinot with bags of fruit, yet elegant balance. Try the others in the range, too.
£179.40 for 12

1990 Château la Vieille Cure, Fronsac
Second year running in my Ideal Cellars and I think one of the best-value clarets on the market from a stunning vintage. American owned, this estate continues to make superb wines – elegant and rich, with maturity beginning to show.
£131.40 for 12

From my £500 cellar I would keep a case each of…

Sainsbury's Cabernet Rosé de Loire
£47.88 for 12
1996 Sanctuary New Zealand Sauvignon Blanc
£77.40 for 12
1996 Sainsbury's South African Reserve Selection Cabernet-Merlot
£59.88 for 12

Finally, to use up the last £40, a mixed case of six each of…

Mendoza Country Red and White
Not great keeping wine, but eminently quaffable from Peñaflor in Argentina, with a touch of Australian Peter Bright's wine-making. Ripe fruit and flavour are the hallmarks.
£35.88 for 6 of each

Total cost: £993.72

OZ CLARKE

£100

It's getting more and more difficult to find exciting wines right down at the rump end of the wine market – but that only spurs me on to try even harder – and all of these are really characterful gluggers.

Les Oliviers French Vin de Table
A delightful red and white pair for not much more than the cost of the bottle, the label and the excise duty.

£12 for 6

Argentinian Dry Red
Hey, trading up! Lots of producers are doing these light, fruity, perfumed reds as Argentina shows its potential.

£18 for 6

ASDA Léon Red
Spain can do it too – but it beats me how this wine keeps its lovely red fruit and vanilla warmth year on year at this sort of price.

£18 for 6

1996 Nagyrede Pinot Blanc and 1996 Tokaji Hárslevelü
Just to show I do like whites too. These are inspired cheap whites from Hungary, full of crisp fruit and perfume for very little money.

£20 for 3 of each

Kourtaki Retsina
Hell, why not – spanking fresh, reeking of pine needles, crying out for a tall glass, a couple of ice cubes and a tall blonde… Well, you know what I mean. Love it or loathe it. I love it.

£17.20 for 6

Viña Patagonia Bonarda
Never heard of it? Well, the winery's spanking new and Bonarda is one of a clutch of little-known European grapes that are set to keep us enthralled with Argentina for years to come.

£12 for 3

Total £97.20

£500

Okay, let's get a bit indulgent here. There's so much excellent stuff at £4.99 nowadays I could simply put together a round hundred of bottles at less than a fiver – but I'm in more adventurous mood. So, here goes…

1995 Estremadura Palha-Canas and 1995 Quinta do Crasto
Well, I'll go all the way to £5.75 a bottle to show I am trying to find more pricey stuff. But when it's this good – why spend more? Two brilliant Portuguese reds blending New Wave imagination with Old World grape varieties and vineyards.

£69 for 6 of each

1996 Urziger Würzgarten Spätlese, Loosen and 1996 Oberhäuser Brücke Spätlese, Dönnhoff
Two stunning modern German whites that are thrilling for their purity of fruit, but much more thrilling for their startling faithfulness to the true flavours of their vineyard – this is what 'terroir' is all about.

£100 for 6 of each

1996 Valdivieso Pinot Noir Reserve and 1997 Morandes Malbec
Further evidence that exhilarating things are happening over the Andes. People are worried you can't make 'great' wine in Chile. If 'great' means you have to wait half a lifetime to appreciate them, then perhaps not. But if 'great' can be a 'here and now' experience – here they are!

£60 for 6 of each

1994 Stoneyfell Metala Shiraz-Cabernet and 1996 Laraghy's Clare Valley Grenache
Australia is back at the front of the pack – if you're prepared to pay the hardly daunting price of £7. For fruit and spice and 'serious' drinkability, these two reds are the business.

£84 for 6 of each

1994 Ribera del Duero Pago de Carraovejas and 1995 Rioja Cosme Palacio

And Spain's back in the tastebud-teasing game. I don't go for many Riojas but Cosme Palacio is one of my favourites.

£95 for 6 of each

1996 Fairview Estate Zinfandel-Cinsaut and 1995 Fairview Estate Bush Vine Pinotage

South Africa has not lived up to the hype: too much dull stuff – and not many bargains. But Fairview Estate gets better with every vintage and these two juicy reds are packed with personality as well as luscious ripe fruit.

£65 for 6 of each

That's £473. Damn, I keep forgetting the fizz! Right, I'll have four bottles of Prosecco la Marca for £19.96 – wonderful, frothy, Italian fizz – and one of gorgeous, biscuity Aussie Seaview Edwards & Chaffey Brut at £9.99.

Total cost: £502.95

£1000

ALL-RIGHT! The Big K. Throwing caution to the wind, I would usually dip into the realms of young red Bordeaux – but with prices going completely barmy at the moment I simply can't bring myself to.

Valdespino Coliseo and Osborne Solera India

These sherries are stunning old – very old – dry Olorosos of such supreme, arresting quality that they'd be underpriced at almost any money. A taste of affordable greatness.

£100 for 5 bottles

1991 Penfolds Bin 707 Cabernet Sauvignon and 1993 Cyril Henschke Cabernet Sauvignon

Top Aussie performers like these two get more expensive every year and yet you still don't feel you're being taken for a ride.

£200 for 6 of each

1996 Palliser Estate Sauvignon Blanc and 1996 Lawsons Dry Hills Sauvignon Blanc

And I don't feel I'm being taken for a ride by Kiwi Sauvignon either. They've never been cheap, but the best ones from a fine year like 1996 have as much gushing, crunchy, mouthwatering fruit as you could want at any price.

£95 for 6 of each

1995 Welschriesling Trockenbeerenauslese, Kracher and 1995 Zweigelt Tu es adorable, Kracher

Okay. These Austrian whites are seriously expensive, but they're wild, brilliantly original, swimming in all the sweet, sensuous flavours you didn't know wine could have – so I'll pay.

£200 for 6 halves of each

1995 Cornas Verset, 1995 Côte-Rôtie Jamet and 1995 Gigondas Domaine de Font-Sane

Right, back to the real world. But what a real world! 1995 produced beautiful wines all along the Rhône Valley and these three reds are classics – at what I can only describe as an eminently reasonable price.

£175 for 6 of each

1994 Bien Nacido Syrah and 1994 Ridge Santa Cruz Merlot

Ah, the kind of wines that California does so well yet does not do nearly often enough. Stunning flavours from two of the great post-technological winemakers.

£190 for 6 of each

And I'm nearly done. What have I left out? Which 'must haves' slipped through my fingers? Ah well, I think I'm satisfied. I've still got 40 quid, so I'll use that to buy three bottles of the best-value Blanc de Blancs Champagnes on the market: Waitrose's own label at £41.85 for 3 – taking me just one mouthful of foaming bubbles over my thousand quid at:

Total cost: £1001.85

AUSTRALIA

Price rises hurt. But don't blame the Australians: they're not conspiring against us. Blame a couple of short harvests – and the Far East, which thinks it has discovered the secret of eternal life

It had to happen, of course. After years of seeing Australian wines as cheap-and-cheerful standbys we're going to have to start forking out more money for them. By the time this book appears we'll already be shelling out another pound or 50p than we were last year on the cheaper wines, and a deal more on the costlier ones. Will we do it willingly? Yes, probably.

The first question is, why are these increases happening? The answer is simple: supply and demand. It's not only us Brits who like Australian wines: the Thais and the Chinese are getting in on the act, too.

The Thais, I hear you say. Come on. But yes, it's true. The king of Thailand has started to drink a couple of glasses of red wine every night for the sake of his health. Never mind whether he likes it or not; his doctors have decreed that it's good for him. And what's good for a king is good for his subjects: Australian giant BRL Hardy reckons it could sell its entire production to Thailand at twice the price it sells for here.

China's going the same way: Li Peng has recommended red wine to the Chinese – and there are an awful lot of Chinese – because of its health-promoting properties. As a result Australian wine exports to China in just one month were more than for the whole of the previous year.

All this suits Australian wine producers just fine. Australians have a deadline – the year 2025 – by which they want to be world players in the wine business. It'll mean more than quadrupling their exports. And yes, they're busy planting vines to cope with it. But vines take time to mature, and in the meantime, especially with poor recent harvests, there are price hikes.

It all means that we have to look at Australian wines in a different light. We're going to have to start thinking hard about the sort of quality we want in return for our pennies – and so are the Australians. Sometimes the quality's already there, so we won't mind paying more. Sometimes it's not – and then we won't pay.

GRAPE VARIETIES

CABERNET SAUVIGNON (red) This can be rich and chocolaty in the Barossa, austere and minty in Victoria's Pyrenees, full of moss, tobacco and cedar flavours in the Eden Valley, and dense, phenolic and black in the Hunter. Sometimes it can be all of these, sometimes it can taste of nothing more than simple blackcurrant jelly. Winemakers tend to give it their best, which can mean too much new wood. But when it's good, it's breathtaking. It's also often blended with other grapes, particularly Shiraz or the Bordeaux varieties Cabernet Franc and/or Merlot. Best: *Clancy's Shiraz-Cabernet, Greenock Creek, Peter Lehmann,*

Rockford, St Hallett Cabernet Merlot, Seppelt's Dorrien (Barossa); *Grosset, Knappstein Cabernet Merlot* (also a good Cabernet Franc), *Leasingham Cabernet-Malbec* and *Classic, Wendouree* (Clare); *Bowen Estate, Hollick's Ravenswood, Katnook, Lindemans' Pyrus, Lindemans' Limestone Ridge* and *Lindemans' St George, Leconfield, Orlando, Parker, Penley Estate, Petaluma, Wynns' Coonawarra* and *John Riddoch, Yalumba* (Coonawarra); *Heggies, Henschke Cyril Henschke, Hill-Smith Estate, Mountadam The Red, Seppelt's Partalunga* (Eden Valley); *Chateau Tahbilk* (Goulburn Valley); *Mt Langi Ghiran* (Great Western); *Frankland Estate,*

Goundrey, Howard Park, Plantagenet (Great Southern); Brokenwood, Lake's Folly, Rothbury Shiraz-Cabernet (Hunter); Chapel Hill The Vicar, Chateau Reynella, Coriole Shiraz-Cabernet, Mount Hurtle, Reynella Basket Press, Shottesbrooke, Wirra Wirra (McLaren Vale); Cape Mentelle, Capel Vale, Chateau Xanadu, Cullen, Devil's Lair, Leeuwin Estate, Lenton Brae, Moss Wood, Sandstone, Vasse Felix (Margaret River); Dromana Estate (Mornington); Taltarni (Pyrenees); Freycinet, Domaine A (Tasmania); Seppelt's Drumborg, Tisdall Mt Helen (Victoria); Coldstream Hills, Mount Mary, Seville Estate, St Hubert's, Yarra Yering (Yarra); Geoff Merrill, Penfolds (various).

CHARDONNAY (white) Australia has done more than most to give this grape mass appeal with its rich, fruity wines. Most are now far more restrained than they were, but the fruit is still there. The best have gained complexity while not losing their original appeal. Best: Shaw & Smith Reserve, Ashton Hills, Petaluma, Bridgewater Mill (Adelaide Hills); Andrew Garrett, Basedow, St Hallett, Greenock Creek, Peter Lehmann (Barossa); Giaconda (Beechworth); Grosset (Clare); Katnook (Coonawarra); Richmond Grove (Cowra); Henschke, Hill-Smith Estate, Mountadam, Seppelt's Partalunga (Eden Valley); Bannockburn (Geelong); Michelton Preece (Goulburn); Frankland Estate, Howard Park, Plantagenet, Wignalls (Great Southern); Allandale, Allanmere, Brokenwood, McWilliams' Mount Pleasant, Rosemount, Scarborough (Hunter); Knappstein, Stafford Ridge (Lenswood); Chateau Reynella, Geoff Merrill, Wirra Wirra, Grant Burge The Custodian (McLaren Vale); Cape Mentelle, Chateau Xanadu, Cullen, Evans & Tate, Leeuwin Estate, Lenton Brae, Moss Wood, Pierro (Margaret River); Dromana Estate (Mornington); Goundry (Mount Barker); Eileen Hardy, Lindemans (Padthaway); Pipers Brook (Tasmania); Tisdall Mt Helen (Victoria), Coldstream Hills (Yarra); Koonunga Hill (various).

CHENIN BLANC (white) The Australian incarnation of this grape ripens to a much

fuller, fruitier and blander style than its steelier Loire counterpart. Moondah Brook (Swan Valley) does a good example; Sandalford (Western Australia) blends it with the Madeira grape Verdelho.

GEWÜRZTRAMINER (white) Fine, faintly spicy cool-climate Gewürztraminers smelling of lychees and honeydew melon are made by Brown Brothers, Delatite and Lillydale (Victoria), and Tim Knappstein (Clare). Orlando Wyndham's Flaxman's (Eden Valley) and Tolleys (Barossa) are always good.

GRENACHE (red) There's more to Aussie reds than Cabernet and Shiraz. The Southern Vales around Adelaide are the heartland of this southern French variety, and the rediscovery of old vines sitting there squeezing out more and more concentrated grapes has resulted in a range of wonderful wines; the Turkey Flat vines have been in constant production since 1847. Grenache's star is in the ascendant. Best: Rockford, Turkey Flat, St Hallett's Gamekeeper's Reserve, Yalumba Bush Vine Grenache and The Reserve, Charles Melton, RBJ, Yaldara Reserve, Whitmore Old Vineyard (Barossa); James Halliday Shiraz-Grenache, Michelton III (Goulburn); d'Arenberg Ironstone Pressings (McLaren Vale).

MARSANNE (white) In Central Victoria, both Chateau Tahbilk and Mitchelton have made big, broad, ripe Marsanne.

MUSCAT (white) There are two types of Muscat in Australia: first, the bag-in-box Fruity Gordo or Muscat of Alexandria – fruity, sweetish, swigging wine, from a heavy-cropping lowish-quality grape grown along the Murray River; second, Liqueur Muscat, made from the Brown Muscat, a strain of the top quality Muscat à Petits Grains, grown in Victoria. It is a sensation: dark, treacly even, with a perfume of strawberry and honeyed raisins. Best producers include All Saints, Baileys, Bullers, Campbells, Yalumba, Chambers, Morris and Stanton & Killeen.

PINOT NOIR (red) Aussie winemakers are still pretty obsessed with Pinot Noir, but it looks increasingly as if New Zealand is going to become its Southern Hemisphere heartland. But Australia makes a few decent ones. Best: *Ashton Hills, Hillstowe, Pibbin* (Adelaide Hills); *Giaconda* (Beechworth); *Mountadam* (Eden Valley); *Bannockburn* (Geelong); *Lenswood, Ashton Hills* (Lenswood); *Wignall's* (Great Southern); *Tyrrell Vat 6* (Hunter); *Henschke, Tim Knappstein* (Lenswood); *Moss Wood* (Margaret River); *Freycinet, Spring Vale, Piper's Brook, Tasmania Wine Co* (Tasmania); *Coldstream Hills, Mt Mary, St Hubert's, Tarrawarra, Yarra Yering* (Yarra).

'PORT' Shiraz and other Rhône-type grapes are often used to make high-quality 'port'. Vintage is wonderful. One day they'll stop calling it port. Best: *Chateau Reynella, Lindemans, Montara, Penfolds, Saltram, Seppelt, Stanton & Killeen, Yalumba.*

RIESLING (white) Australia makes highly individual Rieslings, all sharing a lime aroma: some clean and crisp (*Ashton Hills, Pewsey Vale, Leeuwin Estate*), some softer and more rounded (*Heritage, Skillogalee*), others that beg to be aged (*Orlando Steingarten, Mount Langhi-Ghiran*). It's a wonderful apéritif and the perfect partner for Thai and Pacific Rim cooking: not many white wines could stand up to those flavours, but Australian Riesling sails through them. Other good ones: *Rockford* (Barossa); *Tim Adams, Jim Barry, Grosset, Tim Knappstein, Mitchell, Petaluma, Pike* (Clare); *Heggies, Hill-Smith Estate, Lindemans' Leo Buring, Orlando St Helga, Seppelt's Partalunga* (Eden Valley); *Frankland Estate, Howard Park* (Great Southern); *Henschke* (Lenswood or Eden Valley); *Pipers Brook* (Tasmania); *Delatite* (Victoria). Best botrytis-afffected wines: *Petaluma, Mt Horrocks* and *St Huberts.*

SAUVIGNON BLANC (white) There is an increasingly assured bunch of Aussie Sauvignon Blancs on the market, proof that the newer cool-climate regions are coming up with the goods. Adelaide Hills is proving its worth, with *Shaw & Smith, Stafford Ridge* and *Lenswood,* while Margaret River's richer styles are like southern hemisphere Graves (*Cullen, Evans & Tate*). Best: *Jim Barry, Pike* (Clare); *Katnook* (Coonawarra); *Hill-Smith Estate* (Eden Valley); *Bannockburn* (Geelong); *Frankland Estate, Wignalls* (Great Southern); *Ribbon Vale, Amberley Estate* (Margaret River); *Mount Hurtle, Wirra Wirra* (McLaren Vale); *Hardy, Lindemans* (Padthaway); *Bridgewater Mill* (various).

SEMILLON (white) This is slowly gaining the respect of the public, and about time too, as Australia's home-grown style. The Lower Hunter leads the way with wines which are lean and grassy when young, and that take on aromas of toast and honey with age (even though they see no wood). In Western Australia it can be powerful and exotically perfumed. Best: *Heritage, Peter Lehmann, Rockford* (Barossa); *Grosset, Mitchell, Mount Horrocks* (Clare); *Hill-Smith Estate* (Eden Valley); *Cassegrain* (Hastings Valley); *Brokenwood, Lindemans, McWilliams, Petersen, Rothbury* (Hunter); *Knappstein* (Lenswood); *Evans & Tate, Moss Wood, Sandstone* (Margaret River); *Simon Hackett* (McLaren Vale); *Brown Bros* (Milawa). Best blends with Sauvignon: *St Hallett* (Barossa); *Brokenwood* (Hunter); *Cape Mentelle, Pierro, Xanadu Secession* (Margaret River); *Wirra Wirra* (McLaren Vale). *Geoff Merrill* blends with Chardonnay. Best sweet wines: *Peter Lehmann, Tim Adams, de Bortoli.*

SHIRAZ (red) The most widely planted red vine in Oz, and the one which squeezes out the most distinctive flavours in wines of the greatest opulence and longevity. Old gnarled Shiraz vines seem to slurp up sunlight, in return offering grapes with the dense, black iron intensity of Clare, the chocolate, earth and moss of the Barossa, the black pepper of the cooler bits of Victoria and WA, or the simple red berry sweetness of the over-irrigated, hot Murray

Valley. Old vine Shiraz should offer more depth of flavour. Try: *Basedow, Grant Burge Meshach, Greenock Creek, Peter Lehmann, Charles Melton, Rockford, St Hallett, Yalumba Octavius* (Barossa); *McWilliams* (Barwang); *Jasper Hill, Passing Clouds* (Bendigo); *Cape Mentelle* (Margaret River); *Tim Adams, Jim Barry The Armagh, Mitchell, Pike's, Wendouree* (Clare); *Bowen, Majella, Wynns, Zema* (Coonawarra); *Craneford, Henschke, David Wynn Patriarch* (Eden); *Bannockburn* (Geelong); *Ch. Tahbilk* (Goulburn); *Mt Langi-Ghiran* (Great Western); *Plantagenet* (Great Southern); *Allandale Matthew, Brokenwood, McWilliams Old Paddock and Old Hill, Tulloch Hector, Rothbury* (Hunter); *Craiglee* (Macedon); *Chapel Hill, Chateau Reynella, d'Arenberg Old Vine, Hardy* (McLaren Vale); *Goundrey* (Mount Barker); *Dalwhinnie, Taltarni* (Pyrenees); *Baileys* (Rutherglen); *Baileys 1920s Block* (Victoria); *Yarra Yering* (Yarra Valley); *Hardy, Penfolds, Yaldara Reserve* (various).

SPARKLING WINES In the lead for quality are *Croser, Green Point* (otherwise known as *Domaine Chandon*), *Yalumba D, Salinger* and *Jansz*. Cheaper ones include: *Seaview, Angas Brut, Orlando Carrington*. Upmarket: *Seppelt's Blanc de Blancs* and *Pinot Noir-Chardonnay*. And try *Yalumba's Cabernet* and *Seppelt's Shiraz* (sparkling red).

OTHER WHITES Australia is growing more sophisticated with a widening range of grape varieties. *Heggies* is increasing its plantings of Viognier, *Michelton* is going the whole hog in its attempt to turn the Goulburn Valley into the Rhône with its *Michelton III* red blend; *St Hallett's Poacher's Blend* is a wonderfully easy-drinking wine, while Verdelho – best known as a Madeira grape – seems to be on the increase. It makes rich, lime-flavoured wines in the heat of Cowra (*Richmond Grove*), the Hunter Valley (*Pendgrves Estate, Rothbury Estate*) and the Swan Valley (*Moondah Brook*).

WINE REGIONS

The new Australian Geographical Indication system, the finer details of which are still being decided, has to encompass certain Australian peculiarities. The main one is the system of inter-regional blending: that is, trucking grapes from several different regions, possibly in different states, to a central winery for blending together. So the Australian system has more layers than most, starting with the most general designation, which is Produce of Australia. Anything sold solely under this appellation will not be able to have a grape variety or a vintage on its label.

The next most general is South-Eastern Australia, an appellation which already exists and is much seen; it covers, in fact, most of the wine-producing areas of the country. Then there is the more specific State of Origin, and then there are zones. A zone is smaller than a state but larger than an individual region: the Central South Australia zone incorporates several regions,

including McLaren Vale and Barossa. Then come sub-regions, like Barossa Valley and Clare Valley, which are both part of the Barossa region. In all there will be about 400 Geographical Indications but, as always, there are arguments over the precise position of boundaries.

ADELAIDE HILLS (South Australia) This area was pioneered by *Petaluma's* search for cooler climate sites for its still whites and sparkling wine. It has now been joined by firms such as *Shaw & Smith, Stafford Ridge, Henschke* and *Lenswood*, who are establishing the area with classically pure Sauvignon Blanc, Chardonnays with great length and some classy Pinot Noir.

BAROSSA VALLEY (South Australia) The heart of the wine industry, planted originally by immigrants from Silesia. Most of Australia's wine passes through the Barossa, if only for bottling or aging. It's also a source of wonderful old-vine Grenache and Shiraz. Best: *Penfolds, Orlando-Wyndham, Peter Lehmann, Mildara-Blass, Rockford, Greenock Creek, Charles Melton, Grant Burge.*

BENDIGO (Victoria) This 19th-century region, destroyed by phylloxera, has been replanted with excellent Cabernet, good Shiraz and some Pinot Noir. *Balgownie* is the leader, with *Chateau Le Amon, Craiglee, Harcourt Valley, Heathcote, Mount Ida, Passing Clouds* and *Yellowglen* important.

CANBERRA DISTRICT (ACT) In the Australian Capital Territory, with some modest wineries producing wines to match.

CENTRAL VICTORIA Goulburn Valley is the most important area, with *Chateau Tahbilk* producing big, old-style Shiraz and Cabernet, and some interesting Marsanne. *Tisdall* makes superbly fruity Cabernet, Chardonnay and Sauvignon; *Mitchelton* is also good. *Delatite* makes delicate whites and intense reds.

CLARE (South Australia) An upland complex of four valleys (Skillogalee, Clare, Watervale and Polish River), Clare is all things to many grapes: cool and dry enough for steely, limy Riesling (*Leo Buring, Tim Knappstein, Jim Barry, Pike* and *Grossett*) and soft, light Chardonnay (*Penfolds*), but warm enough for rounded Semillon (*Mitchell*) and long-living reds (*Wendouree, Knappstein, Skillogalee, Leasingham* and *Watervale*).

COONAWARRA (South Australia) A big, flat, wide open landscape with the famous cigar-shaped strip of *terra rossa* soil at its heart. It is Australia's most profitable red wine vineyard, and its incredibly expensive land is jam-packed with great names. Coonawarra is best at Cabernet and unirrigated Shiraz. Try: *Bowen, Brand's Laira, BRL Hardy, Hollick, Katnook, Lindemans, Majella, Mildara, Orlando, Penfolds, Penley, Petaluma, Rouge Homme, Rosemount, Rymill, Wynns* and *Zema.* In recent years, more

white grapes have been planted, but these are best for sparkling wines.

EDEN VALLEY (South Australia) Home to some of Australia's oldest vineyards, like *Henschke*'s 120-year-old Hill of Grace, and some of the newest and most high-tech (*Mountadam* and *Seppelt's Partalunga*). Most of the major Barossa companies take fruit from these rolling uplands. The *Yalumba* winery is here too, with its *Heggies* and *Hill-Smith Estate* vineyards.

GEELONG (Victoria) Best are intense Cabernets from vineyards like *Idyll* and *Bannockburn*, Pinot Noir from *Prince Albert* and *Bannockburn*, whites from *Idyll*.

GLENROWAN-MILAWA (Victoria) Famous for *Baileys* torrid, palate-blasting reds from Cabernet and Shiraz and (more importantly) Liqueur Muscats. These are intensely sweet, the very essence of the overripe brown Muscat grape, full of an exotic tangle of orange and honey. *Brown Brothers* makes a wide range, but its best are from the *Koombahla* vineyard, and the high-altitude *Whitlands* site.

GOULBURN VALLEY (Victoria) One of Victoria's biggest premium regions, this houses *Mitchelton*, a medium-sized modern winery, and *Chateau Tahbilk*, one of the nation's oldest, still making traditional intense reds and long-lived Marsanne. Tiny, high-tech *Delatite* is nearby.

GRANITE BELT (Queensland) The vines are planted high up in what is otherwise a banana and mango belt. Most wines serve the local market and some (*Ballandean, Koninos Wines, Rumbalara, Robinsons Family* and *Stone Ridge*) are good. *Ironbark Ridge* is one to watch.

GREAT SOUTHERN (Western Australia) One of Australia's most promising wine areas. It has Rieslings as good as those of the Clare and Eden Valleys, and delightful limy Chardonnays. Its Shiraz is lithe and peppery; its Pinot lush and fleshy; its Cabernet magnificent, full of cedar, spice, moss, fern and earth. Cabernet from here will soon give Margaret River a very hard run for its money. Wineries are *Goundrey, Alkoomi, Plantagenet* and the new *Frankland Estate*. Also fairly new is the stunning *Howard Park*, home of *Madfish Bay* blends.

GREAT WESTERN (Victoria) Historic area best known as the source of base wine for *Seppelt's Great Western* fizz, but more exciting for its reds. Shiraz is superb, full of chocolate, coconut and cream as at *Cathcart Ridge*, or dry, liquoricy and with impressive pepper as at *Mount Langi-Ghiran*. *Best's, Montara* and *Seppelt* are other top names. There is also excellent Chardonnay from *Best's* and *Seppelt*, good Cabernet Sauvignon from *Mount Langi-Ghiran* and 'vintage port' from *Montara*.

HUNTER VALLEY (New South Wales) This old-established region is home to wonderfully individual Semillons that will last for decades, and great leathery Shiraz. Best producers include: *McWilliams Mount Pleasant, Tyrrells, Rosemount* and its *Roxburgh* vineyard, *Reynolds, Rothbury* and *Allandale*.

LOWER GREAT SOUTHERN (Western Australia) A vast, rambling area of great promise, especially round Mount Barker. *Alkoomi, Forest Hill, Goundrey, Howard Park* and *Plantagenet* are good. The whites are fragrant and appetizing, with zesty Riesling and Sauvignon, but the reds are best, with spicy, tobaccoey Cabernets.

MARGARET RIVER (Western Australia) A source of increasingly poised wines that reek of a sense of place, combining richness of fruit with elegance of structure. *Moss Wood, Cape Mentelle, Cullen, Pierro, Vasse Felix* and *Leeuwin Estate* are the names to watch, and while Semillon and Sauvignon (as varietals and blends),

Cabernet and Chardonnay are the most common wines, experimentation is continuing. Cape Mentelle is making great Zinfandel and there are experiments with Malbec, Sangiovese and Nebbiolo.

MCLAREN VALE (South Australia) This area has been under threat from the spread of the Adelaide suburbs, and sadly some wonderful old Shiraz vineyards are now under tarmac. Thankfully, the building has been slowed by a revival of interest in the singular quality of the area's fruit, in particular the boldness of the black pepper Shiraz and the sweet concentration of Grenache. Recommended are *Chateau Reynella Basket Press Shiraz, Coriole Redstone Shiraz-Cabernet, d'Arenberg Shiraz-Grenache, Old Vine Shiraz* and *Ironstone Pressings, Geoff Merrill Chardonnay* and *Cabernet, Mount Hurtle Cabernet.*

MORNINGTON PENINSULA (Victoria) One of the coolest Aussie wine zones, this is a weekend playground for the Melbourne rich. Good for light Chardonnay, sparkling wine and sometimes Pinot Noir. Among the best wineries are *Dromana, Stonier's Merricks* and *Moorooduc Estate*.

MUDGEE (New South Wales) Though Mudgee was established on Shiraz (*Montrose* is outstanding), the best reds have been tarry, plummy Cabernets. But Chardonnay is even better, usually rich, soft and full of fruit-salad flavours. Best: *Montrose, Craigmoor, Huntington, Miramar*.

MURRUMBIDGEE IRRIGATION AREA/GRIFFITH (New South Wales) The vast irrigated MIA provides ten to 15 per cent of the total Australian crop. Most is bulk wine, but *McWilliams* makes some attractive wines, as does *de Bortoli*, including a Sauternes-style Semillon and marmalade-flavoured Rare Dry Botrytis Semillon.

ORANGE (New South Wales) A new cool-climate region already making intense

Loire-style Sauvignon Blanc (*Highland Heritage*) and cashew nut Chardonnay (*Rosemount*), while the reds, notably Shiraz Cabernet and Merlot (from *Bloodwood, Reynolds* and *Rosemount*) are outstanding.

PADTHAWAY (South Australia) High quality and increasingly important for whites, notably Chardonnay, Riesling and Sauvignon Blanc. Grapes are grown here for sparkling wine, and there is some excellent sweet Riesling. Best: *Hardy, Lindemans, Seppelt*; major names like *Orlando* and *Penfolds* also use the grapes.

PEMBERTON (Western Australia) New region showing promise for Pinot Noir.

PYRENEES (Victoria) Very dry Shiraz and Cabernet reds, and mostly Sauvignon whites. Tops: *Dalwhinnie, Mount Avoca, Redbank, Taltarni, Warrenmang*, and for fizz, *Chateau Remy* (also stylish Cabernet and Chardonnay) and *Taltarni*.

RIVERLAND (South Australia) A vast irrigation project on the Murray River providing a large chunk of the national crop. Dominated by the huge *Angove's* winery, and the even bigger *Berri-Renmano-Loxton* group (part of BRL Hardy), it makes huge amounts of bag-in-box wines of consistently good quality. But it also yields fresh, fruity Rhine Riesling, Chardonnay, Sauvignon, Colombard, Chenin, Cabernet and Shiraz.

RUTHERGLEN (Victoria) The centre of the fortified wine tradition. The white table wines are generally dull, except for the reliably fine *St Leonards*. The reds are rich and robust. The fortifieds, either as solera-method 'sherries', as 'vintage ports', or as intense, brown sugar-sweet Tokays, are all memorable. The true heights are achieved by Liqueur Muscats, unbearably rich but irresistible with it. Best: *Bullers, Campbells, Chambers, Morris, Stanton & Killeen*.

SWAN VALLEY (Western Australia) This hot region made its reputation on big, rich reds and whites, but even the famous *Houghton Supreme* is now much lighter and fresher. Good names: *Bassendean, Evans & Tate, Houghton, Moondah Brook, Sandalford*.

TASMANIA Only tiny amounts, but there is some remarkable Chardonnay from *Pipers Brook* and *Tasmanian Wine Co.*, and Cabernet from *Freycinet* and *Domaine A*. Pinot Noir can be terrific.

YARRA VALLEY (Victoria) Victoria's superstar. It suits the Champagne grapes, Pinot Noir and Chardonnay, for fizz, plus Riesling and Gewürztraminer, and even Cabernet and Pinot for superb reds. The scale is quite small, the quality very high. Best producers include: *Coldstream Hills, de Bortoli, Diamond Valley, Lillydale, Mount Mary, St Huberts, Seville, Tarrawarra, Yarra Burn, Yarra Ridge, Yarra Yering* and *Yeringberg*.

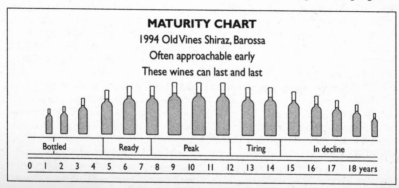

MATURITY CHART
1994 Old Vines Shiraz, Barossa
Often approachable early
These wines can last and last

Bottled	Ready	Peak	Tiring	In decline

0   1   2   3   4   5   6   7   8   9   10   11   12   13   14   15   16   17   18 years

PRODUCERS WHO'S WHO

TIM ADAMS ★★★★(★) (South Australia) Spellbinding Semillon and a dense, full-flavoured Shiraz.

ALLANDALE ★★★(★) (Lower Hunter) One of the best Hunter Semillons; also complex, slightly honeyed Chardonnay and the excellent Matthew Shiraz.

BAILEYS OF GLENROWAN ★★★(★) (Victoria) Attempts to modernize this traditional winery famous for stunning liqueur Muscats have led to alarming dips in quality, particularly for reds. But latest Muscats and Tokays are reassuringly rich and reds are full and correct, though lacking the sense of history.

BANNOCKBURN ★★★★ (Victoria) Some of cool-climate Geelong's best wines: a rich Pinot Noir, full-bodied Chardonnay and Shiraz.

BAROSSA VALLEY ESTATES ★★(★) (South Australia) BRL Hardy-owned, this specializes in good quality, cheap wine.

JIM BARRY ★★★★ (South Australia) Clare Valley winery; outstanding unwooded Chardonnay, Rhine Riesling, Sauvignon Blanc and a splendid Shiraz, The Armagh.

BASEDOW ★★★★ (South Australia) Barossa winery with big, toasty, oaky Chardonnay, fine Watervale Riesling, hearty, chocolaty Shiraz and Cabernet.

WOLF BLASS ★★★(★) (South Australia) The wines are good once more at this Mildara-owned winery – modern, well plumped out with fruit and oak – but rarely match the silky, come-hither brilliance of the old days. Voluptuous Chardonnay, good Riesling and five styles of red which are, in rising price order, red, yellow, grey, brown and black labels.

DE BORTOLI ★★★(★) (New South Wales) Rich sweet Noble One Botrytis Semillon, plus a string of well-priced basics. New Rare Dry Botrytis Semillon has bags of marmalade flavour but little subtlety. De Bortoli's Yarra Valley property makes good Chardonnay, Cabernet and Shiraz.

BOWEN ESTATE ★★★★ (South Australia) The best value in Coonawarra: elegant Cabernet-Merlot and razor-fine Shiraz renowned for consistency and quality. Very good Riesling and Chardonnay.

BRL HARDY★★★★ (South Australia) Huge company making both high standard, cheap own-labels and Hardy's impressive range from Nottage Hill to Chateau Reynella and Eileen Hardy. Look out, too, for Hardy's rich, sweet Botrytized Riesling.

BROKENWOOD ★★★★(★) (New South Wales) Small, high-class Hunter Valley winery noted for eclectic blends such as Hunter/Coonawarra Cabernet and latterly Hunter/McLaren Vale Semillon/Sauvignon Blanc. Low-yielding Graveyard vineyard produces one of Australia's best Shiraz: concentrated, profound and long-living.

BROWN BROTHERS ★★★ (Victoria) A huge range of good wine. The best vineyards are the cool Koombahla and even cooler Whitlands; look for Muscat, Semillon, Chardonnay, Koombahla Cabernet, Whitlands Gewürz and Riesling, the last in every style up to sweet and botrytized.

CAPE MENTELLE ★★★★(★) (Western Australia) Excellent Cabernet and variations on the Semillon/Sauvignon theme as well as Shiraz – and Zinfandel.

CHAPEL HILL ★★★★ (McLaren Vale) Impressive wines with restraint and style include toasty Eden Valley Riesling, unwooded Chardonnay and chocolaty, blackberry-flavoured The Vicar, a blend of Cabernet and Shiraz.

CHATEAU TAHBILK ★★★★
(Victoria) Historic Goulburn Valley winery with great traditional Shiraz and Cabernet Sauvignon, and excellent Marsanne.

COLDSTREAM HILLS ★★★★
(Victoria) World-class Pinot Noir, exciting Chardonnay and Cabernet. Recently bought by giant Southcorp, which seems to want to maintain quality.

CULLEN ★★★★(★) (Margaret River)
Cullen has made consistently intense wines from the word go, and is getting better with each vintage. Releases include a benchmark Sauvignon Blanc and a richly elegant Cabernet. Good Pinot Noir, too.

D'ARENBERG ★★★★ (McLaren Vale)
Firmly traditional winemaking produces powerfully rich Shiraz capable of almost infinite aging, sweetly fruity Custodian Grenache and the densely structured Ironstone Pressings. Dead Arm is Cabernet and Shiraz; The Other Side is Chardonnay; Twentyeight Road is Mourvèdre and Nostalgia is 12-year-old fortified.

DELATITE ★★★★ (Victoria) Wines
with individuality of style plus superb wine-making which puts them in the top class. Dry Riesling is delicious, the sweet version superb, while Pinot Noir, Gewürz, Cabernet and Shiraz are brilliant.

DROMANA ★★★(★) (Victoria)
Excellent Chardonnay, promising Pinot Noir and Cabernet-Merlot in the Mornington Peninsula, as well as the good-value Schinus-Molle label.

EVANS & TATE ★★★(★) (Western
Australia) Beautifully crafted, stylish wines; in particular weighty Semillon (straight and blended with Sauvignon), Merlot and Shiraz.

GOUNDREY ★★★(★) (Western
Australia) Wines of real concentration, including the Windy Hill pairing of Chardonnay and Cabernet, and the soft, coffee bean aromas of Shiraz from Mount Barker.

GREEN POINT ★★★★ (Yarra Valley)
Moët & Chandon's Australian outpost, making possibly Australia's best sparklers, from Champagne grape varieties.

HENSCHKE ★★★★★ (South Australia)
Old red vines, some of them 100 years old, that yield deep, dark, currancy wines of top class. Cyril Henschke Cabernet Sauvignon is terrifically rich. Whites equally stunning – Riesling, Semillon and Chardonnay.

HERITAGE ★★★(★) (Barossa) In a
region filled with boisterous winemakers, Heritage is a hidden gem, quietly producing classic wines from a wide range of varieties – limy Riesling, softly honeyed Semillon and an elegant Cabernet Franc.

HILL-SMITH/YALUMBA ★★★★
(South Australia) A large Barossa company producing good wines under the Yalumba and Hill-Smith labels, and exceptional ones under the Signature, Heggies and Pewsey Vale Vineyard labels, where dry and sweet Rieslings are some of the finest in Australia. Yalumba D is very good fizz. Look out for The Octavius III Shiraz and Antipodean – Sauvignon Blanc, Semillon and Viognier – from Yalumba.

HOLLICK ★★★ (South Australia) Some
of Coonawarra's suavest reds; rich Wilgha Shiraz/Cabernet and an outstanding Cabernet cuvée, Ravenswood. There is also fine Pinot and Chardonnay fizz and the district's most successful Riesling.

HOWARD PARK ★★★(★) (Western
Australia) Expensive but superb, long-living wines. Intense, structured Chardonnay and rich Cabernet Merlot. Both need cellaring.

KNAPPSTEIN ★★★ (South Australia) Ageworthy Riesling, spicy, restrained Traminer, nutty, long Chardonnay and ripe, grassy Cabernet Franc.

LAKE'S FOLLY ★★★★ (New South Wales) Tiny Hunter Valley winery making highly idiosyncratic Chardonnay and Cabernet, very exciting with age.

LEEUWIN ESTATE ★★★★ (Western Australia) Ultra-high profile, ultra-high prices for exciting Chardonnay and Pinot Noir, blackcurrant-and-leather Cabernet Sauvignon, good Riesling and Sauvignon. Prelude Cabernet Sauvignon is tops.

LINDEMANS ★★★★ (Victoria) Vineyards in the Hunter, Padthaway, Coonawarra and Barossa. Exceptionally good basic varietals, while Coonawarras, Padthaways and Hunters are among Australia's finest. Coonawarra reds Limestone Ridge and St George are tip-top, as is the Bordeaux blend, Pyrus.

MCWILLIAMS ★★(★) (New South Wales) Old-fashioned giant now rapidly improving its quality. Blends like the Hillside Colombard-Chardonnay show what can be done with fairly basic fruit. Unoaked Elizabeth Semillon repays aging.

CHARLES MELTON ★★★★ (South Australia) A 1000-case Barossa winery with Grenache-based Nine Popes and a Shiraz of exceptional concentration and character.

GEOFF MERRILL ★★★(★) (South Australia) Wines here include worthy Cabernet, full Chardonnay, crisp Sauvignon-Semillon and thirst-quenching Grenache rosé at Mount Hurtle.

MILDARA-BLASS ★★★ (South Australia) Rapidly expanding, cash-rich company. Own labels include Jamieson's Run and Robertson's Well and the Coonawarra reds are beginning to live up to their potential, while prices stay reasonable. Chardonnay is also improving, but Sauvignon and Pinot Noir need a bit of work yet. See also entries for subsidiaries Baileys, Wolf Blass, Rothbury, St Hubert's and Tisdall.

MITCHELTON ★★★(★) (Victoria) Wide range of styles, notably fine, full-flavoured Rieslings, good Chardonnay under the Preece label and the speciality of the house, Marsanne. Also new Rhône blends: Mitchelton III white is Marsanne, Roussanne and Mourvèdre; Mitchelton III red is Shiraz, Grenache and Mourvèdre.

MOORILLA ESTATE ★★(★) (Tasmania) A polished range of crisp, cool-climate wines. Pinot Noir is a speciality; aromatic Riesling, Chardonnay and Gewürztraminer are also good.

MATURITY CHART
1995 Clare Riesling
The best age as well as German Rieslings but go into a shell between three and six years old

Bottled	Ready	Peak	Tiring	In decline

0 1 2 3 4 5 6 7 8 9 10 11 12 13 14 15 16 17 18 19 20 years

MORRIS ★★★★(★) (Rutherglen) The leading producer of sweet liqueur Muscat and Tokay which give a new meaning to the words 'intense' and 'concentrated'.

MOSS WOOD ★★★★ (Western Australia) Superbly original wines. Semillon, with and without wood-aging, is some of the best in Australia. Pinot Noir is daring and delicious, Chardonnay less daring but just as delicious, Cabernet rich and structured. All have lots of polished fruit.

MOUNTADAM ★★★★(★) (South Australia) French-trained Adam Wynn makes complex, Burgundian Chardonnay, substantial Pinot Noir, idiosyncratic Riesling and lean Cabernet. The Red is a Cabernet/Merlot blend, and there's good rosé fizz, too.

MOUNT LANGI-GHIRAN ★★★★ (Victoria) Great Western winery making richly flavoured, dry, intense Shiraz and long-lived Cabernet. New is Pinot Grigio.

MOUNT MARY ★★★★ (Victoria) Finely structured Cabernet-based Bordeaux blend and a Pinot Noir improving with age. Tiny production, much sought-after.

ORLANDO ★★★ (South Australia) Barossa winery with fine quality at every level. Its boxed wine is outstanding, its RF Cabernet, Riesling and Chardonnay are usually the best in the price bracket, and St Helga Riesling, St Hilary Chardonnay and St Hugo Cabernet are among the best. Excellent Jacaranda Ridge Cabernet from Coonawarra.

PENFOLDS ★★★★★ (South Australia) Great red winemakers, and now good in whites too, particularly Old Vine Barossa Valley Semillon. Its basics are clean and tasty, its varietals packed with flavour, and its special selection reds, culminating in the deservedly legendary Grange Hermitage, are superlative, hugely structured wines of world class. If you can't afford Grange, try Bin 28, Bin 128, Bin 389 or the 407 Cabernet Sauvignon.

PENLEY ESTATE ★★★★ (South Australia) There's rich, concentrated Shiraz/Cabernet from here as well as ageworthy Cabernet Sauvignon, supple Phoenix Cabernet and elegant Chardonnay.

PETALUMA ★★★★(★) (South Australia) Croser fizz is always correct, and his tip-top Chardonnay deserves ageing. Riesling is limy and elegant. Red Coonawarra is good, but the whites are even better.

PIPERS BROOK ★★★★ (Tasmania) Steely aromatic Riesling, classically reserved Chardonnay, serious Pinot Noir and tasty, barrel-fermented Sauvignon Blanc are joined by elegant Tamar Cabernet and rounder Bordeaux blend Opimian.

PLANTAGENET ★★★(★) (Western Australia) Noted for peppery Shiraz, melony/nutty Chardonnay, fine limy Riesling and elegant Cabernet Sauvignon. Sparkling wine is good too, as is Pinot Noir.

REYNOLDS ★★★★ (Upper Hunter Valley) This recently established estate has already built a reputation with excellent chocolaty Cabernet, powerful Shiraz and well-structured Semillon.

ROCKFORD ★★★★(★) (South Australia) The individuality of Rocky O'Callaghan's wines, especially his Basket Press Shiraz, has made him a Barossa cult. Grenache and Riesling are marvellous, too, and all improve with aging.

ROSEMOUNT ★★★(★) (New South Wales) The company which did more than any to help Australia take Britain by storm with Chardonnay, Fumé Blanc and Cabernet. The last two are no longer so good, though Chardonnay is on the way back and the single-vineyard Roxburgh and Show Reserve Chardonnays are impressive. Also surprising Pinot Noir and excellent Semillon and Shiraz.

ROTHBURY ★★★★ (New South Wales) Idiosyncratic but successful under Len Evans' obsessive control, and too early to say what new owners Mildara Blass will do here. Capable of producing the Hunter's greatest Semillon and juicy, fat crowd-pleasing Chardonnays. Some great Shiraz and Pinot Noir on occasion, too.

ST HALLETT ★★★★ (South Australia) Full, oaky Semillon and Chardonnay and a rich Shiraz, Old Block, from old vines. Gamekeeper's Reserve is Shiraz, Grenache, Mourvèdre and Touriga Nacional, brambly and spicy. One of the leading names in the Barossa revival.

ST HUBERTS ★★★(★) (Victoria) At best produces superb Chardonnays, exciting Cabernets and Pinots plus the odd thrilling sweetie, but has never settled into a totally reliable groove and some vintages fail to convince.

SEPPELT ★★★ (Victoria) Leading makers of quality fizz from Champagne grapes, peaking with Salinger. Also fruity, easy-drinking styles, and blackberryish sparkling red Shiraz.

SHAW & SMITH ★★★★ (South Australia) Fine Sauvignon Blanc and Chardonnay, including unoaked Chardonnay.

STAFFORD RIDGE ★★★★(★) (Adelaide Hills) Crisply intense and pure Sauvignon Blanc and delicate but long Chardonnay.

STONIER'S MERRICKS ★★★ (Victoria) Good cool climate Chardonnay and Cabernet from this Mornington Peninsula winery.

TALTARNI ★★★ (Victoria) Remarkable bone-dry, grassy-sharp Fumé Blanc; fine Cabernet and Shiraz which soften (after about a decade) into classy, if austere reds.

TISDALL ★★★ (Victoria) Mildara-owned winery with excellent grape sources, but has never quite lived up to its exceptional potential. If less oak were used the fruit would sing through. That said, there's good Chardonnay here and Mount Ida Reserve Shiraz is a cracker.

TYRRELL'S ★★★(★) (New South Wales) Eccentrically brilliant Hunter winery which sells 'port' and 'blackberry nip' to tourists through the front door while making some classic wines out the back. Vat 1 Semillon is excellent, as is the 'plonk' – Long Flat Red and White, named after the vineyard.

VASSE FELIX ★★★★ (Western Australia) One of the original Margaret River wineries, producing a classic regional style of rich, leafy, curranty Cabernet and spicy, fleshy Shiraz. Classic Dry White is a blend of Chardonnay, Semillon and Sauvignon Blanc.

WIRRA WIRRA ★★★★ (South Australia) Fine, concentrated reds, whites and sparkling wine, and exceptional Angelus Cabernet.

WYNNS ★★★★ (South Australia) Big, oaky Chardonnay, refined Cabernet and Shiraz from this Coonawarra company. Top-line John Riddoch Cabernet is expensive but worth every penny.

YARRA YERING ★★★★★ (Victoria) Wonderful Yarra Valley winery, where Bailey Carrodus labels his Cabernet-based wine Dry Red No.1 and his Shiraz-based wine Dry Red No.2: exceptional, powerful and concentrated yet fragrant reds. Fine Pinot Noir and Chardonnay as well, in a very personal style.

AUSTRALIA PRICE GUIDES

RED

Under £4.00

Non-vintage
Dalwood Dry Red Penfolds £3.45 (SOM)
1996
Shiraz/Cabernet Hardys Southern Creek
£3.99 (WAI)
★ Malbec/Ruby Cabernet Angove's Nanya
Estate £3.99 (BOT) £3.99 (THR) £3.99
(WR)

£4.00 → £4.49

Non-vintage
Dry Red David Wynn £4.35 (FLE)
1996
Shiraz/Cabernet Lindemans Cawarra
£4.49 (MAJ)
Shiraz/Cabernet Sauvignon Hardys Stamp
£4.49 (CO) £4.49 (SAF) £4.49 (VIC) £4.49
(SAI)
Shiraz/Merlot Barramundi £4.29 (CO)
1995
Rawson's Retreat Bin 35 Penfolds £4.35
(SOM)
Shiraz/Cabernet Lindemans Cawarra
£4.49 (SAI) £4.49 (UN)
Shiraz/Cabernet Orlando Jacob's Creek
£4.39 (WR) £4.39 (BOT) £4.39 (THR)
1994
Jacob's Creek Red Orlando £4.49 (FUL)
Shiraz/Cabernet Penfolds Rowlands
Brook £4.49 (JON)
1992
Shiraz Lindemans Bin 50 £4.49 (FUL)
1990
Grenache Peter Lehmann £4.49
(FUL)

£4.50 → £4.99

1996
Grenache Peter Lehmann £4.99 (ASD)
★ Grenache Salisbury £4.99 (VIC)
Jacob's Creek Red Orlando £4.99 (SAI)
Rawson's Retreat Bin 35 Penfolds £4.99
(VIC)
Shiraz/Cabernet Orlando Jacob's Creek
£4.99 (GRE)
Tarrango Brown Brothers £4.99 (POR)
£4.99 (WAI) £4.99 (VIC)
1995
Cabernet Sauvignon Deakin Estate £4.99
(VIC)
Cabernet Sauvignon/Shiraz Hardys
Nottage Hill £4.99 (GRE) £4.99 (VIC)
Cabernet Sauvignon/Shiraz Yalumba
Oxford Landing £4.99 (NI) £4.99 (NA)
Jacob's Creek Red Orlando £4.50 (HOG)
£4.99 (NEW)
Long Flat Red Tyrrells £4.99 (HOG)
Rawson's Retreat Bin 35 Penfolds £4.95
(WS) £4.95 (POR) £4.99 (WR) £4.99 (BOT)
£4.99 (THR) £4.99 (SAF)
Shiraz/Cabernet Orlando Jacob's Creek
£4.99 (VIC) £4.99 (SAF)
Shiraz/Cabernet Yalumba Oxford Landing
£4.99 (BOT) £4.99 (WR) £4.99 (THR)
Shiraz/Mourvèdre Penfolds Bin 2 £4.80
(SOM)
Shiraz/Mourvèdre Adam Wynn Canoe
Tree £4.85 (AUR)
Tarrango Brown Brothers £4.99 (JON)
1994
Cabernet Sauvignon Lindemans Bin 45
£4.99 (UN)
Rawson's Retreat Bin 35 Penfolds £4.99
(JON)

MERCHANTS SPECIALIZING IN AUSTRALIA
see Merchant Directory (page 413) for details

Everybody wants to buy Australian wines,
and virtually every merchant will be able to
sell you something. But if you want
something other than the usual names, try:
Adnams (AD), Australian Wine Centre
(AUS), Averys of Bristol (AV), Bennetts
(BEN), Bibendum (BIB), Anthony Byrne (BY),
Direct Wine (DI), Eldridge Pope (EL), Lay &
Wheeler (LAY), Oddbins (OD), James
Nicholson (NI), The Nobody Inn (NO),
Terry Platt (PLA), Philglas & Swiggot,
Raeburn Fine Wines (RAE), Roberson (ROB),
Sainsbury (SAI), Safeway (SAF), Sommelier
Wine Co (SOM), Tanners (TAN), Thresher
(THR), The Ubiquitous Chip (UB), Wine
Society (WS)

Shiraz Lindemans Bin 50 £4.99 (UN)
Shiraz/Cabernet Penfolds Koonunga Hill
£4.99 (SO)
Shiraz/Mourvèdre Penfolds Bin 2 £4.99
(HOG)
Shiraz/Mourvèdre Adam Wynn Canoe
Tree £4.95 (BU)
1993
Shiraz/Mourvèdre Penfolds Bin 2 £4.99
(FUL)
1992
Cabernet Sauvignon Lindemans Bin 45
£4.99 (FUL)
Cabernet Sauvignon/Shiraz Yalumba
Oxford Landing £4.99 (FUL)
1990
Cabernet Sauvignon/Shiraz Hardys
Nottage Hill £4.99 (SO)

£5.00 → £5.49

1996
Tarrango Brown Brothers £5.10 (ROS)
£5.29 (NA) £5.35 (PLA)
1995
Cabernet Sauvignon Lindemans Bin 45
£5.49 (MAJ) £5.49 (SAI) £5.49 (VIC)
Cabernet Sauvignon Red Cliffs
Coonawarra £5.49 (BOT) £5.49 (THR)
£5.49 (WR)
Cabernet Sauvignon Sunnycliff £5.49 (JON)
Shiraz/Mourvèdre Penfolds Bin 2 £5.30
(NO) £5.45 (WS) £5.49 (POR) £5.49 (VIC)
£5.49 (WAI)
1994
Cabernet Sauvignon Berri £5.24 (ROS)
Cabernet Sauvignon Lindemans Bin 45
£5.44 (PEN)
Cabernet Sauvignon/Shiraz Penfolds
Koonunga Hill £5.20 (SOM) £5.39 (HOG)
Shiraz/Mourvèdre Penfolds Bin 2 £5.49
(JON)
1993
Cabernet Sauvignon Orlando £5.02
(HOG)
Cabernet Sauvignon Orlando RF £5.29
(VIC)
Dry Red David Wynn £5.40 (HIC)
1992
Cabernet Sauvignon/Shiraz Berri £5.49
(FUL)
Long Flat Red Tyrrells £5.39 (JON)
Shiraz/Cabernet Sauvignon Rouge
Homme £5.49 (FUL)
Shiraz/Mourvèdre Penfolds Bin 2 £5.19
(WATT)

£5.50 → £5.99

1996
Cabernet/Shiraz Rosemount £5.99 (ASD)
Jacob's Creek Red Orlando £5.50 (FOR)
Shiraz David Wynn £5.55 (SOM)
Shiraz/Cabernet Rosemount £5.99 (NEW)
£5.99 (SAF)
Tarrango Brown Brothers £5.78 (NO)
1995
Cabernet Sauvignon Lindemans Bin 45
£5.50 (WHI) £5.59 (JON)
Cabernet Sauvignon Sunnycliff £5.75 (POR)
Cabernet Sauvignon David Wynn £5.55
(SOM)
Long Flat Red Tyrrells £5.50 (GRE)
Pinot Noir David Wynn £5.55 (SOM)
Shiraz Lindemans Bin 50 £5.50 (WHI)
£5.79 (MAJ)
Shiraz Rosemount £5.99 (MAR)
Shiraz Wyndham's Bin 555 £5.99 (MAJ)
Shiraz/Cabernet Penfolds Koonunga Hill
£5.99 (WR) £5.99 (BOT) £5.99 (THR)
Shiraz/Cabernet Rosemount £5.99 (SAI)
1994
Cabernet Sauvignon Berri £5.95 (UN)
Cabernet Sauvignon Rosemount £5.99 (BO)
Cabernet Sauvignon Salisbury Estate
£5.64 (ROS)
Cabernet Sauvignon Seaview £5.69 (OD)
★ Cabernet Sauvignon Wakefield £5.99 (UN)
Cabernet Sauvignon/Shiraz Yalumba
Oxford Landing £5.69 (JON)
Long Flat Red Tyrrells £5.70 (PIP) £5.99
(AME)
Shiraz Mildara £5.99 (DI)
Shiraz Rothbury £5.99 (FUL)
Shiraz Wynns £5.99 (BOT) £5.99 (THR)
Shiraz/Cabernet Penfolds Koonunga Hill
£5.99 (JON)
Shiraz/Cabernet Sauvignon Krondorf
£5.92 (HOG)
Shiraz/Mourvèdre Penfolds Bin 2 £5.50 (VIG)
1993
Shiraz/Cabernet Penfolds Koonunga Hill
£5.95 (WS)

£6.00 → £6.49

1996
Shiraz d'Arenberg Old Vine £6.49 (OD)
1995
Cabernet Sauvignon Rosemount £6.49
(BOT) £6.49 (THR) £6.49 (WR)
Cabernet Sauvignon Wolf Blass Yellow
Label £6.15 (HOG)

Cabernet Sauvignon/Shiraz Penfolds
Koonunga Hill £6.45 (SAI) £6.49 (OD)
£6.49 (POR) £6.49 (VIC)
Cabernet/Mourvèdre Grant Burge
Oakland £6.25 (STA) £6.30 (AS)
Grenache Basedow Bush Vine £6.49 (VIC)
Long Flat Red Tyrrells £6.00 (TAN)
Shiraz Baileys £6.35 (GRE)
Shiraz Best's Victoria £6.39 (NI)
Shiraz/Cabernet Penfolds Koonunga Hill
£6.49 (SAF)

1994

Cabernet Sauvignon Basedow £6.45 (VIC)
Shiraz Baileys £6.49 (CO)
Shiraz Best's Victoria £6.49 (FUL)
Shiraz Lindemans Bin 50 £6.15 (BEN)
Shiraz Taltarni £6.45 (REI)
Shiraz Wynns £6.49 (WHI)

1993

Cabernet Sauvignon Rosemount £6.49 (FUL)
Cabernet Sauvignon/Shiraz Penfolds
Koonunga Hill £6.49 (BO)
Pinot Noir Tyrrells £6.32 (PEN)
Shiraz/Cabernet Penfolds Koonunga Hill
£6.33 (NO)
Shiraz/Cabernet Sauvignon Rouge
Homme £6.49 (WHI)

1989

Cabernet Sauvignon Seppelt Partalunga
£6.49 (FUL)
Cabernet Seppelt Dorrien £6.49 (FUL)

£6.50 → £6.99

1996

Cabernet/Merlot Tyrrells Old Winery
£6.75 (STA)
Shiraz David Wynn £6.99 (AD)
Shiraz/Cabernet Rosemount £6.50 (FOR)

1995

Cabernet Sauvignon Wolf Blass £6.89 (WHI)
Cabernet/Merlot Tyrrells Old Winery
£6.95 (SAI)
Cabernet/Shiraz Riddoch £6.99 (OD)
Long Flat Red Tyrrells £6.60 (GN)
Shiraz Lindemans Bin 50 £6.55 (BY)
Shiraz Rosemount £6.99 (VIC)
Shiraz Wynns £6.99 (MAJ)
Shiraz/Cabernet Sauvignon Stonyfell
Metala £6.95 (POR)

1994

Cabernet Sauvignon Brown Bros £6.99 (DI)
Cabernet Sauvignon Rosemount £6.99
(SAI) £6.99 (SO)
Cabernet Sauvignon Wolf Blass Yellow
Label £6.99 (SAF) £6.99 (SO)

Cabernet Sauvignon David Wynn £6.95
(AD)
Cabernet Sauvignon/Franc/Merlot St
Hallett £6.65 (REI)
Cabernet/Merlot Tyrrells Old Winery
£6.99 (UN)
Cabernet/Shiraz Riddoch £6.99 (BO)
Pinot Noir David Wynn £6.99 (NI)
Shiraz Baileys £6.79 (AME) £6.95 (STA)
Shiraz Brown Bros £6.85 (ROS) £6.99 (DI)
Shiraz Chateau Tahbilk £6.95 (WS)
Shiraz Leasingham £6.99 (TES)
Shiraz Rothbury £6.99 (DI) £6.99 (OD)
Shiraz St Hallett £6.65 (REI)
Shiraz Wyndham's Bin 555 £6.79 (NA)
Shiraz/Cabernet Sauvignon Stonyfell
Metala £6.99 (SAF)

1993

Cabernet Sauvignon Brown Bros Milawa
£6.99 (JON)
Cabernet Sauvignon Wolf Blass Yellow
Label £6.69 (POR)
Cabernet Sauvignon Wyndham's Bin 444
£6.79 (NA)
Cabernet Sauvignon/Franc/Merlot St
Hallett £6.95 (SOM)
Cabernet/Merlot Chateau Reynella £6.99
(CO)
Shiraz Basedow £6.72 (HOG)
Shiraz Brown Bros £6.99 (GRE)
Shiraz Penfolds Kalimna Bin 28 £6.80 (SOM)
Shiraz Wynns £6.95 (POR)

1992

Cabernet/Malbec Leasingham £6.99 (CO)
Shiraz Penfolds Coonawarra Bin 128
£6.90 (SOM)

1990

Cabernet Sauvignon Taltarni £6.85 (REI)

£7.00 → £7.49

1995

Cabernet Sauvignon Brown Bros £7.40 (PIP)
Cabernet Sauvignon Rosemount £7.49
(NEW)
Shiraz Best's Victoria £7.46 (PLA)
Shiraz Brown Bros £7.39 (WHI) £7.40 (PIP)
Shiraz/Cabernet Penfolds Koonunga Hill
£7.14 (GN)

> *Stars (★) indicate wines
> selected by Oz Clarke in the
> Best Buys section which begins
> on page 12.*

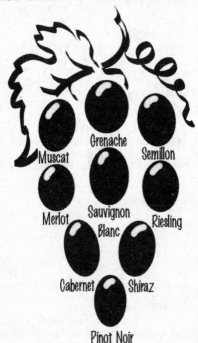

1994

Cabernet Sauvignon Brown Bros £7.49 (CO)
Cabernet Sauvignon Peter Lehmann £7.49
(SAF)
Cabernet/Merlot Cape Mentelle £7.25 (REI)
Cabernet/Merlot St Hallett £7.49 (AUS)
Cabernet/Shiraz Riddoch £7.00 (BIB)
Coonawarra Red Jamiesons Run £7.43
(HOG)
Shiraz Brown Bros £7.49 (NA)
Shiraz/Cabernet Peter Lehmann Clancy's
£7.45 (SAI)

1993

Cabernet Sauvignon Brown Bros £7.49 (NA)
Cabernet Sauvignon Capel Vale £7.33 (FLE)
Cabernet Sauvignon Chateau Tahbilk
£7.25 (GRE)
Cabernet Sauvignon Penfolds Bin 407
£7.35 (SOM)
Cabernet/Shiraz Riddoch £7.49 (BOT)
£7.49 (WR) £7.49 (THR)
Shiraz Penfolds Coonawarra Bin 128
£7.19 (HOG)
Shiraz Penfolds Kalimna Bin 28 £7.19 (HOG)
Shiraz Riddoch Limited Release £7.49
(BOT) £7.49 (WR) £7.49 (THR)
Shiraz/Cabernet Sauvignon Rouge
Homme £7.45 (ROB)

1992

Shiraz Penfolds Kalimna Bin 28 £7.49 (WATT)

1991

Cabernet/Shiraz Hill-Smith £7.25 (WS)

£7.50 → £7.99

Non-vintage

Shiraz Penfolds Coonawarra Bin 128
£7.99 (BO)

1996

Cabernet Sauvignon Mitchelton Preece
£7.50 (GRE)
Shiraz Chateau Yaldara Reserve £7.81 (PLA)

1995

Cabernet Sauvignon Rosemount £7.50 (FOR)
Cabernet Sauvignon Wolf Blass Yellow
Label £7.67 (BY)
Cabernet/Shiraz Wirra Wirra Church
Block £7.99 (AUR)
Shiraz Baileys £7.70 (GN)
Shiraz Montara Estate £7.72 (FLE)
Shiraz Penfolds Kalimna Bin 28 £7.99 (BOT)

1994

Cabernet Franc Tim Knappstein £7.93 (PLA)
Cabernet Sauvignon Best's £7.50 (FLE)
Cabernet Sauvignon Brown Bros £7.76
(PEN) £7.80 (TAN) £7.95 (AD)

Cabernet Sauvignon Penfolds Bin 407
£7.99 (BOT) £7.99 (THR) £7.99 (WR)
Cabernet/Malbec Leasingham £7.99 (GRE)
Cabernet/Merlot Cape Mentelle £7.99 (NI)
Cabernet/Merlot Goundrey Langton
£7.79 (WHI)
Cabernet/Shiraz Wirra Wirra Church
Block £7.95 (WS)
Grenache Tim Gramp £7.73 (FLE)
Grenache Rockford Dry Country £7.95
(FLE)
Shiraz Basedow £7.99 (VIC)
Shiraz Brown Bros £7.76 (PEN) £7.80
(TAN) £7.95 (POR)
Shiraz Campbell's Bobbie Burns £7.95 (UB)
Shiraz Cape Mentelle £7.99 (NI)
Shiraz Mitchell Peppertree £7.90 (SOM)
£7.99 (JON)
Shiraz Penfolds Coonawarra Bin 128
£7.99 (SO)
Shiraz Penfolds Kalimna Bin 28 £7.99
(BOT) £7.99 (WR) £7.99 (THR)
Shiraz St Hallett £7.99 (AUS) £7.99 (BOT)
£7.99 (WR) £7.99 (THR)
★ Shiraz St Hallett Blackwell £7.99 (AUS)
★ Shiraz The Willows £7.99 (AUS)
Shiraz David Wynn Patriarch £7.95 (SOM)

1993

Cabernet Sauvignon Mitchell £7.99 (JON)
Cabernet/Merlot St Hallett £7.50 (FLE)
Grenache Rockford Dry Country £7.99
(FUL)
Shiraz Leasingham £7.99 (GRE)
Shiraz/Grenache/Mourvèdre Penfolds Old
Vine £7.80 (SOM)

1992

Cabernet Sauvignon Pewsey Vale £7.95
(SAI)
Cabernet/Merlot St Hallett £7.56 (LON)
Coonawarra Red Jamiesons Run £7.95 (GRE)
Merlot Taltarni £7.95 (WS)
Shiraz Cape Mentelle £7.75 (REI)
Shiraz Charles Melton £7.95 (SOM)

1991

Cabernet Sauvignon Cassegrain £7.65 (ROB)
Cabernet Sauvignon Taltarni £7.95 (WS)

Please remember that
Webster's *is a price
guide and not a price list. It
is not meant to replace up-
to-date
merchants' lists.*

1990
Cabernet Sauvignon Orlando St Hugo
£7.69 (HOG)
1987
Cabernet Sauvignon Vasse Felix £7.50 (REI)

£8.00 ➜ £8.49

1996
Shiraz/Grenache Veritas Christa-Rolf
£8.20 (LAY)
1995
Cabernet/Merlot St Hallett £8.11 (DOM)
Merlot Trentham £8.03 (ELL)
Shiraz Basedow £8.00 (BIB)
Shiraz Mitchell Peppertree £8.45 (AD)
£8.49 (POR)
Shiraz/Cabernet Peter Lehmann Clancy's
£8.25 (EL)
1994
Cabernet Sauvignon Jim Barry £8.00 (TAN)
Pinot Noir Tasmanian Wine Company
£8.15 (PEN)
Shiraz Wirra Wirra R.S.W. £8.40 (SOM)
★ Shiraz/Malbec/Cabernet Hollick Wilgha
£8.20 (LAY)
1993
Shiraz Penfolds Kalimna Bin 28 £8.10
(PEN) £8.20 (TAN)
1992
Cabernet Sauvignon Montara Estate £8.25
(BU)
Cabernet Sauvignon/Merlot Hollick
Coonawarra £8.45 (SOM)
1991
Cabernet Sauvignon Capel Vale £8.49 (AME)
Cabernet Sauvignon Penfolds Bin 407
£8.13 (WATT)

£8.50 ➜ £8.99

1995
Cabernet Sauvignon Brown Bros £8.70 (GN)
★ The Fergus Tim Adams £8.99 (AUS)
Grenache Rockford Dry Country £8.70
(PIP)
Pinot Noir Hollick £8.95 (LAY)
Pinot Noir Montara £8.95 (PIP)
Pinot Noir Yarra Valley Hills £8.99 (EL)
Shiraz Brown Bros £8.70 (GN)
Shiraz Taltarni £8.62 (AV)
1994
Angelus Wirra Wirra £8.95 (SOM)
Cabernet Sauvignon Leconfield £8.95 (POR)
Cabernet Sauvignon Mitchell £8.95 (POR)
Cabernet/Merlot Cape Mentelle £8.95
(POR)

Cabernet/Merlot Chateau Reynella £8.99
(ASD)
Grenache Tim Gramp £8.72 (NO)
Grenache Rockford Dry Country £8.75
(WS)
Richardsons Red Block Rouge Homme
£8.99 (AME)
Shiraz Tim Adams £8.99 (TES) £8.99 (AUS)
Shiraz Cape Mentelle £8.99 (PLA)
Shiraz Penfolds Coonawarra Bin 128
£8.99 (POR)
Shiraz Penfolds Kalimna Bin 28 £8.99 (POR)
Shiraz Penley Estate Hyland £8.50 (AUS)
Shiraz Taltarni £8.50 (STA)
Shiraz David Wynn Patriarch £8.54 (FLE)
Zinfandel Cape Mentelle £8.95 (STA)
1993
Cabernet Sauvignon Houghton Gold
Reserve £8.95 (WS)
Cabernet Sauvignon Penfolds
Coonawarra £8.50 (SOM)
Cabernet Sauvignon Wynns £8.99 (UN)
Cabernet Sauvignon Wynns Coonawarra
£8.95 (VIG)
Cabernet/Shiraz Penfolds Bin 389 £8.65
(SOM)
Shiraz Best's Victoria £8.95 (GRE)
Shiraz Penfolds Coonawarra Bin 128
£8.65 (BY) £8.90 (BEN) £8.99 (TES)
1992
Cabernet Sauvignon Penfolds Bin 407
£8.99 (SAF)
Cabernet/Shiraz Penfolds Bin 389 £8.99
(FUL)
1991
Cabernet Sauvignon Wynns Coonawarra
£8.99 (AME)
Merlot Taltarni £8.99 (AME)
Shiraz Taltarni £8.99 (AME)

£9.00 ➜ £9.99

1996
Pinot Noir Coldstream Hills £9.65 (NEZ)
Pinot Noir Stonier's £9.99 (WAT)
1995
Grenache Rockford Dry Country £9.10
(TAN)
Shiraz Campbell's Bobbie Burns £9.40
(PIP)
Shiraz Chateau Reynella Basket Pressed
£9.99 (WAI)
Shiraz Mitchell Peppertree £9.20 (PIP)
Shiraz Pikes Polish Hill River £9.95 (LEA)
Shiraz Rothbury Reserve £9.99 (DI)
Shiraz Veritas Heysen Vineyard £9.50 (LAY)

1994

Cabernet Sauvignon Katnook £9.99 (VIC)

Cabernet Sauvignon Penfolds Bin 407
£9.90 (GN)

Cabernet Sauvignon Wolf Blass
President's Selection £9.41 (HOG) £9.99
(GRE)

Cabernet/Merlot Chateau Reynella £9.95
(SAI)

Cabernet/Shiraz Penfolds Bin 389 £9.99
(BOT) £9.99 (THR) £9.99 (WR)

Pinot Noir Pipers Brook £9.75 (SOM)

Richardsons Red Block Rouge Homme
£9.99 (DI)

Sangiovese Coriole £9.80 (GAU)

Shiraz Campbell's Bobbie Burns £9.59 (DI)
£9.78 (GN)

Shiraz Cape Mentelle £9.04 (NO) £9.95 (AD)

Shiraz Coriole £9.20 (TAN)

Shiraz Mount Langi Ghiran £9.99 (GRE)

Shiraz Penfolds Kalimna Bin 28 £9.20 (PIP)

Shiraz Taltarni £9.40 (PEN)

Shiraz Wirra Wirra R.S.W. £9.99 (AUR)

Zinfandel Cape Mentelle £9.49 (NO) £9.95
(VIG) £9.95 (POR)

1993

Angelus Wirra Wirra £9.99 (FUL)

Cabernet Sauvignon Best's £9.99 (AUS)

Cabernet Sauvignon Penfolds Bin 407
£9.13 (NO)

Cabernet Sauvignon Penfolds
Coonawarra £9.99 (CO) £9.99 (MAJ)

Cabernet Sauvignon Rosemount Show
Reserve £9.99 (TES)

Cabernet Sauvignon Wynns Coonawarra
£9.99 (VIC) £9.99 (MAJ)

Cabernet Sauvignon/Merlot Hollick
Coonawarra £9.95 (LAY)

Cabernet Sauvignon/Shiraz Penley Estate
Coonawarra £9.50 (AUS)

Sangiovese Coriole £9.95 (ROB)

Shiraz Baileys 1920 Block £9.75 (BU)

Shiraz Best's Victoria £9.99 (UN)

Shiraz Hardy McLaren Vale £9.45 (BER)

Shiraz David Wynn Patriarch £9.85 (NI)

Shiraz/Cabernet Henschke Eden Valley
Keyneton Estate £9.99 (SOM)

Shiraz/Cabernet Penley Estate £9.50 (AUS)

1992

Cabernet Sauvignon Best's £9.99 (UN)

Cabernet Sauvignon Cape Mentelle £9.65
(NI)

Cabernet Sauvignon St Huberts £9.99 (JON)

Merlot Katnook £9.99 (VIC)

Pinot Noir Cullens £9.70 (GAU)

1991

Cabernet Sauvignon Katnook £9.99 (VIC)

Cabernet Sauvignon Mount Langi Ghiran
£9.99 (DI)

Cabernet Sauvignon Taltarni £9.25 (STA)

Cabernet Sauvignon Wynns Coonawarra
£9.99 (POR)

1990

Cabernet Sauvignon Orlando St Hugo
£9.75 (UN)

1989

Cabernet Sauvignon Merricks Estate
£9.95 (VIG)

Cabernet Sauvignon Taltarni £9.95 (AME)

Coonawarra Red Jamiesons Run £9.26 (NO)

£10.00 → £10.99

1996

Nine Popes Charles Melton £10.99 (AUS)

Shiraz Charles Melton £10.99 (AUS)

1995

Pinot Noir Coldstream Hills £10.15 (PIP)

Shiraz Charles Melton £10.95 (AD)

1994

Angelus Wirra Wirra £10.25 (WS)

Cabernet Sauvignon Bowen Estate £10.10
(TAN) £10.99 (AUS)

Cabernet Sauvignon Katnook £10.95 (BIB)
£10.99 (BO)

Cabernet Sauvignon Wolf Blass
President's Selection £10.35 (WHI)

Cabernet/Shiraz Penfolds Bin 389 £10.81
(HOG)

Nine Popes Charles Melton £10.90 (SOM)

Pinot Noir Cullens £10.49 (AME)

Shiraz Bowen Estate £10.99 (AUS)

Shiraz Plantagenet £10.49 (NA) £10.75 (GRE)

Shiraz/Grenache/Mourvèdre Penfolds Old
Vine £10.56 (PEN)

1993

Cabernet Sauvignon Penfolds
Coonawarra £10.74 (BY)

Cabernet Sauvignon Plantagenet £10.49
(NA)

Cabernet Sauvignon Rouge Homme
£10.12 (AV)

Cabernet Sauvignon Wolf Blass
President's Selection £10.39 (HA)
£10.99 (VIC)

Cabernet/Merlot Reynolds £10.39 (GN)

Cabernet/Shiraz Penfolds Bin 389 £10.74
(BY) £10.75 (NO)

Nine Popes Charles Melton £10.95 (POR)

Shiraz St Hallett Old Block £10.50 (REI)

Shiraz Wirra Wirra R.S.W. £10.95 (AD)

1992
Cabernet Sauvignon Cape Mentelle
£10.50 (REI)
Shiraz Seppelt Black Label £10.25 (BER)
Shiraz/Cabernet Henschke Eden Valley
Keyneton Estate £10.99 (JON)
1990
Shiraz Tyrrells Vat 9 Winemakers
Selection £10.75 (REI)

£11.00 → £11.99

1996
Pinot Noir Stonier's £11.30 (GN)
Pinot Noir Yarra Valley Hills £11.99 (OD)
1995
Pinot Noir Pipers Brook £11.75 (GRE)
1994
Angelus Wirra Wirra £11.99 (AUR)
Cabernet Sauvignon/Merlot Petaluma
Coonawarra £11.99 (OD)
Cabernet/Shiraz Penfolds Bin 389 £11.95
(POR) £11.99 (OD)
Gaia Grosset £11.63 (DOM)
Pinot Noir Henschke Giles Lenswood
£11.95 (SOM)
Pinot Noir Mountadam £11.99 (WR)
£11.99 (THR) £11.99 (BOT)
Shiraz Jim Barry Macrae Wood £11.20
(TAN)
Shiraz Mount Langi Ghiran £11.95 (VIG)
Shiraz Rockford Basket Press £11.82 (FLE)
Shiraz St Hallett Old Block £11.50 (POR)
1993
Cabernet Sauvignon Cape Mentelle
£11.80 (TAN)
Cabernet/Shiraz Henschke Keyneton
Estate £11.39 (NO)
Durif Mick Morris £11.21 (NO)
Pyrus Lindemans £11.75 (PEN)
Shiraz Baileys 1920 Block £11.25 (DI)
Shiraz St Hallett Old Block £11.90 (FLE)
£11.95 (AD) £11.99 (WR) £11.99 (BOT)
1992
Cabernet Sauvignon Cape Mentelle
£11.39 (NO)
Cabernet/Shiraz Henschke Keyneton
Estate £11.50 (FLE)
Pinot Noir Cullens £11.15 (NO)
Shiraz Rockford Basket Press £11.99 (FUL)
1991
Cabernet Sauvignon/Merlot Cullens
£11.90 (GAU)
1990
Cabernet Sauvignon/Merlot Cullens
£11.99 (YOU)

1988
Shiraz Penfolds Magill Estate £11.70 (SOM)
1987
Cabernet Sauvignon Vasse Felix £11.50
(YOU)
Cabernet Sauvignon/Merlot Petaluma
Coonawarra £11.65 (SOM)

£12.00 → £13.99

1995
Nine Popes Charles Melton £12.50 (ENO)
£12.63 (FLE)
Pinot Noir Cullens £12.03 (NO)
Shiraz Charles Melton £12.50 (ENO)
1994
Cabernet Sauvignon Moss Wood £13.87
(NO)
Cabernet Sauvignon/Merlot Cullens
£13.50 (DI)
Cabernet Sauvignon/Merlot Howard Park
£13.50 (BAN)
Pinot Noir Henschke Giles Lenswood
£13.50 (NI) £13.95 (LAY)
Shiraz Jim Barry Macrae Wood £12.99
(OD) £13.00 (PIP) £13.95 (AD)
Shiraz Charles Melton £12.95 (ROB)
Shiraz Mount Langi Ghiran £12.00 (WS)
Shiraz Plantagenet £12.50 (LEA)
Shiraz Rockford Basket Press £13.50
(ENO) £13.99 (DI)
Shiraz Wirra Wirra R.S.W. £12.75 (BER)
1993
Cabernet Sauvignon De Bortoli £12.83
(NO) £13.95 (VIG)
Cabernet Sauvignon/Merlot Petaluma
£13.60 (BEN)
Limestone Ridge Lindemans £12.25 (WS)
£12.99 (POR) £12.99 (OD)
Pinot Noir Mountadam £12.70 (NO)
Pyrus Lindemans £12.99 (UN) £12.99 (SAF)
£12.99 (OD)
St George Lindemans £12.93 (PEN)
Shiraz De Bortoli £12.07 (NO) £12.50
(AUS) £12.95 (LEA) £12.99 (VIC)
Shiraz Plantagenet £12.00 (WS) £12.90 (BER)
Shiraz Rockford Basket Press £13.25 (AME)
Shiraz St Hallett Old Block £12.20 (LAY)
1992
Cabernet Sauvignon Moss Wood £12.97
(NO)
Cabernet Sauvignon/Merlot Cullens
£12.50 (WS)
Cabernet Sauvignon/Shiraz Penley Estate
Coonawarra £12.75 (DI)
Pinot Noir Wignalls £12.75 (ROB)

Pyrus Lindemans £12.99 (VIC)
Shiraz Rockford Basket Press £12.90 (GAU)
1991
Cabernet Sauvignon Cape Mentelle
£12.04 (NO) £12.04 (PLA)

Cabernet Sauvignon Vasse Felix £13.95
(ROB)
Durif Mick Morris £12.41 (NO)
Pinot Noir Mountadam £13.51 (NO)
Pinot Noir Pipers Brook £12.07 (PEN)
Pinot Noir Tyrrells £12.50 (REI)
Pyrus Lindemans £12.90 (NO)
St George Lindemans £12.90 (NO)
1990
Pyrus Lindemans £13.00 (NO)
Shiraz Tyrrells Vat 9 Winemakers
Selection £13.97 (HOG)
1989
Limestone Ridge Lindemans £12.29 (NO)
St George Lindemans £12.83 (BY)
1988
Cabernet Sauvignon Brown Bros Family
Reserve £12.50 (GRE)

£14.00 ➜ £15.99

1995
Nine Popes Charles Melton £14.75 (WRI)
Pinot Noir Coldstream Hills Reserve
£14.99 (OD)
1994
Cabernet Sauvignon Penley Estate
Coonawarra £14.99 (AUS)
Pinot Noir Yeringberg £14.50 (BIB)
Shiraz Jasper Hill Georgia's Paddock
£14.95 (YAP)
Shiraz/Cabernet Henschke Eden Valley
Keyneton Estate £15.65 (GN)
1993
Cabernet Sauvignon Penley Estate
Coonawarra £14.99 (AUS)
Cabernet Sauvignon/Merlot Petaluma
Coonawarra £14.95 (ROB)
Shiraz Henschke Mount Edelstone £14.55
(SOM)

1992
Cabernet Sauvignon Penley Estate
Coonawarra £14.99 (AUS)
Cabernet Yarra Yering Dry Red No.1
£15.95 (SOM)
Shiraz E&E Black Pepper Barossa Valley
£14.86 (NO)
Shiraz Henschke Mount Edelstone £15.99
(JON)
1991
Cabernet Sauvignon Penley Estate
Coonawarra £14.29 (YOU)

£16.00 ➜ £19.99

1994
Cabernet Sauvignon/Merlot Howard Park
£17.99 (YOU)
Pinot Noir Bannockburn £16.95 (BEN)
Pinot Noir Henschke Giles Lenswood
£16.10 (GN)
Shiraz Baileys 1920 Block £17.99 (GRE)
Shiraz Bannockburn £16.95 (BEN)
1993
Cabernet Sauvignon Dalwhinnie £16.90
(GAU)
Cabernet Yarra Yering Dry Red No.1
£18.00 (WS)
Pinot Noir Giaconda £18.86 (NO)
Shiraz E&E Black Pepper Barossa Valley
£19.95 (GRE)
Shiraz Henschke Mount Edelstone £17.95
(DI) £19.50 (ROB) £19.75 (YOU)
1992
Cabernet Sauvignon Henschke Cyril
Henschke £18.25 (NI) £19.95 (DI)
Cabernet Sauvignon Hollick Ravenswood
£16.99 (YOU)
Cabernet Sauvignon Penfolds Bin 707
£16.31 (NO) £18.06 (BY)
Cabernet Sauvignon Wolf Blass Black
Label £17.75 (GRE)
Meshach Grant Burge £17.50 (BU)
Shiraz Henschke Mount Edelstone £16.35
(NI)
Shiraz Penfolds Magill Estate £16.45 (PEN)
Shiraz Rockford Basket Press £16.17 (NO)
Shiraz Yarra Yering Dry Red No.2 £19.95
(BEN)

> *In each price band wines*
> *are listed in vintage order.*
> *Within each vintage they*
> *are listed in A–Z order.*

£20.00 → £29.99

1994
Cabernet Sauvignon Penfolds Bin 707 £24.95 (POR)
Shiraz Jim Barry The Armagh £29.99 (OD)
Shiraz Henschke Mount Edelstone £22.95 (LAY) £24.17 (GN)
1993
Cabernet Sauvignon Henschke Cyril Henschke £24.95 (LAY) £25.99 (YOU)
Cabernet Sauvignon Hollick Ravenswood £22.95 (LAY)
Cabernet Sauvignon Penfolds Bin 707 £22.47 (HOG) £24.99 (UN) £24.99 (VIC)
Meshach Grant Burge £21.71 (GN)
Shiraz Jim Barry The Armagh £24.10 (TAN)
Shiraz Henschke Mount Edelstone £21.02 (NO) £21.50 (BEN)
Shiraz Wynns Michael £24.95 (POR)
1992
Cabernet Sauvignon Hollick Ravenswood £20.95 (BER)
Cabernet Sauvignon Wynns John Riddoch £24.99 (TES)
Pinot Noir Coldstream Hills Reserve £20.95 (UB)

1991
Cabernet Yarra Yering Dry Red No.1 £22.00 (BER)
1990
Pinot Noir Yarra Yering £21.50 (WRI) £22.50 (BEN)
1989
Pinot Noir Yarra Yering £24.72 (NO)
1987
Cabernet Sauvignon Wynns John Riddoch £24.95 (VIG)
1986
Limestone Ridge Lindemans £20.00 (VIG)
Pyrus Lindemans £20.00 (VIG)
1985
Cabernet Sauvignon Rouge Homme £25.00 (BU)
Cabernet Sauvignon Wolf Blass Black Label £24.50 (POR)

£30.00 → £39.99

1994
Cabernet Sauvignon Wynns John Riddoch £35.95 (GN)
1985
Cabernet Sauvignon Wynns John Riddoch £35.00 (VIG)

£40.00 → £59.99

1992
Shiraz Henschke Hill of Grace £44.20 (NI)
1991
Shiraz Henschke Hill of Grace £59.85 (NO)
1990
Cabernet Sauvignon Penfolds Bin 707 £55.00 (REI)
Grange Penfolds £43.91 (PEN) £52.55 (BY)
1978
Cabernet/Shiraz Henschke Keyneton Estate £46.99 (YOU)
1977
Shiraz Henschke Mount Edelstone £56.79 (YOU)

£60.00 → £99.99

1992
Shiraz Henschke Hill of Grace £70.00 (ROB)
1991
Grange Penfolds £60.50 (BY) £99.00 (VIG)
Shiraz Henschke Hill of Grace £60.00 (BEN)
1982
Cabernet Sauvignon Wynns John Riddoch £92.00 (UB)

£105.00 → £250.00

1990
Grange Penfolds £166.46 (WATT)
1987
Grange Penfolds £133.46 (FA) £154.00 (REI)
1985
Grange Penfolds £182.00 (REI)
1982
Grange Penfolds £158.63 (FA) £250.00 (VIG)
1981
Grange Penfolds £250.00 (VIG)
1980
Grange Penfolds £250.00 (VIG)
1973
Grange Penfolds £182.00 (REI)

WHITE

Under £4.00

1996
Colombard/Chardonnay Lindemans Cawarra £3.50 (SOM)
Riesling Penfolds Bin 202 £3.50 (SOM) £3.99 (ASD) £3.99 (THR) £3.99 (BOT)
1995
Chardonnay Hardy £3.49 (SAF)
Dalwood Dry White Penfolds £3.45 (SOM)

£4.00 → £4.49

Non-vintage
Dry White David Wynn £4.35 (FLE)
Semillon/Chardonnay Barramundi £4.29 (CO) £4.45 (SAI)
1996
Chardonnay Penfolds Koonunga Hill £4.35 (SOM) £4.49 (HOG)
Colombard/Chardonnay Sunnycliff £4.49 (POR)
Rawson's Retreat Bin 21 Penfolds £4.27 (HOG) £4.49 (SAF) £4.49 (BOT) £4.49 (WR) £4.49 (THR)
Riesling Penfolds Bin 202 £4.49 (WAI)
Semillon/Chardonnay Hardys Stamp £4.49 (SAI) £4.49 (SAF) £4.49 (VIC)
Semillon/Chardonnay Orlando Jacob's Creek £4.20 (HOG) £4.39 (THR) £4.39 (WR) £4.39 (BOT)
Semillon/Chardonnay Penfolds Barossa Valley £4.35 (SOM)
Stirling Hills Dry White Penfolds £4.40 (HAH)
1995
Colombard/Chardonnay Red Cliffs £4.29 (THR) £4.29 (BOT) £4.29 (WR)
Dry White David Wynn £4.10 (SOM)
Rawson's Retreat Bin 21 Penfolds £4.49 (UN)
Semillon/Chardonnay Lindemans Bin 77 £4.49 (UN)
Semillon/Chardonnay Orlando Jacob's Creek £4.49 (FUL)
Semillon/Chardonnay Penfolds Rowlands Brook £4.49 (JON)
1994
Chardonnay Lindemans Bin 65 £4.35 (SOM)
Colombard/Chardonnay Sunnycliff £4.45 (JON)

£4.50 → £4.99

1996
Chardonnay Deakin Estate £4.99 (VIC)
Chardonnay Hardy Nottage Hill £4.99 (GRE) £4.99 (ASD) £4.99 (VIC) £4.99 (SAF)
Chardonnay Lindemans Bin 65 £4.95 (WS) £4.99 (MAR) £4.99 (WR) £4.99 (VIC) £4.99 (SAI) £4.99 (NEW) £4.99 (MAJ) £4.99 (CO) £4.99 (THR) £4.99 (OD)
Chardonnay Orlando Jacob's Creek £4.99 (BOT) £4.99 (WR) £4.99 (THR)
Chardonnay Penfolds Koonunga Hill £4.95 (WS) £4.99 (BOT) £4.99 (THR) £4.99 (WAI) £4.99 (SAI) £4.99 (WR)

Chardonnay Yalumba Oxford Landing
£4.99 (BOT) £4.99 (THR) £4.99 (WR)
Colombard/Chardonnay Lonsdale Ridge
£4.50 (BIB)
Jacob's Creek White Orlando £4.99 (VIC)
Rawson's Retreat Bin 21 Penfolds £4.69
(VIC) £4.69 (CO) £4.69 (SAI) £4.75 (WS)
Riesling Orlando Jacob's Creek Dry £4.59
(TES) £4.65 (SAI)
Riesling Wynns Coonawarra £4.99 (SAI)
★ Sauvignon Blanc Deakin Estate £4.50 (BIB)
£4.99 (VIC)
Sauvignon Blanc Sunnycliff £4.95 (POR)
Sauvignon Blanc Yalumba Oxford Landing
£4.99 (THR) £4.99 (NI) £4.99 (BOT) £4.99
(SAF)
★ Semillon Peter Lehmann £4.99 (ASD)
£4.99 (SAF)
Semillon/Chardonnay Orlando Jacob's
Creek £4.59 (CO) £4.59 (SAF) £4.59 (SAI)
£4.59 (UN) £4.59 (NEW) £4.59 (GRE)
£4.59 (VIC) £4.99 (TES)
Semillon/Chardonnay Penfolds Koonunga
Hill £4.99 (OD)
1995
Chardonnay Hardy Nottage Hill £4.99
(FUL) £4.99 (UN)
Chardonnay Lindemans Bin 65 £4.99 (POR)
Chardonnay Penfolds Koonunga Hill
£4.70 (WATT) £4.95 (POR) £4.99 (VIC)
Chardonnay Red Cliffs £4.99 (WR) £4.99
(BOT) £4.99 (THR)
Chardonnay Yalumba Oxford Landing
£4.95 (HOG) £4.99 (NA) £4.99 (NI)
Rawson's Retreat Bin 21 Penfolds £4.99
(POR)
Riesling Orlando Jacob's Creek Dry £4.59
(VIC)
Sauvignon Blanc Sunnycliff £4.89 (JON)
1994
Chardonnay Hardy Nottage Hill £4.99 (CO)
Chardonnay Lindemans Bin 65 £4.99 (FUL)
Chardonnay Penfolds Koonunga Hill
£4.99 (SO) £4.99 (FUL)
Chardonnay Penfolds Rowlands Brook
£4.99 (JON)
Chardonnay Rothbury £4.99 (FUL)
Chardonnay Yalumba Oxford Landing
£4.99 (FUL)
Jacob's Creek White Orlando £4.99 (SO)
Semillon Penfolds Barrel Fermented £4.99
(MAJ)
1993
Chardonnay Hardy Nottage Hill £4.99
(SO)

£5.00 → £5.49

1996
Chardonnay Lindemans Bin 65 £5.09 (WHI)
Muscat Brown Bros Dry £5.20 (PIP)
Sauvignon Blanc Deakin Estate £5.00 (BIB)
Semillon/Chardonnay Penfolds Barossa
Valley £5.49 (BOT) £5.49 (THR)
1995
Chardonnay Orlando RF £5.02 (HOG)
£5.29 (VIC) £5.49 (NEW)
Chardonnay Sunnycliff £5.49 (JON)
Marsanne Mitchelton Un-oaked £5.49 (OD)
Muscat Brown Bros Dry £5.39 (WHI)
£5.42 (ROS) £5.49 (NA) £5.49 (POR)
Rawson's Retreat Bin 21 Penfolds £5.19 (BY)
1994
Chardonnay Lindemans Bin 65 £5.09 (SO)
Long Flat White Tyrrells £5.39 (JON)
Muscat Brown Bros Dry £5.20 (HOG)
Semillon/Sauvignon Blanc Rosemount
£5.29 (FUL)
1993
Muscat Brown Bros Dry £5.49 (AME)

£5.50 → £5.99

1996
Chardonnay Deakin Estate Alfred Barrel
Fermented £5.99 (OD)
Chardonnay Krondorf £5.99 (DI)
Chardonnay Penfolds Koonunga Hill
£5.51 (BY)
Chardonnay Rothbury £5.97 (HOG) £5.99
(CO)
Chardonnay Sunnycliff £5.75 (POR) £5.80
(HAH)
Chardonnay Wyndham's Bin 222 £5.99
(MAJ)
Chardonnay David Wynn £5.70 (SOM)
Chardonnay Adam Wynn Canoe Tree
£5.79 (AUR)
Long Flat White Tyrrells £5.50 (GRE)
Riesling Pewsey Vale £5.99 (TES)
Semillon/Chardonnay Penfolds Barossa
Valley £5.59 (WAT) £5.99 (ASD)
Semillon/Chardonnay Rosemount £5.99
(SAF) £5.99 (THR) £5.99 (WR) £5.99 (BOT)
Semillon/Sauvignon Blanc Rosemount
£5.99 (SAI)
1995
Chardonnay Chittering Estate £5.99 (OD)
Chardonnay Penfolds Private Bin £5.75 (BY)
Chardonnay Rothbury £5.75 (GRE) £5.99
(UN)
Chardonnay Saltram £5.79 (JON)

★ Chardonnay/Semillon Penfolds Clare Valley £5.99 (SAF)
Long Flat White Tyrrells £5.70 (PIP) £5.99 (AME)
Muscat Brown Bros Dry £5.65 (STA) £5.70 (PEN) £5.95 (AD)
Riesling David Wynn £5.55 (SOM)
Semillon/Chardonnay Penfolds Barossa Valley £5.95 (POR)

1994
Chardonnay Orlando RF £5.50 (GRE) £5.99 (UN)
Chardonnay Adam Wynn Canoe Tree £5.99 (BU)
Chenin Blanc Houghton Moondah Brook £5.69 (VIC)
Chenin Blanc Houghton Wildflower Ridge £5.82 (ROS)
Marsanne Chateau Tahbilk £5.50 (VIG) £5.80 (HOG)
Muscat Brown Bros Dry £5.65 (GRE) £5.65 (WRI) £5.75 (DI) £5.75 (UB)
Sauvignon Blanc David Wynn £5.55 (SOM)
Semillon Penfolds Barrel Fermented £5.99 (WAI)

1993
Semillon/Chardonnay Rosemount £5.99 (BO)

1992
Chardonnay Penfolds Padthaway £5.99 (SO)
Chardonnay Rouge Homme £5.99 (AME)

1989
Semillon Lindemans Botrytis ½ bottle £5.99 (POR) £5.99 (UN) £5.99 (JON)

£6.00 → £6.49

1996
Chardonnay d'Arenberg Olive Grove £6.49 (OD)
Chardonnay Goundrey Langton Mount Barker £6.40 (SOM)
Chardonnay Madfish Bay £6.25 (BAN)
Chardonnay Penfolds Koonunga Hill £6.28 (AV)
Chardonnay Rosemount £6.49 (ASD)
Chardonnay David Wynn £6.25 (FLE)
Semillon/Chardonnay Rosemount £6.45 (SAI)

1995
Long Flat White Tyrrells £6.00 (TAN)
Muscat Brown Bros Dry £6.20 (GN)
Riesling Brown Bros King Valley £6.40 (STA)
Sauvignon Blanc David Wynn £6.25 (FLE)
Semillon Basedow £6.49 (VIC)

1994
Chardonnay Houghton Wildflower Ridge £6.29 (ROS)
Chardonnay Rosemount £6.49 (FUL)
Marsanne Chateau Tahbilk £6.25 (GRE)
Riesling Mount Langhi Ghiran £6.25 (SOM) £6.37 (FLE)
Semillon/Sauvignon Blanc Rosemount £6.49 (SAT)
Semillon/Sauvignon Blanc St Hallett £6.25 (REI)

1993
Chardonnay Penfolds South Australia £6.49 (FUL)
Chardonnay Tyrrells Old Winery £6.32 (PEN)
Semillon Leasingham £6.49 (CO)

1990
Semillon Leasingham £6.30 (NO)

£6.50 → £6.99

1996
Chardonnay Allandale £6.65 (REI)
Chardonnay Penfolds Private Bin £6.56 (BY)
Chardonnay Rosemount £6.99 (UN) £6.99 (CO) £6.99 (WHI) £6.99 (VIC) £6.99 (TES)
Chardonnay Rosemount Diamond £6.99 (SAI)
Chardonnay Rothbury Barrel-Fermented £6.99 (DI)
Chardonnay Wolf Blass £6.75 (WHI)
Chardonnay Wyndham's Bin 222 £6.60 (TAN)
★ Chardonnay David Wynn £6.99 (AD)
Riesling Tim Knappstein £6.76 (ELL)
Semillon Peter Lehmann £6.99 (EL)

1995
Chardonnay Lindemans Padthaway £6.80 (SOM)
Chardonnay Riddoch £6.99 (THR)
Chardonnay Rosemount £6.99 (SAF)
Chardonnay St Hallett £6.65 (REI)
Chardonnay Wolf Blass £6.75 (WHI) £6.99 (NEW)
Chardonnay Wyndham Estate Oak-Aged £6.99 (MAJ)
Chardonnay Wyndham's Bin 222 £6.80 (NA)
Marsanne Chateau Tahbilk £6.95 (WAI)
Riesling Jim Barry Watervale £6.50 (TAN)
Sauvignon Blanc Brown Bros £6.99 (DI)
Sauvignon Blanc David Wynn £6.99 (NI)
Semillon/Chardonnay Peter Lehmann £6.99 (SAF)
Semillon/Sauvignon Blanc St Hallett £6.99 (AUS)

1994

Chardonnay Leasingham £6.99 (GRE)
Chardonnay Rosemount £6.99 (BO)
Chardonnay Wolf Blass £6.69 (POR)
Marsanne Chateau Tahbilk £6.50 (UB)
Muscat Brown Bros Dry £6.95 (BER)
Riesling Howard Park £6.95 (BAN)
Sauvignon Blanc David Wynn £6.95 (AD)
Semillon Lindemans Hunter River £6.50
  (VIG)
Semillon Penfolds Barrel Fermented £6.99
  (VIC)

1993

Chardonnay Rothbury Barrel-Fermented
  £6.99 (JON)
Chardonnay Wynns Coonawarra Estate
  £6.99 (FUL) £6.99 (POR)

£7.00 → £7.49

1996

Chardonnay Madfish Bay £7.30 (SOM)
Chardonnay Ninth Island £7.25 (SOM)
Riesling Tim Adams £7.49 (AUS)
Sauvignon Blanc Brown Bros £7.10 (PIP)
Semillon Basedow £7.00 (BIB)

1995

Chardonnay Basedow £7.49 (VIC) £7.49
  (FUL)
Chardonnay Ninth Island £7.37 (HOG)
Chardonnay Wynns Coonawarra Estate
  £7.45 (SAI) £7.49 (VIC)
Fumé Blanc Tim Knappstein £7.25 (GRE)
Semillon Brown Bros £7.25 (NA) £7.25 (GRE)
Semillon/Chardonnay Wolf Blass £7.49 (VIC)

1994

Chardonnay Penfolds Barrel Fermented
  £7.20 (PIP)
Chardonnay Riddoch £7.49 (POR)
Chardonnay Tyrrells Old Winery £7.10
  (PIP)
Riesling Tim Adams £7.25 (REI)
Riesling Mitchell Watervale £7.15 (HAH)
  £7.25 (JON)
Semillon Brown Bros £7.11 (ROS)
Verdelho Houghton Gold Reserve £7.19
  (EL)

1993

Riesling Mountadam £7.35 (SOM)

Stars (★) indicate wines
selected by Oz Clarke in the
Best Buys section which begins
on page 12.

1992

Chardonnay Orlando St Hilary £7.25 (HOG)

£7.50 → £7.99

1996

Chardonnay Allandale £7.50 (AUS)
★ Chardonnay Chapel Hill Unwooded £7.99
  (AUS)
Chardonnay Madfish Bay £7.99 (NI)
Chardonnay Ninth Island £7.75 (GRE)
★ Chardonnay Water Wheel £7.99 (AUS)
Chardonnay Wirra Wirra £7.99 (OD)
Chardonnay Wolf Blass £7.67 (BY)
Riesling Pikes Polish Hill £7.95 (LEA)

1995

Chardonnay Brown Bros King Valley
  £7.83 (ROS) £7.99 (NA) £7.99 (JON)
Chardonnay Chateau Reynella £7.99 (ASD)
Chardonnay Richard Hamilton £7.95 (POR)
Chardonnay Jamiesons Run £7.95 (GRE)
Chardonnay Saltram Mamre Brook £7.99
  (GN)
Riesling Mitchell Watervale £7.75 (POR)
Riesling Mountadam £7.99 (TES)
Riesling Rockford £7.70 (FLE)
Sauvignon Blanc Petaluma Bridgewater
  Mill £7.50 (GRE)
Semillon Amberley Estate £7.95 (SOM)
Semillon Brown Bros £7.60 (STA) £7.95 (AD)
Semillon Coriole £7.75 (WS)
Semillon Mitchell Wood-aged £7.95 (POR)
Semillon/Sauvignon Blanc Cape Mentelle
  £7.99 (RAE) £7.99 (POR) £7.99 (NI)

1994

Chardonnay Brown Bros £7.99 (DI)
Chardonnay Coriole £7.95 (WS)
Chardonnay Hill-Smith £7.95 (WS)
Chardonnay Houghton Gold Reserve
  £7.75 (WS)
Chardonnay Jamiesons Run £7.99 (BO)
Chardonnay Tim Knappstein £7.99 (OD)
Chardonnay Ninth Island £7.99 (BO)
Chardonnay Rothbury Barrel-Fermented
  £7.50 (DI)
Chardonnay St Hallett £7.99 (BOT)
Semillon/Chardonnay Henschke Tilly's
  Vineyard Eden Valley £7.60 (SOM)
Semillon/Sauvignon Blanc Cape Mentelle
  £7.92 (NO)
Verdelho Houghton Gold Reserve £7.75
  (ROB)

1993

Chardonnay Jamiesons Run £7.99 (SO)
Chardonnay Lindemans Padthaway £7.69
  (HOG)

Chardonnay Meadowbank £7.75 (BU)
Chardonnay St Hallett £7.56 (LON)
Marsanne Mitchelton Reserve £7.75 (GRE)
1992
Marsanne Mitchelton Wood-Matured
£7.65 (UB)
1991
Semillon Brown Bros £7.69 (AME)
1990
Verdelho Willespie £7.95 (LAY)

£8.00 → £8.99

Non-vintage
Chardonnay Capel Vale £8.20 (EL)
1996
Chardonnay Ninth Island £8.25 (STA)
£8.50 (BU)
Chardonnay Shaw & Smith Un-oaked
£8.99 (TES)
Riesling Henschke Julius Eden Valley £8.95
(WS)
Sauvignon Blanc Hill-Smith £8.19 (HA)
Sauvignon Blanc Katnook £8.69 (THR)
£8.69 (BOT) £8.69 (WR) £8.99 (OD)
Sauvignon Blanc Pikes Polish Hill River
£8.95 (LEA)
Semillon Coriole £8.70 (TAN)
Semillon/Sauvignon Blanc Cape Mentelle
£8.17 (DOM) £8.50 (TAN) £8.60 (HAH)
£8.99 (MAJ) £8.99 (WAI)
1995
Chardonnay Basedow £8.00 (BIB)
Chardonnay Brown Bros £8.10 (PIP) £8.46
(PEN)
Chardonnay Goundrey Langton Mount
Barker £8.49 (UN)
Chardonnay Ninth Island £8.13 (NO)
Chardonnay Plantagenet £8.49 (NA)
Chardonnay Rosemount Show Reserve
£8.99 (THR) £8.99 (WR) £8.99 (BOT)
Chardonnay Wynns Coonawarra Estate
£8.30 (BY)
Riesling Petaluma £8.99 (AUS)
Riesling Rockford £8.95 (VIG)
Sauvignon Blanc Shaw & Smith £8.66 (FLE)
★ Semillon Tim Adams £8.95 (WS) £8.99
(AUS) £8.99 (TES)
Semillon/Sauvignon Blanc Cape Mentelle
£8.37 (NO) £8.40 (PLA) £8.69 (JON)
£8.99 (EL)
1994
Chardonnay Brown Bros £8.70 (TAN)
Chardonnay Rymill Winery The Riddoch
Run £8.25 (HAH)
Chardonnay St Hallett £8.11 (DOM)

Riesling Henschke Green Hill Eden Valley
£8.10 (SOM)
Riesling Henschke Julius Eden Valley £8.61
(NO)
Sauvignon Blanc Katnook £8.99 (BO)
Semillon Tim Adams £8.99 (AUS) £8.99
(BOT) £8.99 (THR) £8.99 (WR)
Semillon Basedow £8.38 (NO)
Semillon Henschke £8.25 (REI)
Semillon/Sauvignon Blanc Cape Mentelle
£8.95 (AD)
1993
Chardonnay Green Point £8.49 (VIC)
Chardonnay Reynolds Yarraman £8.95 (LAY)
Chardonnay Rosemount Show Reserve
£8.99 (FUL)
Chardonnay Wirra Wirra £8.95 (WS)
Marsanne Mitchelton Wood-Matured
£8.65 (WRI)
Semillon Henschke £8.95 (WRI)
1992
Chardonnay Wirra Wirra £8.49 (FUL)
Semillon Rockford £8.99 (ENO)
1990
Marsanne Mitchelton Reserve £8.74 (NO)
Semillon Mitchell Wood-aged £8.91 (NO)

£9.00 → £9.99

1996
Chardonnay Coldstream Hills £9.65 (NEZ)
Chardonnay Howard Park £9.95 (BAN)
Chardonnay Pikes Polish Hill River £9.95
(LEA)
Sauvignon Blanc Shaw & Smith £9.15 (REI)
£9.30 (PIP)
Semillon Amberley Estate £9.20 (PIP)
Semillon/Sauvignon Blanc Marienberg
£9.95 (BIB)
1995
Chardonnay Best's £9.99 (WHI)
Chardonnay Brown Bros King Valley
£9.52 (GN)
Chardonnay Cape Mentelle £9.25 (REI)
£9.75 (NI) £9.75 (NI) £9.91 (NO)
Chardonnay Green Point £9.99 (DI)
Chardonnay Jeffrey Grosset £9.93 (LON)
Chardonnay Pipers Brook £9.85 (SOM)
Chardonnay Plantagenet Mount Barker
£9.60 (GN)
Chardonnay Rosemount Show Reserve
£9.45 (HA) £9.95 (SAI) £9.99 (VIC) £9.99
(WAI) £9.99 (MAJ) £9.99 (CO)
Chardonnay Shaw & Smith £9.95 (BEN)
Chardonnay Shaw & Smith Un-oaked
£9.60 (NI) £9.85 (WRI)

Riesling Henschke Julius Eden Valley £9.99
(AUS)
Sauvignon Blanc Shaw & Smith £9.60 (NI)
£9.95 (BEN)
Semillon Amberley Estate £9.95 (BEN)
£9.99 (BOT) £9.99 (THR) £9.99 (WR)
Semillon Moss Wood £9.99 (RAE)
Semillon/Chardonnay Henschke Tilly's
Vineyard Eden Valley £9.49 (EL) £9.49 (DI)
Viognier Heggies Estate £9.45 (NI)
1994
Chardonnay Geoff Merrill £9.99 (SAF)
Chardonnay Penley Estate £9.50 (AUS)
Riesling Petaluma Rhine £9.95 (BEN)
Semillon Henschke £9.50 (LAY) £9.99
(AUS) £9.99 (ELL)
1993
Chardonnay Cape Mentelle £9.85 (NO)
Chardonnay Rosemount Show Reserve
£9.99 (SAF)
Riesling Mountadam £9.95 (ROB)
Semillon Rockford £9.69 (PLA) £9.95 (VIG)
1992
Riesling Rockford £9.22 (NO)
1991
Chardonnay Stafford Ridge £9.99 (RAE)

1989
Marsanne Chateau Tahbilk £9.50 (VIG)
Semillon McWilliams Mount Pleasant
Elizabeth £9.75 (GRE)

£10.00 → £12.99

1996
Chardonnay Pipers Brook £12.50 (STA)
Chardonnay Shaw & Smith Un-oaked
£10.30 (TAN)
Sauvignon Blanc Shaw & Smith £10.30
(TAN)
1995
Chardonnay Coldstream Hills £10.10
(PIP)
Chardonnay Cullens £10.60 (SOM) £11.30
(FLE)
Chardonnay Henschke Eden Valley
£12.99 (AUS)

Chardonnay Katnook £10.95 (BIB)
Chardonnay Penley Estate £10.95 (LAY)
Chardonnay Petaluma £11.50 (GRE)
Chardonnay Pipers Brook £11.75 (GRE)
£12.50 (POR) £12.99 (EL)
Chardonnay Tyrrells Vat 47 £10.85 (REI)
£11.82 (NO) £12.99 (UN)
Riesling Henschke Green Hill Eden Valley
£10.50 (LAY) £11.40 (BEN)
Riesling Henschke Julius Eden Valley
£11.66 (GN)
Riesling Petaluma £10.80 (AD)
Riesling David Wynn £11.85 (UB)
Sauvignon Blanc Cullens £11.61 (FLE)
Semillon Moss Wood £10.75 (NO) £10.95
(VIG)
1994
Chardonnay Cape Mentelle £11.70 (AD)
Chardonnay Mountadam £10.50 (SOM)
£11.40 (FLE) £12.48 (ELL) £12.99 (WR)
£12.99 (BOT) £12.99 (THR)
Chardonnay Petaluma £10.95 (REI) £11.99
(OD)
Chardonnay Plantagenet Mount Barker
£12.50 (LEA) £12.80 (BER)
Chardonnay Tyrrells Vat 47 £11.22 (NO)
Chardonnay Wignalls £11.99 (AUS)
Riesling Jasper Hill £10.95 (YAP)
Semillon Tim Adams £10.50 (GRE)
Semillon Henschke £10.99 (GN) £11.49
(DI)
1993
Chardonnay Coldstream Hills Reserve
£10.35 (NEZ)
Chardonnay Cullens £12.50 (GAU)
Chardonnay De Bortoli £10.01 (NO)
£10.25 (WRI) £11.49 (NA) £11.50 (VIG)
Chardonnay Giaconda £11.43 (NO)
Chardonnay Henschke Eden Valley
£10.35 (SOM)
Chardonnay Mountadam £11.99 (AME)
Chardonnay Wignalls £11.99 (AUS)
Semillon Henschke £10.95 (ROB)
1992
Chardonnay Giaconda £11.43 (NO)
Chardonnay Pipers Brook £12.95 (LEA)
1991
Chardonnay Shaw & Smith £11.00 (REI)
Riesling Brown Bros Family Reserve
£10.50 (NO)
Sauvignon Blanc Cullens £11.99 (YOU)
1990
Chardonnay Cullens £11.99 (YOU)
Chardonnay Pipers Brook £12.06 (PEN)
Marsanne Chateau Tahbilk £10.46 (NO)

Semillon Tyrrells Vat I £12.61 (NO)
Semillon Willespie £10.58 (NO)
1989
Chardonnay Mountadam £12.90 (GAU)

£13.00 → £15.99

1996
Chardonnay Henschke Eden Valley
£13.75 (LAY)
1995
Chardonnay Cullens £13.50 (DI) £15.95
(BER)
Chardonnay Howard Park £13.95 (VIG)
£14.99 (YOU)
Chardonnay Moss Wood £13.87 (NO)
Chardonnay Pipers Brook £13.99 (GN)
£14.25 (ROB)
Viognier Heggies Estate £13.45 (AD)
1994
Chardonnay Bannockburn £13.50 (BEN)
Chardonnay Cullens £13.95 (AD)
Chardonnay Mountadam £13.25 (HIC)
Chardonnay Petaluma £13.00 (TAN)
£13.60 (BEN) £14.95 (ROB)
Chardonnay Wignalls £13.95 (BER)
1993
Chardonnay Lakes Folly £14.50 (LAY)
£14.95 (ROB)
Chardonnay Tarrawarra £13.00 (WS)
1989
Marsanne Yeringburg £15.95 (VIG)

£16.00 → £19.99

1995
Chardonnay Henschke Croft Lenswood
£16.95 (BEN)
Chardonnay Tyrrells Vat 47 £16.60 (STA)
1994
Chardonnay Bannockburn £17.25 (UB)
Chardonnay Leeuwin Art Series £18.21
(DOM)
1993
Chardonnay Dalwhinnie £19.05 (NO)
Chardonnay Leeuwin Estate £19.99 (OD)
Chardonnay Rosemount Roxburgh
£17.99 (UN)

> *Please remember that*
> **Webster's** *is a price*
> *guide and not a price list. It*
> *is not meant to replace up-*
> *to-date*
> *merchants' lists.*

1992
Chardonnay Leeuwin Art Series £19.69
(YOU)
1991
Chardonnay Petersons £16.50 (REI)
Chardonnay Rosemount Roxburgh
£16.49 (AME)
Semillon Tyrrells Vat I £16.60 (STA)
1990
Chardonnay Yarra Yering £18.88 (NO)

ROSÉ

c. £7.50

1995
Rose of Virginia Charles Melton £7.29 (FLE)

SPARKLING

Under £5.50

Non-vintage
Angas Brut £5.15 (SOM)
Killawarra Rosé £3.99 (SOM)
Penfolds Rowlands Brook Bottle
Fermented £4.99 (JON)
Penfolds Rowlands Brook Rosé, Bottle
Fermented £4.99 (JON)
Seaview £5.46 (NEW)
Seppelt Great Western Brut £4.99 (WR)
£4.99 (THR) £4.99 (BOT)
Seppelt Great Western Rosé £4.99 (BOT)
£4.99 (WR) £4.99 (THR)

£5.50 → £5.99

Non-vintage
Angas Brut £5.75 (NI) £5.99 (FUL)
Angas Brut Rosé £5.75 (NI) £5.99 (FUL)
Barramundi Sparkling £5.75 (BO)
Cockatoo Ridge Brut £5.99 (SAI)
Orlando Carrington Extra Brut £5.75
(GRE) £5.99 (SAF) £5.99 (JON)
★ Richmond Royal Brut £5.75 (WHI)
Seaview £5.95 (WS) £5.99 (FUL)

£6.00 → £7.99

Non-vintage
Angas Brut £6.49 (THR) £6.49 (CO) £6.49
(FLE) £6.49 (SAI) £6.49 (WR) £6.49 (BOT)
£6.49 (OD) £6.95 (BEN) £6.95 (AD)
Angas Brut Rosé £6.49 (OD) £6.49 (CO)
£6.49 (THR) £6.49 (WR) £6.49 (BOT)
£6.49 (TES) £6.49 (FLE) £6.95 (AD)
Killawarra Brut £6.60 (GN)

Seaview £6.49 (BO) £6.49 (WAI) £6.49 (CO)
£6.49 (POR) £6.49 (POR) £6.50 (GRE)
Seppelt Sparkling Shiraz £7.95 (POR)
Taltarni Brut Taché £6.95 (REI) £7.46
(HOG)
Wolf Blass Brut £7.99 (GRE)
Yalumba Pinot Noir/Chardonnay £7.90
(NI) £7.99 (FUL)
Yalumba Pinot Noir/Chardonnay Cuvée
One Prestige £7.25 (SOM)
Yalumba Sparkling Cabernet £7.75 (NI)
1994
Seaview Pinot Noir/Chardonnay £7.99
(BOT) £7.99 (WR) £7.99 (THR) £7.99
(WAI)
1991
Seaview Pinot Noir/Chardonnay £7.99
(JON)
1990
Seaview Pinot Noir/Chardonnay £7.49
(MAJ)
Seppelt Sparkling Shiraz £7.95 (POR) £7.99
(BO)

£8.00 → £9.99

Non-vintage
Seaview Pinot Noir/Chardonnay £8.49
(POR)
Seppelt Salinger Brut £9.95 (POR)
Seppelt Sparkling Shiraz £9.20 (LAY) £9.89
(ROS)
Taltarni Brut Taché £8.75 (BEN) £8.99
(MAJ) £9.49 (AME)
Taltarni Cuvée Brut £8.95 (STA) £9.45 (AD)
Yalumba Pinot Noir/Chardonnay £8.49
(THR) £8.49 (BOT) £8.49 (WR) £8.99 (MAJ)
Yalumba Pinot Noir/Chardonnay Cuvée
One Prestige £8.95 (AD)
1994
Seaview Pinot Noir/Chardonnay £8.49
(SAF)
Yalumba Pinot Noir/Chardonnay £8.49
(SAI)
1993
Croser £9.25 (SOM)
Green Point Brut Domaine Chandon
£9.30 (SOM)
Seaview Pinot Noir/Chardonnay £8.49 (SAI)
1992
★ Seaview Edwards & Chaffey £9.99 (SAF)
Seppelt Sparkling Shiraz £8.99 (OD)
1991
Seppelt Salinger Brut £8.99 (AME) £8.99
(OD) £9.49 (MAJ) £9.99 (FUL)
Seppelt Sparkling Shiraz £8.99 (TES)

£10.00 → £11.99

1994
Croser £11.99 (WR) £11.99 (THR) £11.99
(OD) £11.99 (BOT)
Green Point Brut Domaine Chandon
£10.00 (HOG) £11.49 (BOT) £11.49 (WAI)
£11.49 (OD) £11.49 (THR) £11.95 (AD)
1993
Clover Hill £10.95 (STA) £11.17 (AV)
£11.99 (AME)
Green Point Brut Domaine Chandon
£10.49 (FUL) £10.49 (TES) £10.95 (GRE)
£11.75 (DI)
Seppelt Sparkling Shiraz £10.95 (GN)
1992
Green Point Brut Domaine Chandon
£10.95 (POR) £11.50 (TAN)
Seppelt Sparkling Shiraz £10.95 (ROB)
Yalumba D £11.25 (SOM)
1991
Green Point Brut Domaine Chandon
£10.89 (JON)
1990
Seppelt Salinger Brut £11.26 (ELL)

£12.00 → £15.99

Non-vintage
Charles Melton Sparkling Red £14.99
(AUS) £15.95 (POR)
1994
Green Point Brut Domaine Chandon
£12.20 (LAY) £12.95 (ROB)
1993
Yalumba D £14.95 (AD)

SWEET & FORTIFIED

Under £5.00

Non-vintage
Morris Liqueur Muscat £4.95 (TES)
1995
Brown Bros Orange Muscat & Flora ½
bottle £4.99 (HOG)

£5.00 → £5.99

Non-vintage
Chambers Rutherglen Liqueur Muscat ½
bottle £5.85 (NO) £5.99 (AUR)
Stanton & Killeen Rutherglen Liqueur
Muscat ½ bottle £5.99 (AME)
1997
Brown Bros Orange Muscat & Flora ½
bottle £5.90 (PIP)

1996
Brown Bros Muscat Late Picked £5.99
(NA)
Brown Bros Orange Muscat & Flora ½
bottle £5.49 (BOT) £5.49 (THR) £5.49
(WR) £5.50 (GRE) £5.53 (ROS) £5.99 (NA)
£5.99 (AME)
1995
Brown Bros Muscat Late Picked £5.48
(HOG) £5.90 (PIP) £5.91 (ROS) £5.99
(AUR) £5.99 (GRE)
Brown Bros Orange Muscat & Flora ½
bottle £5.49 (UN) £5.49 (CO) £5.55
(JON) £5.99 (WHI)
1994
Brown Bros Muscat Late Picked £5.99 (JON)
Brown Bros Orange Muscat & Flora £5.79
(WAT)
Brown Bros Orange Muscat & Flora ½
bottle £5.29 (FUL) £5.95 (POR) £5.99
(HAL)
1992
Brown Bros Muscat Late Picked £5.99 (UB)

£6.00 → £6.99

Non-vintage
Campbell's Liqueur Muscat ½ bottle £6.30
(PIP)
Rothbury Museum Reserve Liqueur
Muscat £6.29 (NO)
Stanton & Killeen Rutherglen Liqueur
Muscat ½ bottle £6.00 (NO) £6.45 (SAT)
£6.45 (SOM)
1996
Brown Bros Muscat Late Picked £6.20
(STA) £6.46 (PEN) £6.75 (AD)
Brown Bros Orange Muscat & Flora ½
bottle £6.00 (TAN) £6.25 (STA) £6.35 (WRI)
1995
Brown Bros Muscat Late Picked £6.50
(WRI) £6.99 (TES)
Brown Bros Orange Muscat & Flora £6.50
(ROB)
Brown Bros Orange Muscat & Flora ½
bottle £6.35 (AUR) £6.65 (UB) £6.95 (GN)
1994
Brown Bros Muscat Late Picked £6.29
(AME) £6.99 (GN)
Brown Bros Orange Muscat & Flora £6.89
(VIN)
Brown Bros Orange Muscat & Flora ½
bottle £6.23 (PEN) £6.29 (BO)
1993
Brown Bros Orange Muscat & Flora ½
bottle £6.60 (NO)

1992
Brown Bros Orange Muscat & Flora ½
bottle £6.95 (SAT)
1984
Brown Bros Noble Riesling ½ bottle £6.15
(ROS) £6.60 (PIP)

£7.00 → £9.99

Non-vintage
Brown Bros Liqueur Muscat £8.45 (JON)
Chambers Rosewood Liqueur Muscat
£9.99 (JON)
Morris Liqueur Muscat £9.99 (GRE)
1996
Brown Bros Orange Muscat & Flora ½
bottle £7.65 (AD)
1991
Yalumba Pewsey Vale Botrytis Late
Harvest Riesling ½ bottle £9.55 (BEN)
1982
Brown Bros Noble Riesling £7.33 (NO)
Brown Bros Noble Riesling ½ bottle £7.94
(GN)

£10.00 → £11.99

Non-vintage
Baileys Founder Liqueur Muscat £10.14
(NO)
Baileys Founder Liqueur Tokay £11.82 (NO)
Baileys Liqueur Muscat £10.20 (BEN)
Brown Bros Liqueur Muscat £10.50 (GRE)
Campbells Rutherglen Liqueur Muscat
£10.92 (NO) £11.95 (ROB)
Chambers Rutherglen Liqueur Muscat
£10.47 (NO) £11.49 (AUS)
Morris Liqueur Muscat £10.08 (NO)
Stanton & Killeen Rutherglen Liqueur
Muscat £10.79 (NO) £10.99 (RAE)
£11.49 (AUS)

£12.00 → £13.99

Non-vintage
Brown Bros Liqueur Muscat £12.75 (PIP)
£13.50 (WRI) £13.89 (WAT) £13.99 (GN)
Chambers Special Liqueur Muscat £13.79
(NO)
Morris Liqueur Muscat £13.95 (UB)
1993
De Bortoli Noble One Botrytis Semillon
£12.95 (LEA)

c. £38.00

Non-vintage
Campbells Old Rutherglen Liqueur
Muscat £37.99 (NO)

CHILE

A round of applause, please, for ever-improving quality – and now can we have lower yields? More concentration? Even better flavours? Even if we have to pay a bit more?

This has to be one of the steepest learning curves in the history of wine. Yes, Chilean wines have been around for a while now – names like Concha y Toro are not exactly unfamiliar. But it's only in the last few years that the red wines have started to lose that lean, stalky, woody character that made me think – yes, these wines have got bags of potential, but I don't think I want to drink them.

That was then. This is now. Now the reds are increasingly vibrant, increasingly exciting, increasingly packed with minty, rich fruit. And the whites? They're fresher. There's Chilean Sauvignon Blanc that has every ounce of the pungent gooseberry and cut grass flavour that I'm looking for; and there's Chardonnay with crisp, lemony fruit and just the right touch of new oak. This being a learning curve, I'm not going to pretend that everything's perfect just yet.

I'd like to see more character in some of the wines. I'd like to see lower yields in many of the vineyards – much, much lower, in some cases. Lower yields will give greater concentration; and greater concentration will give wines that last better. Too many cheaper Chilean wines still fade away rather too early.

I'm happy to see so many joint ventures between Chilean and foreign – notably Bordelais – producers, but I'd like to see better wine from them. So far they haven't been the stars I'd hoped.

The reason so many Bordelais want to dip their toes in Chilean vats is, of course, the potential of Chilean Cabernet. Cabernet is everybody's idea of the classic Chilean wine – but don't neglect the Merlot. And don't be afraid to pay a little bit extra for something special: you'll get your money's worth.

GRAPE VARIETIES

CABERNET SAUVIGNON (red) Characterized by relatively soft, well-rounded tannins; Chilean Cabernet often doesn't need Merlot to fill it out, unlike Cabernet from many other places. However, it can be slightly hollow in the middle: doughnut wine. Unoaked versions are best within two years of the vintage. Over-oaking was a problem in the past, especially with premium wines, but greater restraint is now being shown. Best unoaked Cabernets: *Monte La Finca, La Rosa, Andes Peak*. Best premium: *Concha y Toro Don Melchor, Canepa Magnificum*.

CHARDONNAY (white) Handling of this grape has improved massively. A good crop of unoaked wines has emerged (like

those of *La Rosa, Luis Felipe Edwards, Casa Porta, Santa Monica*) and at the top end of the quality range there are experiments with fermenting wines in oak barrels using wild yeasts (*Viña Casablanca, Errázuriz, Montes*). As with Cabernet, subtler oaking is increasingly the norm. Cool-climate Casablanca tends to produce a crisper, more citrus-fresh Chardonnay than its Central Valley counterparts.

GEWÜRZTRAMINER (white) The lychee and rose petal packed *Viña Casablanca* version of this grape sells out almost immediately, but few others are trying. *Concha y Toro*'s vineyards in southerly Mulchen are showing good results, but frost is a major problem.

MERLOT (red) The grape of the moment. Bursting with colour and vibrant, plummy fruit. Try *La Rosa, Santa Monica, Carta Vieja, La Fortuna, Canepa* (all for drinking young); *Errázuriz Reserve, Casa Lapostolle, Carmen, Viña Porta, Mont Gras, Montes, Concha y Toro* and *Segu Ollé* (all with aging potential).

PINOT NOIR (red) Only two wineries, *Valdivieso* and *Cono Sur*, have managed to tame this grape and produce juicy, good-value versions. *Concha y Toro's* new Casablanca Pinot shows some promise.

RIESLING (white) Only minimal amounts of the great German grape are grown in Chile, and it's not being pursued with any great zeal. Nor are the results terribly exciting. *Miguel Torres* makes a good Gewürztraminer-Riesling blend in the Curicó Valley, however; *Santa Monica* makes a minerally varietal; and *Santa Rita's* example has good varietal character though otherwise seems unlikely to thrill.

SAUVIGNON BLANC (white) Most of the inferior Sauvignonasse (which used to be mistaken, accidentally or not, for Sauvignon Blanc) has now gone, and new clones, better canopy management and handling in the winery are resulting in cleaner flavours. Casablanca still leads and is the only region with a distinct style (ripe gooseberry and asparagus fruit, and firm acidity). *Viña Casablanca's Santa Isabel Estate, Villard, Concha y Toro* and *Caliterra* are the labels to watch. Outside Casablanca, the Curicó Valley is producing some goodies (*Viña Casablanca White Label, Montes, San Pedro*).

SEMILLON (white) Widely planted but rarely used in blended whites for the domestic market. For exports, *Carmen's* Alvaro Espinoza uses it in a good Chardonnay blend and a rich, oily Late Harvest Semillon. The quality of the few other varietal wines suggests efforts should be concentrated on other grapes. *Viña San Carlos* is decent.

WINE REGIONS

Although grapes are grown in the far north and pretty far south, only a 400km strip of the Central Valley is responsible for producing quality wine. Frost and rain limit development further south, searing heat and desert to the north.

Recent appellation legislation splits the main wine growing region into Aconcagua (incorporating the sub-region of Casablanca), the Central Valley (including Maipo, Rapel, Curicó and Maule) and the Southern Region (including the valleys of Itata and Bío-Bío).

ACONCAGUA VALLEY Dominated by one producer (*Errázuriz*) in Panqueheu. The main vine is Cabernet Sauvignon (*Errázuriz' Don Maximiano* is one of the top Cabernets in Chile) and new plantings of Sangiovese, Nebbiolo and Zinfandel add to the red bias.

CASABLANCA VALLEY Chile's premier white wine region, and the only one with an identifiable style. Chardonnay dominates, with Sauvignon Blanc and Gewürztraminer making up the white balance, and small amounts of Cabernet Sauvignon, Merlot and Pinot Noir yielding impressive results. Chardonnay tends to be green and citrus-flavoured, often with figgy aromas, and Sauvignons are grassy and crisp with firm acidity. Best: *Viña Casablanca, Caliterra, Concha y Toro, Villard.*

CURICÓ Mainly known for its Chardonnay (*Valdivieso, Montes, San Pedro, Caliterra*). Valdivieso has emerged as the leading producer, also making beautiful Pinot Noir, Merlot and Cabernet.

MAIPO VALLEY Birthplace of the Chilean wine industry and home to some of the biggest and most traditional players (*Santa Rita, Concha y Toro, Santa Carolina*). Alto Maipo (*Aquitania, Cousiño Macul, William Fèvre*) has colder nights, so the grapes keep their acidity better. Cabernet Sauvignon made the valley's name and is still the main grape, although excellent Chardonnay is made here, too. The spread of Santiago's suburbs and smog is creating pressure on some producers. Most innovative: *Carmen, Canepa, Concha y Toro.*

MAULE A handful of producers (*Terra Noble, Domaine Oriental, Carta Vieja, Segu Ollé*) are achieving variable results, with reds

(particularly Merlot) so far beating whites hands down on quality.

RAPEL A seedbed of new winery activity, particularly in the Colchagua Valley where new arrivals *Mont Gras, Luis Felipe Edwards* and *Casa Lapostolle* are producing good Chardonnay and Cabernet. Top Pinot Noir from *Cono Sur*, and Merlot from *La Rosa* and *Concha y Toro. Viña Porta* and *Santa Monica* make top-class Cabernet and Merlot.

SOUTHERN REGION *Concha y Toro* has produced a top-class Gewürztraminer from Mulchen.

PRODUCERS WHO'S WHO

AQUITANIA ★★★ Bruno Prats of Ch. Cos d'Estournel and Paul Pontallier of Ch. Margaux know their real estate, but there are less polluted areas to make great Cabernet. It's questionable whether the Domaine Paul Bruno is worth its hefty price tag.

CANEPA ★★★★ The company behind many of the best own-labels here, Canepa also makes the good Montenuevo and Rowan Brook. Merlot, Zinfandel and Magificum Cabernet are its top reds.

CARMEN ★★★★ State-of-the-art sister operation to Santa Rita. Reds are best; beautiful Merlot Reserve and Grande Vidure Cabernet. Petite Sirah is on the way.

CARTA VIEJA ★★★ Old Maule Valley winery with new quality drive and ability to deliver good value, inexpensive wine. Reds are superior to whites. Very good Merlot.

CASA LAPOSTOLLE ★★★(★) Grassy Sauvignon, rich, buttery Chardonnay and spectacular oak-aged Merlot.

CONCHA Y TORO ★★★★ Chile's biggest winery has resources to reach both good value and premium ends. New Trio

red and white are superb, as is the Amelia Chardonnay, a new Syrah, and constantly improving Don Melchor Cabernet. Latest is a joint venture with Ch. Mouton-Rothschild in Bordeaux.

CONO SUR ★★★★ Superb Pinot Noir and Isla Negra red are excellent value.

COUSIÑO MACUL ★★ Traditionalist making old-style reds under the Santiago smog. A new location and a new wine-making philosophy would help.

ECHEVERRIA ★★★ One of the leading boutique wineries with vineyards in Curico Valley. Good reserve Chardonnay and Cabernet Sauvignon.

LUIS FELIPE EDWARDS ★★★(★) Large specialist in Chardonnay and Cabernet.

ERRÁZURIZ ★★★★ Chardonnay and Reserve Merlot have improved; there is also a wild yeast Chardonnay. Second label

The Price Guides for this section begin on page 76.

Caliterra ★★★(★) is now in a joint venture with Robert Mondavi of California.

LA FORTUNA ★★★ Malbec is best here, but Merlot and Cabernet are both good. Decent whites.

MONT GRAS ★★★ Go for the reds here: Cabernet and Merlot are both good. Whites are less impressive so far.

MONTES ★★★ Slightly erratic, but currently on form with intense Malbec, good Merlot and juicy unoaked La Finca Cabernet.

LOS ROBLES ★★★ Upfront flying winemaker-style Cabernet and Merlot.

LA ROSA ★★★★ Top unwooded Chardonnay and Merlot. Watch out for new Cabernet from Palmeria Estate.

SAN PEDRO ★★★ There have been big improvements in quality here. Best of the Castillo de Milina range is the Chardonnay Reserve.

SANTA CAROLINA ★★★ Reliable producer of reds, particularly Merlot from San Fernando. Whites are dull compared with the vibrant wines of its sister company Viña Casablanca.

SANTA INÉS ★★★ Small company making good quality wines.

SANTA MONICA ★★★ Small family-run winery; excellent Riesling and Merlot.

SANTA RITA ★★★ Erratic quality in recent years. The 120 range is the most reliable, and the latest release of premium Casa Real shows welcome restraint with the new oak.

SEGU OLLÉ ★★★ Merlot is the star turn here, but the Cabernet Sauvignon is also good and worth a punt.

TERRA NOBLE ★★★★ Winery based at Talca in the Maule Valley, where Touraine wizard Henri Marionnet makes very good Sauvignon Blanc and Merlot.

TORRÉON DE PAREDES ★★★(★) Large winery based in Rapel. Good wines throughout, particularly an award-winning Merlot.

TORRES ★★★ Another piece of foreign investment that hasn't delivered the goods. Whites are above average but not spectacular.

UNDURRAGA ★★★ One of the old camp that needs an injection of inspiration. Merlot and Cabernet are good.

VALDIVIESO ★★★★ Traditional sparkling wine producer, now top of the premium still wine league. Excellent oaked Pinot Noir, Merlot, and new red blend Caballo Loco.

LOS VASCOS ★★★ Bordeaux Château Lafite-Rothschild's joint venture in Chile. So far, the Cabernet has not lived up to its potential.

VILLARD ★★★★ Good Sauvignon and Chardonnay from Casablanca, and fruity Merlot.

VIÑA PORTA ★★★★ Boutique winery delivering consistently good oak-aged Chardonnay and Cabernet. A good Merlot here, too.

VIÑA CASABLANCA ★★★★ White label wines come from outside the Casablanca area (good new El Bosque Cabernet is from Maipo). Santa Isabel Estate Sauvignon, Chardonnay and Gewürztraminer are all excellent.

VIÑA SAN CARLOS ★★★ The blend of Cabernet and Malbec is worth trying; also ripe Semillon.

CHILE PRICE GUIDES

RED

Under £4.00

1996
★ Cabernet Sauvignon Casa Leona £3.99 (MAR)
Cabernet Sauvignon Valdivieso £3.99 (VIC)
★ Merlot Carta Vieja £3.99 (MAJ)
Merlot La Palma £3.99 (WAI) £3.99 (OD)
★ Merlot las Colinas £3.99 (BOT) £3.99 (WR) £3.99 (THR)
1995
Cabernet Sauvignon Santa Helena £3.95 (EL)
★ Cabernet Sauvignon/Merlot Vinicola las Taguas £3.99 (ASD)
Merlot Concha y Toro £3.99 (FUL)

£4.00 → £4.49

1996
Cabernet Sauvignon Caliterra £4.49 (CO)
Cabernet Sauvignon Concha y Toro £4.49 (POR)
Cabernet Sauvignon Isla Negra £4.35 (WAI)
Cabernet Sauvignon/Merlot Concha y Toro £4.25 (AUR) £4.45 (STA)
★ Merlot Villa Rosa £4.35 (WHI)
Pinot Noir Cono Sur £4.49 (VIC)
1995
Cabernet Sauvignon Carmen £4.49 (FLE)
Cabernet Sauvignon Montes £4.49 (AME)
Cabernet Sauvignon/Merlot Concha y Toro £4.20 (UB)
Merlot Santa Carolina £4.29 (CO) £4.49 (WR) £4.49 (BOT) £4.49 (THR)
1994
Cabernet Sauvignon Caliterra £4.35 (GRE) £4.49 (BO) £4.49 (FUL)
Cabernet Sauvignon Concha y Toro £4.49 (JON)
1993
Cabernet Sauvignon Santa Carolina £4.35 (GRE)

£4.50 → £4.99

1996
Cabernet Sauvignon Montes £4.75 (PIP)
Merlot Errázuriz £4.99 (THR) £4.99 (BOT)
Merlot Valdivieso £4.55 (BO)
Pinot Noir Cono Sur £4.75 (WS)
1995
★ Cabernet Franc Palo Alto £4.99 (AV)
Cabernet Sauvignon Canepa Estate Oak-Aged £4.99 (UN)
Cabernet Sauvignon Carmen £4.99 (NA)
Cabernet Sauvignon Concha y Toro £4.85 (GRE) £4.99 (BOT) £4.99 (WR) £4.99 (THR)
Cabernet Sauvignon Errázuriz £4.99 (VIC) £4.99 (FUL)
Cabernet Sauvignon Montes £4.65 (AS)
Cabernet Sauvignon Undurraga £4.85 (WRI)
Malbec Villa Montes £4.99 (POR)
Merlot Concha y Toro £4.75 (TAN) £4.85 (GRE) £4.99 (UN) £4.99 (BOT) £4.99 (THR) £4.99 (WR)
Pinot Noir Cono Sur £4.99 (FUL)
Pinot Noir Santa Rita "120" £4.99 (DI)
Pinot Noir Undurraga £4.95 (GRE) £4.99 (TES)
1994
Cabernet Sauvignon Castillo de Molina £4.95 (ROB)
★ Cabernet Sauvignon Rowan Brook Reserve £4.99 (ASD)
Cabernet Sauvignon Santa Carolina £4.91 (BY)
Cabernet Sauvignon Santa Rita Reserva £4.99 (MAJ)
Cabernet Sauvignon Torres £4.93 (HOG) £4.99 (POR)
Cabernet Sauvignon Torres Santa Digna £4.75 (GRE)
Cabernet Sauvignon Undurraga £4.50 (GRE)

MERCHANTS SPECIALIZING IN CHILE
see Merchant Directory (page 413) for details

This is another country where few merchants stock a long list. The following, however, have a good choice: Lay & Wheeler (LAY), Oddbins (OD) – few independent merchants have as much variety, Thos. Peatling, Safeway (SAF), Tanners (TAN), Thresher (THR), The Ubiquitous Chip (UB)

Cabernet Sauvignon Viña Casablanca Miraflores Estate £4.99 (NI)
Cabernet Sauvignon Vina Portal del Alto £4.95 (HAH)
Merlot Concha y Toro £4.99 (JON)
Merlot Santa Carolina £4.91 (BY)
Merlot Santa Rita 120 £4.99 (DI)
Merlot Villa Montes Gran Reserva £4.99 (SAF)

1993
Cabernet Sauvignon Montes £4.69 (WHI)
Cabernet Sauvignon Torres £4.99 (UN)
Cabernet Sauvignon Torres Santa Digna £4.59 (WHI)
Malbec Santa Carolina £4.69 (BOT) £4.69 (THR)

£5.00 ➔ £5.99

1997
Cabernet Sauvignon Valdivieso £5.00 (BIB)
Merlot Valdivieso £5.00 (BIB)
1996
Cabernet Sauvignon Torres Santa Digna £5.99 (GN)
Malbec Santa Carolina £5.20 (AD)
Merlot Errázuriz £5.49 (VIC) £5.99 (QUE)
1995
Cabernet Sauvignon Los Vascos £5.85 (STA)
Cabernet Sauvignon Valdivieso Reserva £5.99 (FUL)
Cabernet Sauvignon Viña Linderos £5.99 (NA)
★ Merlot Carmen Reserve £5.50 (BER) £5.99 (POR) £5.99 (GRAP)
Merlot Casa Lapostolle Selection £5.99 (FUL)
1994
Cabernet Sauvignon Cousiño Macul £5.45 (NI)
Cabernet Sauvignon Los Vascos £5.04 (HOG) £5.25 (REI) £5.45 (GRE) £5.73 (WATT) £5.79 (NO) £5.91 (PLA)
Cabernet Sauvignon Torres Curico £5.49 (AME)
Casillero del Diablo Concha y Toro £5.85 (GRE) £5.95 (WRJ)
1993
Cabernet Sauvignon Los Vascos £5.63 (PEN) £5.69 (ROS) £5.95 (VIG)
Cabernet Sauvignon Marqués de Casa Concha £5.99 (VIC)
Cabernet Sauvignon Montes Nogales Estate Oak-Aged Reserve £5.80 (PIP)
Merlot Marqués de Casa Conche £5.95 (WS)

1992
Cabernet Sauvignon Cousiño Macul £5.10 (UB)
Cabernet Sauvignon Santa Carolina Special Reserve £5.49 (WR) £5.49 (BOT) £5.49 (THR)
Cabernet Sauvignon Undurraga Reserve Selection £5.99 (GRE)
1990
Cabernet Sauvignon Undurraga Reserve Selection £5.99 (JON)
1989
Cabernet Sauvignon Cousiño Macul Antiguas Reservas £5.89 (BO)

£6.00 ➔ £6.99

1996
Merlot Errázuriz £6.35 (HAH)
Merlot Viña Porta £6.49 (OD)
Pinot Noir Cono Sur Selection Reserve £6.49 (OD)
1995
★ Cabernet Sauvignon Carmen Grande Vidure £6.99 (NA)
Cabernet Sauvignon Carmen Reserve £6.45 (WS) £6.99 (NA)
Cabernet Sauvignon Los Vascos £6.60 (GN)
★ Cabernet Sauvignon Viña Casablanca Santa Isabel Estate £6.99 (OD)
Merlot Montes £6.65 (AD)
Pinot Noir Cono Sur Selection Reserve £6.59 (FUL) £6.60 (WS)
1994
Cabernet Sauvignon Cousiño Macul Antiguas Reservas £6.50 (GRE) £6.95 (WRI)
Cabernet Sauvignon Los Vascos £6.35 (HAH)
Cabernet Sauvignon Viña Casablanca Miraflores Estate £6.99 (EL)
Merlot Cousiño Macul £6.50 (GRE)
1993
Cabernet Sauvignon Cousiño Macul Antiguas Reservas £6.29 (VIC) £6.70 (TAN) £6.95 (POR)
Cabernet Sauvignon Montes £6.70 (TAN)
Cabernet Sauvignon Santa Helena Seleccion del Directorio £6.25 (WRI)

Stars (★) indicate wines selected by Oz Clarke in the Best Buys section which begins on page 12.

Cabernet Sauvignon Undurraga Reserve
Selection £6.87 (PEN)
1992
Cabernet Sauvignon Cousiño Macul
Antiguas Reservas £6.35 (UB) £6.59 (NI)
£6.59 (JON)
1991
Cabernet Sauvignon Marqués de Casa
Concha £6.85 (GRE)

£7.00 → £7.99

1995
Cabernet Sauvignon Valdivieso Reserva
£7.00 (BIB)
Merlot Cousiño Macul £7.25 (STA)
1994
Cabernet Sauvignon Cousiño Macul
Antiguas Reservas £7.25 (STA)
1993
Cabernet Sauvignon Cousiño Macul
Antiguas Reservas £7.00 (MV) £7.70
(GN)
Cabernet Sauvignon Marqués de Casa
Concha £7.50 (TAN)
1992
El Bosque Viña Casablanca £7.25 (WS)

£8.00 → £9.99

Non-vintage
Caballo Loco Valdivieso £9.95 (BIB) £9.95
(WAI)
1996
Pinot Noir Valdivieso Reserve £8.00 (BIB)
1995
Cabernet Sauvignon Montes Alpha £9.65
(AD)
Merlot Casa Lapostolle Cuvée Alexandre
£8.95 (WS) £8.99 (OD)
1994
Merlot Casa Lapostolle Cuvée Alexandre
£9.99 (EL)
1993
Cabernet Sauvignon Montes Alpha £8.95
(AME) £8.99 (OD) £9.39 (PLA) £9.55 (QUE)
Merlot Montes £8.90 (BER)
1992
Cabernet Sauvignon Montes Alpha £9.30
(WRI)

£10.00 → £13.99

1994
Cabernet Sauvignon Carmen Gold
Reserve £11.79 (NA)
Cabernet Sauvignon Concha y Toro Don
Melchor £12.95 (STA)

1993
Cabernet Sauvignon Concha y Toro Don
Melchor £10.50 (TAN) £11.30 (UB)
Cabernet Sauvignon Santa Rita Casa Real
£13.99 (EL)
1989
Cabernet Sauvignon Concha y Toro Don
Melchor £12.85 (GRE)

WHITE

Under £4.00

1996
Sauvignon Blanc Montenuevo £3.75 (WAI)
Sauvignon Blanc Undurraga £3.99 (MAJ)
1995
Sauvignon Blanc Caliterra £3.99 (TES)

£4.00 → £4.99

1997
Sauvignon Blanc Torres £4.95 (STA)
Sauvignon Blanc Valdivieso £4.50 (BIB)
1996
Sauvignon Blanc Santa Carolina £4.92 (BY)
Chardonnay Andes Peaks £4.49 (POR)
£4.69 (EL) £4.75 (BU)
Chardonnay Caliterra £4.35 (GRE) £4.49
(SAF)
Chardonnay Carmen £4.99 (NA)
Chardonnay Carta Vieja £4.99 (MAJ)
Chardonnay Casa Porta £4.99 (OD)
Chardonnay Concha y Toro £4.85 (GRE)
£4.99 (POR) £4.99 (UN)
Chardonnay Isla Negra £4.99 (WAI)
Chardonnay Santa Carolina £4.49 (CO)
Chardonnay Valdivieso £4.99 (WAI)
Chardonnay Viña Casablanca £4.95 (WS)
Chardonnay/Semillon Santa Carolina
£4.69 (WR) £4.69 (BOT) £4.69 (THR)
Gewürztraminer Cono Sur £4.45 (WS)
£4.49 (VIC)
Sauvignon Blanc Andes Peaks £4.45 (WS)
£4.49 (POR) £4.50 (BU) £4.69 (EL)
Sauvignon Blanc Caliterra £4.35 (GRE)
Sauvignon Blanc Concha y Toro
Casablanca £4.49 (POR) £4.99 (OD)
Sauvignon Blanc Errázuriz £4.49 (THR)
£4.49 (WR) £4.49 (BOT) £4.99 (VIC)
Sauvignon Blanc Montes £4.50 (ELL) £4.60
(PIP)
Sauvignon Blanc Santa Rita Reserva £4.99
(MAJ)
Sauvignon Blanc Torres £4.21 (HOG)
£4.75 (POR)

Sauvignon Blanc Torres Santa Digna £4.49 (GRE)

Sauvignon Blanc Undurraga £4.50 (GRE) £4.85 (WRJ)

Sauvignon Blanc Villard Aconcagua £4.68 (HOG)

Sauvignon Blanc Viña Casablanca Lontué Valley £4.95 (WS)

Sauvignon Blanc Viña Casablanca Santa Isabel Estate £4.99 (VIC) £4.99 (CO)

1995

Chardonnay Caliterra £4.49 (BO)

Chardonnay Carmen £4.49 (VIC)

Chardonnay Casillero del Diablo, Concha y Toro £4.99 (OD)

Chardonnay Concha y Toro £4.59 (JON)

Chardonnay Santa Carolina £4.65 (GRE)

Chardonnay Viña Casablanca £4.99 (BO)

Chenin Blanc Santa Carolina £4.69 (THR) £4.69 (BOT) £4.92 (BY)

Sauvignon Blanc Carmen £4.49 (FLE)

Sauvignon Blanc Concha y Toro Casablanca £4.85 (GRE)

Sauvignon Blanc Torres Santa Digna £4.59 (WHI)

£5.00 → £5.99

1997

Chardonnay Cousiño Macul £5.95 (STA)

Chardonnay Valdivieso £5.00 (BIB)

1996

Chardonnay Andes Peaks £5.95 (SAT)

Chardonnay Caliterra £5.49 (CO)

Chardonnay Cousiño Macul £5.50 (TAN) £5.50 (GRE)

Chardonnay Errázuriz £5.49 (OD) £5.49 (VIC) £5.49 (TES)

Chardonnay Santa Carolina £5.12 (BY)

Chardonnay Santa Rita Reserve £5.50 (PIP) £5.99 (DI)

Chardonnay Villa Montes £5.86 (PLA)

Gewürztraminer Viña Casablanca £5.97 (ELL) £5.99 (OD)

Sauvignon Blanc Torres Santa Digna £5.50 (GN)

Sauvignon Blanc Viña Casablanca Lontué Valley £5.29 (JON) £5.49 (WR) £5.49 (THR) £5.49 (BOT) £5.68 (COU)

1995

Chardonnay Caliterra £5.49 (THR) £5.49 (BOT) £5.49 (WR)

Chardonnay Marqués de Casa Concha £5.99 (VIC)

Chardonnay Undurraga £5.03 (PEN) £5.18 (ROS) £5.50 (WRJ)

Chardonnay Viña Casablanca £5.49 (POR) £5.68 (COU)

Sauvignon Blanc Undurraga £5.03 (PEN) £5.18 (ROS)

1994

Chardonnay Marqués de Casa Concha £5.95 (WS)

Sauvignon Blanc Santa Rita Reserva £5.49 (BO)

£6.00 → £6.99

1996

Chardonnay Carmen Reserve £6.99 (NA)

Chardonnay Casillero del Diablo, Concha y Toro £6.25 (STA)

Chardonnay Errázuriz £6.35 (HAH)

Gewürztraminer Viña Casablanca £6.49 (POR) £6.99 (EL)

Sauvignon Blanc Carmen £6.05 (PLA)

Sauvignon Blanc Errázuriz £6.84 (HA)

Sauvignon Blanc Viña Casablanca Lontué Valley £6.40 (BER)

1995

Chardonnay Viña Casablanca £6.49 (EL)

★ Chardonnay Viña Casablanca Santa Isabel Estate Barrel-Fermented £6.99 (OD)

1994

Chardonnay Casa Lapostolle Selection £6.99 (EL)

Chardonnay Marqués de Casa Concha £6.85 (GRE)

£7.00 → £8.99

1996

Chardonnay Montes £7.25 (BER)

Chardonnay Valdivieso Reserva £7.00 (BIB)

1995

Chardonnay Errázuriz Reserve £7.34 (ELL) £7.49 (TES)

Chardonnay Santa Carolina Reserva Familia £8.99 (OD)

Chardonnay Viña Casablanca Barrel-Fermented £8.49 (OD) £8.99 (EL)

ROSÉ

Under £5.00

1996

Cabernet Sauvignon Torres Santa Digna Rosado £4.22 (HOG) £4.49 (POR)

1995

Cabernet Sauvignon Torres Santa Digna Rosado £4.59 (WHI) £4.99 (JON)

EASTERN EUROPE

It's not surprising that we buy so many flying winemaker wines from Eastern Europe: we know they're going to be reliable. But unreliability among other makers seems set to be the problem here for a while longer

Talk about Eastern Europe and the first phrase that comes to mind is 'flying winemakers'. And that's perfectly fair: where else in the wine world have such vast changes been effected so quickly by so few?

Before the shredding of the Iron Curtain the only wines from Eastern Europe that were enjoyable were the reds of Bulgaria. They're still going strong, and we're still drinking them, but the whites remain pretty uneven. Just as well, then, that Hungary, under the influence of flying winemakers like Hugh Ryman, is producing fruity, fresh, clean Sauvignons and Chardonnays – and, more excitingly, dry wines from Tokaji grape varieties, especially Furmint.

What else is there? Well, Slovenia produces good whites and a few good reds, but prices tend to be too high to be competitive. And forget about the oxidised Laski Rizling of yesteryear: Slovenian Laski Rizling can be very good – if it's fresh.

There's inexpensive wine by the bucketful in Romania, but is it any good? The answer is that when it's good it's very, very good, and when it's bad it's horrid. Quality is unpredictable: a superb shipment can be followed by a dud. It's often safer to stick to the young wines.

There were brilliant older reds coming out of Moldova a few years back, but they all seem to have been drunk now. But Moldovan reds can still be excellent: they've got acres and acres of Cabernet Sauvignon there and, it seems, good oak. Head east of Moldova and increasingly you're in uncharted territory, where familiar European grape varieties give way to strange, tannic whites and even stranger reds, where flying winemakers have yet to land.

GRAPE VARIETIES

ALIGOTÉ (white; Romania, Bulgaria, Moldova) Used for sparkling wine and some passable neutral dry white. Often blended with Chardonnay.

BURGUND MARE (red; Romania) Probably the Blauburgunder grape by another name. Produces a light shadow of Pinot Noir style.

CABERNET FRANC (red; Hungary, Moldova, Bulgaria) Lovely velvety, fruity young reds in Hungary.

CABERNET SAUVIGNON (red; Macedonia, Bulgaria, Romania, Moldova, SW Hungary) Capable of producing ripe, long-lived wines in Romania, Moldova and Bulgaria.

CHARDONNAY (white; Bulgaria, Hungary, Moldova, Romania) Good dry whites. Yields are a bit too high in Hungary.

DIMIAT (white; Bulgaria) Bulk producer, blended with Muscat and Rhine Riesling.

FETEASCĂ ALBĂ/LEANYKA/ MÄDCHENTRAUBE (white; Romania, Hungary) Rich, floral, short-lived, flabby wines.

FETEASCĂ NEAGRĂ (red; Romania) At best dark, slightly vegetal with sooty tannins. Can easily become too vegetal.

FURMINT (white; Hungary) The top Tokaji grape; good acidity, concentration, long life.

GAMZA (red; Bulgaria) Soft, light, and early maturing.

GEWÜRZTRAMINER (white; everywhere) Usually known as Traminer, and has typical spicy style. Amazing dessert wines in Moldova.

GRÜNER VELTLINER (white; CZ, Slovakia) Intense greengage fruit at best; hard acidity if not ripened properly.

HÁRSLEVELÜ (white; Hungary) Earthy, big, peachy, long-lived.

IRSAY OLIVER (white; CZ, Slovakia, Hungary) A Muscat cross, very perfumed.

KADARKA (red; Hungary) Seldom allowed to produce the weight and tannin which made its reputation. Usually small, tough, green wines.

KÉKFRANKOS/FRANKOVKA/ BLAUFRANKISCH (red; Hungary, CZ, Slovakia) Vegetal young reds. Yields have to be small for good quality.

KÉKOPORTO/BLAUER PORTUGUEISER (red; Hungary) Light, ordinary, short-lived reds.

MAVRUD (red; Bulgaria) Hefty dark reds.

MERLOT (red; everywhere except CZ and Slovakia) Very successful in Romania, good in southern Bulgaria.

MISKET (white; Bulgaria) Claims not to be a Muscat, but has a lightly perfumed style, and a tendency to blow over quickly.

MÜLLER-THURGAU (white; CZ, Slovakia, Hungary) Floral, early-drinking Germanic type. Widely cultivated.

MUSCAT OTTONEL (white; everywhere) Good but short-lived, vulgar Muscat styles.

PAMID (red; Romania, Bulgaria) Short-lived, empty, can blend well with Merlot.

PINOT BLANC (white; Hungary, CZ, Slovakia) Very similar to dry Alsace at best.

PINOT GRIS (white; Hungary, CZ, Slovakia, Romania, Moldova) Can make outstanding dry and off-dry wines with wonderful spicy aroma.

PINOT NOIR (red; Romania, Hungary, Moldova, Slovakia) Can be true to type and elegant, but often too poorly handled.

RHINE RIESLING (white; everywhere) Can be lemony and true to type; rarely as intense as good German versions.

ST LAURENT/BLAUER LIMBERGER/ SVATOVAVRINECKE (red; CZ, Slovakia) Delicious soft reds with black cherry flavours when allowed to ripen.

SAPERAVI (red; Moldova) Very good spicy wine; lots of potential.

SAUVIGNON (white; everywhere) Needs good technology; grassy and vegetal otherwise.

SMEDEREVKA (white; Macedonia and elsewhere in former Yugoslavia) Can make good, fresh wine; often poorly handled.

TĂMÎIOASĂ ROMANEASCĂ/ TAMIANKA (white; Romania, Bulgaria) Classic noble rot grape. Very sweet, raisiny flavours, long-lived.

VRANAC (red; Macedonia) Good solid performer. Takes well to oak.

WELSCHRIESLING/LASKI RIZLING/ VLASSKY RIZLING/ OLASZ RIZLING/ RIZLING ITALICO (white; everywhere) Nothing to do with Rhine Riesling. Earthy, lowish-acid, but can be good; ages well occasionally.

WINE REGIONS AND PRODUCERS

ASSENOVGRAD (Bulgaria) Source of reliable Mavrud and Cabernet.

BALATON (Hungary) Region centred on Lake Balaton. Well structured wines.

BALATONBOGLÁR (Hungary) Go-ahead region south of Lake Balaton, source of wines made by flying winemaker Kym Milne.

BOHEMIA (Czech Republic) Region making light whites from Riesling, Traminer and others. Quality is fair.

COTNARI (Romania) Region producing excellent, ageworthy botrytized wines from Tămîioasă, Grasa and Fetească Albă grapes.

DEALUL MARE (Romania) Rich, slightly jammy reds come from this region; also some whites. Tămîioasă can be good.

DISZNÓKÖ (Hungary) Western-owned company in Tokaji. Tremendous dry Furmint.

DRAVA VALLEY (Slovenia) Delimited wine region, otherwise known as Podravski. Good, well-structured, aromatic whites.

EGER (Hungary) Home of Bull's Blood, a red which these days is a shadow of its former self.

GYÖNGYÖS (Hungary) An estate, and also a region. The estate is the source of Hugh Ryman's pioneering Chardonnay and Sauvignon Blanc.

HASKOVO (Bulgaria) Region making good Controliran (see box) Merlot.

HINCESTI (Moldova) Western investment at this winery is producing very good Chardonnay, again made by Hugh Ryman.

HUNGAROVIN (Hungary) This used to be the name (in small print) on every bottle of Hungarian wine exported. Now it's German owned. It's still exporting, but these are not Hungary's finest.

KHAN KRUM (Bulgaria) Winery producing some of Bulgaria's best, freshest whites, especially Chardonnay (oaked and unoaked) and Sauvignon.

LITTORAL (Slovenia) Wine region making fairly northern Italian-style reds, especially Refosco, Barbera, Cabernet and Merlot. The region is known as Primorski in Slovenia.

LOVICO SUHINDOL (Bulgaria) Bulgaria's first privatized winery, making good quality reds. Best are Cabernet, Merlot, Gamza.

LJUTOMER-ORMOZ (Slovenia) Leading white region capable of producing excellent Laski Rizling, the best of which seems to stay *in situ* while the poor stuff comes here.

MASSANDRA (Ukraine) The Tsar's old cellars (or the old Tsar's cellars, if you prefer) made fortified wines in every

EASTERN EUROPEAN CLASSIFICATIONS

Quality wine, equivalent to France's Appellation Contrôlée, is Minöségi bor in Hungary, Controliran in Bulgaria, and in Slovenia Vrhunsko Vino or, below this, Kakovostno Vino. Romania's system is too complicated to give in full, but the best are VSOC, which can be late harvest up to nobly rotten; VSO from specific grapes and regions; and VS for quality wine.

conceivable style, aping port, sherry, Madeira and a few other things besides. They're still making them, too.

MÓR (Hungary) Good quality region, especially for whites.

MORAVIA (Czech Republic) Region with similar grapes (though not always as good quality) as neighbouring Austria.

MURFATLAR (Romania) Black Sea region producing erratic quality. Botrytized Chardonnay is a speciality, but can lack acidity.

NOVI PAZAR (Bulgaria) Winery making some of Bulgaria's better Chardonnay.

ORIACHOVITZA (Bulgaria) There's good Reserve Cabernet from this region.

PLOVDIV (Bulgaria) A plodding name for a region that is making far from plodding Cabernet.

PRESLAV (Bulgaria) Winery making decent whites. Make sure they're young.

ROYAL TOKAJI WINE COMPANY (Hungary) Excellent quality new-style Tokaji from this joint venture between British, Danish and Hungarian investors.

SAKAR (Bulgaria) Region producing characterful Merlot which can age for a few years.

SAVA VALLEY (Slovenia) Region with promising whites from Sauvignon Blanc and Laski Rizling, and light reds.

SLIVEN (Bulgaria) Lots of Cabernet and Merlot here, and good country wine.

SLOVAKIA Most of the former Czechoslovakia's vineyards ended up here: there's even a chunk of Hungary's Tokaj. Good, spicy whites; fair reds.

SOPRON (Hungary) Region just south of Austria's Neuseidlersee, producing mostly red wines.

STARA ZAGORA (Bulgaria) The name sounds far too glamorous to be a mere wine region; but the Cabernets and Merlots are good.

SVISHTOV (Bulgaria) Winery making good quality Cabernet.

TÎRNAVE (Romania) Cool region making promising whites, especially Feteasca. Best winery: Jidvei.

TOKAJ (Hungary) Tokaj is the region, Tokaji its wine. We've all adopted the Hungarian spelling of this luscious sweet white now; the English always used to spell it Tokay. The style has also changed: from being oxidized and tasting like cheap sherry, it is now (as a result of Western investment) fresher and infinitely more delicious. The grape varieties used to make it are Furmint, Hárslevelü and Muscat Lunel. Some people, notably the Hungarian producers, prefer the old oxidized style: not me. It's made from botrytized grapes (known as *aszú*) which are added to dry base wine in measures known as *puttonyos*. A three-puttonyos Tokaji will be sweet, a four-puttonyos one sweeter, and a five or six-puttonyos one very concentrated and rich. Aszú Eszencia is sweeter again, and Eszencia on its own means juice too sweet to ferment to more than a few per cent alcohol. You could almost stand a spoon up in it; but you almost certainly won't be able to buy it in your local shop. It's used for blending in tiny quantities into lesser wines to pep them up or (according to legend) for reviving dying monarchs. Western-made Tokajis of three to six puttonyos are a more practical buy: wonderful dessert wines, they have a smokiness to their fruit which stands them apart from all other botrytized wines. And they'll age superbly. Best producers: *Royal Tokaji Wine Company, Disznókö.*

EASTERN EUROPE PRICE GUIDES

BULGARIA RED

Under £2.50

Non-vintage
Russe Cabernet Sauvignon/Cinsaut £2.43 (WIW)
Suhindol Cabernet Sauvignon/Merlot £2.40 (WIW)
Suhindol Merlot/Gamza £2.40 (WIW)
1995
Svischtov Debut Merlot £2.49 (WIW)

£2.50 → £2.99

Non-vintage
Bulgarian Cabernet Sauvignon £2.99 (SAI)
Bulgarian Cabernet Sauvignon/Merlot £2.95 (GRE) £2.99 (UN) £2.99 (OD)
Pavlikeni Cabernet Sauvignon/Merlot £2.99 (VIC)
Russe Cabernet Sauvignon/Cinsaut £2.79 (CO) £2.99 (WR) £2.99 (THR) £2.99 (BOT)
Sliven Merlot/Pinot Noir £2.79 (CO) £2.99 (VIC)
Suhindol Cabernet Sauvignon/Merlot £2.99 (WR) £2.99 (BOT) £2.99 (THR)
1995
Bulgarian Cabernet Sauvignon/Merlot £2.99 (SAI)
Sliven Merlot/Pinot Noir £2.89 (CO)
1994
Bulgarian Merlot £2.89 (WHI)
1993
Suhindol Cabernet Sauvignon £2.85 (ASD)
Suhindol Gamza Reserve £2.89 (KWI)
1992
Oriahovitza Cabernet Sauvignon Reserve £2.83 (WIW) £2.99 (ASD)
Sakar Mountain Cabernet Sauvignon £2.83 (WIW)
1991
Bulgarian Cabernet Sauvignon £2.99 (WHI)
Suhindol Gamza £2.83 (WIW)

1990
Assenovgrad Mavrud £2.83 (WIW)
Bulgarian Gamza Reserve £2.99 (SAI)

£3.00 → £3.99

Non-vintage
★ Noble Oak Merlot £3.99 (TES)
Oriahovitza Cabernet Sauvignon Reserve £3.79 (FUL)
Russe Cabernet Sauvignon Reserve £3.89 (VIC)
Suhindol Cabernet Sauvignon £3.79 (FUL)
Svischtov Cabernet Sauvignon £3.78 (LAY)
1995
Iambol Reserve Cabernet Sauvignon £3.69 (THR) £3.69 (BOT) £3.69 (WR)
1993
Suhindol Reserve Merlot £3.49 (OD)
Svischtov Cabernet Sauvignon £3.49 (MAR)
1992
Haskovo Merlot £3.49 (POR)
Iambol Reserve Cabernet Sauvignon £3.79 (SAI)
Oriahovitza Cabernet Sauvignon/Merlot £3.75 (SAI)
Russe Cabernet Sauvignon Reserve £3.69 (CO)
Suhindol Gamza Reserve £3.49 (OD)
Suhindol Reserve Merlot £3.60 (WS) £3.75 (SAI)
1991
Bulgarian Merlot £3.49 (UN)
Oriahovitza Special Reserve Cabernet Sauvignon £.99 (SAI)
Russe Cabernet Sauvignon £3.49 (POR)
Suhindol Cabernet Sauvignon/Merlot £3.79 (SAF)
Suhindol Cabernet Sauvignon Special Reserve £3.99 (VIC) £3.99 (SAI)
Svischtov Cabernet Sauvignon £3.29 (JON)
1990
Plovdiv Cabernet Sauvignon £3.49 (THR) £3.49 (WR) £3.49 (BOT)

MERCHANTS SPECIALIZING IN EASTERN EUROPE
see Merchant Directory (page 413) for details

If you want to look beyond bargain Cabernet Sauvignon, try the following merchants: Butlers Wine Cellar (BU) – good for curiosities, Morris & Verdin (MV),

Thos. Peatling, Sainsbury (SAI), Safeway (SAF), T&W Wines (TW) – good for old Tokaji, Thresher (THR), Wines of Westhorpe (WIW)

Russe Cabernet Sauvignon Reserve £3.99
(MAJ)
Stambolovo Merlot Reserve £3.69 (SO)
£3.99 (UN)
Svischtov Reserve Cabernet Sauvignon
£3.29 (WHI) £3.99 (SAI)
Yantra Valley Cabernet Sauvignon £3.65
(SAI)
1989
Haskovo Merlot £3.58 (SAT)
Russe Cabernet Sauvignon Reserve £3.75
(JON) £3.79 (GRE)

£4.00 → £4.99

1989
Svischtov Cabernet Sauvignon £4.85 (WHI)
1987
Oriahovitza Cabernet Sauvignon Reserve
£4.35 (SAT)
Svischtov Cabernet Sauvignon £4.49 (THR)
£4.49 (BOT) £4.49 (WR)
1985
Sakar Mountain Cabernet Sauvignon
£4.53 (SAT)

BULGARIA WHITE

Under £3.00

Non-vintage
Burgas Muscat/Ugni Blanc £2.89 (FUL)
£2.99 (MAJ) £2.99 (UN)
Preslav Chardonnay £2.99 (FUL)

ESTATE BOTTLED ℮ 75cl
Bulgarian
Chardonnay
PRESLAV REGION
A fine white wine
12% vol
Produced and bottled in Bulgaria by Vinimpex, Sofia
Sole importer in the UK BULGARIAN VINTNERS Co. Ltd. London EC1R 5AD

Preslav Riesling Dimiat £2.99 (OD)
1996
Russe Debut Sauvignon Blanc £2.69 (WIW)
1993
Khan Krum Chardonnay Reserve £2.88
(WIW)

£3.00 → £3.99

Non-vintage
Khan Krum Special Reserve Chardonnay
£3.69 (FUL)

1996
Preslav Chardonnay £3.25 (OD)
1995
Novi Pazar Chardonnay £3.58 (WIW)
1994
Khan Krum Special Reserve Chardonnay
£3.49 (OD)
1992
Khan Krum Chardonnay Reserve £3.79
(WR) £3.79 (THR) £3.79 (BOT)

HUNGARY WHITE

Under £3.00

1996
Chapel Hill Irsai Oliver £2.99 (SAI) £2.99
(CO)

£3.00 → £3.99

1996
Chapel Hill Chardonnay £3.49 (SAI)
Chapel Hill Chardonnay Oaked £3.29 (CO)
Gyöngyös Estate Chardonnay £3.69 (CO)
Nagyréde Pinot Blanc £3.29 (SAF)
Tokaji Szamorodni Dry ½ litre, Bodrog-
Várhegy £3.91 (WIW)
1995
Chapel Hill Chardonnay Oaked £3.29 (JON)
Gyöngyös Estate Chardonnay £3.69 (THR)
£3.69 (BOT) £3.69 (WR) £3.99 (UN)
1994
Gyöngyös Estate Sauvignon Blanc £3.49
(FUL)
1993
Gyöngyös Estate Sauvignon Blanc £3.69 (SO)
Tokaji Furmint Château Megyer £3.80 (UB)

£4.00 → £5.99

1996
Tokaji Furmint Château Megyer £5.25 (GRE)
1995
Chapel Hill Barrique-Aged Chardonnay
£5.29 (SAF)
Tokaji Furmint Disznókö £4.50 (WS)
Tokaji Furmint Château Megyer £5.25 (BU)
1994
Dry Furmint Disznókö £4.99 (JON)
1993
Tokaji Furmint Disznókö £4.85 (BOT)
1989
Tokaji Szamorodni Sweet ½ litre, Oremus
£5.95 (DI)
1988
Tokaji Aszú 5 Putts ½ litre, Bodrog-
Várhegy £5.48 (WIW)

£6.00 → £9.99

Non-vintage
Tokaji Aszú 4 Putts ½ litre, Tokaji
Kereskedöhóz £8.95 (SAT)
1990
Tokaji Fordítás Dessewffy £6.50 (WS)
1988
Tokaji Aszú 5 Putts ½ litre, Tokaji
Kereskedöhóz £6.89 (AUR)
Tokaji Szamorodni Dry ½ litre, Château
Megyer £6.50 (BU) £6.95 (ROB)
Tokaji Szamorodni Sweet ½ litre, Tokaji
Kereskedöhóz £6.99 (UN)

£10.00 → £19.99

1992
Tokaji Aszú 5 Putts ½ litre, Disznókö
£13.95 (WS) £15.50 (VIG)
1991
Tokaji Aszú 5 Putts ½ litre, Royal Tokaji
Wine Co. £14.75 (REI) £16.90 (TAN)
1988
Tokaji Aszú 5 Putts ½ litre, Château
Megyer £12.75 (BU) £15.99 (GRE)
Tokaji Aszú 5 Putts ½ litre, Disznókö
£10.50 (POR) £10.99 (JON)
Tokaji Aszú 6 Putts ½ litre, Bodrog-
Várhegy £10.43 (WIW)
1983
Tokaji Aszú 3 Putts ½ litre, Tokaji
Kereskedöhóz £11.45 (ROB)
Tokaji Aszú 5 Putts ½ litre, Tokaji
Kereskedöhóz £10.95 (STA) £11.99 (UN)

£20.00 → £55.00

1991
Tokaji Aszú 5 Putts ½ litre, Birsalmàs
Secundae Classis £27.95 (VIG)
Tokaji Aszú 5 Putts ½ litre, Nyulaszo 1st
Growth £36.00 (HIG) £39.39 (TAN)
1990
Tokaji Aszú 5 Putts ½ litre, Birsalmàs
Secundae Classis £25.00 (HIG)
Tokaji Aszú 5 Putts ½ litre, Nyulaszo 1st
Growth £32.50 (REI)
Tokaji Aszú 5 Putts ½ litre, Royal Tokaji
Wine Co. £25.00 (BER)
1988
Tokaji Aszú Essencia ½ litre, J Monyok
£37.82 (WIW)
1964
Tokaji Aszú 6 Putts ½ litre £52.88 (WY)
1953
Tokaji Szamorodni Dry ½ litre £43.48 (WY)

£75.00 → £87.00

1993
Tokaji Aszú Essencia ½ litre, Royal Tokaji
  Wine Co. £79.50 (BER)
1964
Tokaji Aszú Essencia ½ litre £75.00 (SOM)

£96.00 → £129.99

1957
Tokaji Aszú Essencia ½ litre £96.50 (UB)
  £125.91 (NO)

HUNGARY RED

Under £3.00

1995
Eger Bull's Blood £2.63 (WIW)
1994
Szekszard Nemes Kadarka £2.74 (WIW)

£3.00 → £4.99

1995
Chapel Hill Cabernet Sauvignon £3.29 (CO)
Eger Bull's Blood £3.19 (CO)
Villány Cabernet Sauvignon £3.49 (BOT)

ROMANIA

Under £3.00

1994
Romanian Merlot/Cabernet £2.99 (CO)

£3.00 → £3.99

1995
Graham Dixon Chardonnay £3.25 (CO)
River Route Merlot, Cernavoda £3.19 (CO)
1994
Pinot Noir Dealul Mare £3.29 (WHI)
1991
Classic Pinot Noir £3.20 (GRE)
1989
Tămîioasă Pietroasele £3.99 (UB)

£4.00 → £5.50

Non-vintage
Tămîioasă Pietroasele £5.49 (SAT)
1995
Tămîioasă Pietroasele £4.20 (GRE)

c. £10.00

1960
Tămîioasă Pietroasele £9.95 (BU)

"BETTER BUY BULGARIAN"

*I*t is still the wisest decision for the discerning wine buyer. The person seeking quality, choice and, above all, outstanding value.

Since Bulgarian Vintners launched Bulgarian wines in the UK back in 1980, sales have risen constantly, with millions enjoying our wines.

However, the emphasis is, as always, on quality - but still at highly affordable prices. During 1996 we are further expanding our range of distinctive white wines and our select range of top quality reds.

As the leading supplier of the best from Bulgaria's vineyards, we at Bulgarian Vintners know that "better buy Bulgarian" is a thought shared by more and more appreciative wine purchasers.

The Bulgarian Vintners

Bulgarian Vintners Company Limited
Nazdrave House, 154 Caledonian Road, London N1 9RD Telephone: 0171 278 8047 Facsimile: 0171 833 3127

FRANCE

How is France keeping up with the New World? By stealing its clothes, that's how

You would be hard put these days to find anybody who isn't French claiming that French wines are the best in the world. Individual French wines may well be world-beaters – a *grand cru* Chablis from a top grower, for example, or Mouton-Rothschild 1982 – but the wine world is now too big and too diffuse for anyone seriously to suggest that any one country is 'the best'.

And yet the influence of France is felt in just about every wine-producing country – through Cabernet Sauvignon, Chardonnay, Merlot and Sauvignon Blanc. These grapes are the four-lane highway that has carried French ideas about wine as far away as California, Bulgaria and New Zealand. France still provides the benchmarks for these wines, and growers in Chile and New South Wales look over their shoulders at the prototypes while making their own – sometimes very different – styles of wine.

But influence almost always works both ways. France has absorbed a great many of the lessons of the New World – and as a result is making fresher, cleaner wine than ever before. The idea that what modern drinkers want is bright fruit flavours was anathema to a great many French producers in the past; but now growers in the Midi are delightedly turning out the sort of wines that would win prizes in Australia – and indeed might even have been made by Australians. France is infinitely flexible – and has enough other cards in her hand (Pinot Noir, Syrah, Viognier, Sémillon, Mourvèdre et al) to keep surprising us for a long time yet.

WINE CLASSIFICATIONS

The French have the most far-reaching system of wine control of any nation, even though its adequacy as a form of quality control is now in question. The key factors are the 'origin' of the wine, its historic method of production and the use of the correct grape types. The three defined levels are: AC, VDQS, and vin de pays.

APPELLATION D'ORIGINE CONTROLÉE (AC, AOC) To qualify
for AC a wine must meet seven requirements:
Land: Suitable vineyard land is minutely defined. **Grape**: Only those grapes traditionally regarded as suitable can be used. **Degree of alcohol**: Wines must reach a minimum (or maximum) degree of natural alcohol. **Yield**: A basic permitted yield is set for each AC, but the figure may be increased or decreased year by year after consultation between the growers of each AC region and the Institut National des Appellations d'Origine (INAO). **Vineyard practice**: AC wines must follow rules about pruning methods and density of planting. **Wine-making practice**: Each AC wine has its own regulations as to what is allowed. Typically, chaptalization – adding sugar during fermentation to increase alcoholic strength – is accepted in the north, but not in the south. **Tasting and analysis**: Since 1979 wines must pass a tasting panel.

VIN DÉLIMITÉ DE QUALITÉ SUPÉRIEURE (VDQS) This second
group is, in general, slightly less reliable in quality. It is in the process of being phased out. No more vins de pays are being upgraded to VDQS but there is still no news on when any of the existing ones will be upgraded to AC status (or downgraded to vin de pays).

VIN DE PAYS The third category gives a regional definition to France's basic blending wines. The rules are similar to AC, but allow a good deal more flexibility and some wonderful cheap wines can be found which may well surprise. Quality can be stunning, and expect fruit, value and competent wine-making. There are also one or two high priced superstars in this category.

VIN DE TABLE 'Table wine' is the title for the rest. No quality control except as far as basic public health regulations demand. Vins de pays are always available for approximately the same price, and offer a far more interesting drink. Many vins de table here are dull and poorly made, and branded, heavily advertised ones are seldom good value.

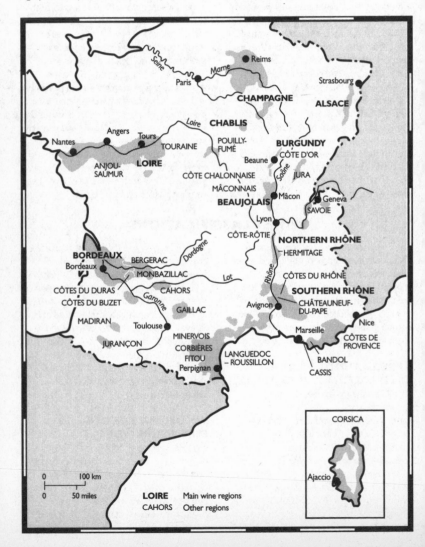

WINE-FINDER: FRANCE

France is packed with famous wine names, but if you don't know whereabouts in the country a wine comes from, life can get confusing. In the following 185 pages we have divided the huge number of appellations in France into eight clearly defined regions: Alsace, Bordeaux, Burgundy, Champagne, Jura & Savoie, Loire, Rhône and Southern France. In Burgundy, we have separated Basic Burgundy and the subregions Beaujolais, Chablis, Côte Chalonnaise, Côte d'Or and Mâconnais. So, if you know the name but are wondering which section to look in, this quick guide to some of the best-known wine names will help.

Aloxe-Corton – *Burgundy, Côte d'Or*
Auxey-Duresses – *Burgundy, Côte d'Or*
Bandol – *Southern France*
Barsac – *Bordeaux (sweet white)*
Beaune – *Burgundy, Côte d'Or*
Blagny – *Burgundy, Côte d'Or*
Bourgueil – *Loire (red)*
Brouilly – *Burgundy, Beaujolais*
Cadillac – *Bordeaux*
Cahors – *Southern France*
Cérons – *Bordeaux*
Chablis – *Burgundy, Chablis*
Chambolle-Musigny – *Burgundy, Côte d'Or*
Chassagne-Montrachet – *Burgundy, Côte d'Or*
Châteauneuf-du-Pape – *Rhône*
Chénas – *Burgundy, Beaujolais*
Chinon – *Loire (red)*
Chiroubles – *Burgundy, Beaujolais*
Chorey-lès-Beaune – *Burgundy, Côte d'Or*
Clairette de Die – *Rhône (sparkling)*
Condrieu – *Rhône (white)*
Corbières – *Southern France*
Cornas – *Rhône (red)*
Coteaux du Tricastin – *Rhône*
Côte-Rôtie – *Rhône (red)*
Côtes de Beaune – *Burgundy, Côte d'Or*
Côtes de Bourg – *Bordeaux*
Côtes de Nuits – *Burgundy, Côte d'Or*
Côtes du Ventoux – *Rhône*
Crozes-Hermitage – *Rhône*
Entre-deux-Mers – *Bordeaux*
Fitou – *Southern France*
Fixin – *Burgundy, Côte d'Or*
Fleurie – *Burgundy, Beaujolais*
Fronsac – *Bordeaux*
Gevrey-Chambertin – *Burgundy, Côte d'Or*
Gigondas – *Rhône (red)*
Givry – *Burgundy, Côte Chalonnaise*
Graves – *Bordeaux (dry white)*
Hautes-Côtes de Beaune – *Burgundy, Côte d'Or*
Hautes-Côtes de Nuit – *Burgundy, Côte d'Or*
Haut-Médoc – *Bordeaux*
Hermitage – *Rhône*
Juliénas – *Burgundy, Beaujolais*
Languedoc-Roussillon – *Southern France*
Listrac – *Bordeaux*

Loupiac – *Bordeaux*
Mâcon – *Burgundy, Mâconnais*
Margaux – *Bordeaux*
Marsannay – *Burgundy, Côte d'Or*
Médoc – *Bordeaux*
Mercurey – *Burgundy, Côte Chalonnaise*
Meursault – *Burgundy, Côte d'Or*
Minervois – *Southern France*
Montagny – *Burgundy, Côte Chalonnaise*
Monthelie – *Burgundy, Côte d'Or*
Morey-St-Denis – *Burgundy, Côte d'Or*
Morgon – *Burgundy, Beaujolais*
Moulin-à-Vent – *Burgundy, Beaujolais*
Moulis – *Bordeaux*
Muscadet – *Loire (dry white)*
Muscat de Beaumes-de-Venise – *Rhône (fortified white)*
Nuits-St-Georges – *Burgundy, Côte d'Or*
Pauillac – *Bordeaux*
Pernand-Vergelesses – *Burgundy, Côte d'Or*
Pessac-Léognan – *Bordeaux*
Pomerol – *Bordeaux*
Pommard – *Burgundy, Côte d'Or*
Pouilly-Fuissé – *Burgundy, Mâconnais*
Pouilly-Fumé – *Loire (dry white)*
Provence – *Southern France*
Puligny-Montrachet – *Burgundy, Côte d'Or*
Régnié – *Burgundy, Beaujolais*
Rully – *Burgundy, Côte Chalonnaise*
St-Amour – *Burgundy, Beaujolais*
Ste-Croix-du-Mont – *Bordeaux*
St-Émilion – *Bordeaux*
St-Estèphe – *Bordeaux*
St-Joseph – *Rhône (red)*
St-Julien – *Bordeaux*
St-Véran – *Burgundy, Mâconnais*
Sancerre – *Loire*
Saumur-Champigny – *Loire (red)*
Sauternes – *Bordeaux (sweet white)*
Sauvignon de St-Bris – *Burgundy, Basic*
Savigny-lès-Beaune – *Burgundy, Côte d'Or*
Tavel – *Rhône (rosé)*
Vins de pays – *various*
Volnay – *Burgundy, Côte d'Or*
Vosne-Romanée – *Burgundy, Côte d'Or*
Vougeot – *Burgundy, Côte d'Or*
Vouvray – *Loire*

ALSACE

**All adventurous cooks should look at Alsace wines: they can be
all things to an awful lot of dishes. But pay
attention to vintages**

These are the ultimate food wines.
Nothing goes quite so well with oriental
cooking or those modish dishes that
combine oriental and western influences;
nothing is quite so perfect with a humble
onion tart. Trout and salmon are
thoroughly at home with Alsace wines, and
people who prefer white to red ought to
head straight for Alsace when serving pâté,
pork or goose. And that's before one even
starts thinking about pudding.

The reason that Alsace wines can be said
to go so well *en bloc* with food is that their
flavours are variations on a theme – and
that theme is ripeness and spice. The
spiciest of all is Gewürztraminer, followed
by Pinot Gris; Riesling is the best all-round
wine for food; Pinot Blanc is more neutral
though still creamily ripe; Sylvaner is more
neutral again. They all have structure and
weight – far more weight (and alcohol) than
the German wines with which they are so
often confused; and you need weight in
wine to drink with food.

How irritating of the Alsaciens, then, not
to make it clear when their wines are not
absolutely dry. Usually they are: usually only
Vendange Tardive wines and upwards are
sweet. But sometimes a very warm year will
produce wines with slightly more sweetness
than is ideal for trout or goose. And for
food wines, that's a serious matter.

GRAPE VARIETIES

In Alsace wines are generally labelled
according to their grape variety. Cheap
blends of two or more varieties are sold as
Edelzwicker; go instead for upmarket ones.

AUXERROIS Usually blended with Pinot
Blanc to add acidity. It's fatter and more
buttery than Pinot Blanc, with a touch of
spice and musk. Best: *André Kientzler, Marc
Kreydenweiss, Jos Meyer, Landmann-Ostholt,
Rolly Gassmann, Bruno Sorg.*

CHASSELAS Rare now in Alsace,
Chasselas has never been complex, but the
few true examples can be vibrantly fruity
and must be drunk young, while they retain
their freshness. Best: *André Kientzler, Jos
Meyer, Schoffit.*

CLASSIC BLENDS These can be
superb, and their producers avoid the
Edelzwicker designation like the plague.
Best: *Hugel Gentil, Marc Kreydenweiss Clos du
Val d'Eléon, Co-op de Ribeauvillé Clos du*
*Zahnacker, Schlumberger Réserve, Jean Sipp
Clos du Schlossberg, Louis Sipp Côtes de
Ribeauvillé, Willm Gentil Clos Gaensbroennel.*
They will almost all be best in riper years.

EDELZWICKER These are mostly
lacklustre blends. Occasionally an
Edelzwicker with an extra dollop of
Gewürztraminer or Tokay-Pinot Gris will be
good. *Schlumberger Cristal-Maree* is about as
good as they get.

GEWÜRZTRAMINER The least dry of
all Alsace, though *Beyer Cuvée des Comtes
d'Eguisheim* and *Trimbach Cuvée des Seigneurs
de Ribeaupierre* are bone dry. Gewürztraminer is the most voluptuous, upfront and
fat of all Alsace wines, overflowing with
exotic aromas. Young Gewürz often smells
of banana and the more it does so, the
more finesse it will have when mature. Best:
*Kuentz-Bas, Ostertag, Trimbach, Weinbach,
Willm Clos Gaensbroennel, Zind-Humbrecht,
Turckheim co-op.*

MUSCAT Light, fragrant, wonderfully grapy. Imagine crushing a fistful of green grapes and gulping the juice. That's how fresh and grapy a good Muscat should be. Hotter years give heavy wines that are far from ideal. Look for *Becker, Ernest Burn, Joseph Cattin, Dirler, Charles Koehly, Marc Kreydenweiss, Kuentz-Bas, Rolly Gassmann, Pfaffenheim co-op, Schlumberger, Bruno Sorg, Weinbach, Zind-Humbrecht.*

PINOT BLANC At its best, this is plump, rich and ripe, with apple or floral overtones and a long creamy finish. Standard supermarket versions are more neutral, but usually perfectly acceptable. Best: *J B Adam, Camille Braun, Théo Cattin, Co-opérative de Cléebourg, Marcel Deiss, Hugel, Charles Koehly, Albert Mann, Rolly Gassmann, Schlumberger, Martin Spielmann, Zind-Humbrecht.* Can also be called Klevner.

PINOT NOIR The Burgundy grape makes light reds, although richer, oakier wines are becoming more common. Typically they are perfumed and strawberryish, but lack complexity. 1990 was an exceptional year, and there's been nothing quite as good for reds since. Best include *J B Adam, Jean Becker, Marcel Deiss, René Fleith, Albert Hertz, Hugel, Jacques Iltis,* *Albert Mann, Co-opérative de Pfaffenheim, Turckheim co-op, Wolfberger.*

RIESLING Powerful, structured, steely wines that grow 'petrolly' with age. It's with Riesling that the subtleties of *grand cru* soils are most evident. Can be long-lived. Best: *Becker, Beyer, Paul Blanck, Deiss, Dirler, Pierre Freudenreich, Pierre Frick, Mader, Frederic Mallo, Frederic Mochel, Edgar Schaller, Schlumberger, Sick-Dreyer, Jean Sipp, Louis Sipp, Bruno Sorg, Trimbach, Weinbach, Wunsch & Mann, Zind-Humbrecht.*

SYLVANER Light, tart, slightly earthy. With age it tastes of tomatoes, for some reason. Best: *Christian Dolder, J Hauller, Ostertag* (especially the *Veilles Vignes*), *Rolly Gassmann, Martin Schaetzel, Schoffit, Albert Seltz, Zind-Humbrecht.*

TOKAY-PINOT GRIS Rich, musky and honeyed, though can run to flab if badly made. Even the lighter ones are luscious behind their dry fruit. The best can age well. Best: *Lucien Albrecht, Barmès-Buecher, Léon Beyer, Ernest Burn, Claude Dietrich, Robert Dietrich, Pierre Frick, Marc Kreydenweiss, Kuentz-Bas, Frédéric Mallo, Schlumberger, Schoffit, Bruno Sorg, Turckheim co-op, Weinbach, Zind-Humbrecht.*

WINE CLASSIFICATIONS

VIN D'ALSACE, AC This is the simple generic appellation that covers the whole Alsace region, and it is normally used in conjunction with a grape name. Thus a wine made from the Riesling grape would be called 'Riesling – Appellation d'Origine Contrôlée Alsace'.

CRÉMANT, AC White, Champagne-method fizz, made mainly from Pinot Blanc. Some producers make the wine from Riesling or Pinot Gris, the former racy and flowery, the latter more musky and rich. But both are atypical. Chardonnay may also be used, and Pinot Noir for rosé. Look for

wines from *Paul Blanck, Robert Dietrich, Dopff & Irion, Dopff Au Moulin, Laugel, Co-opérative de Pfaffenheim, Co-opérative de Turckheim, Wolfberger.*

GRAND CRU A decree of 1992 classified 50 historically excellent vineyards as *grands crus.* They must meet stricter regulations than ordinary Alsace, and can only be planted with Riesling, Tokay-Pinot Gris, Gewürztraminer or Muscat. Notably lower (but still high) yields apply. They can be recognized from the words 'Appellation Alsace Grand Cru Contrôlée' which appear on the label.

The fascination of *grands crus* is that they reflect the great variety of soils to be found in Alsace – limestone, schist, granite, clay, sandstone – offering a superb palate of flavours and nuances. But great wine can only be made, even from *grand cru* sites, if yields are modest. Otherwise the wines do not reflect the *terroirs* that were the reason why the *grand cru* sites were selected.

SÉLECTION DE GRAINS NOBLES (SGN) The higher of the two 'super-ripe' legal descriptions, applying to very sweet wines made from botrytized grapes. It applies only to wines made from Riesling, Tokay-Pinot Gris, Muscat (very rare) and Gewürztraminer; the wines are not dissimilar to Sauternes in style, though the flavour is different. Acidity levels can be lower, especially from Pinot Gris or from Gewürztraminer. All benefit from aging, for ten years or more.

VENDANGE TARDIVE The lesser of the 'super-ripe' categories, made from late-picked grapes, as opposed to the botrytized ones used for *sélection de grains nobles*. Only applies to Riesling, Tokay-Pinot Gris, Muscat (rare) and Gewürztraminer. They are very full, fairly alcoholic and vary in sweetness from richly dry to dessert-sweet. They, too, can be aged, particularly if from *grand cru* vineyards. Up to ten years is a good rule of thumb.

ALSACE VINTAGES

1996   A mostly good, ripe vintage with nice acidity levels. Small quantities of *vendange tardive* and even *sélection des grains nobles* were made.

1995   Similar to 1994, but possibly with lower acidity. Stick to good names.

1994   Mixed: some wines are too light; but conversely other producers made phenomenally rich late-harvest wines.

1993   Good to average wines. Gewürztraminer is fresh, and mostly needs drinking before it loses that freshness. There is excellent Riesling.

1992   The wines are sound, and range from dilute to excellent. How to tell the difference from the label? Choose good producers only.

1991   Fresh, clean wines, but it is not a late-harvest year. Not one to keep, either.

1990   With healthy grapes and no noble rot, 1990 was a *vendange tardive* year. Rieslings are powerful and will age well.

1989   Very good but not top quality. The wines have lively fruit, though some are low in acidity. Abundant and superb late-harvest wines.

1988   Pleasant, but hardly inspiring wine. Tokay-Pinot Gris and Riesling are the most successful wines from this year.

1987   Not great, but better than first thought. Good single-vineyard wines.

1986   The best are at their peak. Good *vendange tardive* and even some SGN.

1985   An absolute corker – wonderful wines to drink now but they will keep.

1983   A great year, but only at the top level. These are brilliant, and will still keep.

ALSACE PRICE GUIDES

WHITE

Under £4.50

1996
Pinot Blanc Cave Co-op. Turckheim
£4.49 (BO)
1993
Pinot Blanc Cave Co-op. Turckheim
£4.49 (FUL)

£4.50 → £4.99

1996
Pinot Blanc Blanck Frères £4.75 (WAI)
Pinot Blanc Tradition, Cave Co-op.
Turckheim £4.75 (GRE) £4.99 (AME)
1995
Pinot Blanc Cave Co-op. Turckheim
£4.59 (SO) £4.99 (NI)
Pinot Blanc Dopff & Irion £4.91 (HOG)
Pinot Blanc Tradition, Cave Co-op.
Turckheim £4.85 (WS)
Pinot Blanc Trimbach £4.99 (SAF)
1994
Pinot Blanc Cave Co-op. Turckheim
£4.99 (OD)
Pinot Blanc Cuvée Reservée, Schaetzel
£4.95 (LEA)
Pinot Blanc Klevner, Metz £4.50 (LEA)
Riesling Cave Co-op. de Ribeauvillé £4.50
(LEA)
Riesling Metz £4.95 (LEA)
1993
Gewürztraminer Mittelwihr, Deiss ½
bottle £4.95 (LEA)

£5.00 → £5.99

1996
Gewürztraminer Cave Co-op. Turckheim
£5.49 (BO) £5.75 (GRE)
1995
Gewürztraminer Cave Co-op. Turckheim
£5.49 (FUL) £5.90 (WS) £5.95 (SO)

Gewürztraminer Hornstein, Cave
Vinicole de Pfaffenheim £5.75 (POR)
Gewürztraminer Turckheim, Dopff £5.99
(WR) £5.99 (THR) £5.99 (BOT)
Muscat Réserve, Cave Co-op. Turckheim
£5.69 (OD)
Pinot Blanc Cave Co-op. Turckheim
£5.02 (ROS)
Pinot Blanc Deiss ½ bottle £5.00 (LEA)
Pinot Blanc Dopff & Irion £5.45 (EL)
Pinot Blanc Horstein, Cave Vinicole de
Pfaffenheim £5.00 (POR) £5.50 (HAH)
Pinot Blanc les Vignards, Hugel £5.95 (WS)
Sylvaner Dopff & Irion £5.15 (EL)
Tokay-Pinot Gris Cave Co-op. Turckheim
£5.59 (BOT) £5.59 (WR) £5.59 (THR)
Tokay-Pinot Gris Cave de Beblenheim
£5.75 (WAI)
Tokay-Pinot Gris Tradition, Cave Co-op.
Turckheim £5.99 (AME)
1994
Pinot Blanc Cave Co-op. Turckheim
£5.11 (FLE)
Riesling Horstein, Cave Vinicole de
Pfaffenheim £5.95 (JON)
Sylvaner Hugel £5.60 (WS)
Tokay-Pinot Gris Cave Co-op. Turckheim
£5.16 (ROS)
1993
Riesling Bennwihr, Deiss ½ bottle £5.00
(LEA)
Tokay-Pinot Gris Cave Co-op. Turckheim
£5.99 (FLE)

£6.00 → £6.99

1996
Riesling Dopff & Irion £6.75 (GRE)
1995
Gentil Hugel £6.50 (DI)
Gewürztraminer Cave Co-op. de
Ribeauvillé £6.99 (FLE)
Gewürztraminer Seigneur d'Alsace, Dopff
& Irion £6.99 (EL)

MERCHANTS SPECIALIZING IN ALSACE
see Merchant Directory (page 413) for details

Adnams (AD), Bennetts (BEN), Bute Wines
(BUT), Butlers Wine Cellar (BU), Anthony
Byrne (BY), Croque-en-Bouche (CRO),
Direct Wine (DI), Eldridge Pope (EL), J E

Hogg (HOG), Lay & Wheeler (LAY), Oddbins
(OD), Thos Peatling, Reid Wines (REI), T&W
Wines (TW), Thresher (THR), The
Ubiquitous Chip (UB), Wine Society (WS)

Pinot Blanc Muré £6.55 (DI) £6.95 (NEZ)
Pinot Blanc Schlumberger £6.99 (GRE)
Riesling Seigneur d'Alsace, Dopff & Irion
£6.59 (EL)
Riesling Tradition, Kuentz-Bas £6.95 (WS)
Sylvaner Schleret £6.25 (YAP)
1994
Gewürztraminer Cave Co-op. Turckheim
£6.11 (FLE)
Gewürztraminer Dopff & Irion £6.63 (HOG)
Gewürztraminer Hornstein, Cave
Vinicole de Pfaffenheim £6.30 (HAH)
Pinot Blanc Hugel £6.95 (STA)
Pinot Blanc Schlumberger £6.44 (HOG)
Pinot Blanc Trimbach £6.41 (HOG) £6.50
(VIG)
Riesling Réserve, Cave Co-op. Turckheim
£6.85 (QUE)
Sylvaner Deiss £6.75 (LEA)
Tokay-Pinot Gris Dopff & Irion £6.63 (HOG)
Tokay-Pinot Gris Tradition, Cave Co-op.
Turckheim £6.35 (QUE)
1993
Gewürztraminer Réserve Prestige, Cave
Co-op. Turckheim £6.85 (NI)
Muscat Réserve, Cave Co-op. Turckheim
£6.35 (QUE)
1992
Gewürztraminer Seigneur d'Alsace, Dopff
& Irion £6.90 (UB)
1991
Pinot Blanc Rolly Gassmann £6.99 (RAE)

£7.00 → £7.99

1995
Pinot Blanc Deiss £7.95 (LEA)
Pinot Blanc Schlumberger £7.63 (PLA)
Riesling Albert Mann £7.95 (BU)
1994
Gewürztraminer Dopff au Moulin £7.65
(GRE)
Gewürztraminer Muré £7.49 (DI)
Gewürztraminer Wiederhirn £7.99 (HIG)
Gewürztraminer Zind-Humbrecht £7.45
(BY)
Muscat Wiederhirn £7.99 (HIG)
Pinot Blanc Schlumberger £7.25 (NI) £7.59
(JON) £7.60 (WRI)
Riesling Wiederhirn £7.44 (HIG)
Sylvaner Vieilles Vignes, Ostertag £7.20 (MV)
Sylvaner Zind-Humbrecht £7.64 (BY)
Tokay-Pinot Gris Wiederhirn £7.99 (HIG)
1993
Gewürztraminer Réserve, Cave Co-op.
Turckheim £7.35 (QUE)

Pinot Blanc Deiss £7.50 (REI)
1992
Pinot Blanc Tradition, Kuentz-Bas £7.95
(BER)
Pinot Blanc Trimbach £7.25 (UB)
Riesling Beyer £7.99 (AME)
Tokay-Pinot Gris Louis Gisselbrecht
£7.15 (WHI)
1991
Riesling les Murailles, Dopff & Irion £7.99
(HOG)

£8.00 → £8.99

1995
Gewürztraminer Albert Mann £8.75 (BU)
£8.95 (WRI)
Gewürztraminer Dopff au Moulin £8.92
(PLA)
Gewürztraminer Hugel £8.99 (OD)
Riesling Hugel £8.60 (STA)
Riesling Muré £8.00 (NEZ)
1994
Gewürztraminer Beyer £8.95 (WS)
Gewürztraminer Schléret £8.25 (YAP)
Muscat Deiss £8.95 (LEA)
Muscat Réserve, Trimbach £8.15 (REI)
£8.35 (WS)
Pinot Blanc Rolly Gassmann £8.00 (BIB)
£8.40 (TAN)
Riesling des Princes Abbés, Schlumberger
£8.99 (GRE)
Riesling les Murailles, Dopff & Irion £8.35
(EL)
Tokay-Pinot Gris Barriques, Ostertag
£8.45 (SOM)
Tokay-Pinot Gris Tradition, Kuentz-Bas
£8.15 (HOG)
1993
Auxerrois Rolly Gassmann £8.45 (REI)
Gewürztraminer les Sorcières, Dopff &
Irion £8.75 (EL)
Gewürztraminer Sipp £8.19 (WHI)
Gewürztraminer Trimbach £8.65 (REI)
Muscat Hugel £8.75 (DI)
Riesling Bennwihr, Deiss £8.45 (LEA)

Riesling Hugel £8.49 (OD)
Riesling Louis Gisselbrecht £8.20 (TAN)
£8.95 (GN)
Riesling Trimbach £8.25 (GRE) £8.60 (WS)
1992
Gewürztraminer Hugel £8.99 (BOT) £8.99
(WR) £8.99 (THR)
Muscat Tradition, Hugel £8.70 (STA)
Riesling des Princes Abbés, Schlumberger
£8.29 (HOG)
Riesling Hugel £8.99 (DI)
1991
Gewürztraminer les Sorcières, Dopff &
Irion £8.20 (HOG)
Gewürztraminer Trimbach £8.79 (HOG)
Tokay-Pinot Gris les Maquisards, Dopff &
Irion £8.18 (HOG)
1989
Muscat les Amandiers, Dopff & Irion
£8.63 (HOG)
Muscat Schlumberger £8.08 (NO)
Riesling Dopff & Irion £8.30 (UB)

£9.00 → £10.49

1995
Gewurztraminer Réserve Personnelle,
Kuentz-Bas £9.99 (UN)
Muscat Réserve, Trimbach £10.25 (BER)
Muscat Rolly Gassmann £10.00 (BIB)
Muscat Schleret £10.25 (YAP)
Tokay-Pinot Gris Koehly £9.10 (HAH)
1994
Gewürztraminer des Princes Abbés,
Schlumberger £10.21 (PLA)
Gewürztraminer Hugel £9.40 (STA)
Gewürztraminer Louis Gisselbrecht £9.00
(TAN)
Gewürztraminer Trimbach £9.80 (BER)
Pinot Blanc Zind-Humbrecht £9.38 (FLE)
£10.45 (NI)
Tokay-Pinot Gris Réserve, Trimbach
£9.95 (WS)
Tokay-Pinot Gris Schlumberger £9.99 (NI)
1993
Gewürztraminer Cuvée Caroline Harth,
Schoffit £9.99 (OD)
Gewürztraminer Hugel £9.99 (DI)
Gewürztraminer Mittelwihr, Deiss £9.95
(LEA)
Gewürztraminer Zind-Humbrecht £9.00
(NI)
Muscat Koehly £9.10 (HAH)
Muscat Réserve, Trimbach £9.20 (GAU)
Muscat Schlumberger £10.44 (PLA)
Riesling Rolly Gassmann £9.85 (RAE)

1992
Gewürztraminer Beyer £9.49 (AME)
Gewürztraminer des Princes Abbés,
Schlumberger £9.25 (WATT)
Gewürztraminer Herrenweg, Zind-
Humbrecht £9.68 (BY)
Muscat Zind-Humbrecht £9.47 (BY)
Riesling Ecaillers, Beyer £9.95 (WS)
Riesling Trimbach £9.50 (BER)
Tokay-Pinot Gris Schlumberger £10.10
(PLA)
1991
Gewurztraminer Réserve Personnelle,
Kuentz-Bas £9.99 (UN)
Gewürztraminer Rolly Gassmann £9.95
(GAU) £9.95 (RAE)
Muscat Réserve, Trimbach £9.60 (PLA)
1990
Riesling Tradition, Hugel £10.15 (REI)
1989
Gewürztraminer Réserve, Trimbach
£9.90 (GAU)
Riesling Réserve, Trimbach £10.00 (VIG)
1987
Muscat Moench Reben, Rolly Gassmann
£9.65 (RAE)
Riesling Clos Haüserer, Zind-Humbrecht
£9.07 (BY)
Riesling Réserve, Trimbach £9.15 (REI)

£10.50 → £12.99

1996
Tokay-Pinot Gris Schleret £11.75 (YAP)
1995
Gewürztraminer Cuvée Caroline Harth,
Schoffit £10.95 (AD)
Gewürztraminer Tradition, Hugel £10.99
(OD)
Riesling Kaefferkopf, Meyer-Fonné £12.95
(LAY)
Riesling Wineck-Schlossberg, Meyer-
Fonné £12.25 (LAY)
★ Tokay-Pinot Gris Patergarten, Blanck
£10.50 (LAY)
1994
Gewürztraminer Clos Gaensbroennel, A.
Willm £11.30 (AS)
Gewürztraminer Schlumberger £10.95 (NA)
Gewürztraminer Tradition, Hugel £11.45
(STA)
Gewürztraminer Zind-Humbrecht £12.04
(BUT)
Pinot Blanc Zind-Humbrecht £11.95 (VIG)
Riesling Clos Haüserer, Zind-Humbrecht
£12.13 (BY)

Riesling Turckheim, Zind-Humbrecht
£11.30 (NI)
Tokay-Pinot Gris Beblenheim, Deiss
£10.95 (LEA)
1993
Gewürztraminer Herrenweg, Zind-
Humbrecht £10.70 (BY)
Pinot Blanc Schlumberger £10.89 (JON)
Riesling Herrenweg, Zind-Humbrecht
£12.49 (WR)
Riesling Saering, Schlumberger £12.75 (GRE)
Riesling Schoenenberg, Dopff au Moulin
£11.72 (HOG) £11.95 (GRE)
Riesling Schoenenberg, Wiederhirn
£11.55 (HIG)
Tokay-Pinot Gris Tradition, Hugel £10.95
(STA) £11.95 (GRE)
Tokay-Pinot Gris Trimbach £11.95 (ROB)
1992
Gewürztraminer Clos Windsbuhl, Zind-
Humbrecht £12.99 (EL)
Gewürztraminer Goldert, Zind-
Humbrecht £12.55 (BY)
Gewürztraminer Rangen, Zind-
Humbrecht £12.53 (BUT)
Gewürztraminer Turckheim, Dopff
£12.22 (HOG)

Pinot Gris des Princes Abbés,
Schlumberger £10.75 (POR)
Riesling Clos Haüserer, Zind-Humbrecht
£11.21 (BY)
Riesling Schoenenberg, Dopff au Moulin
£12.42 (NO)
Tokay-Pinot Gris Millesime, Rolly
Gassmann £12.50 (RAE)
Tokay-Pinot Gris Rolly Gassmann £12.80
(TAN)
Tokay-Pinot Gris Tradition, Hugel £10.99
(DI)
1991
Riesling Clos Haüserer, Zind-Humbrecht
£12.75 (BY)
Riesling Herrenweg, Zind-Humbrecht
£10.53 (BY) £11.75 (NI)
Riesling Saering, Schlumberger £10.95 (HOG)
1990
Riesling Réserve, Trimbach £12.50 (BEN)
1989
Riesling Réserve Particulière, Faller
£10.57 (BUT)
Riesling Rolly Gassmann £12.80 (TAN)
Riesling Schlossberg, Domaine Weinbach
£12.04 (BUT)
Tokay-Pinot Gris Koehly £12.53 (BUT)
1988
Riesling Herrenweg, Zind-Humbrecht
£10.93 (BY)
1987
Gewürztraminer Hengst, Zind-
Humbrecht £12.55 (BY)
1976
Riesling Schoenenberg, Dopff au Moulin
£12.50 (NO)

£13.00 → £14.99

1995
Gewürztraminer Furstentum Vieilles
Vignes, Blanck £13.45 (AD)
Tokay-Pinot Gris Hatschbourg, Cattin
£13.95 (VIG)
1994
Gewürztraminer Herrenweg, Zind-
Humbrecht £14.88 (BUT)
Tokay-Pinot Gris Hatschbourg, Cattin
£13.50 (VIG)
1993
Gewürztraminer Goldert, Zind-
Humbrecht £13.57 (BY)
Gewürztraminer Hengst, Zind-
Humbrecht £13.57 (BY)
Muscat Moench Reben, Rolly Gassmann
£13.90 (GAU)

1992

Riesling Frédéric Émile, Trimbach £14.49
(FA)

Riesling Furstentum, Blanck £13.75 (AD)

Riesling Muenchberg, Ostertag £14.50 (MV)

1991

Muscat Goldert, Zind-Humbrecht £13.57
(BY)

Riesling Brand, Zind-Humbrecht £14.59
(BY)

1990

Gewürztraminer Deiss £14.95 (LEA)

Gewürztraminer Seigneurs de
Ribeaupierre, Trimbach £14.98 (FA)

Riesling Silberberg, Rolly Gassmann
£13.50 (GAU)

1989

Riesling Kitterlé, Schlumberger £14.50
(HOG)

Tokay-Pinot Gris Domaine Weinbach
£13.02 (BUT)

1988

Gewürztraminer Jubilee, Hugel £14.00 (WS)

Gewürztraminer Seigneurs de
Ribeaupierre, Trimbach £14.36 (HOG)

Riesling Réserve, Trimbach £13.51 (TW)

1985

Gewürztraminer Hengst, Zind-
Humbrecht £13.57 (BY)

£15.00 → £19.99

1994

Gewürztraminer Kessler, Schlumberger
£15.95 (GRE)

Gewürztraminer Steingrubler, Albert
Mann £17.59 (YOU)

Gewürztraminer Steingrubler Vendange
Tardive, Albert Mann ½ litre £18.95 (LAY)

Muscat Goldert, Zind-Humbrecht £15.95
(VIG)

Riesling Clos Haüserer, Zind-Humbrecht
£15.96 (BUT)

Riesling Kappelweg, Rolly Gassmann
£16.50 (GAU)

1993

Gewürztraminer Jubilee, Hugel £15.00 (WS)

Gewürztraminer les Sorcières, Dopff &
Irion £15.30 (UB)

Riesling Brand, Zind-Humbrecht £15.20
(BY)

Riesling Frédéric Émile, Trimbach £17.50
(GRE) £19.99 (BOT)

Tokay-Pinot Gris Jubilee, Hugel £15.95 (WS)

Tokay-Pinot Gris Réserve Personnelle,
Trimbach £19.95 (VIG)

1992

Gewürztraminer Seigneurs de
Ribeaupierre, Trimbach £15.99 (UN)

Riesling Brand, Zind-Humbrecht £15.00
(BY)

Riesling Frédéric Émile, Trimbach £18.95
(LAY) £19.95 (ROB)

1991

Gewürztraminer Clos Windsbuhl, Zind-
Humbrecht £19.70 (GAU)

Gewürztraminer Goldert, Zind-
Humbrecht £15.00 (BY)

Gewürztraminer Kessler, Schlumberger
£16.80 (TAN) £16.95 (POR) £17.14 (PLA)

Riesling Kitterlé, Schlumberger £17.50
(POR) £17.95 (VIG)

1990

Gewürztraminer Jubilee, Hugel £15.99 (DI)

Muscat Goldert, Zind-Humbrecht £15.96
(BUT)

Riesling Frédéric Émile, Trimbach £16.77
(HOG) £17.45 (PLA) £17.50 (REI)

1989

Gewürztraminer Comtes d'Eguisheim,
Beyer £16.00 (WS)

Gewürztraminer Herrenweg Vendange
Tardive, Zind-Humbrecht £18.48 (BY)

Gewürztraminer Kappelweg, Rolly
Gassmann £17.90 (GAU)

Gewürztraminer Kessler, Schlumberger
£17.50 (BEN) £18.95 (VIG)

Riesling Bennwihr Vendange Tardive,
Deiss £17.95 (AD)

Riesling Frédéric Émile, Trimbach £15.82
(NO) £16.10 (GAU)

Tokay-Pinot Gris Kitterlé, Schlumberger
£19.95 (LAY)

Tokay-Pinot Gris Réserve, Rolly
Gassmann £17.00 (BIB)

1988

Riesling Brand, Zind-Humbrecht £17.46 (BY)

Riesling Frédéric Émile, Trimbach £17.00
(WS)

Riesling Jubilee, Hugel £16.00 (WS) £17.50
(GRE)

Riesling Jubilee Réserve Personnelle,
Hugel £15.95 (STA)

1986

Riesling Frédéric Émile, Trimbach £18.50
(TW)

Riesling Kitterlé, Schlumberger £16.95 (BEN)

1985

Gewürztraminer Hengst, Zind-
Humbrecht £15.47 (BUT)

Gewürztraminer Jubilee, Hugel £17.50 (GRE)

Gewürztraminer Seigneurs de
  Ribeaupierre, Trimbach £15.40 (GAU)
Riesling Brand, Zind-Humbrecht £17.46
  (BY)
Riesling Jubilee, Hugel £15.99 (DI)
1983
Riesling Réserve Personnelle, Hugel
  £17.33 (TW)

£20.00 → £24.99

1994
Pinot Gris Kitterlé, Schlumberger £21.95
  (VIG)
Riesling Brand, Zind-Humbrecht £23.79
  (BUT)
1992
Gewürztraminer Clos Windsbuhl, Zind-
  Humbrecht £20.25 (NI)
1991
Riesling Clos Ste-Hune, Trimbach £24.28
  (FA)
1990
Gewürztraminer Seigneurs de
  Ribeaupierre, Trimbach £22.85 (BER)
Gewürztraminer Vendange Tardive,
  Wiederhirn £22.72 (HIG)
Tokay-Pinot Gris Kitterlé, Schlumberger
  £21.00 (BEN)
1989
Gewürztraminer Kitterlé, Schlumberger
  £21.20 (HOG)
1986
Gewürztraminer Kitterlé, Schlumberger
  £22.50 (STA) £23.50 (GRE)
1985
Gewürztraminer Schlumberger £24.49 (BO)
1983
Gewürztraminer Vendange Tardive,
  Ostertag £20.99 (YOU)
Gewürztraminer Vendange Tardive,
  Wiederhirn £22.72 (HIG)
Riesling Vendange Tardive, Dopff & Irion
  £24.15 (HOG)
Tokay-Pinot Gris Vendange Tardive,
  Dopff & Irion £24.15 (HOG)
1981
Riesling Frédéric Émile, Trimbach £22.50
  (REI) £23.26 (TW)
1969
Muscat Trimbach £23.50 (FA)

£25.00 → £29.99

1991
Riesling Clos Ste-Hune, Trimbach £29.95
  (VIG)

1990
Riesling Kuentz-Bas £29.00 (BER)
1989
Gewürztraminer Herrenweg Vendange
  Tardive, Zind-Humbrecht £29.67 (FA)
Gewürztraminer Vendange Tardive,
  Hugel £27.99 (JON)
1987
Riesling Clos Ste-Hune, Trimbach £29.95
  (VIG)
1986
Riesling Clos Ste-Hune, Trimbach £25.75
  (FA) £28.00 (WS) £28.50 (GRE) £29.95 (LAY)
1985
Gewürztraminer Cuvée Christine,
  Schlumberger £28.50 (REI)
1983
Gewürztraminer Rangen, Zind-
  Humbrecht £29.95 (BY)
Gewürztraminer Vendange Tardive, Dopff
  & Irion £27.75 (GRE) £28.15 (HOG)
Riesling Frédéric Émile, Trimbach £29.50
  (VIG)

£30.00 → £39.99

1991
Gewürztraminer Cuvée Christine,
  Schlumberger £35.00 (GRE) £36.20 (TAN)
1990
Gewürztraminer Cuvée Christine,
  Schlumberger £31.15 (HOG)
Gewürztraminer Vendange Tardive,
  Trimbach £32.00 (WS)
Riesling Clos Ste-Hune, Trimbach £34.50
  (REI)
1989
Gewürztraminer Vendange Tardive,
  Hugel £32.59 (DI)
Gewürztraminer Vendange Tardive
  Sélection Personnelle, Hugel £32.50 (STA)
Riesling Frédéric Émile Vendange Tardive,
  Trimbach £39.95 (VIG)
1986
Riesling Clos Ste-Hune, Trimbach £31.43
  (PLA) £33.95 (ROB) £36.00 (BER)
1985
Gewürztraminer Cuvée Anne Vendange
  Tardive, Rolly Gassmann £33.50 (RAE)
1983
Gewürztraminer Sélection de Grains
  Nobles, Dopff & Irion £34.90 (HOG)
Riesling Frédéric Émile Vendange Tardive,
  Trimbach £33.59 (FA) £39.95 (VIG)
Riesling Sélection de Grains Nobles, Dopff
  & Irion £31.20 (HOG) £33.50 (GRE)

£40.00 → £49.99

1989
Riesling Frédéric Émile Vendange Tardive,
  Trimbach £41.50 (BER)
1983
Riesling Clos Ste-Hune, Trimbach £49.00
  (GAU)
Riesling Vendange Tardive, Hugel £45.00
  (BEN)
Tokay-Pinot Gris Sélection de Grains
  Nobles, Beyer £45.00 (REI)
1981
Gewürztraminer Vendange Tardive,
  Hugel £45.00 (VIG)
1976
Riesling Vendange Tardive, Hugel £49.50
  (REI)

£50.00 → £59.99

1994
Tokay-Pinot Gris Rangen Vendange
  Tardive, Zind-Humbrecht £54.64 (BUT)
1989
Gewürztraminer Cuvée Anne,
  Schlumberger £52.50 (GRE) £54.20 (TAN)
1988
Gewürztraminer Sélection de Grains
  Nobles, Hugel £59.99 (VIN)
Tokay-Pinot Gris Sélection de Grains
  Nobles, Dopff au Moulin £55.00 (BER)
1983
Gewürztraminer Sélection de Grains
  Nobles, Hugel £55.75 (REI)
1976
Riesling Vendange Tardive, Hugel £52.88
  (TW)
Tokay-Pinot Gris Vendange Tardive,
  Hugel £51.99 (YOU) £52.88 (TW)

£60.00 → £76.99

1993
Gewürztraminer Rangen Sélection de
  Grains Nobles, Zind-Humbrecht
  £61.98 (FA)
1989
Gewürztraminer Sélection de Grains
  Nobles, Hugel £61.50 (STA)
1976
Riesling Clos Ste-Hune, Trimbach £76.38
  (TW)
Riesling Sélection de Grains Nobles,
  Hugel £70.00 (REI)
Riesling Vendange Tardive Sélection de
  Grains Nobles, Hugel £73.45 (NO)

c. £85.50

1993
Tokay-Pinot Gris Clos St-Urbain, Zind-
  Humbrecht £85.48 (FA)

£145.00 → £180.00

1989
Gewürztraminer Rangen Sélection de
  Grains Nobles, Zind-Humbrecht
  £176.25 (BUT)

RED

Under £10.00

1993
Pinot Noir Hugel £9.45 (STA)
1992
Pinot Noir Rolly Gassmann £9.70 (RAE)

£10.00 → £17.99

1995
Pinot Noir Schleret £10.25 (YAP)
1994
Pinot Noir Herrenweg, Zind-Humbrecht
  £11.34 (BY)
1992
Pinot Noir Herrenweg, Zind-Humbrecht
  £10.70 (BY)
1989
Pinot Noir Herrenweg, Zind-Humbrecht
  £13.16 (BY)
1985
Pinot Noir Réserve Personnelle, Hugel
  £17.03 (TW)

c. £22.00

1990
Pinot Noir Réserve, Rolly Gassmann
  £22.00 (BIB)

SPARKLING

Under £9.00

Non-vintage
Crémant d'Alsace Cuvée Julien, Dopff au
  Moulin £8.50 (HOG)
Crémant d'Alsace Dopff & Irion £8.67 (EL)

£9.00 → £9.99

Non-vintage
Crémant d'Alsace Cuvée Julien, Dopff au
  Moulin £9.75 (GRE) £9.95 (BEN) £9.95
  (STA) £10.50 (ROB)

BORDEAUX

**Is Bordeaux a by-word for expensive, status-symbol wine, or is it a
by-word for the cheap and not necessarily cheerful? Both can be
true – but there is a middle way**

The polarisation to be seen throughout the world of wine today can be seen in microcosm in Bordeaux. And it is, simply, that the very best is ever more expensive, while the cheapest is ever more reliable, but too often ever more standard, as well.

Let's look at the top end first. Britain is no longer a prime market for the leading classed growths: they go to Germany, to Singapore, to the US. These days middle-aged wine merchants gather at trade tastings and reminisce over the days when they could afford a bottle of Lafite on a Saturday night. They talk enviously of friends who bought 1961s when the wines were young, and who, as a result, can actually afford to drink them. With Lafite

1995 selling en primeur for around £600 a case in bond UK, you'd need more than a mere Saturday night to justify opening a bottle.

But the attraction of Bordeaux – one might even say the point of Bordeaux – is that it has wines at all levels. Basic Bordeaux Rouge and Blanc is probably better made now than ever before in its history, especially the Blanc. But the vines (particularly those for the reds) are sometimes so heavily overcropped that in less good years the wines run the risk of being too dilute and chaptalized (fermented with added sugar) to have real character.

What about the middle ground? This is where Bordeaux should in theory be able

BUYING CLARET EN PRIMEUR

In the spring after the vintage the Bordeaux châteaux make their opening offers. This means that they do not have to sit on very expensive stock for a further two years until the wines are bottled and ready to ship. In theory this also means that you can buy the wine at a preferential price. Traditionally merchants would buy for stock while offering their customers the chance to take advantage of the opening prices as well. In the heady days of the 1980s, however, the market really took off.

There is a lot to be said for buying en primeur. For one thing, you may be able to find the finest and rarest wines far more cheaply than they will ever appear again. This was especially true of the 1982 and 1990 vintages.

But you should be aware of the risks: as they say in the investment world, prices can go down as well as up. They may easily not increase significantly in the few years after the campaign (witness prices for 1985s and 1989s). The second risk is that the merchant you bought the wine from may not still be around to deliver it to you two years later. Buy from a merchant you can trust, one with a solid trading base in other wines.

Once the wines are shipped you may want your merchant to store the wine for you. If so, you should insist that (1) you receive a stock certificate; (2) your wines are stored separately from the merchant's own stocks, and (3) your cases are identifiable as your property and are labelled accordingly. All good merchants will offer these safeguards as a minimum service. Of course, in an ideal world your house is equipped with its own temperature controlled cellar, because the best solution is certainly to take possession of your cases yourself.

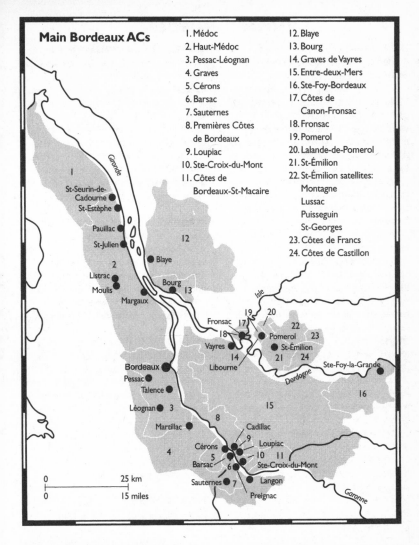

Main Bordeaux ACs

1. Médoc
2. Haut-Médoc
3. Pessac-Léognan
4. Graves
5. Cérons
6. Barsac
7. Sauternes
8. Premières Côtes de Bordeaux
9. Loupiac
10. Ste-Croix-du-Mont
11. Côtes de Bordeaux-St-Macaire
12. Blaye
13. Bourg
14. Graves de Vayres
15. Entre-deux-Mers
16. Ste-Foy-Bordeaux
17. Côtes de Canon-Fronsac
18. Fronsac
19. Pomerol
20. Lalande-de-Pomerol
21. St-Émilion
22. St-Émilion satellites:
    Montagne
    Lussac
    Puisseguin
    St-Georges
23. Côtes de Francs
24. Côtes de Castillon

to combine the best of both worlds; of low(ish) prices and high quality. Is it happening?

Sometimes, yes, it is. In Fronsac, for example, where standards are rising faster than prices and where few châteaux are individually famous. In the southern Graves, too, and in Bergerac; and for sweet whites, in Monbazillac and Loupiac, where the wines never have the intensity of Sauternes but these days often have something of the flavour.

The answer for the consumer is to go for the less obvious names, before the world discovers them. How to find such wines? Well, in the next few pages I'll be steering you towards them – and, I hope, away from the duds.

GRAPE VARIETIES

Fine claret (the English term for red Bordeaux) has the most tantalizing and unlikely combination of flavours of any red wine. There's the blast of pure, fragrant blackcurrant fruit, and then the exotic, dry perfumes of lead pencil shavings, fresh-wrapped cigars and cedar to weave an endlessly fascinating balance of sweet and dry tastes with, increasingly, the buttery overlay of new oak barrels.

Bordeaux's vineyards are so poised on the knife-edge of ripening their grapes or failing to do so that every vintage is fascinatingly different. If the year gets too hot, the flavour can be rich, strong and burnt, more like the Californian or Italian attempts at claret. If the summer rains and autumn gales roll in off the Bay of Biscay and the grapes can't ripen, then the taste may be thin and green, resembling the Cabernets of the Loire Valley. But in the years of balance, like 1966, '70, '78, '83, '85, '86, '88, '89 and '90, those astonishing sweet and dry, fruity and tannic flavours mix to produce the glory that is claret.

As for the whites – well, for years the sweet, botrytized wines of Sauternes and Barsac were the only ones which could compete in quality with the reds, and not always successfully. But recent years have seen a revolution. The sweet whites have improved beyond measure, helped by massive investment and a run of excellent vintages in the 1980s, but so have the dry ones. Inexpensive Bordeaux Blanc, based on Sauvignon, is increasingly crisp and grassy, while fine oak-aged white Graves has taken its place among the great dry whites of France.

CABERNET FRANC (red) The lesser of the two Cabernets, giving lighter-coloured, softer wines than Cabernet Sauvignon, often slightly earthy but with good, blackcurrant fruit. It's always blended in Bordeaux. In St-Émilion and Pomerol it can give fine flavours and is widely planted.

CABERNET SAUVIGNON (red) This world-famous Bordeaux grape nevertheless covers only a fifth of the vineyards. Crucially, a wine built to age needs tannin and acidity, and the fruit and extract to keep up with them. Cabernet Sauvignon has all these in abundance. It gives dark, tannic wine with a strong initial acid attack, and stark blackcurrant fruit. When aged in new oak, it can be stunning. It's the main grape of the Haut-Médoc, but other varieties soften it and add complexity.

MALBEC (red) A rather bloated, juicy grape, little seen nowadays in Bordeaux, though it appears in some blends, especially in Bourg and Blaye. In Bordeaux it tastes rather like a feeble version of Merlot, soft and low in acidity. Upriver in Cahors it has real style, which probably explains why there's lots of it there and little in Bordeaux.

MERLOT (red) Bordeaux has more Merlot than Cabernet Sauvignon. It is the main grape in St-Émilion and Pomerol, whereas in the Médoc and Graves it's used to soften and enrich the Cabernet. It ripens early and gives a gorgeous, succulent, minty, blackcurrant or plummy wine, which explains why Pomerols and St-Émilions are easier to enjoy than Médocs. It also makes less long-lived wine than Cabernet, and tends to peak and fade sooner.

MUSCADELLE (white) A very little (up to five per cent) of this headily perfumed grape often goes into the Sauternes blend. In dry white blends a few per cent can add a very welcome honeyed softness. It is now being produced in small quantities as a varietal: dry, lean, but perfumed.

PETIT VERDOT (red) A dark, tough grape with a liquorice-and-plums taste, and a violet perfume, used for colour. Little planted in the past but on the increase now because it adds quality in a late, ripe year.

SAUVIGNON BLANC (white) There has been a rush to plant more of this fashionable grape in Bordeaux in recent years, but with a couple of exceptions – such as Malartic-Lagravière, Couhins-Lurton and Smith-Haut-Lafitte – Sauvignon by itself here often gives rather muddy, tough wine. Even so, many dry white Bordeaux are entirely Sauvignon, particularly at the cheaper end, and can be fresh and flowery if from careful winemakers like Mau, Dourthe, Ginestet and Coste. The best are almost always blended with Sémillon. A little Sauvignon adds acidity to Sauternes and other sweet whites.

SÉMILLON (white) The most important grape of Sauternes, and vital to the best dry wines, too. With modern techniques one can hardly tell a good dry Sémillon from a Sauvignon, except that it's a little fuller. But ideally they should be blended, with Sémillon the main variety. It gives a big, round dry wine, slightly creamy but with an aroma of fresh apples and a lanolin smoothness in the mouth. The result is a wonderful, soft, nutty dry white, often going honeyed and smoky as it ages for seven to 15 years. Like this it produces one of France's great whites, and is an antidote to anyone getting just a little tired of varietals.

WINE REGIONS

BARSAC, AC (sweet white) The only one of the five Sauternes villages with the right to use its own name as an official appellation (it may also call itself Sauternes – or Sauternes-Barsac for that matter). The wines tend to be lighter, and the best combine marvellous richness with a certain delicacy of texture.

BORDEAUX BLANC, AC (dry white) This AC is the catch-all name for all white Bordeaux. Château wines are usually the best and should generally be drunk as young as possible. Recommended names include: *Birot, Grand-Mouëys, du Juge, Lamothe, Reynon*. Good blends are likely from the following merchants: *Coste, Dourthe, Dubroca, Ginestet, Joanne, Lurton, Mau, Sichel* and *Univitis*.

Some classy properties in red areas make good, dry white which is only allowed this AC. *Château Margaux*'s white, for instance, is a simple AC Bordeaux Blanc. Many great Sauternes châteaux have started to make a dry wine from the grapes deemed unsuitable for Sauternes. These also make use of the Bordeaux Blanc AC and are often named after the initial letter of the château's name – as in 'G' of *Guiraud*, 'R' of *Rieussec* and 'Y' of *Yquem*. 'Y' can really be spectacular.

BORDEAUX BLANC SUPÉRIEUR, AC (dry white) Rarely used, but requires higher basic strength and lower vineyard yield than Bordeaux Blanc AC.

BORDEAUX ROUGE, AC (red) Unless qualified by one of the other ACs below, this is the everyday red wine of Bordeaux, either from co-ops, from properties in undistinguished localities, or wine disqualified from one of the better ACs. It can come from anywhere in Bordeaux. Still, reasonably priced, for drinking young, it is a delicious, appetizing meal-time red when good – and a palate-puckering disappointment when bad.

BORDEAUX SUPÉRIEUR, AC (red) Similar to Bordeaux Rouge but with more alcohol and produced from a slightly lower yield. The same comments on quality apply, but from a good estate the wines can be delicious. Best results are often from properties producing white Entre-Deux-Mers and from the Premières Côtes. Best châteaux: *Brethous, Cayla, Domaine de Terrefort, Fayau, la Gabory, le Gay, Grand-Mouëys, Gromel Bel-Air, Jalousie-Beaulieu, Jonqueyres, du Juge, Lacombe, Méaume, Peyrat, Pierredon, Reynon, la Roche, Tanesse, Thieuley, de Toutigeac, de la Vieille Tour*.

CADILLAC, AC (sweet white) This small region can produce attractive sweet whites, but since the price is low, many properties now produce dry white and red – which do *not* qualify for the AC Cadillac. The AC is in any case so involved that few growers bother with it.

CÉRONS, AC (sweet white) Good, fairly sweet whites, but many growers now prefer to produce dry whites instead, which can be sold as Graves. *Château Archambeau* is typical, producing tiny amounts of very good Cérons and larger amounts of good, fresh dry Graves. *Château Cérons* makes splendidly complex sweet whites worthy of the AC of Barsac. Other good names to look out for: *Grand Enclos du Château Cérons, Haura.*

CÔTES DE BOURG, AC (red) The rather full, savoury style of these reds is backed up by sweet Merlot fruit and occasionally a touch of new oak. As Médoc and St-Émilion prices spiral, Bourg wines are slowly coming into their own. Best châteaux: *de Barbe, du Bousquet, Brûle-Sécaille, la Croix, Dupeyrat, Grolet, Guionne, Haut-Guiraud, Haut-Rousset, de Millorit* and wines from the co-op at *Tauriac.*

CÔTES DE CASTILLON, AC (red) and **CÔTES DE FRANCS, AC** (red) Two small regions which are turning out an increasing number of exciting wines. They can be a little too earthy, but at their best they combine a grassy Cabernet Franc freshness with a gorgeous, juicy, minty Merlot sweetness. Best châteaux in the Côtes de Castillon: *Beau-Séjour, Belcier, Brisson, Canon-Monségur, Ferrasses, Fonds Rondes, Grand Taillac, les Hauts-de-Grange, Lessacques, Moulin-Rouge, Parenchère, Pitray, Rocher-Bellevue.* The Côtes de Francs is increasingly producing fruity, light, delicious wines to drink early, using a lot of Cabernet Franc. Best châteaux here are *la Claverie, de Francs, Lauriol, du Moulin-la-Pitié, la Prade, Puygueraud.*

CÔTES DE FRONSAC, AC (red) with the (in theory) superior **CANON-FRONSAC, AC** (red) Lesser St-Émilion lookalikes, sometimes a bit grassy and tannic, but often supple, balanced clarets of some elegance – even in bad years like 1992. Best: *Barrabaque, Canon-de-Brem, Canon-Moueix, Cassagne Haut-Canon, Dalem, de la Dauphine, Fonteuil, Mayne-Vieil, Mazeris, Moulin Haut-Laroque, Moulin Pey-Labrie, Plain Point, la Rivière, la Truffière, Tourmalin, la Valade, La Vieille Cure.*

ENTRE-DEUX-MERS, AC (dry white) The AC is for dry whites, which are of varying quality, but every vintage produces more good, fresh, grassy ones. Many properties make red, which take the AC of Bordeaux or Bordeaux Supérieur. Best: *Bonnet, Ducla, de Florin, Fondarzac, Moulin-de-Launay, Tertre du Moulin, Thieuley, Union des Producteurs de Rauzan.*

GRAVES, AC (red, dry white) Red Graves run the gamut of claret flavours, and are less easy to sum up than others. Though the Cabernet Sauvignon is the dominant grape in the North, as in the Médoc, there's more stress on Merlot, so the wines are slightly softer. They tend to have some of the blackcurrant and cedar of the Médoc, but without the sheer size of, say, Pauillac; they have some of the full, plummy richness of St-Émilion, yet it never dominates; and there is a slightly gravelly quality in many of them, too. The less well-known châteaux are good value.

Modern white Graves, even at the level of commercial blends, can be sharply fruity and full in style, while at the best properties, with some oak aging employed, the wines are among the most delicious dry whites in France. Best châteaux: *Archambeau, Bouscaut, Cabannieux, Carbonnieux, Domaine de Chevalier, Couhins-Lurton, de Cruzeau, Domaine la Grave, de Fieuzal, la Garance, la Garde, Haut-Brion, Landiras, Laville-Haut-Brion, la Louvière, Malartic-Lagravière, Montalivet, Rahoul, Respide, Rochemorin,*

Roquetaillade-la-Grange, Smith-Haut-Lafitte and la Tour-Martillac.

(Note that in 1987 the prestigious properties in the North were grouped into a separate AC, Pessac-Léognan.)

GRAVES SUPÉRIEURES, AC (sweet or dry white) Graves with a minimum natural alcohol of 12 degrees. Often made sweet. Best property: *Clos St-Georges*.

HAUT-MÉDOC, AC (red) Geographically, the prestigious southern part of the Médoc, nearest Bordeaux. The AC, however, covers the less exciting vineyards because the really juicy business gets done at Margaux, St-Julien, Pauillac, St-Estèphe, Listrac and Moulis, which have their own ACs. Even so, the AC Haut-Médoc has five Classed Growths including two superb ones – *Cantemerle* and *la Lagune* – and an increasing number of fine *bourgeois* properties like *Beaumont, de Castillon, Cissac, Hanteillan, Lamarque, Lanessan, Liversan, Pichon, Sociando-Mallet* and *la Tour-du-Haut-Moulin* – plus lots of lesser properties, such as châteaux *Bernadotte, Cambon-la-Pelouse, Coufran, le Fournas, Grandis, du Junca, Larose-Trintaudon, Malescasse, Maucamps, Moulin de Labarde, Quimper, Sénéjac* and *Verdignan*.

LALANDE-DE-POMEROL, AC (red) Pomerol's equally tiny northern neighbour, is often accused of being overpriced, but since it can produce rich, plummy wines with a distinct resemblance to those of Pomerol at a distinctly less painful price, this criticism is not entirely justified. Best: *Annereaux, Bel-Air, Belles-Graves, Bertineau-St-Vincent, Clos des Moines, Clos des Templiers, la Croix Bellevue, la Fleur St-Georges, Grand Ormeau, Haut-Ballet, les Hauts-Tuileries, Lavaud-la-Maréchaude, Siaurac, les Templiers, Tournefeuille.*

LISTRAC, AC (red) One of the less prestigious communes of the Haut-Médoc. The wines contain a higher proportion of Merlot than elsewhere, but nevertheless are rather tough and charmless, only lightly perfumed wines. But some properties rise above this, such as *la Bécade, Cap-Léon-Veyrin, Clarke, Fonréaud* (since 1988), *Fourcas-Dupré, Fourcas-Hosten, Fourcaud, Lestage* and the *Grand Listrac* co-op.

LOUPIAC, AC (sweet white) These wines are not as sweet as Sauternes, and most are light, lemony, honeyed Barsac styles. The general improvement in Bordeaux's sweet wines has filtered down here, as well. Best: *Domaine du Noble, Loupiac-Gaudiet, Ricaud.*

MARGAUX, AC (red) Rather sludgy, solid wines at one extreme, and the most fragrant, perfumed red wines France has yet dreamed up at the other. The best include: *d'Angludet, la Gurgue, d'Issan, Labégorce-Zédé, Margaux, Monbrison, Palmer, Prieuré-Lichine, Rauzan-Ségla, du Tertre.* Among the next best are *Durfort-Vivens, Giscours, Lascombes, Marquis d'Alesme-Becker, Marquis de Terme, Siran* and *la Tour-de-Mons.*

MÉDOC, AC (red) This name covers the long tongue of land north of Bordeaux town, between the Gironde river and the sea, including the Haut-Médoc and all its famous communes. As an AC it refers to the less-regarded but important northern part of the area. Médoc reds, with a high proportion of Merlot grapes, are drinkable more quickly than Haut-Médocs and the best have a refreshing, grassy, juicy fruit, backed up by just enough tannin and acidity. Easily the best property is *Potensac*, where Michel Delon of *Léoville-Las-Cases* makes wine of Classed Growth standard. Other good wines are *le Bernadot, Cardonne, Cassan d'Estevil, David, d'Escot, a Gorce, Greysac, Grivière, Haut-Canteloup, Lacombe-Noaillac, Noaillac, Ormes-Sorbet, Patache d'Aux, la Tour-de-By, la Tour-St-Bonnet, Loudenne, Vieux-Château-Landon.* Most of the co-ops – especially *Bégadan, Ordonac* and *St-Yzans* – make good fruity stuff.

MOULIS, AC (red) Another lesser commune of the Haut-Médoc next door to, and similar to, Listrac, but with more potentially outstanding properties and a softer, more perfumed style in the best which can equal Classed Growths. Best are *Bel-Air-Lagrave, Brillette, Chasse-Spleen, Duplessis-Fabre, Dutruch-Grand-Poujeaux, Grand-Poujeaux, Gressier-Grand-Poujeaux, Maucaillou, Moulin-à-Vent, Poujeaux.*

PAUILLAC, AC (red) The most famous of the Haut-Médoc communes, Pauillac has three of the world's greatest red wines sitting inside its boundaries: *Latour, Lafite* and *Mouton-Rothschild.* This is where the blackcurrant really comes into its own. The best wines are almost painfully intense, a celestial mixture of blackcurrant and lead pencil sharpenings that sends well-heeled cognoscenti leaping for their cheque books. Best: *d'Armailhac (formerly known as Mouton-Baronne-Philippe), Grand-Puy-Lacoste, Haut-Bages-Avérous, Haut-Bages-Libéral, Lafite-Rothschild, Latour, Lynch-Bages, Mouton-Rothschild, Pichon-Baron, Pichon-Lalande.* Next best: *Batailley, Clerc-Milon-Rothschild, Duhart-Milon, Grand-Puy-Ducasse, Haut-Bages-Monpelou.*

PESSAC-LÉOGNAN, AC (red, dry white) An AC in its own right since September 1987 for the area traditionally the Graves' best and containing all the *crus classés.* The whites at their best offer a depth surpassed only by the best Burgundies. They start out with a blast of apricot, peach and cream ripeness and slowly mature to a superb nutty richness with a dry savoury finish. The reds have a biscuity, bricky warmth. Best reds: *Carbonnieux, Carmes-Haut-Brion, Cruzeau, Domaine de Chevalier, Domaine de Gaillat, Domaine la Grave, Ferrande, de Fieuzal, Haut-Bailly, Haut-Brion, Haut-Portets, la Louvière, Malartic-Lagravière, la Mission-Haut-Brion, Pape-Clément (since 1985), Rahoul, Rochemorin, de St-Pierre, Smith-Haut-Lafitte (since 1988), Roquetaillade-la-Grange,*

la Tour Martillac, Tourteau-Chollet. Best whites: *Bouscaut, Carbonnieux (from 1988), Couhins-Lurton, Domaine de Chevalier, de Fieuzal, Haut-Brion, la Louvière, Malartic-Lagravière, Rochemorin, Smith-Haut-Lafitte, la Tour Martillac.*

POMEROL, AC (red) The Merlot grape is even more dominant in Pomerol than in St-Émilion, and most Pomerols have a deeper, rounder flavour, the plummy fruit going as dark as prunes in great years, but with the mineral backbone of toughness preserving it for a very long time. Pomerol has no classification, but it harbours the world's greatest red wine, *Château Pétrus,* and the world's (currently) most expensive red, *Château Le Pin.* Best: *le Bon Pasteur, Bourgneuf-Vayron, Certan-de-May, Certan-Giraud, Clinet, Clos René, Clos du Clocher, Clos l'Église, la Conseillante, la Croix de Gay, l'Église Clinet, l'Évangile, le Gay, la Grave-Trigant-de-Boisset, Lafleur, Lafleur-Gazin, la Fleur-Pétrus, Lagrange-à-Pomerol, Latour-à-Pomerol, Petit-Village, Pétrus, le Pin, Trotanoy, Vieux-Château-Certan.*

PREMIÈRES CÔTES DE BLAYE, AC (red, dry white) The reds are too often a little 'cooked' in taste and slightly jammy-sweet. They're cheap, but have a lot more improving to do. Good names: *Bas Vallon, Bourdieu, Charron, Crusquet-Sabourin, l'Escadre, Fontblanche, Grand Barail, Haut-Sociondo, Jonqueyres, Peybonhomme.*

PREMIÈRES CÔTES DE BORDEAUX, AC (red, white) Some very attractive reds and excellent dry whites in the bang-up-to-date, fruit-all-the-way style, as well as some reasonable sweetish wines. Best châteaux include: *de Berbec, Brethous, Cayla, Fayau, Grands-Moüeys, du Juge, Lamothe, de Lucat, Peyrat, la Roche, Reynon, Tanesse.*

ST-ÉMILION, AC (red) Soft, round and rather generous wines, because the main grape is the Merlot, aided by Cabernet

Franc and Malbec, and only slightly by Cabernet Sauvignon. St-Émilions don't always have Pomerol's minerally backbone, and the sweetness is usually less plummy and more buttery, toffeed or raisiny. Top wines add to this a blackcurranty, minty depth. It's a well-known name, yet with few famous châteaux: the top ones are *Cheval-Blanc* and *Ausone*. Some satellite areas also annex the name, like St-Georges-St-Émilion or Puisseguin-St-Émilion. They're okay, but would be better value if they didn't trade greedily on the St-Émilion handle. Best in satellites: *St-Georges, Montaiguillon, Tour du Pas St-Georges* (St-Georges-St-Émilion); *Haut-Gillet, de Maison Neuve* (Montagne-St-Émilion); *Bel Air, la Croix-de-Berny* (Puisseguin-St-Émilion); *Lyonnat* (Lussac-St-Émilion). Best St-Émilion: *l'Angélus, l'Arrosée, Ausone, Balestard-la-Tonnelle, Beauséjour-Duffau-Lagarosse, Canon, Canon-la-Gaffelière, Cheval-Blanc, Clos des Jacobins, la Dominique, Figeac, Fonroque, Larmande, Magdelaine, Pavie, Pavie-Decesse, Soutard, Tertre-Rôteboeuf, Troplong-Mondot.* Next best: *Belair, Cadet-Piola, Berliquet, Cap de Mourlin, Cardinal Villemaurine, Carteau, Clos Fourtet, Corbin-Michotte, Côtes Daugay, Couvent des Jacobins, Destieux, de Ferrand, Fombrauge, Franc-Mayne, la Gaffelière, Grand-Mayne, Gravet, Magnan-la-Gaffelière, Mauvezin, Monbousquet, Pavie-Macquin, Rolland-Maillet, Tour-des-Combes, la-Tour-du-Pin-Figeac, Trappaud, Trottevieille, Villemaurine.*

ST-ESTÈPHE, AC (red) The northernmost of the great Haut-Médoc communes is a more everyday performer. There are few famous names, and most are relatively cheap. Best: *Calon-Ségur, Chambert-Marbuzet, Cos d'Estournel, Haut-Marbuzet, Lafon-Rochet, Marbuzet, Meyney, Montrose, les Ormes-de-Pez, de Pez.* Next best: *Andron-Blanquet, Beausite, du Boscq, Cos Labory, le Crock, Lavillotte, Phélan-Ségur.*

ST-JULIEN, AC (red) There are two main styles here. One is almost honeyed: gentle, round, wonderfully easy-to-love. The other has glorious cedar-cigar-box fragrance and just enough fruit to make it satisfying as well as exciting. Best: *Beychevelle, Ducru-Beaucaillou, Gruaud-Larose, Lagrange, Lalande-Borie, Langoa-Barton, Léoville-Barton, Léoville-Las-Cases, St-Pierre, Talbot.* Next: *Branaire-Ducru, Gloria, Hortevie, Léoville-Poyferré* and *Terrey-Gros-Caillou.*

STE-CROIX-DU-MONT, AC (sweet white) Very attractive when properly made. *Château Loubens* is the best-known wine, but *Château Lousteau-Vieil* is producing better wine every year, and *Domaine du Tich, la Grave, la Rame, des Tours* and the minuscule *de Tastes* are also good.

SAUTERNES, AC (sweet white) The overall appellation for a group of five villages: Sauternes, Bommes, Fargues, Preignac and Barsac. (Barsac wines may use their own village name if they wish.) Concentrated by noble rot, the Sémillon, along with a little Sauvignon and Muscadelle, produces at its glorious best a wine that is brilliantly rich and glyceriny. It combines honey and cream, pineapple and nuts when young, and becomes oily and penetrating as it ages. The sweetness begins to have an intensity of volatile flavours, rather like a peach, bruised and browned in the sun, then steeped in the sweetest of syrups. These are the fine wines; but in recent years the average quality has soared, and the wines are infinitely better, as indeed they ought to be given their high prices. And in bad years those châteaux that can afford it can now practise cryoextraction – a method of freezing the grapes before fermentation which can increase the richness of the juice pressed out. It can be the saving of a vintage in those years where it just won't stop raining. Best include: *Bastor-Lamontagne, Climens, Doisy-Daëne, Doisy-Védrines, de Fargues, Gilette, Guiraud, Lafaurie-Peyraguey, Lamothe-Guignard, Rabaud-Promis, Raymond-Lafon, Rayne-Vigneau, Rieussec, St-Amand, Suduiraut, la Tour Blanche, d'Yquem.*

THE 1855 CLASSIFICATION

This is the most famous and enduring wine classification in the world – but it was intended merely as an impromptu guide to the Bordeaux wines entered for the Great Paris Exhibition of 1855, based on the prices the wines had obtained over the previous century.

Since this classification applies only to the Médoc and one château, Haut-Brion, in the Graves, all the wines are red. The Graves has its own classification, for reds and whites, and Sauternes and St-Émilion are also classified. Pomerol steers clear of any official hierarchy. The only change so far has been the promotion of Mouton-Rothschild to First Growth in 1973.

In general, classified properties do deserve their status, but that's never yet stopped anyone from arguing about it.

CLARET CLASSIFICATIONS

First Growths (1ers crus)
Margaux – *Margaux*; Lafite-Rothschild, Latour, Mouton-Rothschild (promoted in 1973) – *Pauillac*; Haut-Brion – *Pessac-Léognan* (formerly *Graves*).

Second Growths (2èmes crus)
Brane-Cantenac – *Cantenac-Margaux*; Durfort-Vivens, Lascombes, Rauzan-Gassies, Rauzan-Ségla – *Margaux*; Pichon-Longueville, Pichon-Longueville-Lalande (formerly Pichon-Lalande) – *Pauillac*; Cos d'Estournel, Montrose – *St-Estèphe*; Ducru-Beaucaillou, Gruaud-Larose, Léoville-Barton, Léoville-Las-Cases, Léoville-Poyferré – *St-Julien*.

Third Growths (3èmes crus)
Boyd-Cantenac, Cantenac-Brown, Kirwan, d'Issan, Palmer – *Cantenac-Margaux*; Giscours – *Labarde-Margaux*; la Lagune – *Ludon-Haut-Médoc*; Desmirail, Ferrière, Malescot-St-Exupéry, Marquis d'Alesme-Becker – *Margaux*; Calon-Ségur – *St-Estèphe*; Lagrange, Langoa-Barton – *St-Julien*.

Fourth Growths (4èmes crus)
Pouget, Prieuré-Lichine – *Cantenac-Margaux*; Marquis-de-Terme – *Margaux*; Duhart-Milon-Rothschild – *Pauillac*; Lafon-Rochet – *St-Estèphe*; Beychevelle, Branaire (formerly Branaire-Ducru), St-Pierre, Talbot – *St-Julien*; la Tour-Carnet – *St-Laurent-Haut-Médoc*.

Fifth Growths (5èmes crus)
du Tertre – *Arsac-Margaux*; Dauzac – *Labarde-Margaux*; Cantemerle – *Macau-Haut-Médoc*; d'Armailhac (formerly Mouton-Baronne-Philippe), Batailley, Clerc-Milon-Rothschild, Croizet-Bages, Grand-Puy-Ducasse, Grand-Puy-Lacoste, Haut-Bages-Libéral, Haut-Batailley, Lynch-Bages, Lynch-Moussas, Pédesclaux, Pontet-Canet – *Pauillac*; Cos Labory – *St-Estèphe*; Belgrave, de Camensac – *St-Laurent-Haut-Médoc*.

SAUTERNES CLASSIFICATONS

Grand 1er cru   d'Yquem – *Sauternes*.

1er crus   Climens, Coutet – *Barsac*; Haut-Peyraguey, Lafaurie-Peyraguey, Rabaud-Promis, Rayne-Vigneau, Sigalas-Rabaud, la Tour-Blanche – *Bommes*; Rieussec – *Fargues*; Suduiraut – *Preignac*; Guiraud – *Sauternes*.

2èmes crus   Broustet, Caillou, Doisy-Daëne, Doisy-Dubroca, Doisy-Védrines, Nairac, de Myrat, Suau – *Barsac*; Romer-du-Hayot – *Fargues*; de Malle – *Preignac*; d'Arche, Filhot, Lamothe, Lamothe-Guignard – *Sauternes*.

PRODUCERS WHO'S WHO

L'ANGÉLUS *grand cru classé St-Émilion* ★★★★(★) Big and well known. A lot of Cabernet in the vineyard makes for a reasonably gutsy red, although rich and soft. The 1985 and '86 are the finest yet, with superb '87, '88 and '89. Excellent in the difficult years of the 1990s.

D'ANGLUDET *cru bourgeois Margaux* ★★★ £ Bourgeois red easily attaining Classed Growth standards. The wine has much of the perfume of good Margaux without ever going through the traditional lean period. Fairly priced. Tremendous value. The 1983 and '90 are the finest ever, and the '85, '86, '88 and '89 are big and classy.

D'ARCHE *2ème cru Sauternes* ★★★(★) A little-known property now increasingly highly thought of. 1983, '86, '88, '89 and '90 are good but I don't think they're that good. A little over-alcoholic, perhaps.

D'ARMAILHAC *5ème cru classé Pauillac* ★★★ (formerly known as Mouton-Baronne-Philippe) A red of very good balance for a Fifth Growth, with the perfume particularly marked: this obviously benefits from having the same ownership as Mouton-Rothschild. 1983 and '86 are very good, with '82 not bad either.

AUSONE *1er grand cru classé St-Émilion* ★★★★(★) Between 1976 and 1994 the wines were made in a very fine, understated style. A new winemaker was appointed for the 1995. Potentially great red at its best. The 1985, '86, '89 and above all the '90, are especially good.

BASTOR-LAMONTAGNE *cru bourgeois Sauternes* ★★★ £ Unclassified property making marvellous, widely available sweet whites, as rich as many Classed Growths, and nearly as expensive. 1983, '86, '88, '89 and '90 epitomize high-quality Sauternes.

BATAILLEY *5ème cru classé Pauillac* ★★★ £ The wines have been getting a lot better. Drinkable young, they age well too. The 1983, '85, '86, '88, '89 and '90 are excellent, and relatively affordable.

BELAIR *1er cru classé St-Émilion* ★★★ Looked as though it was rapidly returning to a top position as a finely balanced, stylish St-Émilion red, but some recent bottles have been strangely unconvincing.

BEYCHEVELLE *4ème cru classé St-Julien* ★★★★ The most expensive Fourth Growth, but deservedly so, since traditional quality puts it alongside the top Seconds. It takes time to mature to a beautifully balanced, scented, blackcurranty – and pricy – red. 1989 and '90 are sublime, but there is still sometimes a tendency to overproduce.

BRANAIRE *4ème cru classé St-Julien* ★★★ Formerly Branaire-Ducru. Used to be soft, smooth red with a flavour of plums and chocolate, achieving a classic, cedary St-Julien perfume in maturity. The 1981, '82, '85 and '86 are good. But the 1980s overall were erratic, with dilute flavours and unclean fruit: 1982, '85 and '86 were clean and fruity, but '83, '87 and '88 were oddly insubstantial. 1989 and '90 saw a welcome return to form, thanks to a change of ownership, with wine of sturdy fruit with backbone.

BRANE-CANTENAC *2ème cru classé Margaux* ★★ A big and famous property which has been underachieving when most of the other Second Growths have been shooting ahead. It has had chances in the last few years to prove itself, but remains behind the rest of the field.

BROUSTET *2ème cru classé Barsac* ★★★ A reliable, fairly rich sweet white not often seen, but worth trying: the 1988 and '90 are especially good. The dry white is rather disappointing.

CABANNIEUX *Graves* ★★★ £ One of the new wave of non-classified Graves which is radically improving its white wine with new oak barrels. The red is good, too. 1986, '88, '89 and '90 show the way.

CALON-SÉGUR *3ème cru classé St-Estèphe* ★★★(★) An intensely traditional claret, it's certainly good on present showing. 1986 and '88 look good, '90 is fine and '94 promising. 1995 is superb.

CANON *1er grand cru classé St-Émilion* ★★★★(★) Mature Canon reeks of the soft, buttery Merlot grape as only a top St-Émilion can. The wines seem to get better and better; marvellous 1982s and '83s were followed by a stunning '85 and a thoroughly impressive '86. 1988 was excellent. 1989 and '90 are keeping up this high standard.

CANTEMERLE *5ème cru classé Haut-Médoc* ★★★(★) Wine that is often up to Second Growth standards, although sometimes a little light. The 1988 and '89 are the best recent vintages by a long way, and the '83 was really good, but though the '85, '86 and '90 are beautifully perfumed, they are a little loose-knit. Interestingly, the perfumed style quite suits the '87.

CARBONNIEUX *cru classé Pessac-Léognan* ★★★(★) This large property has been using 50 per cent new oak for its whites since 1988 – and you can taste the difference. The 1990 is the best yet, and '92 and '93 are good. The red is increasingly complex.

CHASSE-SPLEEN *cru bourgeois Moulis* ★★★(★) A tremendously consistent wine, at the top of the *bourgeois* tree. It already sells above the price of many Classed Growths. The wines were impressive, chunky and beautifully made right through the 1980s, except for a rather over-elegant 1985. Choose 1982 and '86, followed by lovely '87 and tip-top '88. The 1989 is a bit fierce, but the '90 is first class, with lots of blackberry fruit backed by a firm structure. Even the difficult years '91 and '92 are impressive.

CHEVAL-BLANC *1er grand cru classé St-Émilion* ★★★★★ There's some sturdy richness here, but wonderful spice and fruit too, perhaps due to the very high proportion of Cabernet Franc. Good years are succulent. Lesser years like 1980 can be successes too, and only '84 and '87 haven't worked. The 1982 is unbelievably good, and the '81, '83, '85 and '86 are not far behind. 1988 and '90 are among the best of the vintage, but '89 is not quite of the intensity I want. 1995 is very promising.

CISSAC *cru grand bourgeois Haut-Médoc* ★★★ £ Traditionalists' delight! This is one of the best-known *bourgeois* reds: dark, dry and slow to mature with lots of oak influence, too – the oak perhaps a little more apparent than the fruit. It is best in richly ripe years like 1982 and '85, but can be a little lean in more austere years like '86. 1988, '89 and '90 were very good.

CLIMENS *1er cru Barsac* ★★★★★ Undoubtedly the best property in Barsac, making some of the most consistently fine sweet wines in France. 1980, '83, '86, '88, '89 and '90 are all excellent. It also makes a delicious second wine called les Cyprès that is well worth seeking out.

COS D'ESTOURNEL *2ème cru classé St-Estèphe* ★★★★★ £ The undoubted leader of St-Estèphe. The wines are dark, tannic and oaky: classically made for long aging despite a high percentage of Merlot. The quality was so good in '85, '88 and '90 that they are probably undervalued, but the price has risen recently. The '91 is decent.

COUHINS-LURTON *cru classé Pessac-Léognan* ★★★★ 100 per cent Sauvignon dry white fermented in new oak barrels, producing a blend of grassy fruit and oaky spice. Recent vintages have been excellent.

COUTET *1er cru Barsac* ★★(★) A great sweet wine property which in recent years has not been living up to its previous exacting standards.

DOISY-DAËNE *2ème cru Barsac* ★★★(★) A very good, consistent property providing relatively light, but extremely attractive sweet wine. Doisy-Daëne Sec is a particularly good dry white.

DOISY-VÉDRINES *2ème cru Barsac* ★★★★ £ A rich, concentrated sweet white which is usually good value. 1980, '83, '86 and '89 are very good.

DOMAINE DE CHEVALIER *cru classé Pessac-Léognan* ★★★★(★) The red has a superb balance of fruit and oak, and the white is simply one of France's greatest. The hottest years are not always the best: 1982 is looking disappointing and the '81, '83, '85, '86 and '88 may yet turn out better. 1987 is a resounding success in a light vintage, as is the '84. 1989 and '90 were classy.

DUCRU-BEAUCAILLOU *2ème cru classé St-Julien* ★★★(★) Potentially one of the glories of the Médoc. It initially distanced itself from most other Second Growths in price and quality, with a flavour so deep and warm, and balance so good, it was worth the money. With its relatively high yields, it has a less startling quality when young than its near rivals Léoville-Las-Cases and Pichon-Longueville-Lalande. The mid- to late 1980s saw problems with the barrels, so while '82 and '85 are top drawer, and '81, '79 and '78 fit for the long haul, other '80s vintages must be approached with caution. The 1995 should be excellent.

L'ÉVANGILE *Pomerol* ★★★(★) Top-line Pomerol, lacking the sheer intensity of its neighbour Pétrus, but perfumed and rich in a most irresistible way. 1982, '85, and '88 are delicious, with first-rate '87 too. 1989 is packed with multi-layered, firm, luscious fruit, and '90 is another blockbuster.

DE FARGUES *cru bourgeois Sauternes* ★★★★(★) Small property owned by d'Yquem, capable of producing stunning, rich wines in the best years.

DE FIEUZAL *cru classé Pessac-Léognan* ★★★★(★) One of the stars of Pessac-Léognan, the white only just behind Domaine de Chevalier, the red well ahead. The red starts plum-rich and buttery, but develops earthiness and cedar scent allied to lovely fruit. It made one of the finest 1984s, outstanding '85s and '86s as well as lovely '87s and thrilling '88s. 1989 was top-notch, the '90 very good. The white, though unclassified, is scented, complex, deep and exciting. Even the '92 is good.

FIGEAC *1er grand cru classé St-Émilion* ★★★★ Figeac shares many of the qualities of Cheval Blanc but it's always ranked as the ever-reliable star of the second team. A pity, since it has a beauty and a blackcurranty, minty scent uncommon in St-Émilion. High quality. High(ish) price. Figeac is always easy to drink young, but deserves proper aging. The excellent 1978 is just opening out, and the lovely '82, '85 and '86 will all take at least as long. 1989 and '90 are already seductive.

FILHOT *2ème cru Sauternes* ★★(★) Well-known Sauternes property producing pleasant but hardly memorable sweet whites, though 1988 looks more hopeful.

LA FLEUR-PÉTRUS *Pomerol* ★★★★ This red is in the top flight, having some of the mineral roughness of much Pomerol, but also tremendous perfume and length. The 1982 and '89 are without doubt the best recent wines; the '85 and '86 seem to lack that little extra class.

GAZIN *Pomerol* ★★★★ This can produce the extra sweetness and perfume Nenin usually lacks. 1987 and '88 showed improved standards, and '89 and '90 are really very fine. 1995 is first rate.

GILETTE *cru bourgeois Sauternes* ★★★★
Remarkable property which ages its sweet
whites in concrete tanks for 20 to 30 years
before releasing them. Usually delicious,
with a dry richness unique in Sauternes
thanks to long maturation and absence of
wood. The 1970 is heavenly, and is the
current vintage. Seriously. The wines come
in different quality levels (not all of which
are made every year), of which Crème de
Tête is the top.

GISCOURS *3ème cru classé Margaux*
★★★ This property excelled right through
the 1970s and into the '80s. But something
went wrong after 1982. Although '86 is
good, and '87 reasonable for the year, '83,
'85 and '88 are not up to par. 1989 and '90
showed a return to form.

GLORIA *cru bourgeois St-Julien* ★★★
The quality of this quick-maturing red has
not always been faithful to the quality of its
hype. 1986, '88 and '89 show some signs
that the wine is finally becoming worthy of
the price.

GRAND-PUY-DUCASSE *5ème cru
classé Pauillac* ★★★ £ With a price that is
not excessive, its slightly gentle but tasty
Pauillac style is one to buy. The 1979 is
lovely now, and the '82 and '83 are very
nice without causing the hand to tremble in
anticipation. Since 1984 there has been a
discernible rise in tempo, and '85 and '86
look to be the best wines yet, but little
exciting wine was made here in the late
1980s.

GRAND-PUY-LACOSTE *5ème cru
classé Pauillac* ★★★★ £ This combines
perfume, power and consistency in a way
that shows Pauillac at its brilliant best.
Blackcurrant and cigar-box perfumes are
rarely in better harmony than here. The
1982, '83, '86 and '88 are tremendous, and
the '84, though very light, is gentle and
delicious. 1989 is gorgeously perfumed with
robust fruit, and '90 is super.

GRUAUD-LAROSE *2ème cru classé St-
Julien* ★★★★(★) Often starts rich, chunky
and sweetish but will achieve its full cedary
glory in time, while still retaining a lovely
sweet centre. The remarkable run of 1982,
'83, '84 and '85 continued with a great '86,
an attractive '87, an exceptional '88 and '89
and, keeping up the standards, an almost
unnervingly juicy, ripe '90.

GUIRAUD *1er cru Sauternes* ★★★★(★)
The wines are difficult to taste when young
but are very special, and the 1983, '86, '88,
'89 and '90 are going to be outstanding.

HAUT-BAILLY *cru classé Pessac-
Léognan* ★★★★ Haut-Bailly red (there is
no white) tastes sweet, rich and perfumed
from its earliest youth, and the high
percentage of new oak adds to this
impression. But the wines do age well.
1981, '82, '85, '86, '88, '89 and '93 are the
best recently.

HAUT-BATAILLEY *5ème cru classé
Pauillac* ★★★ Once dark, plummy and slow
to sweeten, this is now a somewhat lighter,
more charming wine. In some years this has
meant it was less satisfying, but 1989 is the
best yet, marvellously concentrated. 1986
and '88 are the best of earlier wines, with
'82, '83 and '85 all good, but just a touch
too diffuse and soft. The vineyard is now
coming of age, so look for some very good
wines in the mid-1990s.

HAUT-BRION *1er cru classé Pessac-
Léognan* ★★★★★ The wines are not big,
but are almost creamy in their gorgeous ripe
taste, deliciously so. If anything, they slightly
resemble the great Médocs. Although 1982
is strangely insubstantial, the next four
vintages are all very fine, and '88 and '89 are
outstanding, while the 1990, although
worthy enough, could not quite compete
with its predecessors. There are also small
quantities of fine, long-lived white, also
appealing when young. The 1985 and 1994
are both spectacular.

D'ISSAN *3ème cru classé Margaux*
★★★★ One of the truest Margaux wines, hard when young (though more use of new oak recently has sweetened things up a bit), but perfumed and deep-flavoured after ten to 12 years. Fabulous in 1983, '88 and '90, first rate in '85 and '86, with a good '87 too. 1989 has excellent fruit, while '90 is a star, rich and concentrated, with lots of liquorice.

LAFAURIE-PEYRAGUEY *1er cru Sauternes* ★★★★(★) Fine sweet wine property, currently returning to top form. Produced remarkably good wines in the difficult years of '82, '84 and '85, and it was stunning in '83, '86, '88 and '90.

LAFITE-ROTHSCHILD *1er cru classé Pauillac* ★★★★★ The most difficult of all the great Médocs to get to know. It doesn't stand for power like Latour, or perfume like Mouton. It stands for balance, the elegant, restrained balance that is the perfection of great claret. 1986, '88, '89 and '90 are the best recent vintages, followed by '82.

LAFLEUR *Pomerol* ★★★★★ The only Pomerol with the potential to be as great as Pétrus. They couldn't be further apart in style, and Lafleur is marked out by an astonishing austere concentration of dark fruit and an intense tobacco spice perfume. The 1982 almost knocks you sideways with its naked power, and the '83 and '85 are also remarkable. 1989 is superbly fruity and displays tremendous finesse.

LAFON-ROCHET *4ème cru classé St-Estèphe* ★★★(★) An improving St-Estèphe, with as much body and a little more perfume than most. 1982, '83 and '85 are all good, though not stunning, while '86, '87, '88, '89 and '90 show real class and a welcome consistency of style. It looks set to move another gear upwards in the 1990s; 1994 and '95 are most impressive.

LAGRANGE *3ème cru classé St-Julien* ★★★(★) Investment is making its presence felt: 1985, '86, '88, '89 and '90 are impressive and '87 was good too. Not great, though: the vineyard is not one of St-Julien's best, and in a way the current technical expertise underlines this, because the wine lacks heart. Make sure you concentrate on more recent vintages.

LA LAGUNE *3ème cru classé Haut-Médoc* ★★★★ Certainly making Second Growth- standard red, with a rich, soft intensity. It is now becoming more expensive, but the wine was consistently good, until the disappointing 1994. The 1982 is wonderfully rich and juicy, with '85 and '88 not far behind, and '83 on their tails. 1986 is burly but brilliant stuff, as is '89. 1987 is more delicate but good.

LAMOTHE-GUIGNARD *2ème cru Sauternes* ★★★ Since 1981 this previously undistinguished sweet white has dramatically improved. 1983, '86 and '88 show the improvement, as will '89 and '90.

LANESSAN *cru bourgeois Haut-Médoc* ★★★ Always correct, if not distinguished. But this may be because the owner resolutely refuses to use new oak and therefore his wines are discreet when young. The 1982, '83 and '88 are exhibiting classic claret flavours now, and '90 is a wine of balance and depth.

LANGOA-BARTON *3ème cru classé St-Julien* ★★★★ £ Very good, in the dry, cedary style, and sometimes regarded as a lesser version of Léoville-Barton. The wine has character and style, and is reasonably priced. 1982 and '85 are exciting, '86 and '87 typical, but the '88 may be the best for 30 years. The '89 vintage almost matched Léoville-Barton for elegance and the '90 was fully its equal.

LASCOMBES *2ème cru classé Margaux* ★★★ Very attractive early on, but the wine can gain flesh and character as it ages. The 1983 and '85 are good, and the '86 is the most serious effort for a long time. 1987 is also good, but '88 is so light you'd think they'd put in every grape on the property. 1989, '90 and '91 are more hopeful.

LATOUR *1er cru classé Pauillac* ★★★★★ The easiest of all the First Growths to comprehend. It's a huge, dark, hard brute when young, calming down as it ages and eventually spreading out to a superb, blackcurrant and cedar flavour. It used to take ages to come round, but some recent vintages have seemed a little softer and lighter, whilst retaining their tremendous core of fruit. Let's hope they age as well as the previous ones, because the 1984 was more true to type than the '85. And though the '82 is a classic, both '81 and '83 are very definitely not. 1986 and '88 seem to be back on course, and '89 and '90 look splendidly powerful. The '91 and '92 are the best wines of their years. The second wine, called les Forts-de-Latour, is getting better and better, while the third wine, Pauillac de Latour, is made in most years to preserve the quality of the two greater wines.

LAVILLE-HAUT-BRION *cru classé Pessac-Léognan* ★★★★ This should be one of the greatest of all white Pessac-Léognan, since it is owned by Haut-Brion, but despite some great successes, the general effect is patchy – especially given the crazy prices.

LÉOVILLE-BARTON *2ème cru classé St-Julien* ★★★★★ £ The traditionalist's dream. Despite all the new fashions and trends in Bordeaux, Anthony Barton simply goes on making superlative, old-fashioned wine for long aging. All the vintages of the 1980s have been attractive, but the '82, '83, '85 and '86 are outstanding, the '87 delicious, and the '88 and '90 are two of the best wines of the Médoc. 1989 keeps up the high standard. All the wines are *wonderfully* fairly priced.

LÉOVILLE-LAS-CASES *2ème cru classé St-Julien* ★★★★★ The most brilliant of the St-Juliens, combining all the sweet, honeyed St-Julien ripeness with strong, dry, cedary perfume. The 1982 is more exciting every time a bottle is broached, and all the vintages of the 1980s are top examples of their year. The second wine, Clos du Marquis, is better than the majority of Classed Growths.

LÉOVILLE-POYFERRÉ *2ème cru classé St-Julien* ★★★★ The Léoville that got left behind, not only in reputation, but also in the quality of the wine, which until recently had a dull, indistinct flavour and an unbalancing dryness compared with other top St-Juliens. Things are now looking up with new investment and renewed commitment, and every vintage shows progress. The 1982, '85, '86 and even the '87 are better, and '88, '89 and '90 continue the good work. '94 is remarkably good.

LOUDENNE *cru bourgeois Médoc* ★(★) The château is owned by Gilbey's and the wine is seen a lot in high street chains. Both red and white are fruity and agreeable, and best drunk young.

LA LOUVIÈRE *cru bourgeois Pessac-Léognan* ★★★★ This property has been making lovely, modern, oak-aged whites since the mid-1970s, and since 1987 the quality has climbed even higher. Reds are also good, and quite earthy.

LYNCH-BAGES *5ème cru classé Pauillac* ★★★★★ This château is so well known that its familiarity can breed contempt, causing its considerable quality to be underestimated. It is astonishingly soft and drinkable when very young, yet ages brilliantly, and has one of the most beautiful scents of minty blackcurrant in all Bordeaux. The most likely to show that character are the 1983, '86 and, remarkably, the '87, but for sheer starry-eyed brilliance the '85, '88 and particularly the '82 are the ones. The '89 is unusually big and powerful; the '90 marginally more restrained and classic.

MAGDELAINE *1er grand cru classé St-Émilion* ★★★★ This wine combines the soft richness of Merlot with the sturdiness needed to age. Expensive, but one of the best. 1982 and '85 are both classics, '88 and '89 tremendously good.

MALARTIC-LAGRAVIÈRE *cru classé Pessac-Léognan* ★★★ £ The quality is good, sometimes excellent, in spite of generous yields from the vines, and while the white is very attractive young, the red is capable of long aging. 1982, '83, '85, '86 and '87 are all successful, with '88 and '89 the finest yet, but the '90s are disappointing. The red, in particular, is rather wishy-washy.

MALESCOT-ST-EXUPÉRY *3ème cru classé Margaux* ★★(★) This seemed in the 1980s to have lost its way: the wines were becoming too light and lacking in depth. So thank goodness for the massive improvement in '88, '89 and '90.

DE MALLE *2ème cru Sauternes* ★★★ Good, relatively light sweet white. It went through a bad patch in the 1980s, but since '88 the wines have been back on course

MARGAUX *1er cru classé Margaux* ★★★★★ A succession of great wines have set Margaux back on the pedestal of refinement and sheer, ravishing perfume from which it had slipped some years ago. The new Margaux is weightier and more consistent than before, yet with all its beauty intact. 1978 and '79 were the harbingers; the '80 was startlingly good in a tricky year, and '82, '83 and '86 are just about as brilliant as claret can be, while the '88 may well be the wine of the vintage. The deep, concentrated '89 doesn't seem to match up to the '88, but the '90 is as fragrant and powerful as the '86 – which is saying a lot. In the difficult '91 and '92 vintages the wines were better than most of the First Growths.

MEYNEY *cru bourgeois St-Estèphe* ★★★(★) £ This epitomizes St-Estèphe reliability, yet is better than that. It is big, meaty and strong, but never harsh. Vintages in the 1970s lacked personality, but recent wines are increasingly impressive, and although it is difficult to taste young, the '82, '83, '85, '86, '88 and '89 are all remarkable, and the '84, '87 and '90 are good.

LA MISSION-HAUT-BRION *cru classé Pessac-Léognan* ★★★(★) La Mission likes to put itself in a class apart, between Haut-Brion and the rest. Yet one often feels this red relies more on weight and massive, dark fruit and oak flavours than on any great subtleties. For those, you go to Haut-Brion or Domaine de Chevalier. 1982, '85 or '86 are recommendable of recent vintages.

MONTROSE *2ème cru classé St-Estèphe* ★★★★ Traditionally famous for its dark, tannic character, and its slow, ponderous march to maturity. For a wine with such a sturdy reputation, some recent vintages have seemed faintly hollow. 1986 made amends with a really chewy, long-distance number, and '87 was densely structured, if hardly classic, but it's taken until '89 and '90 vintages for the wine really to return to form. The château, which tends to pick rather early, came into its own in '89 and '90, and even made a decent '91 and a better '92. The second wine, Dame de Montrose, has been a bargain lately.

MOUTON-ROTHSCHILD *1er cru classé Pauillac* ★★★★★ Wine with an astonishing flavour, piling intense cigar-box and lead-pencil perfume on to the rich blackcurrant fruit. The 1982 is already a legend, the '86 and '89 are likely to join '82, and the '83, '84 and '85 are well worth the asking price. The 1988 and '90, though, are below par, but the '95 is fabulous.

NENIN *Pomerol* ★★ A thoroughly old-fashioned red, rather chunky and solid and with quite a tough core for a Pomerol. This toughness doesn't always disperse into mellow fruitfulness. The 1985 and '86 aren't bad, but, really, the '82, the '83 and the '88, all generally good vintages in Pomerol, were pretty feeble here.

PALMER *3ème cru classé Margaux* ★★★★ Palmer can occasionally out-perform some of the First Growths in tastings. It was consistently brilliant in the 1960s and 1970s (excepting '64), but the 1980s have seen it lose some of its sure touch, and the '83 lacks some of its neighbours' class. 1987 and '88 are very good. 1989 is cedary and elegant, rich but tannic, in a year when not all Margaux wines had great depth of fruit. In 1990 Palmer was better than most, but not all, of its neighbours.

PAPE-CLÉMENT *grand cru classé de Graves* ★★★★(★) One of the top properties in Pessac-Léognan, capable of mixing considerable sweetness from ripe fruit and new oak with a good deal of tough structure. 1975 was great, but then we had a very poor decade until 1985. Recent years are outstanding, with the 1990 an example of Pessac-Léognan at its best.

PAVIE *1er grand cru St-Émilion* ★★★★ Until recently good without being wonderful, stylish without being grand. Still, Pavie does have the true gentle flavours of good St-Émilion and recent releases are showing a deeper, more passionate style which puts it into the top flight. 1985, '86, '87, '88, '89 and '90 are good examples of the new, '82 of the old.

PETIT-VILLAGE *Pomerol* ★★★★ A fairly pricy red, it is not one of the soft, plummy Pomerols, and until recently there was quite a bit of Cabernet giving backbone. The wine is worth laying down, but the price is always high. 1983, '85 and the juicy '82 are all very good, but the '88, '89 and '90 look likely to be the best yet.

PÉTRUS *Pomerol* ★★★★★ One of the world's most expensive reds, and often one

of the greatest. Astonishingly, its fame has only been acquired since 1945, and in particular since 1962, when the firm of Jean-Pierre Moueix took a half-share. Christian Moueix says his intention is to ensure no bottle of Pétrus ever disappoints. 1982 and '89 were stupendously great. 1985 isn't far off it, nor is '81; and the only example from the last 20 years which seemed atypical is the rather Médoc-like 1978.

DE PEZ *cru bourgeois St-Estèphe* ★★★ One of the most famous *bourgeois* châteaux, the wine is almost always of Classed Growth standard, big, reliable, rather plummy and not too harsh. 1982 and '83 were both very attractive, though some prefer the more unashamedly St-Estèphe-style wines of the 1970s, which saw a bit of a comeback with the excellent '86.

PICHON-LONGUEVILLE *2ème cru classé Pauillac* ★★★★ Often described as more masculine than its 'sister', Pichon-Longueville-Lalande, this tremendously correct but diffident Pauillac (formerly Pichon-Longueville-Baron) was until 1987 only hinting at its potential. New management meant that the '87 was very good, the '88 superb, the '89 *tremendous*, broodingly intense, while the '90 is one of the Médoc's greatest reds. However, the difficult vintages since have not been mastered so well.

PICHON-LONGUEVILLE-LALANDE *2ème cru classé Pauillac* ★★★★(★) Formerly known as Pichon-Lalande, it makes a rich, oaky, concentrated red of tremendous quality. Its price has climbed inexorably and it wishes to be seen as equal to St-Julien's leading pair, Léoville-Las-Cases and Ducru-Beaucaillou. 1982, '83, '85 and '86 all brim with exciting flavours. '87 and '88 are good, but both '89 and '90 are below par, and easily outclassed by Pichon-Longueville over the road. But since then Lalande has been clearly back on form, especially with its brilliant '95.

PONTET-CANET *5ème cru classé Pauillac* ★★★ Famous but unpredictable, and still trying to find its traditionally reliable form. 1985 and '86 are hopeful, '87 and '88 less so, '90 hopeful again, and '94 much better.

POTENSAC *cru bourgeois Médoc* ★★★(★) **£** Wines with a delicious, blackcurrant fruit, greatly improved by a strong taste of oak. Not expensive for the quality. Beats many *crus classés* every year for sheer flavour.

PRIEURÉ-LICHINE *4ème cru classé Margaux* ★★★ One of the more reliable Margaux wines: fairly priced and, although not that perfumed, good and sound. 1983, '86, '88 and '89 are all good, but the '90 was the first really exciting wine to have been made for some time, and '91 and '92 continued the improvement.

RABAUD-PROMIS *1er cru Sauternes* ★★★(★) At last! The 1986, '88, '89 and '90 are excellent and show a long-awaited return to First Growth sweet wine quality.

RAHOUL *cru bourgeois Graves* ★★(★) A leader of the new wave of cool-fermented, oak-aged whites among the Graves properties. Also generally good red. Ownership changes are worrying, though, and the 1988, '89 and '90 were not as special as previous vintages, though they are still good.

RAUZAN-SÉGLA *2ème cru classé Margaux* ★★★★(★) A change of ownership in 1983 saw a return to quality. 1983, '85 and '86 were triumphs. 1987 was declassified as Château Lamouroux but is still delicious. The '88, '89, '90, '93 and '94 are all very good. The older spelling of the name, with a z, is now being used again.

RAUZAN-GASSIES *2ème cru classé Margaux* ★★ Leagues below most Second and Third Growth reds in quality, and so far hasn't taken the hint from Ségla that quality pays in the end.

RAYMOND LAFON *cru bourgeois Sauternes* ★★★★ Owned by the former manager of neighbouring d'Yquem, this is

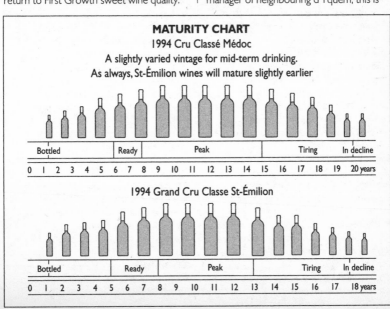

MATURITY CHART
1994 Cru Classé Médoc
A slightly varied vintage for mid-term drinking.
As always, St-Émilion wines will mature slightly earlier

| Bottled | Ready | Peak | Tiring | In decline |

0 1 2 3 4 5 6 7 8 9 10 11 12 13 14 15 16 17 18 19 20 years

1994 Grand Cru Classe St-Émilion

| Bottled | Ready | Peak | Tiring | In decline |

0 1 2 3 4 5 6 7 8 9 10 11 12 13 14 15 16 17 18 years

CLARETS OUT OF THEIR CLASS

One of the most exciting things for a wine devotee is to catch a château at the beginning of a revival in its fortunes. While a reputation is being built or re-built, the quality will keep ahead of the price – for a while.

Some wines, notably Cos d'Estournel and Léoville-Barton, have kept quality up and prices (relatively) down, though Cos has recently raised its prices. These are my best buys of the Bordeaux wines on the market now.

Médoc *Minor châteaux performing like top bourgeois:* Grands Chênes, Malescasse, Moulin Rouge, Potensac, Tour Haut-Caussan, Tour du Haut-Moulin, Tour-de-By, Tour-St-Bonnet.

Top bourgeois performing like Classed Growths: d'Angludet, Chambert-Marbuzet, Chasse-Spleen, Citran, Haut-Marbuzet, Labégorce-Zédé, Lanessan, Meyney, Monbrison, Ormes-de-Pez, Phélan-Ségur, Pibran, Poujeaux, Siran, Sociando-Mallet, Tour-de-Mons.

Classed Growths performing above their station: Clerc-Milon-Rothschild, Grand-Puy-Lacoste, la Lagune, Léoville-Barton, Léoville-Las-Cases, Montrose, Pichon-Longueville-Lalande, Pontet-Canet (from '94), Rauzan-Ségla.

Graves and Pessac-Léognan
Outperformers: White: Cabannieux, Carbonnieux, Couhins-Lurton, de Fieuzal, Montalivet, Olivier, Smith-Haut-Lafitte. *Red:* de Fieuzal, Haut-Bailly, Pape-Clément, Roquetaillade la Grange, la Tour-Martillac.

Pomerol
Outperformers: Beauregard, Bon-Pasteur, Certan-de-May, Clinet, l'Église-Clinet, l'Évangile, Gazin.

St-Émilion
Outperformers: l'Angélus, l'Arrosée, Beau-Séjour-Bécot, Bellefont-Belcier, la Dominique, Grand-Mayne, Larmande, Pavie-Macquin, Tertre Rôteboeuf, Troplong- Mondot, Valandraud.

Sauternes
Outperformers: Bastor-Lamontagne, Chartreuse, Climens, Doisy-Daëne, de Fargues, Gilette, Liot, de Malle, Nairac, Roumieu Lacoste, St-Amand.

Satellites
Outperformers: Canon-de-Brem, Canon Moueix, Charlemagne, Cassagne-Haut-Truffière – *Canon-Fronsac;* Lyonnat – *Lussac-St-Émilion;* Tour-du-Pas-St-Georges – *St-Georges-St-Émilion;* la Prade, de Francs – *Côte de Francs;* des Annereaux, Bertineau-St-Vincent – *Lalande-de-Pomerol.*

---

fine wine but not quite as fine as the increasingly daunting price would imply.

RIEUSSEC *1er cru Sauternes* ★★★★(★) One of the richest, most exotic Sauternes; the property made particularly good wines during the 1980s. The 1982 is good, the '83, '86 and '88 really special, the '89 and '90 wonderful. Well on form.

ST-AMAND *cru bourgeois Sauternes* ★★★(★) £ Splendid property making truly rich wines that age well, at an affordable price. Also seen as Château de la Chartreuse.

ST-PIERRE *4ème cru classé Médoc* ★★★★ Small St-Julien property producing superb, underrated, old-fashioned red. The wines of the 1980s are possibly even better than those that went before.

DE SALES *Pomerol* ★★★ £ A truly enormous estate, the biggest in Pomerol by a mile. This vastness shows in a wine which, though it is good round claret, doesn't often seem to excite. The 1985 is nice, the '82 and '83 are very nice.

SIRAN *cru bourgeois Margaux* ★★★ Sometimes mistaken for a Classed Growth in blind tastings. The 1983 and '85 are the most successful wines of recent years, but all vintages have been good lately. The '88 was a bit clumsy, but the '89 and '90 vintages are both showing well.

SMITH-HAUT-LAFITTE *cru classé Pessac-Léognan* ★★★★ A late convert to cool fermentation and oak-aging, but since 1985 making superb white wines. Also making increasingly good, and better-known, reds.

SUDUIRAUT *1er cru Sauternes* ★★★(★) Rich, exciting wines, frequently deeper and more intensely perfumed than any other Sauternes except for d'Yquem, but unfortunately not as reliable as it should be. A remarkable 1982 was followed by a fine '83, a very good '85 but disappointing '86 and ditto in 1988. 1989 was a leap up again, though.

TALBOT *4ème cru classé St-Julien* ★★★ This has seemed in recent years to be lagging behind in quality. The vintages of the mid- to late 1980s haven't shaped up as well as they should have done, with the 1988 in particular showing poorly (though the '82, '83 and '84 were very good). The '90 seems to lack something in the way of concentration.

DU TERTRE *5ème cru classé Margaux* ★★★(★) This wine is unusually good, with a lot of body for a Margaux, but that weight is all ripe, strong fruit and the flavour is direct and pure. Funnily enough, it's not cheap for a relative unknown but neither is it expensive for the quality. The 1985 is rich and dense and yet keeps its perfume intact, while the '86, '83 and '82 are rich and blackcurranty – already good and sure to improve for ten years more. 1988 was not quite so good, for some reason, but '89 was back to normal.

TROTANOY *Pomerol* ★★★★ If you didn't know Pétrus existed, you'd say this had to be the perfect Pomerol – rich, plummy, chocolaty fruit, some mineral hardness, and tremendous fat perfume. It's very, very good, and makes Pétrus' achievement in eclipsing it all the more amazing. The 1982 is brilliant, and although the '85 is also wonderfully good, the vintages of the mid- and late 1980s haven't been quite as thrilling as the previous examples of this château.

D'YQUEM *grand 1er cru classé Sauternes* ★★★★★ This incredible wine is the pinnacle of achievement in great sweet wines. Almost every vintage of d'Yquem is a masterpiece and its outlandish price is almost justified, since d'Yquem at its best is undoubtedly the greatest sweet wine in the world. And it lasts – well, forever, really. There's also a dry white made here, called Ygrec, which can be remarkable.

THE COST OF A BOTTLE

	1994 Cru Bourgeois	£12.50
	VAT	1.86
	Mark-up	3.00
	Duty	1.06
	Distribution	0.17
	Shipping	0.16
	Wine	6.25

BORDEAUX VINTAGES

Generic wines like Bordeaux Rouge rarely need any aging. A petit château wine from a good vintage might need five years to be at its best, a good bourgeois might need ten, and a premier cru might need 20. Pomerols and St-Émilions come round faster than Médocs.

1996   The 1994s were hyped, the 1995s were hyped, and the 1996s too. Increasingly they look good but not great, and they're certainly expensive. Sauternes are good in parts. The market is greatly overheated – the ideal now would be a good, big 1997 vintage.

1995   Red wines of charm and structure, with a handful of really great wines at the top. There's plenty of tannin, but it's generally ripe. Overall, a very fine vintage, and one to keep. Not much noble rot in Sauternes, though the dry whites of the Graves look good.

1994   Most successful in Pomerol, though most regions produced reds with good concentration. A tiny crop of fair quality in Sauternes; dry whites came off better.

1993   A dilute year, in which the best bets are fresh, fruity wines to drink young. St-Émilion and Pomerol are probably best. Decent dry whites but little of quality in Sauternes.

1992   An unripe vintage: stick to reliable names and drink early. Even better, pick another vintage. Oddly enough there are some nice simple wines in Fronsac.

1991   Wildly variable for reds, and few thrills in Sauternes. Dry whites were good. Most should have been drunk by now.

1990   Excellent quality; the third of a great trio of vintages. Reds are immensely rich, as are Sauternes; lesser regions like Monbazillac and Loupiac also came up trumps. It was a bit too hot for the dry whites, though.

1989   A wonderful Médoc year, although Pomerol and St-Émilion also did well. Graves and Pessac-Léognan were somewhat uneven, as was Sauternes (though good at their best). Dry whites were rather overripe.

1988   Classically balanced reds and very fine Sauternes. For dry whites, stick to good producers.

1987   These have proved to be soft, wonderfully drinkable reds - but drink them now. They won't keep. Dry whites were better than sweet; again, they need drinking.

1986   Superb Sauternes, dripping with noble rot, and drinking beautifully now. Reds are good, sometimes very good, but not quite as good as 1988.

1985   Pretty well all the reds are delicious now, though the top wines are only just starting to come round. Sauternes are pleasant but light: not thrilling.

1984   A fruitless, joyless year in which the Merlot failed. Only the best Classed Growths from the Médoc are showing some lean but fragrant Cabernet class.

1983   Classics, especially in Margaux, and there's no hurry to drink them. Superb rich, exciting Sauternes: the beginning of the great 1980s Sauternes revival.

1982   Fabulous fat, ripe, juicy wines. The best still need a year or two to reach their peak; some of the lesser wines are lovely now and shouldn't be kept that much longer. Sauternes was mixed in quality.

MATURITY CHART
1995 Cru Classé Médoc
A vintage for the medium to long term

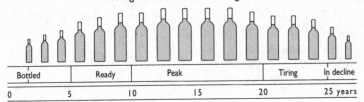

| Bottled | Ready | Peak | Tiring | In decline |

| 0 | 5 | 10 | 15 | 20 | 25 years |

1995 Good Cru Bourgeois Médoc

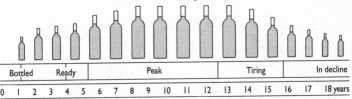

| Bottled | Ready | Peak | Tiring | In decline |

0 1 2 3 4 5 6 7 8 9 10 11 12 13 14 15 16 17 18 years

1994 Good Cru Bourgeois Médoc
More mixed quality for earlier drinking

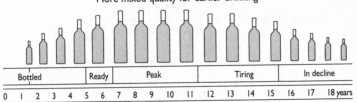

| Bottled | Ready | Peak | Tiring | In decline |

0 1 2 3 4 5 6 7 8 9 10 11 12 13 14 15 16 17 18 years

1993 Good Cru Bourgeois Médoc
The best are good, but won't keep

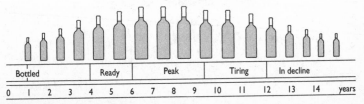

| Bottled | Ready | Peak | Tiring | In decline |

0 1 2 3 4 5 6 7 8 9 10 11 12 13 14 years

EARLIER BORDEAUX VINTAGES

1981 Good but not spectacular. Quite light wines, but those from top properties could still age a bit. A slightly graceless year in Sauternes.

1980 Nice light, grassy claret, which should have been drunk by now. The best Sauternes are still drinking well.

1979 The top wines can still be kept another year or so, but others should be drunk up. There was attractive, mid-weight Sauternes.

1978 All the Classed Growths are delicious now, but lesser wines are starting to dry out. Graves and St-Émilion are lovely, and won't improve.

1976 Rather soft and sweet; not inspiring, drink up. Best Sauternes are still fat and rich.

1975 Very tannic wines; frequently they went stale and brown before they had time to soften. The best may yet bloom; I'm not sure when. Nice, well-balanced Sauternes.

1966 All the wines are ready, and some are tipping over the edge.

1961 Still wonderful wines. I marvel at how great claret can match richness and perfume with a bone-dry structure of tannin and acidity.

Most other vintages of the 1960s will now be risky; '64s can still be good, rather solid wines and '62, one of the most gorgeous, fragrant vintages since the war, is showing its age. If your godfather's treating you, and offers '59, '55 or '53, accept with enthusiasm. If he offers you '49, '47 or '45, get it in writing before be begins to change his mind.

MATURITY CHART
1990 Cru Classé Sauternes
May turn out to be one of the greatest vintages of the century

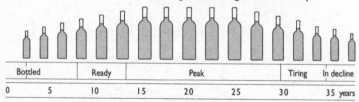

| Bottled | Ready | Peak | Tiring | In decline |

| 0 | 5 | 10 | 15 | 20 | 25 | 30 | 35 years |

1990 Cru Classé White Pessac-Léognan

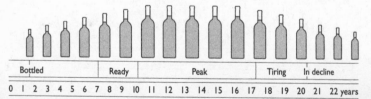

| Bottled | Ready | Peak | Tiring | In decline |

| 0 | 1 | 2 | 3 | 4 | 5 | 6 | 7 | 8 | 9 | 10 | 11 | 12 | 13 | 14 | 15 | 16 | 17 | 18 | 19 | 20 | 21 | 22 years |

RED BORDEAUX

l'Abbaye *Puisseguin-St-Émilion*
1989 £7.73 (FOR)

d'Aiguilhe *Côtes de Castillon*
1993 £6.99 (WR) £6.99 (THR) £6.99 (BOT)

Amiral-de-Beychevelle *St-Julien*
1994 £16.99 (NA) £17.29 (GN)
1993 £13.34 (ROS) £13.95 (LEA) £14.69 (DOM)
1992 £12.50 (BU)
1988 £19.25 (WRI)

Andron-Blanquet *cru grand bourgeois exceptionnel St-Estèphe*
1989 £13.35 (WHI) £14.60 (PIP) £16.30 (GN)

l'Angélus *grand cru classé St-Émilion*
1995 EC £455.00 (WAT) £459.00 (LAY) £650.00 (BUT)
1994 £43.95 (LAY)
1994 EC £500.00 (BUT)
1993 £35.00 (BER)
1990 IB £1,120.00 (FA)
1989 IB £640.00 (FA)

d'Angludet *cru bourgeois supérieur exceptionnel Margaux*
1995 EC £120.00 (BUT)
1993 £12.60 (BER) £12.62 (HA) £14.59 (NI)
1993 IB £135.00 (BUT)
1991 £15.50 (JON)
1990 £17.00 (JON) £19.95 (BER) £20.49 (TAN)
1990 IB £190.00 (GOE)
1989 £22.75 (STA)
1988 £15.99 (JON)
1988 IB £140.00 (BIB)

1986 £30.50 (ROB)
1985 £18.11 (WY) £33.00 (UB)
1983 £30.00 (ROB)
1978 £28.00 (CRO) £30.00 (VIG)
1970 magnum £60.00 (REI)

des Annereaux *Lalande-de-Pomerol*
1993 £9.95 (ROB) £10.25 (GN) £10.49 (AME) £10.96 (PLA)

Anthonic *cru bourgeois supérieur Moulis*
1993 £13.16 (FOR)
1990 £12.90 (CRO)
1986 £13.50 (PLA)

Archambeau *Graves*
1991 £9.95 (SAT)

d'Arche *Graves*
1979 £11.75 (BU)

d'Armailhac (was Mouton-Baronne-Philippe) *5ème cru classé Pauillac*
1995 IB £145.00 (FA)
1995 EC £120.00 (NEW) £130.00 (BUT)
1993 £18.50 (POR)
1991 £19.92 (PLA)
1990 £15.86 (FLE) £30.50 (JON)
1990 IB £254.00 (BIB)
1989 £21.54 (WAT) £25.50 (BEN)
1988 £23.50 (WY)
1986 £37.21 (WY)
1986 IB £200.00 (FA)
1985 £26.95 (ROB) £35.25 (WY)
1985 IB £273.00 (BIB)
1981 £19.95 (LEA)
1979 £28.39 (WY)
1975 £26.04 (PEN)

MERCHANTS SPECIALIZING IN BORDEAUX
see Merchant Directory (page 413) for details

Virtually all merchants have some Bordeaux, but for better ranges: Adnams (AD), Averys of Bristol (AV), Bennetts (BEN), Berry Bros. & Rudd (BER), Bibendum (BIB), Bute Wines (BUT), Butlers Wine Cellar (BU), Anthony Byrne (BY), Châteaux Wines (CHA), Corney & Barrow (CB), Croque-en-Bouche (CRO), Direct Wine (DI), Eldridge Pope (EL), Farr Vintners (FA), Forth Wines (FOR), Gelston Castle, Goedhuis (GOE), Great Western Wine, Harveys (HAR), High Breck (HIG), Justerini & Brooks, Lay & Wheeler (LAY), Oddbins (OD), Thos. Peatling, Christopher Piper (PIP), Raeburn Fine Wines (RAE), Reid Wines (REI), T&W Wines (TW), Tanners (TAN), Thresher (THR), The Ubiquitous Chip (UB), Wine Society (WS), Peter Wylie (WY)

1970 £25.00 (BU) £26.50 (REI) £30.00 (VIG)
1966 £49.35 (WY)
1962 £45.00 (VIG)
1961 £129.25 (WY)
1955 £129.25 (WY)
1945 £223.25 (WY)

l'Arrosée *grand cru classé St-Émilion*
1995 EC £205.00 (BUT) £225.00 (WAT)
1994 £18.39 (LAY)
1994 IB £159.00 (RAE)
1994 EC £170.00 (BUT)
1993 £21.75 (HIC)
1990 £46.50 (ROB)
1989 IB £220.00 (GOE)
1988 £19.90 (CRO)
1986 £29.38 (FA)
1985 £39.00 (CRO) £51.41 (WY)

Ausone *1er grand cru classé St-Émilion*
1995 IB £1,150.00 (GOE)
1995 EC £935.00 (WAT) £950.00 (BUT)
1994 EC £600.00 (BUT)
1993 £51.40 (WAT) £69.00 (UN)
1993 IB £550.00 (BUT)
1990 IB £950.00 (BIB)
1989 IB £900.00 (FA) £900.00 (BIB)
  £910.00 (BUT)
1986 £97.50 (ROB)
1985 £87.14 (WY) £98.50 (ROB)
1985 IB £78.30 (FA) £835.00 (BUT)
1983 £70.00 (CRO) £83.35 (UB)
1982 IB £1,850.00 (FA) £2,050.00 (WY)
1979 £57.00 (CRO) £120.00 (ROB)
1978 £60.00 (REI)
1978 IB £770.00 (FA)
1970 £62.50 (REI)
1967 £75.00 (VIG)
1964 £141.98 (WY)
1964 IB £1,370.00 (FA)
1961 £259.48 (WY)
1961 IB £3,700.00 (FA)

Bahans-Haut-Brion *Graves*
1995 IB £195.00 (GOE)
1995 EC £175.00 (WAT)
1994 ½ bottle £7.88 (WAT)
1993 £13.51 (WAT)
1989 £31.73 (FA) £31.82 (WAT)
1989 IB £450.00 (BUT)
1988 £15.28 (FA)
1988 ½ bottle £11.50 (REI)
1986 £22.50 (BU)
1986 ½ bottle £11.75 (REI)
1985 £21.95 (BO)

de Barbe *Côtes de Bourg*
1989 £8.95 (BU)

Baret *Pessac-Léognan*
1993 £7.95 (WS) £8.75 (EL) £9.99 (HIG)
1991 £8.25 (BER)

Barreyres *cru bourgeois Haut-Médoc*
1959 £35.00 (REI)

Batailley *5ème cru classé Pauillac*
1995 EC £110.00 (HIG)
1994 £16.75 (DI)
1993 £11.95 (BER) £12.99 (FUL) £14.00
  (HIG) £14.50 (REI) £23.75 (ROB)
1990 £19.75 (BER)
1989 £27.19 (PLA)
1989 IB £185.00 (BIB)
1989 magnum £35.25 (HIG)
1989 double magnum £78.33 (HIG)
1988 magnum £35.25 (HIG)
1986 £20.95 (DI)
1986 IB £195.00 (BIB)
1985 £30.00 (RES)
1985 IB £240.00 (GOE)
1983 £22.50 (BU) £26.44 (WY)
1982 £63.00 (UB)
1982 magnum £53.50 (REI) £70.00 (ROB)
1982 imperial £240.00 (REI)
1975 double magnum £115.00 (REI)
1971 £16.50 (REI)
1970 £31.00 (CRO) £35.00 (VIG) £41.12
  (WY) £44.10 (TW)
1970 magnum £80.00 (RES)
1967 £9.40 (FA)
1966 £41.12 (WY)
1961 £76.37 (WY) £95.00 (RES) £95.00 (VIG)
1945 £195.00 (REI)

Beau-Séjour-Bécot *grand cru classé St-Émilion*
1995 IB £240.00 (GOE)
1995 EC £225.00 (WAT) £225.00 (TAN)
  £249.00 (LAY) £250.00 (BUT)
1994 £19.27 (LAY) £20.60 (TAN)

EC (ex-cellar) price per dozen, excl shipping, duty and VAT. IB (in bond) price per dozen, excl duty and VAT.
All other prices, per bottle incl VAT.

1994 EC £154.00 (MV) £175.00 (BUT)
1993 £29.50 (WR) £29.50 (BOT)
1989 £21.15 (BY)
1981 £35.00 (VIG)

Beau-Site *cru grand bourgeois exceptionnel St-Estèphe*
1993 £5.99 (NA) £10.55 (HAH)
1971 £29.37 (WY)

Beaumont *cru grand bourgeois Haut-Médoc*
1994 £8.76 (HA) £9.01 (FOR)
1993 £8.40 (WS) £8.79 (EL) £9.01 (FOR) £9.49 (FUL) £12.44 (PLA) £12.95 (NA)
1990 IB £140.00 (BUT)
1989 £12.95 (WRI) £12.95 (ROB)
1989 IB £140.00 (GOE)
1986 £15.25 (ROB) £17.30 (TAN)
1979 £19.95 (VIG)

Beausejour *Côtes de Castillon*
1995 £4.98 (LON)
1962 £26.50 (REI)

Beauséjour-Duffau-Lagarrosse *1er grand cru classé St-Émilion*
1992 £6.75 (WHI)
1990 IB £1,950.00 (FA)

Bédats-Bois-Montet *1ères Côtes de Bordeaux*
1990 £5.75 (GAL)

Bel-Air *Puisseguin-St-Émilion*
1993 £7.99 (SAT)
1986 £26.59 (NI)

Bel-Orme-Tronquoy-de-Lalande *cru grand bourgeois Haut-Médoc*
1978 £23.00 (CRO)

Belair *1ères Côtes de Blaye*
1994 £5.99 (NA)
1990 £6.75 (BU)

Belair *1er grand cru classé St-Émilion*
1990 £27.50 (WS) £32.25 (ROB)
1989 £33.69 (JON)
1989 IB £230.00 (BUT)
1985 £32.00 (WS) £42.50 (REI)
1985 IB £190.00 (BUT) £210.00 (GOE)
1983 £27.50 (BU)
1982 £27.50 (REI)
1981 £26.01 (BY)

de Belcier *Côtes de Castillon*
1992 £7.99 (AME)

Belgrave *5ème cru classé Haut-Médoc*
1994 £13.95 (SAI)
1985 £12.95 (BU) £21.50 (RES)
1970 £34.49 (TW)

Bellevue *grand cru classé St-Émilion*
1985 £22.50 (ROB)

Beychevelle *4ème cru classé St-Julien*
1995 IB £170.00 (FA)
1995 EC £165.00 (BUT)
1994 £21.95 (STA) £29.50 (NA) £30.25 (GN)
1994 IB £190.00 (WY)
1993 £18.11 (WY) £18.50 (ROB) £20.50 (UN)
1992 £17.02 (BY) £17.62 (WY)
1991 £16.95 (WRI) £18.95 (SAI) £19.60 (BY)
1990 £25.78 (BY) £35.25 (WY)
1990 IB £250.00 (FA) £275.00 (BIB)
1989 £27.99 (OD) £31.82 (WAT) £35.00 (REI) £37.50 (GAL) £39.50 (RES) £41.95 (ROB) £53.50 (UB)
1989 IB £295.00 (BIB)
1989 ½ bottle £23.50 (ROB)
1988 £29.95 (POR)
1988 IB £260.00 (BIB)
1986 £49.00 (PIP)
1985 £38.38 (HA) £49.95 (ROB)
1985 magnum £95.00 (ROB) £95.00 (RES)
1983 £28.20 (FA) £28.95 (POR) £29.18 (WAT) £29.50 (REI) £48.95 (ROB)
1983 IB £280.00 (GOE)
1983 magnum £64.62 (WY)
1982 £49.99 (JON) £54.64 (WAT) £60.00 (REI) £75.00 (RES) £75.00 (ROB) £81.96 (PLA)

1982 IB £440.00 (GOE) £580.00 (FA)
1982 magnum £111.63 (FA)
1981 £29.37 (WY) £29.95 (ROB) £35.00 (VIG)

1978 £23.50 (REI) £39.95 (WY) £47.95 (ROB)
1978 magnum £82.25 (WY)
1976 £24.50 (REI)
1976 ½ bottle £11.75 (REI)
1975 £37.75 (ROB)
1970 £42.57 (FA) £49.95 (RES)
1966 £37.50 (BU) £62.50 (ROB)
1966 ½ bottle £23.50 (WY)
1962 £45.00 (BU)
1961 £109.66 (WY)
1959 £88.12 (WY)
1953 £76.38 (FA)
1945 £628.62 (WY)
1922 ½ bottle £76.37 (WY)

le Bon-Pasteur *Pomerol*
1995 EC £205.00 (BUT)
1994 £20.10 (TAN)
1994 EC £180.00 (BUT)
1993 £18.50 (BER)
1992 £17.90 (GAL)
1990 IB £360.00 (FA)
1988 £32.50 (POR) £35.00 (RES)
1985 £43.00 (UB)
1985 IB £480.00 (BUT)

Bonnet *Bordeaux Supérieur*
1995 £6.75 (EL)
1994 £6.40 (FOR) £8.29 (SAT)
1993 £6.85 (NI) £6.99 (THR) £6.99 (WR) £6.99 (BOT)

le Boscq *cru bourgeois supérieur St-Estèphe*
1988 £11.95 (WS)

Bourgneuf-Vayron *Pomerol*
1995 EC £151.80 (TAN)
1990 £24.91 (NO)
1989 £21.91 (BY)
1988 £18.50 (NI) £20.95 (LAY)
1986 £21.99 (BO)
1979 £17.50 (BU)

de Bourgueneuf *Pomerol*
1992 £9.50 (BU)

Bouscaut *cru classé Pessac-Léognan*
1993 £15.49 (UN)
1990 £13.75 (WS)
1989 £12.85 (WS) £12.95 (RAE)
1988 £12.85 (WS) £13.50 (PLA)
1986 £12.95 (RAE)
1985 £19.95 (RES)

Branaire *4ème cru classé St-Julien*
1995 IB £175.00 (FA)
1995 EC £164.16 (TAN) £165.00 (BUT)
1994 IB £135.00 (FA) £158.00 (BIB)
1990 £25.00 (WS) £33.29 (WY)
1989 £32.95 (DI) £32.99 (OD) £33.67 (FOR) £38.00 (STA) £38.75 (HIC)
1989 IB £260.00 (FA) £270.00 (BIB)
1988 £27.80 (BY) £41.60 (UB)
1986 £19.99 (FUL)
1985 £21.50 (REI)
1983 £22.50 (BU)
1982 £29.38 (FA)
1978 IB £190.00 (FA) £210.00 (WY)
1970 £29.75 (REI) £32.00 (CRO) £38.77 (WY)
1962 £32.50 (REI)
1959 £72.95 (WY) £89.50 (REI)

Brane-Cantenac *2ème cru classé Margaux*
1994 IB £153.00 (RAE)
1990 £33.67 (FOR)
1990 IB £208.00 (BIB)
1989 £19.85 (RAE)
1989 IB £190.00 (GOE)
1988 £16.99 (RAE)
1985 magnum IB £250.00 (FA)
1983 £32.90 (WY)
1983 IB £270.00 (GOE)
1982 £28.50 (REI) £38.77 (WY) £46.25 (ROB) £48.99 (NI)
1982 magnum IB £350.00 (WY)
1981 £37.00 (NA)
1979 £19.97 (WY)
1978 £23.50 (WY)
1978 IB £240.00 (FA)
1975 magnum IB £250.00 (FA)
1971 £18.50 (BU)
1970 magnum £75.00 (ROB)
1967 £22.95 (RAE)
1966 £41.12 (WY) £50.00 (VIG)
1961 £56.40 (WY)
1955 £45.00 (BU)
1952 £88.12 (WY)
1948 £75.00 (VIG)

du Breuil *cru bourgeois supérieur Haut-Médoc*
1994 EC £65.00 (BUT)
1992 £9.76 (PLA)
1990 £9.90 (LON) £10.20 (TAN)

Cabannieux *Graves*
1994 £12.79 (NA)

Cadet-Piola *grand cru classé St-Émilion*
1989 £23.00 (BER)
1981 £30.00 (VIG)

Calon-Ségur *3ème cru classé St-Estèphe*
1995 IB £220.00 (GOE)
1995 EC £190.00 (WAT)
1993 £17.95 (SAI)
1990 £32.00 (BER) £33.68 (HA) £33.78
    (WY)
1990 IB £260.00 (FA) £343.00 (BIB)
1989 £27.50 (RES) £32.95 (ROB) £35.25
    (WY) £39.00 (UB)
1989 IB £275.00 (BIB)
1986 £27.00 (CRO)
1986 IB £240.00 (BIB)
1985 £32.90 (WY) £36.00 (NA)
1983 £32.50 (ROB)
1982 £53.85 (WY) £70.00 (ROB)
1982 IB £460.00 (FA)
1981 £16.50 (REI)
1970 £41.12 (WY)
1966 £47.00 (WY) £60.00 (VIG)
1964 £27.50 (BU)
1959 £45.00 (BU)
1957 £75.00 (VIG)
1955 £75.00 (REI)
1947 £140.00 (CRO)

de Camensac *5ème cru classé Haut-
    Médoc*
1988 £123.38 (FA)
1988 IB £140.00 (GOE)
1982 £25.00 (RES)
1970 £19.50 (REI)

Canon *1er grand cru classé St-Émilion*
1995 IB £225.00 (GOE)
1995 EC £215.00 (BUT) £249.00 (LAY)
1994 EC £200.00 (BUT)
1993 IB £180.00 (GOE)
1990 £28.20 (FA)
1989 £29.00 (RAE) £37.70 (WAT)
1989 IB £340.00 (GOE) £360.00 (BUT)
1987 £26.00 (RES)
1985 £38.00 (RES) £49.00 (PIP) £50.00
    (STA) £60.71 (PLA)
1983 £28.65 (REI) £45.00 (RES)
1982 £83.90 (BEN)
1982 IB £800.00 (BIB)
1981 £35.00 (RES)

Canon de Brem *Canon-Fronsac*
1995 EC £80.00 (BUT) £83.00 (MV)
1989 £10.49 (JON)

Canon-la-Gaffelière *grand cru classé St-
    Émilion*
1995 IB £240.00 (GOE)
1995 EC £248.00 (WAT) £350.00 (BUT)
1994 EC £305.00 (BUT)
1989 IB £215.00 (BUT)
1982 £18.50 (BU)
1979 £16.50 (BU)
1967 £40.00 (VIG)

Cantemerle *5ème cru classé Haut-Médoc*
1995 EC £120.00 (BUT)
1993 £15.50 (UN)
1992 £14.50 (NI) £14.95 (POR)
1990 £22.50 (HOG) £23.95 (ROB) £24.85
    (SOM) £24.95 (LEA) £31.00 (STA)
1990 IB £170.00 (FA) £205.00 (WY)
1989 £21.80 (FOR) £22.50 (HOG) £29.95
    (LEA)
1989 IB £230.00 (FA) £260.00 (BUT)
1988 £19.99 (NEW) £21.00 (BER) £22.03
    (ELL)
1985 £24.00 (HOG) £30.00 (ROB)
1983 £32.90 (WY)
1983 IB £230.00 (BIB)
1982 £39.95 (ROB)
1981 £15.27 (WY)
1979 £17.62 (WY) £22.95 (ROB)
1978 £18.50 (BU)
1978 IB £195.00 (WY)
1975 £13.75 (BU)
1970 £46.50 (UB)
1966 £29.37 (WY)
1955 £75.00 (REI)
1950 £65.00 (REI)

Cantenac-Brown *3ème cru classé
    Margaux*
1991 £18.70 (BY)
1990 IB £240.00 (GOE)
1989 £26.50 (ROB)
1989 IB £240.00 (GOE)
1988 £18.99 (FUL)
1961 £55.00 (REI)
1959 £85.00 (VIG)
1950 £48.50 (REI)

Cap-de-Faugères *Côtes de Castillon*
1994 ½ bottle £5.12 (HAL)

Cap-de-Mourlin *grand cru classé St-
    Émilion*
1993 £12.50 (GAL)
1992 £11.95 (BY)
1990 £20.95 (ROB)

Carbonnieux *cru classé Pessac-Léognan*
1990 £25.95 (ROB)
1988 IB £140.00 (GOE)
1986 £25.50 (REI)
1985 £21.95 (ROB)
1969 magnum £18.50 (REI)
1959 £99.87 (WY)

Cardeneau *Fronsac*
1989 £10.59 (NI) £12.10 (HAH)
1988 £9.95 (WS)

la Cardonne *cru grand bourgeois Médoc*
1992 £8.31 (HOG) £9.40 (FOR)
1991 £7.99 (HOG)
1988 £13.60 (PIP)

les Carmes-Haut-Brion *Pessac-Léognan*
1982 £51.70 (WY)

Caronne-Ste-Gemme *cru grand bourgeois exceptionnel Haut-Médoc*
1993 £8.95 (EL) £9.15 (HAH) £9.44 (HOG)
1987 ½ bottle £4.95 (ROB)
1986 £9.95 (AME)
1982 £14.00 (CRO)
1979 £13.50 (REI)

Carruades de Lafite (Moulin des Carruades until 1987) *Pauillac*
1995 IB £145.00 (FA)
1995 EC £165.00 (BUT) £175.00 (HIG)
1992 £14.06 (BY) £18.95 (NA) £26.44 (PLA)
1991 £18.27 (BY)
1989 £20.07 (WAT) £35.18 (PLA)
1989 IB £160.00 (BUT)
1988 £29.95 (DI)
1988 IB £140.00 (BUT)
1987 £18.00 (BU)
1986 IB £300.00 (BUT)
1955 £95.00 (REI)

Carteau-Côtes-Daugay *grand cru St-Émilion*
1990 £12.50 (WS)

Castéra *cru bourgeois Médoc*
1996 £4.49 (SAF)

Certan-de-May *Pomerol*
1995 EC £395.00 (BUT) £399.00 (WAT)
1994 IB £250.00 (FA)
1994 EC £250.00 (BUT)
1993 £24.95 (LAY)
1993 IB £225.00 (BUT)

1992 £23.50 (WS) £31.50 (REI)
1991 £21.00 (MV)
1988 IB £305.00 (BUT)
1987 £32.95 (ROB)
1986 IB £400.00 (GOE)
1983 £32.50 (REI) £42.54 (FA)
1982 IB £2,200.00 (FA)
1981 £80.00 (RES)
1979 £68.50 (BEN)

Certan-Giraud *Pomerol*
1994 £21.50 (STA)
1989 £22.50 (REI)

Charron *Ières Côtes de Blaye*
1993 £7.39 (PLA)

Chasse-Spleen *cru grand bourgeois exceptionnel Moulis*
1995 IB £139.00 (GOE)
1995 EC £135.00 (BUT) £140.00 (WAT)
1994 £24.30 (PIP)
1994 EC £115.00 (BUT)
1994 magnum £28.20 (WAT)
1993 £12.53 (WAT) £15.25 (BER)
1990 £25.00 (NI) £26.70 (TAN)
1990 IB £250.00 (BUT)
1989 £24.80 (NO) £35.00 (ROB)
1989 IB £310.00 (WY)
1988 £21.95 (LAY)
1987 £12.85 (REI)
1986 £21.39 (JON) £25.00 (CRO)
1985 £19.05 (JON) £20.00 (CRO) £22.52 (WAT)
1983 £22.00 (CRO)
1982 £25.40 (JON) £32.80 (WY) £32.95 (RES)
1982 IB £310.00 (FA)
1981 £17.50 (REI)
1978 £29.00 (CRO) £32.00 (ROB)
1975 £33.00 (CRO)
1961 £75.00 (VIG)

Chauvin *grand cru classé St-Émilion*
1990 IB £190.00 (GOE)

Cheret-Pitres *Graves*
1994 £7.50 (ROS)
1993 £7.46 (CHA)
1990 £9.95 (WS) £10.00 (CHA)

All châteaux are listed alphabetically regardless of class.

Cheval-Blanc *1er grand cru classé St-Émilion*
1995 EC £955.00 (WAT) £990.00 (BUT)
1994 £99.88 (PEN)
1994 EC £695.00 (BUT)
1994 ½ bottle £28.59 (WAT)
1994 magnum £114.36 (WAT)
1993 £44.74 (LAY) £47.00 (AV) £48.76 (WAT) £63.00 (BY)
1993 IB £565.00 (WY) £600.00 (BUT)
1990 £282.00 (WAT) £410.00 (ROB)
1990 IB £2,750.00 (FA)
1990 magnum IB £2,750.00 (FA)
1989 £105.75 (BEN)
1989 IB £1,020.00 (FA) £1,075.00 (BUT) £1,100.00 (BIB)
1989 magnum £198.77 (WY)
1989 magnum IB £1,020.00 (FA)
1988 £84.70 (WY) £120.00 (RES)
1988 magnum £185.00 (RES)
1986 £123.37 (WY) £145.00 (ROB)
1986 IB £1,075.00 (BIB) £1,145.00 (FA)
1985 £150.00 (UB) £150.79 (WY) £175.00 (RES) £195.00 (DI) £225.00 (ROB)
1985 IB £1,300.00 (GOE) £1,450.00 (BIB)
1984 £53.00 (UN)
1983 £145.00 (REI) £162.15 (WY)
1983 IB £1,550.00 (FA)
1983 magnum IB £1,600.00 (WY)
1982 £420.00 (REI) £448.45 (WAT) £458.25 (WY) £665.00 (ROB) £931.78 (FA)
1982 IB £4,200.00 (BIB)
1981 £85.77 (WY)
1981 ½ bottle £49.50 (ROB)
1979 £82.80 (HA)
1979 magnum £215.42 (WY)
1978 £103.40 (WY) £130.00 (ROB)
1978 IB £870.00 (FA)
1978 magnum £246.75 (WY)
1975 £125.00 (REI)
1975 IB £1,120.00 (FA)
1970 £139.82 (WY) £157.00 (ROB)
1970 IB £1,270.00 (FA) £1,350.00 (BIB)
1967 £90.00 (VIG)
1966 IB £2,050.00 (FA)
1964 £275.00 (BEN) £295.00 (VIG)
1962 £120.00 (REI)
1959 £245.00 (REI)
1955 IB £5,150.00 (FA)
1953 £123.38 (FA) £220.00 (REI)
1953 magnum £987.00 (WY)
1952 £125.00 (REI)
1949 £276.12 (WY)
1947 IB £2,250.00 (FA)
1945 £446.50 (WY)

Cheval-Noir *St-Émilion*
1989 £9.65 (WAT)

Chicane *Graves*
1994 £8.60 (TAN)
1991 £9.95 (VIG)

Cissac *cru grand bourgeois exceptionnel Haut-Médoc*
1995 EC £90.00 (BUT) £94.92 (TAN)
1994 £13.00 (TAN) £13.18 (AV)
1994 EC £85.00 (BUT)
1993 £11.25 (HIC) £12.10 (EL)
1992 £7.99 (CO) £11.29 (AV) £11.79 (PLA)
1990 £11.99 (HA) £13.50 (WRI) £13.55 (JON) £13.75 (LON) £14.31 (AV) £17.40 (TAN)
1989 £12.99 (JON) £13.50 (REI) £13.75 (LON) £13.90 (GAL) £14.25 (WRI)
1988 £14.30 (TAN) £14.75 (EL)
1988 magnum £35.00 (RES)
1987 £10.80 (TAN)
1986 £11.99 (CO) £14.25 (JON) £15.50 (WRI) £16.60 (TAN) £18.50 (RES)
1985 £13.25 (WRI) £14.92 (LON)
1984 £10.99 (JON)
1983 £14.50 (REI)
1982 £23.01 (WAT)
1981 £14.50 (REI) £14.50 (BU)
1981 magnum £40.80 (PLA)
1978 £23.00 (CRO)
1975 £18.00 (CRO)
1970 magnum £48.07 (EL) £55.00 (RES)
1964 £30.00 (VIG)

Citran *cru grand bourgeois exceptionnel Haut-Médoc*
1967 £14.50 (BU)

Clarke *cru bourgeois Listrac*
1993 £9.95 (ROB)
1989 £18.50 (ROB)
1988 £11.63 (PEN) £14.95 (ROB)
1983 £22.50 (ROB)

la Claverie *Côtes de Francs*
1988 £10.50 (PIP)

Clerc-Milon *5ème cru classé Pauillac*
1995 EC £185.00 (BUT) £185.00 (WAT)
1994 £21.50 (DI)
1993 £15.18 (WAT)
1992 £17.95 (POR)
1988 £24.28 (WAT)
1985 £35.25 (WY)
1982 £20.50 (FLE) £35.74 (WAT)

Clinet *Pomerol*
1995 IB £800.00 (FA) £895.00 (BIB)
1995 EC £848.00 (WAT) £980.00 (BUT)
1994 £56.30 (WAT)
1994 IB £550.00 (GOE) £665.00 (WY)
1993 IB £375.00 (WY)
1992 £28.20 (WY) £29.50 (REI) £34.95 (ROB)
1990 £90.00 (ROB)
1989 IB £2,000.00 (FA)
1985 £39.50 (RES)
1982 £58.75 (WY)

Clos Beauregard *Pomerol*
1994 £11.53 (LON)

Clos de l'Eglise *Lalande-de-Pomerol*
1991 £14.50 (BY)
1987 £13.99 (MAR)

Clos des Jacobins *grand cru classé St-Émilion*
1989 £19.49 (BO)

Clos du Clocher *Pomerol*
1995 EC £125.00 (BUT) £148.00 (WAT)
1994 £14.68 (WAT)
1994 EC £120.00 (BUT)
1993 £14.20 (WAT)
1992 £13.58 (ROS)
1983 £18.50 (REI)

Clos du Marquis *St-Julien*
1995 EC £160.00 (WAT) £160.00 (BUT) £174.00 (LAY)
1994 £15.16 (LAY)
1993 £21.95 (LEA)
1992 £14.37 (BY) £15.95 (LEA) £17.75 (ROB)
1990 £27.40 (TAN) £32.50 (ROB)
1989 £20.36 (WAT) £25.20 (STA) £25.95 (ROB)
1989 IB £180.00 (GOE) £210.00 (BUT)
1988 IB £195.00 (BUT)
1987 £13.99 (JON)
1986 £23.01 (WAT) £28.95 (ROB)
1983 £27.50 (ROB)
1978 £33.95 (ROB)

Clos Fourtet *1er grand cru classé St-Émilion*
1993 £17.14 (LAY)
1989 £27.10 (BER)
1988 £28.40 (PIP)
1982 £23.36 (WAT) £25.46 (WY)
1962 £31.50 (REI)
1955 £35.00 (REI)

Clos René *Pomerol*
1995 EC £130.00 (BUT) £134.88 (TAN)
1982 £32.90 (WY)
1978 £33.00 (CRO)
1970 £17.50 (REI)

la Clotte *grand cru classé St-Émilion*
1989 £20.95 (HAH)

Connétable Talbot *St-Julien*
1993 £12.95 (LEA)
1990 £19.99 (MAR)
1989 £15.09 (JON)
1982 £27.50 (REI)

la Conseillante *Pomerol*
1995 IB £490.00 (GOE)
1995 EC £460.00 (BUT) £485.00 (WAT)
1994 £35.05 (WAT) £37.50 (LAY) £58.75 (PEN)
1994 IB £340.00 (GOE)
1994 EC £345.00 (BUT)
1993 £26.24 (WAT)
1993 IB £275.00 (RES) £325.00 (BUT)
1992 £24.50 (REI) £35.10 (BY)
1990 IB £1,300.00 (BIB) £1,320.00 (FA)
1989 £125.82 (WAT)
1989 IB £1,270.00 (BUT) £1,270.00 (FA)
1988 £39.16 (AV)
1986 £44.65 (FA)
1986 IB £440.00 (GOE)
1985 £65.62 (AV)
1982 IB £1,320.00 (FA)
1982 magnum £264.38 (FA)
1979 £35.25 (FA)
1978 IB £370.00 (FA)
1961 £293.75 (FA)
1943 £120.00 (REI)

Cos d'Estournel *2ème cru classé St-Estèphe*
1995 EC £315.00 (WAT) £375.00 (BUT)
1994 IB £255.00 (FA)
1994 EC £300.00 (BUT)
1994 magnum £51.70 (WAT)
1993 £24.28 (WAT) £24.50 (UN) £24.68 (BER) £25.00 (GAL) £39.50 (LAY)
1993 IB £220.00 (GOE) £220.00 (BUT)
1992 £25.57 (BY)
1991 £28.00 (BER)
1991 IB £180.00 (GOE)
1990 £48.15 (TAN) £52.00 (REI) £65.75 (ROB) £85.95 (NI)

1990 IB £505.00 (FA) £565.00 (WY)
1990 magnum £97.00 (HIG)
1989 £38.67 (WAT) £38.78 (FA) £42.59 (WY) £54.75 (LAY) £59.38 (FOR)
1989 IB £450.00 (BIB) £520.00 (BUT)
1988 £31.75 (STA) £41.50 (REI) £47.50 (LAY)
1988 IB £340.00 (GOE)
1987 £23.50 (RES)
1986 £63.16 (WAT) £75.00 (RES)
1986 IB £640.00 (FA) £650.00 (BUT) £650.00 (BIB) £700.00 (WY)
1986 jeroboam £393.63 (FA)
1985 £70.50 (WY) £79.50 (LAY)
1985 IB £640.00 (FA)
1985 magnum £145.00 (RES)
1984 magnum £27.50 (BU)
1983 £27.50 (BU) £38.00 (WS) £41.00 (STA) £41.61 (WY) £45.00 (RES)
1983 IB £450.00 (GOE)
1982 £88.00 (JON) £110.00 (BEN) £110.16 (WAT) £123.37 (WY)
1982 IB £1,100.00 (GOE) £1,120.00 (FA)
1982 magnum £235.00 (WY)
1981 £31.82 (WY)
1979 £29.37 (WY)
1979 IB £310.00 (FA)
1978 £44.06 (WY) £47.49 (WAT)
1978 IB £410.00 (FA)
1975 £38.77 (WY)
1970 £44.00 (CRO) £58.75 (WY)
1970 IB £720.00 (BUT)
1961 magnum £305.50 (FA)
1957 £75.00 (VIG)
1955 £95.47 (WY)
1955 IB £920.00 (FA)
1947 £175.00 (REI)

Cos Labory 5ème cru classé St-Estèphe
1993 £15.20 (PIP)
1986 £14.75 (WRI) £20.75 (STA)
1970 £16.50 (REI)

Coufran cru grand bourgeois Haut-Médoc
1994 £11.28 (ROS)
1982 £27.95 (RES)
1975 £14.50 (REI)
1973 £7.50 (REI) £10.75 (BU)
1970 £22.50 (BU)

Couvent-des-Jacobins grand cru classé St-Émilion
1993 £16.75 (BER)
1989 £21.95 (STA)
1988 £24.50 (ROB)

le Crock cru grand bourgeois exceptionnel St-Estèphe
1994 IB £99.00 (RAE)
1993 £11.39 (PLA)
1991 £9.95 (BER)
1990 IB £140.00 (GOE)

la Croix Pomerol
1993 £22.43 (NO)
1989 £39.60 (NO)

la Croix-de-Gay Pomerol
1989 £26.50 (TAN) £28.50 (ROB)
1985 £43.00 (UB)
1973 £11.75 (BU)

la Croix-de-Pez St-Estèphe
1990 £10.58 (FLE)

la Croix-des-Moines Lalande-de-Pomerol
1992 £9.99 (RAE)
1990 £12.99 (JON) £14.80 (BER) £15.40 (UB)

la Croix-du-Casse Pomerol
1995 IB £145.00 (FA)
1995 EC £168.00 (WAT)
1994 £16.92 (LAY)
1988 £29.95 (RES)

Croizet-Bages 5ème cru classé Pauillac
1989 £23.25 (STA)
1982 £33.06 (BY)
1970 £22.50 (REI)

Croque-Michotte grand cru classé St-Émilion
1970 £18.00 (BU)

Curé-Bon-la-Madeleine grand cru classé St-Émilion
1989 £27.26 (TW)

la Dame de Montrose St-Estèphe
1992 £14.82 (BY)
1990 £51.95 (ROB)

Dassault grand cru classé St-Émilion
1993 £17.95 (VIG)

Stars (★) indicate wines selected by Oz Clarke in the Best Buys section which begins on page 12.

de la Dauphine *Fronsac*
1995 EC £95.00 (BUT)
1989 £11.79 (JON)

Dauzac *5ème cru classé Margaux*
1988 £15.50 (WRI)
1982 £33.38 (PLA)

Desmirail *3ème cru classé Margaux*
1990 £16.99 (HIG)
1989 £13.95 (RAE)
1988 £12.95 (RAE)

Deyrem-Valentin *cru bourgeois Margaux*
1994 £12.80 (STA)

Domaine de Chevalier *cru classé*
  Pessac-Léognan
1995 EC £190.00 (BUT)
1994 IB £175.00 (BIB)
1994 EC £175.00 (BUT)
1993 IB £162.00 (RAE) £165.00 (BUT)
1992 £21.75 (ROB)
1991 £17.95 (RAE)
1990 £25.99 (OD)
1990 ½ bottle £17.67 (HAL)
1989 £29.00 (RAE)
1989 IB £300.00 (GOE) £330.00 (BUT)
1988 £29.99 (OD)
1985 £34.99 (OD) £37.50 (BER)
1985 IB £330.00 (FA)
1983 £29.50 (CRO) £79.00 (LEA)
1983 IB £300.00 (GOE)
1982 £49.50 (AD) £70.50 (TW)
1982 IB £340.00 (FA) £450.00 (GOE)
1981 £33.50 (REI)
1979 IB £275.00 (FA)
1975 £24.50 (REI) £35.00 (BU)
1975 IB £230.00 (FA)
1966 £58.00 (CRO)
1961 £112.00 (REI)

Domaine de Curebourse *Margaux*
1989 £12.50 (WS)

Domaine de Dupeyrat *1ères Côtes de*
  Blaye
1993 £6.95 (SAT)

Domaine de l'Eglise *Pomerol*
1994 £18.95 (DI)
1989 £26.73 (PLA)
1988 £23.20 (TAN)
1986 £22.50 (REI)
1982 £30.00 (RES)

Domaine la Grave *Graves*
1993 £7.99 (HIG)

la Dominique *grand cru classé St-Émilion*
1995 IB £245.00 (BIB)
1995 EC £255.00 (WAT) £260.00 (BUT)
1994 IB £253.00 (BIB)
1994 EC £250.00 (BUT)
1989 IB £390.00 (FA)
1955 £38.77 (WY)

Ducluzeau *cru bourgeois Listrac*
1993 £9.95 (AD)
1990 £10.30 (NI)

Ducru-Beaucaillou *2ème cru classé St-*
  Julien
1995 EC £335.00 (WAT) £396.00 (LAY)
  £400.00 (BUT)
1994 £28.50 (DI)
1994 EC £320.00 (BUT)
1994 ½ bottle £13.41 (WAT)
1994 magnum £53.66 (WAT)
1993 £19.45 (BER) £21.05 (WY) £22.89
  (BY) £23.30 (WAT) £24.50 (UN)
1992 £20.93 (BY)
1990 £29.95 (RAE) £32.80 (WY) £37.50 (REI)
1990 IB £413.00 (BIB)
1990 ½ bottle £19.00 (REI)

1989 £38.68 (WAT) £39.95 (RES)
1989 IB £350.00 (BUT) £415.00 (WY)
1989 imperial £229.13 (FA)
1988 £25.50 (RAE) £33.50 (LAY) £33.78
  (WAT) £37.50 (RES) £38.06 (PLA)
1988 IB £900.00 (BUT)
1986 £47.85 (DI) £65.00 (RES)
1986 IB £390.00 (GOE) £450.00 (BIB)
  £460.00 (FA) £490.00 (BUT) £510.00 (WY)
1986 magnum IB £460.00 (FA)
1985 £32.99 (OD) £42.50 (REI) £45.00
  (BER) £47.49 (WY) £69.70 (UB)
1985 IB £440.00 (GOE) £460.00 (FA)
1983 £35.00 (REI) £36.03 (WAT) £41.13
  (WY) £48.95 (STA)
1983 IB £340.00 (GOE) £350.00 (FA)

1983 magnum £65.00 (RES)
1983 jeroboam £300.00 (REI)
1982 £60.00 (RES) £62.09 (NO) £81.27
  (WAT) £81.50 (BEN) £92.70 (TAN)
1982 IB £820.00 (FA) £840.00 (GOE)
1982 ½ bottle IB £950.00 (WY)
1982 double magnum £528.75 (WY)
1982 imperial £787.25 (FA)
1981 double magnum £134.50 (REI)
1979 £31.33 (WAT) £32.50 (REI)
1978 £46.02 (WY) £48.00 (PIP) £55.00 (RES)
1978 IB £405.00 (FA)
1976 £32.50 (REI) £40.00 (VIG)
1975 £33.50 (REI) £41.12 (WY)
1975 magnum £67.50 (REI)
1970 £68.15 (WY) £79.00 (CRO) £85.00
  (BEN) £115.00 (LEA) £125.00 (VIG)
1970 IB £800.00 (FA)
1970 magnum IB £870.00 (FA)
1967 £40.00 (VIG)
1967 ½ bottle £25.00 (VIG)
1967 magnum £75.00 (VIG)
1966 £60.00 (BU)
1964 £57.77 (WY)
1964 IB £540.00 (FA)
1961 £220.00 (CRO)
1961 IB £2,250.00 (FA)
1949 £250.00 (REI)

Duhart-Milon-Rothschild *4ème cru*
  classé Pauillac
1995 EC £152.00 (WAT)
1993 £19.50 (UN)
1990 £28.95 (BEN)
1989 £37.50 (FOR)
1985 £39.50 (PIP) £70.00 (VIG)
1985 IB £350.00 (GOE)
1982 £30.00 (VIG)

Durand-Laplagne *Puisseguin-St-Émilion*
1994 £6.95 (AD)

Durfort-Vivens *2ème cru classé Margaux*
1994 £19.75 (STA)
1989 £22.50 (FOR) £32.25 (HA)
1982 £29.50 (RES)
1970 £25.99 (RAE)

l'Église-Clinet *Pomerol*
1995 IB £1,100.00 (FA) £1,300.00 (BIB)
1995 EC £1,400.00 (BUT) £1,500.00
  (WAT)
1994 £48.76 (WAT)
1994 EC £590.00 (BUT)
1993 £35.00 (BER)

1989 IB £600.00 (FA) £625.00 (BUT)
1988 IB £370.00 (FA)
1985 IB £1,340.00 (FA)
1983 £39.50 (RES)
1983 IB £405.00 (FA)
1982 £65.00 (RES)
1982 IB £760.00 (FA)

l'Enclos *Pomerol*
1995 EC £117.00 (NEW)
1994 £14.00 (TAN) £19.00 (STA)
1993 £24.50 (ROB)
1992 £15.00 (PIP)
1990 £39.85 (ROB)
1983 £29.75 (ROB)
1970 £12.50 (BU)

l'Ermitage de Chasse-Spleen *Haut-*
  Médoc
1993 £8.95 (FOR) £10.50 (CHA)
1991 £8.95 (FOR)

l'Escadre *1ères Côtes de Blaye*
1994 £5.38 (HOG)

l'Estage Simon *Haut-Médoc*
★ **1990** £9.95 (WS)

l'Etoile *Graves*
1994 £5.70 (TAN) £6.80 (AD)

l'Évangile *Pomerol*
1995 IB £800.00 (FA) £990.00 (GOE)
1995 EC £805.00 (WAT) £850.00 (BUT)
1994 £55.62 (WAT) £67.50 (LAY)
1994 IB £500.00 (GOE)
1994 EC £630.00 (BUT)
1993 £38.97 (WAT)
1993 IB £375.00 (RES)
1992 £22.81 (BY)
1992 IB £210.00 (FA)
1990 IB £1,270.00 (FA)
1986 £50.00 (RES)
1986 IB £370.00 (FA)
1985 IB £900.00 (FA) £950.00 (BUT)
1983 £41.75 (TAN)
1982 IB £1,950.00 (FA)
1952 £125.00 (REI)

Ferrande *Graves*
1978 £14.75 (BU)
1975 £12.75 (BU)

Ferrière *3ème cru classé Margaux*
1993 £16.95 (SAI)

Feytit-Clinet *Pomerol*
1990 £28.50 (POR)
1988 £18.15 (AD) £18.59 (JON)
1986 £15.95 (AD)
1982 £30.00 (REI)

les Fiefs-de-Lagrange *St-Julien*
1995 EC £84.30 (GAL)
1994 £17.95 (NA)
1993 £10.99 (AME) £12.87 (DOM) £13.50
   (BU)
1992 £13.95 (ROB)
1989 £13.98 (HOG) £20.99 (BO)
1986 £21.50 (ROB)

de Fieuzal *cru classé Pessac-Léognan*
1995 EC £165.00 (BUT)
1994 £18.50 (TAN)
1994 EC £160.00 (BUT)
1993 £12.93 (FA) £13.20 (TAN)
1993 IB £135.00 (BUT)
1990 £24.95 (BER)
1990 IB £240.00 (GOE)
1990 ½ bottle £13.83 (HAL)
1989 IB £185.00 (BUT) £200.00 (GOE)
1988 IB £180.00 (GOE)
1986 £20.50 (REI)

Figeac *1er grand cru classé St-Émilion*
1995 EC £296.00 (MV) £300.00 (BUT)
1994 £14.77 (NO)
1994 EC £275.00 (BUT)
1993 £16.13 (NO)
1989 £38.00 (STA) £44.15 (FOR)
1989 IB £260.00 (BUT)
1988 IB £385.00 (BIB)
1986 magnum £82.25 (FA)
1985 £49.50 (POR) £58.00 (STA)
1983 IB £385.00 (FA)
1982 £99.00 (VIG) £109.27 (WY)
1982 IB £880.00 (GOE) £970.00 (FA)
1982 magnum IB £970.00 (FA)
1978 £32.50 (REI)
1976 £28.50 (REI) £47.00 (WY)
1975 £84.60 (WY) £125.00 (ROB)
1971 magnum £89.50 (REI)
1970 £90.00 (ROB) £95.00 (RES)
1970 IB £720.00 (FA)
1966 £92.04 (WY)
1959 £120.00 (REI)

la Fleur-Pétrus *Pomerol*
1995 EC £420.00 (LAY)
1994 EC £470.00 (BUT)
1993 £28.50 (LAY)

1993 IB £285.00 (BUT)
1987 £64.62 (WY)
1982 £175.00 (RES)
1978 £49.50 (REI)
1978 IB £310.00 (FA)
1970 £130.00 (ROB)
1947 £225.00 (ROB)

Fombrauge *grand cru St-Émilion*
1993 £13.50 (BER)
1966 £14.50 (REI)

Fonbadet *cru bourgeois supérieur Pauillac*
1991 £12.00 (BER)
1983 £12.50 (HOG)

Fonpiqueyre *cru bourgeois Haut-Médoc*
1978 £14.50 (CRO)

Fonplégade *grand cru classé St-Émilion*
1989 £17.95 (RES)
1988 £19.75 (SAT)
1967 £12.75 (BU)

Fonréaud *cru bourgeois Listrac*
1993 £8.67 (HA)
1966 £20.00 (BU)

Fonroque *grand cru classé St-Émilion*
1989 £19.99 (JON)

les Forts-de-Latour *Pauillac*
1994 £16.44 (HA)
1994 IB £190.00 (WY)
1994 EC £220.00 (BUT)
1993 £22.91 (BY)
1991 £19.20 (PIP) £19.75 (RAE) £22.75
   (ROB) £24.46 (BY)
1990 IB £500.00 (BUT) £540.00 (FA)
1988 £22.03 (WY) £26.90 (BY) £30.80 (NI)
1987 £22.81 (BY)
1983 £23.50 (PEN) £28.50 (REI)
1982 £90.00 (ROB)
1979 £21.70 (CRO) £33.95 (ROB)
1975 £47.98 (WY)
1973 £18.50 (REI)
1970 £59.93 (FA)

Fourcas-Dupré *cru grand bourgeois*
   exceptionnel Listrac
1990 £11.55 (FOR) £12.34 (SOM) £13.28
   (HA) £13.95 (RES) £14.50 (BEN)
1989 £12.25 (WHI) £12.50 (WS) £13.60
   (PIP) £16.75 (ROB)
1983 £13.00 (CRO)

Fourcas-Hosten *cru grand bourgeois exceptionnel Listrac*
1994 £10.50 (STA)
1993 £9.50 (HIG) £10.55 (HAH) £11.86 (AV)
1990 £12.50 (WRI)
1989 £14.10 (BER) £14.95 (ROB)

de Francs *Côtes de Francs*
1993 £6.99 (WR) £6.99 (THR) £6.99 (BOT)
1990 £12.95 (ROB)

la Gaffelière *1er grand cru classé St-Émilion*
1994 IB £156.00 (RAE) £180.00 (GOE)
1989 £23.00 (UB) £31.50 (ROB)
1970 £40.00 (RES)
1962 £32.50 (REI)

la Garde *Pessac-Léognan*
1995 EC £93.00 (WAT)
1993 £5.75 (BU)

le Gay *Pomerol*
1994 EC £135.00 (MV)
1993 £17.50 (MV)
1985 £31.72 (WY)
1971 £76.37 (WY)
1970 £21.50 (REI)

Gazin *Pomerol*
1995 EC £350.00 (BUT)
1994 EC £240.00 (BUT)
1993 £16.16 (MV) £19.50 (WS) £25.95 (LEA)
1993 IB £170.00 (BUT)
1992 £17.99 (FUL)
1989 IB £345.00 (BUT)
1988 £36.00 (NI)
1983 £37.00 (UB)
1966 £27.50 (REI)

Giscours *3ème cru classé Margaux*
1989 £29.86 (WY) £42.89 (PLA)
1986 IB £240.00 (BIB)
1985 £35.20 (NI)
1982 £38.97 (WAT) £43.08 (WY)
1981 £22.00 (CRO)
1978 £50.00 (ROB) £52.87 (WY)
1976 £20.00 (VIG)
1975 IB £420.00 (GOE)
1970 £80.29 (WY) £87.50 (LEA)
1970 IB £845.00 (FA) £850.00 (GOE)
1966 £52.50 (REI) £76.37 (WY)
1959 £85.00 (REI) £152.75 (WY)

du Glana *cru grand bourgeois exceptionnel St-Julien*
1975 £16.43 (PLA)

Gloria *cru bourgeois St-Julien*
1994 £19.40 (PIP)
1993 £15.99 (EL)
1990 £18.56 (CHA) £23.42 (HOG)
1989 £18.90 (BER) £25.95 (ROB)
1987 £19.95 (RES)
1986 £41.70 (UB)
1985 £28.67 (BY)
1983 £18.50 (BU) £35.00 (RES)
1983 IB £195.00 (BIB)
1983 magnum £52.00 (ROB)
1982 £29.38 (FA)
1964 £18.00 (BU) £40.00 (VIG)

Grand-Corbin *grand cru classé St-Émilion*
1993 £13.99 (GN)
1990 £17.99 (AME)
1970 £22.50 (BU)

Grand-Lartigue *St-Émilion*
1993 £9.95 (STA) £9.99 (UN)
1992 £8.89 (BO) £9.99 (UN)

Grand-Mayne *grand cru classé St-Émilion*
1995 EC £195.00 (BUT) £222.96 (TAN)
1994 £23.95 (LAY)
1994 EC £145.00 (BUT)
1993 £17.14 (HIG)

Grand-Pey-Lescours *St-Émilion*
1994 £8.97 (ROS)

Grand-Pontet *grand cru classé St-Émilion*
1989 £21.50 (ROB)
1962 £25.00 (BU)

Grand-Puy-Ducasse *5ème cru classé Pauillac*
1995 EC £122.00 (WAT)
1994 magnum £26.63 (WAT)
1993 £14.99 (BOD) £14.99 (SUN)

EC (ex-cellar) price per dozen, excl shipping, duty and VAT. *IB* (in bond) price per dozen, excl duty and VAT.
All other prices, per bottle incl VAT.

1990 £36.25 (STA)
1989 £18.60 (WAT) £22.50 (HOG)
1989 IB £180.00 (GOE)
1985 £22.50 (BU)
1983 £21.95 (POR)
1978 £32.95 (NI)
1966 £35.25 (WY)
1961 £54.05 (WY) £55.00 (REI)
1957 £65.00 (REI)

Grand-Puy-Lacoste *5ème cru classé*
  Pauillac
1995 IB £250.00 (GOE)
1995 EC £178.32 (TAN) £190.00 (WAT)
1994 £17.95 (DI) £27.39 (GN)
1994 IB £135.00 (FA)
1993 £16.85 (BY) £18.80 (WY) £18.90 (GAL)
1992 £13.50 (WS) £14.58 (BY) £16.95 (LEA)
1991 £18.61 (BY) £20.27 (SOM)
1990 £32.95 (LAY) £42.45 (ROB)
1989 £41.24 (NO)
1989 IB £250.00 (FA) £260.00 (BUT)
  £260.00 (GOE)
1988 £16.30 (RAE) £26.50 (REI) £28.95 (AD)
1988 IB £250.00 (GOE)
1986 £32.50 (REI) £36.99 (JON)
1985 £35.25 (WY)
1983 £27.50 (BU) £32.50 (HOG) £32.80 (WY)
1982 £41.12 (HA) £73.50 (BEN)
1982 IB £550.00 (GOE) £740.00 (FA)
1979 £23.50 (REI)
1978 £33.29 (WY) £40.00 (CRO)
1975 £45.00 (ROB)
1970 £54.00 (CRO) £81.90 (UB)
1964 £45.00 (VIG)
1961 £92.00 (CRO)

de la Grave *Côtes de Bourg*
1994 £4.95 (WS)

la Grave-Figeac *grand cru St-Émilion*
1994 £11.95 (LEA)

la Grave-Trigant-de-Boisset *Pomerol*
1990 £35.25 (WY)
1970 £32.50 (REI)

Gravet *grand cru St-Émilion*
1990 £9.00 (FOR) £9.50 (BU) .
1989 £9.20 (FOR)

Gressier-Grand-Poujeaux *cru*
  bourgeois supérieur Moulis
1993 £12.55 (DI)
1989 £28.00 (NI)
1986 £18.92 (SOM)

Greysac *cru grand bourgeois Médoc*
1993 £6.72 (HOG) £8.95 (POR) £8.95 (ROB)
1990 £12.99 (OD)

Gros-Caillou *St-Estèphe*
1994 £7.29 (NEW)

Gruaud-Larose *2ème cru classé St-Julien*
1994 IB £190.00 (FA)
1993 £24.00 (UN) £27.62 (NO)
1993 IB £175.00 (FA)
1993 ½ bottle IB £180.00 (FA)
1993 magnum IB £175.00 (FA)
1992 £16.99 (FUL) £19.45 (WR)
1992 IB £120.00 (FA)
1992 ½ bottle IB £125.00 (FA)
1991 £19.00 (BER) £24.99 (BOT)
1991 IB £145.00 (FA)
1990 £31.73 (PEN) £35.95 (BOT) £35.95
  (ROB) £35.95 (WR) £41.17 (HA) £47.00
  (TW) £48.00 (BER)
1990 IB £290.00 (GOE)
1989 £28.99 (JON) £33.95 (WR) £33.95
  (BOT) £34.75 (POR) £44.72 (VIN)
1989 IB £280.00 (GOE) £285.00 (BUT)
  £285.00 (FA) £330.00 (WY)
1989 ½ bottle IB £290.00 (FA)
1988 £24.99 (FUL) £28.88 (WAT) £29.99
  (OD) £31.50 (BEN) £35.95 (ROB) £35.95
  (WR) £35.95 (BOT) £38.00 (BER) £38.50
  (LEA) £44.35 (PLA) £45.00 (RES)
1988 IB £240.00 (GOE) £250.00 (FA)
  £280.00 (WY) £284.00 (BIB)
1987 £22.95 (RES) £28.50 (ROB)
1986 £37.50 (RES) £43.50 (ROB) £53.00
  (BEN) £54.34 (WAT)
1986 IB £400.00 (GOE) £540.00 (FA)
1986 magnum IB £540.00 (FA)
1985 £36.99 (OD) £38.00 (CRO) £43.47
  (WY) £44.45 (JON)
1985 IB £390.00 (BIB) £390.00 (FA)

1985 ½ bottle £19.70 (CRO)
1983 £35.00 (REI) £36.00 (GAL) £38.97 (WAT) £46.50 (ROB) £48.17 (WY)
1983 IB £365.00 (BIB) £375.00 (GOE)
1983 double magnum £282.00 (WY)
1982 £81.27 (WAT) £81.50 (BEN)
1982 IB £820.00 (FA) £840.00 (GOE)
1981 £35.25 (WY)
1979 £29.37 (WY)
1978 £30.84 (WY) £36.50 (REI) £45.15 (JON) £49.50 (ROB) £49.50 (RES)
1978 IB £300.00 (GOE) £488.00 (BIB)
1975 £29.50 (BU) £31.80 (TAN) £39.50 (ROB) £40.14 (WY)
1970 £47.00 (WY) £47.20 (TAN)
1970 magnum £99.87 (WY)
1969 double magnum £85.00 (REI)
1966 £76.37 (WY)
1964 £50.00 (VIG)
1962 £75.00 (REI)
1961 ½ bottle £100.36 (FA)
1955 £60.00 (REI)
1949 £223.25 (TW)

Guillot Pomerol
1990 £21.00 (WS) £22.69 (BY)

Guionne Côtes de Bourg
1994 £4.88 (HOG)

Hanteillan cru grand bourgeois Haut-Médoc
1989 £10.95 (BU)

Haut-Bages-Avérous cru bourgeois Pauillac
1993 £17.38 (BY)
1992 £16.50 (BY)
1990 £19.75 (REI) £29.75 (ROB)

Haut-Bages-Libéral 5ème cru classé Pauillac
1995 EC £132.00 (WAT)
1994 magnum £24.67 (WAT)
1993 £10.57 (WAT) £12.95 (BER)
1990 £20.07 (WAT) £24.95 (LEA)
1989 £15.95 (BU) £20.07 (WAT)
1988 £20.50 (ROB) £26.50 (STA)
1985 £26.40 (PIP)
1982 £28.50 (REI)
1979 £20.00 (BU)

Haut-Bages-Monpelou cru bourgeois Pauillac
1992 £8.99 (FUL)

Haut-Bailly cru classé Pessac-Léognan
1995 EC £176.00 (MV)
1994 £16.34 (LAY)
1994 IB £159.00 (RAE) £170.00 (WY)
1994 EC £150.00 (BUT)
1993 £12.93 (FA) £14.95 (WS) £17.20 (BER) £17.90 (GAL)
1993 IB £132.00 (RAE)
1990 IB £210.00 (FA)
1989 £35.50 (ROB)
1988 £21.50 (REI)
1988 IB £240.00 (GOE)

Haut-Batailley 5ème cru classé Pauillac
1995 EC £142.00 (MV)
1994 £18.75 (STA)
1993 £17.50 (UN)
1992 £12.50 (WS) £13.95 (LEA)
1990 £31.75 (STA)
1990 IB £240.00 (GOE)
1988 £16.85 (REI)
1987 £30.95 (ROB)
1985 £23.50 (WY)
1985 magnum £57.95 (ROB)
1979 £18.50 (REI) £20.00 (BU)
1979 magnum £35.25 (WY)
1978 IB £240.00 (GOE)
1976 £17.50 (REI)
1975 magnum £38.50 (REI)
1970 £31.50 (REI) £35.00 (BU)
1966 £60.00 (VIG)

Haut-Bergey Pessac-Léognan
1994 £11.49 (OD)

Haut-Beychevelle-Gloria St-Julien
1982 £28.75 (ROB)

Haut-Brion 1er cru classé Pessac-Léognan
1995 IB £975.00 (BIB)
1995 EC £765.00 (LAY) £795.00 (WAT) £1,000.00 (BUT)
1994 £63.50 (LAY) £82.25 (PEN)
1994 IB £713.00 (BIB)
1994 EC £710.00 (BUT)
1994 magnum £114.36 (WAT)
1993 £47.78 (WAT) £48.30 (DI) £54.33 (BY)
1993 IB £520.00 (BUT)
1992 £44.84 (BY) £51.00 (BOT) £51.00 (WR)
1992 IB £410.00 (WY)
1991 magnum IB £350.00 (FA)
1990 £165.00 (ROB)
1990 IB £1,100.00 (FA) £1,150.00 (BIB) £1,220.00 (WY)
1989 £263.88 (WAT) £279.06 (WY)

1989 IB £2,850.00 (FA)
1989 imperial £249.69 (WAT)
1988 £68.00 (BEN) £77.55 (WY)
1988 IB £620.00 (FA) £650.00 (BIB)
1988 imperial £628.62 (WY)
1986 £82.03 (BY) £83.95 (ROB) £87.64 (WY)
1986 IB £840.00 (FA) £840.00 (BUT)
1986 double magnum £340.75 (FA)
1986 imperial £681.50 (FA)
1985 £96.45 (WY) £125.00 (ROB)
1985 IB £920.00 (FA) £930.00 (BUT)
1985 double magnum £323.13 (FA)
1984 £41.00 (UN)
1983 £93.50 (JON) £99.50 (STA)
1983 IB £625.00 (BIB) £640.00 (FA)
1983 magnum IB £640.00 (FA)
1982 £180.00 (BEN) £188.00 (WY)
1982 IB £1,845.00 (FA)
1982 imperial £2,144.37 (WY)
1981 £60.00 (ROB)
1981 IB £505.00 (FA) £610.00 (WY)
1981 magnum £109.66 (WY)
1979 IB £775.00 (BIB)
1978 £75.00 (REI) £95.00 (BEN) £97.92
   (WY) £126.00 (UB) £134.75 (ROB)
1978 IB £840.00 (FA)
1975 £97.92 (WY)
1975 magnum £195.83 (WY)
1975 magnum IB £840.00 (FA)
1974 £38.75 (BU)
1970 £95.00 (REI) £117.50 (WY)
1970 IB £1,140.00 (BIB)
1970 magnum £258.50 (WY)
1966 £141.00 (FA) £182.12 (WY)
1964 IB £1,470.00 (FA)
1959 £495.00 (CRO)
1952 £95.00 (BU) £164.50 (WY)
1949 £405.37 (WY)
1948 £305.50 (WY)
1945 £360.00 (REI)

Haut-Faugères *grand cru St-Émilion*
1990 ½ bottle £7.85 (HAL)

Haut-Gardère *Pessac-Léognan*
1993 £8.79 (WAT)

Haut-Marbuzet *cru grand bourgeois
   exceptionnel St-Estèphe*
1993 £18.99 (AME)
1990 IB £230.00 (FA)
1989 IB £265.00 (BIB)
1989 ½ bottle IB £265.00 (BIB)
1988 £18.25 (WRI)
1988 magnum IB £245.00 (BIB)

de Haut-Sociondo *1ères Côtes de Blaye*
1995 EC £38.00 (WAT)
1990 £7.29 (WAT)

Hortevie *cru bourgeois St-Julien*
1988 £11.95 (WS)

d'Issan *3ème cru classé Margaux*
1992 £15.50 (CHA)
1989 £17.20 (NI)
1989 IB £180.00 (GOE)
1988 £18.99 (RAE) £42.00 (UB)
1988 IB £180.00 (GOE)
1986 £17.62 (WY) £28.50 (RES)
1985 £34.50 (ROB)
1983 £26.00 (CRO) £27.50 (VIG)
1982 £25.00 (RES)

Jonqueyres *Bordeaux Supérieur*
1995 EC £45.00 (WAT)
1990 £13.95 (RES)

Kirwan *3ème cru classé Margaux*
1994 £17.50 (GAL) £20.95 (DI)
1993 £12.99 (FUL) £21.59 (NA)
1988 £19.83 (AV) £22.95 (POR) £25.10
   (HAH) £25.75 (WRI)

Labégorce-Zédé *cru bourgeois supérieur
   Margaux*
1995 EC £125.00 (BUT) £125.40 (TAN)
1994 EC £105.00 (BUT)
1993 IB £140.00 (GOE)
1992 £10.95 (RAE) £12.80 (STA)
1989 £35.92 (NO)
1988 £16.50 (WS)
1985 £35.00 (VIG)

Lacombe *Bordeaux Supérieur*
1993 £5.99 (SAT)

Lacoste-Borie *Pauillac*
1994 £10.75 (WS) £15.95 (NA) £16.38 (GN)
1993 £11.82 (BY) £13.25 (EL)
1989 IB £140.00 (GOE)

Lafite-Rothschild *1er cru classé Pauillac*
1995 IB £860.00 (FA)
1995 EC £864.00 (LAY) £935.00 (WAT)
1994 IB £600.00 (GOE)
1994 EC £590.00 (BUT)
1994 ½ bottle £26.14 (WAT)
1994 magnum £104.57 (WAT)
1993 £39.50 (LAY) £47.78 (WAT) £50.00
   (UN) £51.02 (BY) £84.49 (WR)

1993 IB £430.00 (FA) £550.00 (BUT)
1992 £42.37 (BY)
1991 £41.25 (AV) £41.61 (WY) £49.66 (BY)
1990 £140.51 (WAT) £169.50 (LAY)
1990 IB £1,250.00 (GOE) £1,400.00 (FA)
  £1,500.00 (BIB)
1989 £103.40 (PEN) £106.24 (WAT)
1989 IB £1,000.00 (FA) £1,050.00 (GOE)
  £1,200.00 (WY)
1988 £99.87 (WY)
1988 IB £970.00 (FA) £990.00 (BUT)

1986 £185.65 (WY) £190.93 (WAT)
1986 IB £1,100.00 (GOE) £1,700.00 (BIB)
1986 magnum IB £1,750.00 (FA)
1985 £97.50 (REI) £105.75 (WY)
1985 IB £900.00 (GOE) £925.00 (BIB)
  £970.00 (FA)
1985 ½ bottle £63.50 (STA)
1985 magnum IB £970.00 (FA)
1984 magnum £90.00 (ROB)
1983 £84.50 (BEN) £85.50 (REI) £89.50 (POR)
1983 IB £800.00 (GOE) £870.00 (FA)
1983 magnum IB £800.00 (FA)
1982 £200.00 (CRO) £337.81 (WAT)
1982 IB £3,150.00 (FA) £3,300.00 (GOE)
1982 magnum IB £3,300.00 (FA)
1981 £90.00 (CRO)
1981 IB £970.00 (WY)
1980 £47.50 (BU)
1979 £65.00 (REI) £75.50 (BEN)
1979 IB £850.00 (GOE)
1979 magnum £161.56 (WY)
1978 £130.00 (ROB)
1978 magnum £158.63 (FA)
1976 £126.90 (FA) £195.00 (VIG)
1975 £129.25 (FA) £146.87 (WY)
1975 magnum £258.50 (FA)
1971 £65.00 (REI)
1970 £125.00 (REI) £141.00 (WY)
1970 magnum £260.00 (ROB) £293.75
  (WY)
1966 £146.87 (WY)
1964 £75.00 (REI) £78.73 (WY)
1961 ½ bottle £158.62 (WY)
1961 magnum £851.88 (FA)

1957 £85.00 (REI)
1956 magnum £340.75 (WY)
1955 £300.00 (REI)
1955 IB £4,200.00 (FA)
1953 magnum £869.50 (WY)
1952 £130.00 (REI) £188.00 (WY)
1949 £264.37 (WY)
1948 £125.00 (REI)
1948 ½ bottle £99.87 (WY)
1945 £669.75 (FA) £699.00 (BEN)
Lafleur *Pomerol*
1994 £136.59 (WAT)
1994 IB £1,000.00 (FA)
1994 EC £1,450.00 (BUT)
1993 IB £815.00 (FA) £820.00 (BUT)
1992 IB £620.00 (FA) £670.00 (WY)
1988 IB £1,650.00 (FA)
1984 £35.00 (REI)
1981 £95.96 (WY)
1971 £146.88 (FA)
1955 £300.00 (REI)

Lafleur-Gazin *Pomerol*
1989 £19.70 (BY)
1979 £18.50 (REI)

Lafon-Rochet *4ème cru classé St-Estèphe*
1995 EC £145.00 (WAT)
1994 £19.95 (STA)
1992 £13.04 (BY)
1984 £8.00 (REI)
1982 £39.95 (WY)
1978 £12.50 (CRO)
1975 £17.50 (BU)

Lagrange *Pomerol*
1995 EC £175.00 (BUT)
1992 £11.40 (TAN)
1988 £22.50 (LAY)
1985 £159.00 (LEA)

Lagrange *3ème cru classé St-Julien*
1994 £6.95 (DI)
1993 £19.09 (WY)
1991 IB £170.00 (WY)
1990 £37.90 (TAN) £39.50 (LEA)
1989 £37.90 (UB)
1989 IB £275.00 (WY)
1988 £24.48 (WY) £32.50 (BER)
1987 £21.00 (RES)
1986 £41.50 (ROB)
1982 £33.09 (WAT)
1962 £23.50 (WY)
1957 £45.00 (VIG)
1947 £145.00 (REI)

la Lagune *3ème cru classé Haut-Médoc*
1995 EC £137.00 (NEW) £142.00 (MV)
1994 ½ bottle £7.54 (WAT)
1994 magnum £30.16 (WAT)
1993 £15.00 (HIG) £18.50 (UN)
1992 £15.19 (BY)
1990 £35.75 (LAY) £42.75 (STA)
1990 IB £260.00 (BIB) £260.00 (FA)
1989 £29.18 (WAT) £29.50 (PIP) £29.50
   (GAL) £32.31 (WY) £34.92 (PLA)
1989 IB £263.00 (BIB) £280.00 (GOE)
1988 £19.99 (HIG) £33.27 (HA)
1988 IB £200.00 (BIB) £220.00 (GOE)
1986 £38.50 (LAY) £41.50 (ROB)
1986 IB £315.00 (WY) £320.00 (GOE)
1985 £26.98 (CHA)
1985 IB £285.00 (FA)
1985 magnum £50.00 (BU)
1985 magnum IB £305.00 (FA)
1983 £25.00 (BU) £31.72 (WY) £39.00 (BER)
1983 magnum £48.50 (REI)
1983 imperial £217.38 (FA)
1982 £53.36 (WY) £61.00 (CRO) £64.63
   (TAN) £67.50 (ROB)
1982 IB £540.00 (FA) £550.00 (GOE)
1982 double magnum £282.00 (WY)
1979 £24.50 (REI)
1978 £28.50 (REI) £33.50 (CRO) £44.50
   (ROB) £46.00 (BER)
1978 IB £270.00 (FA)
1976 £32.50 (REI)
1976 magnum £65.00 (REI)
1975 £32.00 (LEA) £35.25 (WY)
1970 £39.50 (REI) £46.00 (CRO)
1966 £45.00 (VIG) £46.50 (REI) £49.94 (WY)
1966 IB £493.00 (BIB)
1962 £47.50 (BEN)

Lalande d'Auvion *Médoc*
1990 £8.19 (JON)

Lalande-Borie *cru bourgeois supérieur St-Julien*
1989 £23.70 (UB)
1983 magnum £32.50 (REI)

Lamothe-Bergeron *cru bourgeois Haut-Médoc*
1993 £9.43 (AV)
1988 £13.40 (UB)
1986 £10.99 (NEW)

Lamothe-Cissac *Haut-Médoc*
1995 £6.50 (GAL)
1992 £7.99 (DI)

Lanessan *cru bourgeois supérieur Haut-Médoc*
1995 EC £107.72 (CHA)
1992 £12.50 (CHA) £12.62 (BY)
1990 £16.50 (EL) £16.80 (PIP) £18.49 (WR)
   £18.49 (BOT) £21.10 (NO)
1989 £15.25 (BER) £16.95 (ROB)
1983 £15.50 (REI) £21.00 (RES)
1982 £21.50 (RES)

Langoa-Barton *3ème cru classé St-Julien*
1995 IB £195.00 (GOE)
1995 EC £186.48 (TAN) £260.00 (BUT)
1994 £21.50 (DI)
1994 IB £145.00 (GOE)
1994 magnum £34.07 (WAT)
1993 £15.75 (BER) £17.99 (DI)
1993 IB £135.00 (GOE)
1992 £15.39 (BY)
1990 £33.05 (JON) £39.95 (NI)
1989 £26.60 (TAN) £27.57 (BY) £27.95
   (LAY)
1989 IB £210.00 (BIB) £275.00 (GOE)
1988 £15.25 (WRI) £24.20 (PIP) £25.60
   (TAN) £26.46 (BY)
1986 £31.80 (TAN) £33.10 (BY) £34.50
   (LAY)
1986 IB £230.00 (BUT) £280.00 (GOE)
1986 magnum £75.00 (ROB)
1985 £32.00 (BY)
1983 £22.50 (BU)
1982 £37.50 (BY)
1978 £26.00 (CRO)
1976 £19.50 (REI)
1961 £60.00 (BU)

Larmande *grand cru classé St-Émilion*
1995 EC £150.00 (BUT) £170.00 (WAT)
   £174.96 (TAN)
1994 IB £145.00 (GOE)
1994 EC £120.00 (BUT)
1989 IB £225.00 (BUT)
1989 £26.00 (BER)
1985 £27.50 (ROB)

Larose-Trintaudon *cru grand bourgeois Haut-Médoc*
1990 £11.63 (HA)

Laroze *grand cru classé St-Émilion*
1990 £19.80 (LAY)

Larrivet-Haut-Brion *Pessac-Léognan*
1983 £15.50 (REI)
1982 £25.26 (PLA)

Lascombes 2ème cru classé Margaux
1994 £17.50 (LON)
1992 £17.39 (NI)
1990 £27.50 (HOG)
1988 magnum £68.25 (ROB)
1982 £34.76 (WAT)
1978 £21.15 (WY)
1961 £76.37 (WY)

Latour 1er cru classé Pauillac
1995 EC £995.00 (WAT) £1,200.00 (BUT)
1994 EC £870.00 (BUT)
1994 magnum £150.00 (WAT)
1993 £49.47 (FA) £50.00 (UN) £58.56 (BY)
1993 IB £420.00 (BUT) £500.00 (GOE)
1992 £39.60 (RAE) £43.51 (BY)
1992 IB £445.00 (WY)
1991 £42.50 (RAE) £43.00 (DI) £47.51 (AV)
1991 IB £465.00 (WY)
1990 £303.54 (WAT)
1990 IB £3,000.00 (GOE) £3,000.00 (FA)
1989 £167.57 (PLA)
1989 IB £890.00 (WY) £950.00 (GOE)
1988 IB £770.00 (FA) £780.00 (GOE)
  £810.00 (BIB)
1988 double magnum £405.37 (WY)
1987 £55.00 (RES)
1986 £88.12 (WY) £110.75 (WR)
1986 IB £800.00 (FA) £900.00 (BIB)
  £900.00 (GOE)
1986 magnum IB £800.00 (FA)
1986 imperial £611.00 (FA)
1985 £70.00 (RES) £106.73 (WY)
1985 IB £850.00 (GOE) £920.00 (FA)
1985 imperial £822.50 (FA)
1984 £35.99 (FUL) £44.00 (UN) £45.00
  (REI) £75.00 (WS)
1983 £57.00 (HOG) £68.15 (PEN) £77.00
  (JON) £82.74 (WY) £96.95 (STA)
1983 IB £700.00 (FA) £750.00 (GOE)

1982 £350.00 (BEN) £352.50 (WY)
  £367.18 (WAT) £375.00 (RES)
1982 IB £3,500.00 (FA) £3,750.00 (BIB)
1982 double magnum £1,762.50 (WY)
1982 imperial £3,818.75 (WY)

1981 £74.91 (WY)
1981 IB £750.00 (BUT)
1979 £79.90 (PEN) £88.12 (PLA)
1979 IB £680.00 (GOE) £690.00 (FA)
1978 £103.40 (FA) £109.66 (WY) £125.00
  (RES) £150.00 (ROB)
1978 IB £850.00 (GOE)
1976 £70.00 (REI) £70.50 (WY) £77.39 (BY)
1976 double magnum £329.00 (WY)
1975 £135.12 (WY) £142.45 (UB)
1971 £65.00 (BU) £96.00 (LEA)
1970 £252.50 (REI) £323.12 (WY) £328.00
  (WAT) £350.91 (FA) £375.00 (ROB)
1969 £38.19 (WY)
1966 £246.75 (FA) £250.00 (CRO) £295.00
  (RES) £340.75 (WY)
1966 IB £3,000.00 (GOE)
1964 £175.00 (REI) £199.75 (FA) £235.00
  (WY) £275.00 (RES)
1963 £48.50 (REI) £99.87 (WY)
1962 IB £2,600.00 (FA)
1961 £595.00 (ROB) £687.37 (WY)
1961 magnum £2,291.25 (WY)
1959 £489.58 (FA) £495.00 (VIG) £500.00
  (ROB) £540.50 (WY) £575.00 (REI)
1957 £85.00 (REI) £165.00 (RES)
1957 magnum £175.00 (REI)
1956 £145.00 (REI) £164.50 (WY)
1955 £305.50 (FA) £320.00 (REI)
1953 IB £2,850.00 (FA)
1953 magnum £851.87 (WY)
1952 £111.62 (WY) £125.00 (BU)
1950 £125.00 (REI) £140.00 (BEN)
1949 magnum £1,498.12 (WY)
1947 £495.00 (REI) £499.37 (WY)
1945 £1,762.50 (WY)

Latour-à-Pomerol Pomerol
1995 EC £320.00 (BUT)
1989 IB £425.00 (WY)
1988 £27.50 (BO) £28.80 (TAN)
1982 IB £1,470.00 (FA)
1981 £39.95 (WY)
1975 IB £400.00 (FA)
1971 £71.50 (REI)

Léoville-Barton 2ème cru classé St-Julien
1995 IB £350.00 (BIB)
1995 EC £305.00 (WAT) £324.00 (LAY)
  £375.00 (BUT)
1994 £24.00 (GAL) £24.50 (DI)
1994 IB £238.00 (BIB)
1994 magnum £55.62 (WAT)
1993 £17.00 (AD) £18.80 (DI) £21.34
  (WAT) £22.50 (UN)

1993 IB £240.00 (GOE)
1992 £17.60 (BY) £23.99 (WR) £23.99 (BOT)
1991 £17.85 (BER)
1990 £42.95 (LAY) £97.00 (HIG)
1990 IB £400.00 (BIB) £420.00 (GOE)
1989 £31.50 (LAY) £32.50 (REI) £32.80
   (WAT) £34.99 (OD) £37.31 (PLA)
1989 IB £290.00 (GOE) £295.00 (BIB)
1988 £20.50 (CRO) £27.00 (TAN) £35.25
   (WY) £44.75 (BOT) £44.75 (WR)
1988 IB £230.00 (FA) £260.00 (GOE)
1986 £34.50 (LAY) £42.50 (REI) £45.00
   (VIG) £45.04 (WAT)
1986 IB £420.00 (GOE)
1985 £35.00 (REI) £47.00 (WY) £57.50 (RES)
1985 IB £420.00 (GOE)
1983 £27.80 (TAN) £29.18 (WAT) £31.70
   (HOG) £42.50 (RES)
1983 IB £320.00 (GOE) £340.00 (WY)
1982 £54.00 (JON) £55.00 (REI) £79.50 (RES)
1982 IB £620.00 (GOE)
1982 double magnum £282.00 (WY)
1981 £30.84 (WY)
1981 IB £240.00 (GOE)
1979 magnum £38.77 (WY)
1976 magnum £55.00 (REI)
1975 £27.50 (REI) £31.60 (TAN)
1974 £14.50 (BU)
1966 £62.27 (WY)
1964 £35.00 (VIG)
1961 £89.00 (CRO) £135.12 (WY)
1961 magnum £220.00 (REI) £305.50
   (WY)
1959 £75.00 (REI)

Léoville-Las-Cases 2ème cru classé St-
Julien
1995 IB £450.00 (FA)
1995 EC £468.00 (LAY) £498.00 (WAT)
   £550.00 (BUT)
1994 IB £330.00 (RAE) £350.00 (GOE)
1994 EC £425.00 (BUT)
1994 ½ bottle £17.43 (WAT)
1993 £27.22 (WAT) £31.82 (WY)
1993 IB £260.00 (BUT) £300.00 (GOE)
1992 £21.36 (BY) £26.95 (SAI)

> Please remember that
> **Webster's** is a price
> guide and not a price list. It
> is not meant to replace up-
> to-date
> merchants' lists.

1992 IB £240.00 (WY)
1991 £28.25 (BER)
1990 £89.50 (POR)
1990 IB £780.00 (FA) £850.00 (BUT)
   £950.00 (GOE) £1,063.00 (BIB)
1989 £58.40 (FOR)
1989 IB £600.00 (FA) £640.00 (WY)
   £683.00 (BIB) £850.00 (GOE)
1989 ½ bottle IB £700.00 (WY)
1989 magnum £100.00 (FA)
1989 magnum IB £675.00 (BUT)
1988 £38.67 (WAT) £46.51 (WY) £57.95
   (BOT) £57.95 (WR)
1988 IB £340.00 (BIB) £390.00 (FA)
   £420.00 (BUT) £420.00 (GOE)
1988 imperial £311.38 (FA) £355.00 (REI)
1986 £83.23 (WAT)
1986 IB £760.00 (BIB) £840.00 (FA)
1986 magnum £170.56 (WAT)
1986 imperial £728.50 (FA) £820.00 (WAT)
1985 £56.00 (BER) £68.75 (LAY)
1985 IB £570.00 (FA) £600.00 (WY)
1985 magnum IB £570.00 (FA)
1985 double magnum £229.13 (FA)
1985 imperial £481.75 (FA)
1983 £38.00 (WS) £39.50 (LAY) £49.99 (OD)
   £51.89 (WY) £52.00 (BER) £59.95 (BOT)
1983 IB £405.00 (FA) £450.00 (GOE)
1983 ½ bottle £17.85 (REI)
1983 magnum £94.99 (OD)
1983 double magnum £150.00 (FA)
1982 £115.00 (RES) £160.00 (BEN)
   £176.05 (WAT) £176.25 (WY)
1982 IB £1,650.00 (FA) £1,850.00 (GOE)
1982 double magnum £705.00 (FA)
1981 £47.50 (LEA) £47.95 (ROB)
1981 IB £330.00 (FA) £370.00 (GOE)
1981 magnum £65.00 (REI) £225.00 (LEA)
1979 £39.17 (WY)
1979 IB £360.00 (FA)
1979 magnum £74.99 (OD)
1979 double magnum £129.25 (FA)
1978 £42.50 (REI) £52.87 (WY) £58.85
   (UB)
1978 IB £470.00 (FA)
1978 double magnum £217.38 (FA)
1976 £28.50 (REI) £42.55 (JON)
1975 £53.00 (LEA)
1971 £27.50 (BU)
1970 £58.75 (WY)
1970 magnum £150.00 (RES) £157.20 (UB)
1966 £92.04 (WY)
1964 £52.87 (WY)
1961 £150.00 (VIG) £175.00 (REI) £229.12
   (WY) £275.00 (RES)

Léoville-Poyferré *2ème cru classé St-Julien*
1995 EC £195.00 (WAT) £200.00 (BUT)
1994 IB £159.00 (RAE)
1993 £18.93 (BY) £21.50 (UN)
1992 £14.95 (RAE)
1990 £40.14 (WY)
1989 £29.95 (ROB) £30.20 (BER)
1989 IB £270.00 (GOE)
1988 £47.00 (UB)
1987 magnum £39.00 (RAE)
1983 £59.00 (LEA)
1983 IB £320.00 (GOE)
1982 £42.50 (REI) £49.95 (NI) £50.90 (TAN)
1982 IB £450.00 (BIB) £500.00 (GOE)
1981 £26.92 (WY)
1975 £24.50 (REI)
1959 £98.00 (ROB)
1949 £99.87 (WY)

Lestage *cru bourgeois supérieur Listrac*
1991 £7.67 (WAT)

Liversan *cru grand bourgeois Haut-Médoc*
1990 £9.52 (HOG) £13.25 (BER) £14.54 (AV)
1989 £18.92 (SOM)
1988 £15.95 (LEA)
1985 £19.90 (CRO)

Livran *cru bourgeois Médoc*
1993 £6.75 (AS)
1990 £6.99 (HOG)
Loudenne *cru grand bourgeois Médoc*
1993 £10.95 (NA)
1990 £8.71 (NO)
1989 £8.90 (HOG)

la Louvière *Pessac-Léognan*
1994 £9.45 (WAI)
1977 £10.00 (VIG)

Lynch-Bages *5ème cru classé Pauillac*
1995 IB £325.00 (GOE)
1995 EC £260.00 (WAT) £275.00 (COU)
1994 IB £215.00 (FA) £255.00 (WY)
1994 magnum £51.70 (WAT)
1993 £20.00 (WS) £25.00 (UN)
1993 IB £250.00 (WY)
1992 £23.13 (BY)
1991 £21.95 (SAI) £25.25 (BER) £25.57 (BY)
1990 £50.00 (GAL) £57.46 (BY) £59.95 (RES)
 £65.50 (PIP) £72.66 (NO) £80.00 (ROB)
1990 IB £545.00 (FA) £550.00 (BUT)
 £575.00 (WY) £580.00 (GOE)

1989 £71.97 (WAT) £80.00 (ROB)
1989 IB £620.00 (GOE) £700.00 (FA)
 £745.00 (WY) £750.00 (BUT)
1989 magnum £135.13 (FA)
1988 £51.89 (WY) £54.25 (STA)
1988 IB £370.00 (FA)
1987 £23.14 (BY)
1986 £50.92 (WY)
1986 IB £530.00 (BIB)
1986 magnum £145.00 (RES)
1985 £42.51 (NO) £74.02 (WY)
1985 IB £670.00 (BIB) £700.00 (FA)
1985 magnum £142.96 (WY)
1985 magnum IB £700.00 (FA)
1983 £50.52 (WY) £60.00 (ROB)
1983 IB £430.00 (BIB)
1982 £95.00 (RES) £99.00 (UB)
1982 IB £950.00 (GOE) £960.00 (FA)

1981 £47.00 (WY) £50.00 (STA) £50.00 (ROB)
1978 £42.57 (FA) £61.50 (ROB)
1978 IB £430.00 (WY)
1975 £41.61 (WY)
1970 IB £1,220.00 (FA)
1967 £60.00 (VIG)
1966 £60.00 (REI) £75.00 (VIG)
1961 £129.25 (WY) £165.00 (RES)
1961 IB £2,250.00 (FA)
1955 £95.00 (REI)
1949 £150.00 (VIG)

Lynch-Moussas *5ème cru classé Pauillac*
1990 £19.95 (RES)
1982 £19.50 (REI)

du Lyonnat *Lussac-St-Émilion*
1993 £9.75 (ROB) £10.01 (PLA)
1990 £8.51 (HOG) £8.68 (EL) £12.45 (UB)

Macquin-St-Georges *St-Georges-St-Émilion*
1995 £7.35 (HAH) £8.19 (AV)
1994 £6.95 (AD) £7.49 (POR) £7.89 (JON)
1993 £5.99 (FUL) £7.49 (JON)
1990 £8.40 (CRO)
1989 £8.35 (SAT)

Magdelaine *1er grand cru classé St-Émilion*
1995 EC £340.00 (BUT)
1994 £26.00 (WS)
1982 IB £545.00 (FA)
1981 £25.85 (WY)
1978 £67.00 (UB)

Malartic-Lagravière *cru classé Pessac-Léognan*
1989 £17.95 (RES)
1978 £14.50 (REI)

Malescasse *cru bourgeois Haut-Médoc*
1993 £12.46 (HIG)
1985 £13.80 (CRO)

Malescot-St-Exupéry *3ème cru classé Margaux*
1993 £19.50 (POR)
1992 £10.20 (HOG)
1989 £22.99 (BO)
1982 £37.50 (RES)
1971 £19.00 (REI)

de Marbuzet *cru grand bourgeois exceptionnel St-Estèphe*
1990 IB £140.00 (GOE)
1989 £14.85 (BER)
1988 IB £140.00 (GOE)
1978 £14.95 (BU)

Margaux *1er cru classé Margaux*
1995 IB £895.00 (FA) £1,195.00 (BIB)
1995 EC £897.00 (LAY) £935.00 (WAT)
1994 £128.08 (PEN)
1994 IB £880.00 (GOE)
1994 EC £700.00 (BUT)
1994 magnum £128.46 (WAT)
1993 £68.34 (WAT)
1993 IB £650.00 (GOE) £650.00 (BUT) £763.00 (BIB)
1992 £45.27 (BY)
1991 £62.66 (WY)
1990 £303.54 (WAT)
1990 IB £2,900.00 (FA)
1990 magnum IB £3,000.00 (FA)
1989 £127.50 (LAY) £150.00 (ROB)

All châteaux are listed alphabetically regardless of class.

1989 magnum IB £1,100.00 (BIB)
1988 £113.95 (LAY)
1988 magnum £176.25 (FA)
1987 £75.00 (ROB) £79.75 (UB)
1986 £180.16 (WY) £185.55 (WAT)
1986 magnum IB £1,750.00 (FA)
1985 £140.41 (FA) £146.38 (WAT) £215.00 (ROB) £215.00 (ROB) £225.00 (RES)
1985 magnum £301.77 (WAT)
1984 £35.00 (REI) £88.50 (ROB)
1983 £175.00 (REI) £175.76 (WAT) £180.16 (WY)
1983 IB £1,650.00 (FA) £1,750.00 (BIB)
1982 £245.00 (REI) £352.50 (WY) £362.29 (WAT) £475.00 (RES)
1982 IB £3,150.00 (FA) £3,300.00 (BIB)
1982 magnum IB £3,300.00 (FA)
1981 £70.50 (WY) £78.00 (CRO)
1979 IB £1,070.00 (FA)
1979 magnum £195.00 (UB)
1978 IB £1,250.00 (BIB) £1,280.00 (FA)
1975 £95.00 (VIG) £97.50 (ROB)
1970 IB £900.00 (BIB)
1970 magnum £188.00 (WY)
1970 magnum IB £800.00 (FA)
1966 £82.25 (WY) £150.00 (RES)
1964 £58.75 (WY)
1964 magnum IB £1,000.00 (FA)
1961 £340.75 (FA)
1959 £350.00 (REI)
1956 £117.50 (WY)
1952 £95.00 (BU) £125.00 (REI)
1950 £75.00 (BU)
1949 £95.00 (REI) £205.62 (WY)
1947 £300.00 (REI)

Marquis d'Alesme-Becker *3ème cru classé Margaux*
1988 £17.95 (NA) £18.29 (EL) £22.99 (WR) £22.99 (BOT)
1966 £25.00 (BU)
1955 £49.50 (BU)

Marquis-de-Terme *4ème cru classé Margaux*
1993 £12.95 (SAI)
1990 ½ bottle £11.97 (HAL)
1984 £10.99 (BO)
1966 £29.50 (BU)

Marsau *Côtes de Francs*
1995 £5.45 (SAI)

de Martouret *Bordeaux*
1994 £5.69 (AME)

Maucaillou *cru bourgeois Moulis*
1989 £15.49 (HA)
1985 £13.49 (FLE)
1979 £20.00 (VIG)
Mayne-Vieil *Fronsac*
1994 £6.59 (HA)

Mazeris *Canon-Fronsac*
1990 £12.65 (AD) £12.80 (HAH) £16.25
(NO)
1989 £12.80 (HAH)
1988 £11.55 (JON)
1985 £13.75 (JON)

Méaume *Bordeaux Supérieur*
1991 £6.31 (HA)

Mendoce *Côtes de Bourg*
1990 £7.45 (BER)

Meyney *cru grand bourgeois exceptionnel*
St-Estèphe
1993 £15.50 (UN) £17.50 (STA)
1992 £12.08 (BY)
1991 £12.86 (HOG) £14.50 (JON)
1990 £16.55 (HOG) £21.95 (DI)
1989 £17.59 (NI) £23.50 (BEN) £24.50 (ROB)
1988 £14.99 (FUL)
1982 £39.95 (ROB)
1981 magnum £53.95 (ROB)
1962 magnum £48.50 (REI)

Millet *Graves*
1990 £14.08 (PLA)
1975 £10.75 (BU)

de Mirefleurs *1ères Côtes de Bordeaux*
1994 £4.99 (VIC)

la Mission-Haut-Brion *cru classé Pessac-*
Léognan
1995 EC £498.00 (WAT) £520.00 (BUT)
1994 EC £340.00 (BUT)
1994 magnum £92.23 (WAT)
1993 £14.75 (FLE) £37.51 (BY) £38.50
(BER)
1991 £40.71 (BY) £46.41 (WY)
1989 £194.36 (WAT)
1989 IB £1,900.00 (FA) £1,950.00 (BUT)
1987 £33.21 (BY)
1986 £63.45 (WY)
1986 IB £570.00 (FA)
1986 magnum IB £570.00 (FA)
1985 £66.58 (WY) £150.00 (UB)
1985 IB £640.00 (FA)

1984 £39.50 (UN)
1983 £50.00 (HOG) £59.50 (BU) £77.55
(WY)
1983 IB £450.00 (GOE) £490.00 (FA)
1982 £148.05 (WAT) £176.25 (WY)
1982 IB £1,600.00 (FA)
1982 magnum IB £1,650.00 (FA)
1981 £51.70 (WY)
1981 magnum £105.75 (WY)
1979 £79.00 (BER)
1978 £76.37 (WY) £111.63 (FA)
1976 magnum £105.75 (WY)
1975 £295.00 (REI)
1975 IB £3,000.00 (FA)
1974 £37.60 (FA)
1970 £127.29 (WY) £195.00 (RES)
1970 IB £850.00 (GOE)
1970 magnum £375.00 (RES)
1966 £139.25 (UB)
1966 IB £2,400.00 (FA)
1966 magnum IB £2,450.00 (FA)
1964 £135.00 (ROB) £154.71 (WY)
1964 IB £1,470.00 (FA)
1962 £123.38 (RES) £168.91 (WY)
1959 £375.00 (RES)
1953 £245.00 (CRO)
1953 IB £3,100.00 (FA)

des Moines *Lalande-de-Pomerol*
1988 £11.99 (SAT)

les Moines *Médoc*
1990 £7.24 (NO)

Monbousquet *grand cru St-Émilion*
1995 EC £170.00 (BUT)
1959 £48.00 (ROB)

Monbrison *cru bourgeois Margaux*
1995 EC £125.00 (BUT) £128.00 (MV)
1994 EC £110.00 (BUT)
1993 £8.50 (REI)
1993 IB £145.00 (BUT)

Monconseil-Gazin *1ères Côtes de Blaye*
1993 £6.75 (AD)

Monlot-Capet *St-Émilion*
1993 £10.95 (BU)
1990 £11.75 (WS)
1983 £8.99 (CO)

Montaiguillon *Montagne-St-Émilion*
1994 £8.50 (PIP) £8.91 (ELL) £9.50 (LEA)
1993 £9.95 (LEA)

Montbrun *cru bourgeois Margaux*
1993 £12.95 (EL)

Montlabert *grand cru St-Émilion*
1989 £21.55 (VIN)

Montrose *2ème cru classé St-Estèphe*
1995 EC £275.00 (BUT) £280.00 (WAT)
1994 EC £245.00 (BUT)
1994 ½ bottle £12.92 (WAT)
1993 £20.40 (BER) £23.30 (WAT) £24.00 (UN)
1993 IB £190.00 (BUT) £190.00 (GOE)
1991 £21.50 (REI)
1990 IB £1,700.00 (FA)
1989 IB £460.00 (FA) £510.00 (BUT)
1988 £28.39 (WY)
1986 £22.50 (WRI) £31.73 (FA)
1986 IB £350.00 (BIB)
1985 £32.80 (WY) £49.50 (PIP)
1984 £18.15 (BY)
1983 £22.50 (BU) £29.18 (WAT) £29.37 (AV)
1983 IB £315.00 (BIB)
1982 £47.50 (REI) £56.79 (WY)
1982 IB £470.00 (FA) £500.00 (GOE)
1981 £29.37 (WY) £45.00 (PIP)
1976 £23.50 (REI)
1975 £27.95 (BEN)
1970 IB £820.00 (FA)
1966 £68.15 (WY) £92.00 (UB)
1964 £50.00 (VIG)
1961 £120.00 (CRO) £204.00 (NI)
1945 £240.00 (REI) £628.62 (WY)

Moulin Rouge *Bordeaux Supérieur Côtes de Castillon*
1986 £8.50 (BU)

Moulinet *Pomerol*
1992 £15.99 (BOT) £15.99 (THR)
1989 £20.27 (SOM)
1988 £13.30 (UB) £19.49 (SAT)
1953 £75.00 (RES)

Mouton-Rothschild *1er cru classé Pauillac*
1995 EC £995.00 (WAT) £2,200.00 (BUT)
1994 £75.00 (DI) £96.35 (PEN)
1994 IB £610.00 (FA) £708.00 (BIB) £750.00 (GOE)
1994 EC £740.00 (BUT)
1994 ½ bottle £31.38 (WAT)
1994 imperial £681.50 (WY)
1993 £50.00 (UN) £52.00 (WS) £58.55 (WAT) £59.67 (BY) £75.00 (ROB)

1993 IB £570.00 (FA) £599.00 (BIB) £650.00 (GOE)
1993 magnum IB £570.00 (FA)
1992 £53.03 (BY) £59.95 (BOT) £59.95 (WR)
1991 IB £500.00 (BIB) £665.00 (WY)
1990 £99.87 (WY) £111.63 (PEN)
1990 IB £1,000.00 (FA) £1,033.00 (BIB) £1,080.00 (BUT)
1990 ½ bottle IB £1,000.00 (FA)
1989 £110.50 (BEN) £114.56 (WY) £116.03 (WAT) £145.00 (ROB)
1989 IB £1,050.00 (BIB) £1,070.00 (FA)
1989 magnum IB £1,070.00 (FA)
1989 double magnum £376.00 (FA)
1988 £88.00 (BEN) £95.00 (RES) £109.50 (LAY) £120.00 (ROB)
1988 IB £900.00 (FA) £950.00 (BIB)
1988 magnum IB £900.00 (FA)
1987 £52.88 (FA) £77.55 (WY)
1986 £315.78 (WY) £321.16 (WAT)
1986 IB £3,050.00 (FA) £3,100.00 (GOE) £3,250.00 (BIB)
1986 imperial £3,150.00 (WAT)
1985 £92.50 (REI) £146.88 (AV) £152.00 (BEN) £220.00 (ROB)
1985 IB £1,340.00 (FA) £1,350.00 (BIB) £1,500.00 (GOE)
1985 double magnum £728.50 (WY)
1984 £82.25 (WY)
1983 £79.50 (LAY) £89.50 (RES) £89.50 (POR) £92.00 (REI) £99.87 (WY) £130.00 (ROB)
1983 IB £920.00 (BIB) £940.00 (FA) £950.00 (GOE)
1983 magnum £170.00 (BEN)
1983 magnum IB £870.00 (FA)

1983 double magnum £487.62 (WY)
1983 jeroboam £505.25 (FA)
1982 £432.00 (REI) £484.68 (WAT)
1982 IB £4,350.00 (BIB) £4,400.00 (FA) £4,500.00 (GOE)

1982 jeroboam £4,053.75 (WY)
1981 £82.25 (WY)
1981 IB £540.00 (FA) £595.00 (BIB)
1981 magnum £175.00 (RES)
1980 £70.00 (VIG)
1979 £69.00 (LEA) £70.50 (WY) £79.50
  (BEN)
1979 IB £700.00 (FA)
1979 jeroboam £500.00 (ROB)
1978 £89.10 (WY) £130.00 (ROB)
1978 IB £850.00 (GOE)
1978 imperial £865.00 (RES)
1977 £47.00 (WY)
1976 £75.00 (REI) £97.52 (WY)
1976 magnum £325.00 (UB)
1975 £82.25 (FA) £101.05 (WY) £125.00
  (ROB) £128.00 (LEA)
1972 £76.37 (WY)
1971 £55.00 (BU) £66.00 (REI) £99.87
  (WY) £110.00 (RES)
1970 £130.00 (REI) £135.13 (FA) £164.50
  (WY) £186.00 (ROB) £225.00 (RES)
1970 IB £1,600.00 (BIB)
1970 magnum £346.62 (WY)
1970 magnum IB £1,650.00 (FA)
1967 £54.83 (WY) £75.00 (ROB)
1966 £175.00 (REI) £217.37 (WY) £295.00
  (RES)
1966 IB £2,600.00 (FA)
1964 £95.00 (REI)
1964 magnum £193.87 (WY)
1963 £340.75 (WY)
1962 £193.87 (WY) £299.00 (RES)
1961 £481.75 (FA) £650.00 (REI)
1961 imperial £11,397.50 (FA)
1959 £475.00 (REI) £575.75 (FA)
1955 £334.88 (FA) £350.00 (VIG)
1953 £245.00 (REI) £775.50 (WY)
1952 £305.50 (WY)
1952 magnum £560.00 (REI)
1950 £687.37 (WY)
1948 £1,075.12 (WY)
1948 magnum £1,938.75 (WY)
1947 £1,645.00 (WY)
1945 £2,056.25 (FA)

Nenin *Pomerol*
1990 IB £245.00 (WY)
1982 £26.50 (BU)
1981 £42.00 (UB)
1959 £99.87 (WY)
1955 £42.50 (REI)

Notton *Margaux*
1980 £9.95 (RAE) £14.45 (UB)

d'Olivier *cru classé Pessac-Léognan*
1992 £12.73 (BY)

les Ormes-de-Pez *cru grand bourgeois
St-Estèphe*
1993 £15.99 (UN)
1992 £15.17 (BY)
1991 £16.50 (BY)
1990 £26.50 (PIP)
1989 £21.00 (ROB)
1986 £15.95 (BU)
1982 £165.00 (LEA)
1978 £21.00 (REI) £22.50 (BU)

les Ormes-Sorbet *cru grand bourgeois
Médoc*
1993 £15.93 (PLA)

Palmer *3ème cru classé Margaux*
1995 EC £348.00 (WAT)
1994 EC £280.00 (BUT)
1994 magnum £67.36 (WAT)
1993 £23.00 (BER) £30.55 (WAT) £32.00 (BY)
1993 IB £260.00 (BUT)
1992 £15.99 (FUL) £26.95 (DI) £27.80 (BY)
1991 £24.95 (BER) £43.08 (WY)
1990 £48.60 (BY) £48.95 (LAY) £52.68
  (WAT) £55.81 (WY)
1990 IB £420.00 (BIB) £520.00 (FA)
  £560.00 (BUT)
1989 £71.48 (WY) £73.35 (JON) £74.22
  (WAT) £75.00 (BEN)
1989 IB £745.00 (FA) £770.00 (BUT)
1988 £29.00 (FUL) £39.99 (JON) £47.98
  (WY) £55.00 (ROB)
1988 IB £480.00 (GOE)
1987 IB £200.00 (BIB)
1986 £44.95 (DI) £47.20 (TAN) £53.36
  (WAT) £62.66 (WY)
1986 IB £520.00 (GOE) £523.00 (BIB)
1986 magnum £75.00 (ROB)
1985 £48.75 (LAY) £49.45 (WAT) £49.50
  (JON) £52.00 (BER) £58.75 (WY)
1985 IB £553.00 (BIB) £580.00 (GOE)
1983 £106.50 (BEN) £110.16 (WAT)
1983 IB £1,100.00 (FA) £1,160.00 (BIB)
1983 magnum £235.00 (REI)
1982 £60.22 (WAT) £64.63 (WY) £69.75
  (LAY) £70.00 (VIG) £84.00 (STA)
1982 IB £600.00 (FA)
1982 magnum £117.50 (FA) £141.00 (WY)
1981 £34.75 (REI) £38.97 (WAT) £47.00 (WS)
1979 £60.00 (ROB)
1978 £56.75 (BEN) £60.71 (WY) £65.00
  (DI) £80.00 (RES) £89.00 (UB)

1978 IB £540.00 (FA)
1976 £42.50 (REI)
1975 £95.00 (ROB)
1971 £58.00 (CRO)
1970 £105.00 (ROB) £110.50 (BEN) £120.00 (REI) £120.92 (WAT) £141.00 (WY)
1970 IB £1,120.00 (FA)
1967 £37.00 (BO)
1966 £199.75 (FA) £263.88 (WAT)
1964 £32.90 (WY)
1962 £75.00 (BU) £421.00 (WAT)
1961 £215.02 (WY) £680.52 (WAT)
1959 £210.00 (ROB)

Panigon *cru bourgeois Médoc*
1990 £8.75 (HA)

Pape-Clément *cru classé Pessac-Léognan*
1995 IB £250.00 (GOE)
1995 EC £245.00 (WAT) £340.00 (BUT)
1994 IB £172.20 (RAE)
1994 EC £180.00 (BUT)
1993 £17.50 (FLE) £23.01 (WAT)
1989 £24.50 (RAE) £27.90 (WAT)
1985 IB £360.00 (BUT)
1970 £32.50 (REI) £41.12 (WY)
1966 £50.00 (VIG)
1959 £48.50 (REI)

Patache d'Aux *cru grand bourgeois Médoc*
1994 £10.50 (ROB)
1993 £8.80 (TAN) £9.99 (WHI) £10.10 (PIP) £10.72 (GN)
1992 £8.95 (ROB)
1990 £9.29 (JON) £11.50 (RES)
1989 £9.60 (CRO)

Paveil-de-Luze *cru bourgeois Margaux*
1995 £8.99 (OD)
1994 £9.79 (EL)
1970 £16.50 (BU)

Pavie *1er grand cru classé St-Émilion*
1995 EC £285.00 (BUT)
1994 IB £189.00 (RAE)
1994 EC £180.00 (BUT)
1993 £32.50 (UN)
1993 IB £180.00 (GOE)
1991 £18.75 (BER)
1989 IB £255.00 (BUT) £320.00 (GOE)
1989 magnum £78.00 (ROB)
1988 £38.60 (PIP)
1986 £64.21 (PLA)
1985 £35.00 (RES) £40.00 (ROB)

1983 magnum £122.00 (UB)
1982 £76.00 (UB)
1982 IB £460.00 (FA)
1975 £34.25 (ROB)

Pavie-Decesse *grand cru classé St-Émilion*
1993 IB £140.00 (GOE)
1990 £32.95 (ROB)
1989 IB £170.00 (BUT) £180.00 (GOE)
1988 £25.80 (PIP) £27.50 (ROB)

Pavie-Macquin *grand cru classé St-Émilion*
1995 IB £225.00 (GOE)
1995 EC £200.00 (BUT) £205.00 (WAT)
1994 EC £160.00 (BUT)

Pavillon-Rouge-du-Château Margaux *Margaux*
1995 IB £180.00 (FA)
1995 EC £198.00 (WAT)
1994 £16.34 (LAY)
1994 EC £160.00 (BUT)
1993 £17.40 (DI) £21.56 (BY)
1987 £19.85 (PEN)
1986 £29.00 (CRO) £51.70 (WY)
1983 £58.75 (WY)
1981 £29.95 (ROB)

Pédesclaux *5ème cru classé Pauillac*
1990 £19.95 (EL)

Petit-Village *Pomerol*
1995 EC £345.00 (BUT)
1994 IB £240.00 (GOE)
1994 EC £230.00 (BUT)
1993 IB £185.00 (BUT) £240.00 (GOE)
1990 IB £380.00 (GOE)
1989 £39.95 (LEA) £49.50 (BER)
1989 IB £340.00 (BUT) £420.00 (GOE)
1986 IB £320.00 (GOE)
1970 £44.50 (REI) £77.80 (BER)
1961 £111.63 (FA)
1952 £72.50 (REI)
1934 £190.00 (CRO)

les Petits Arnauds *Côtes de Blaye*
1994 £5.38 (HOG)

Pétrus *Pomerol*
1995 IB £5,600.00 (FA)
1994 £332.43 (WAT)
1994 IB £2,850.00 (FA)
1993 £273.67 (WAT)
1993 IB £2,450.00 (FA)
1992 IB £1,750.00 (FA)

1990 £734.37 (WY) £742.20 (WAT)
1990 IB £6,800.00 (FA)
1989 £550.00 (REI) £683.45 (WAT)
£705.00 (WY)
1989 IB £6,120.00 (BIB) £6,600.00 (FA)
1989 magnum £1,341.49 (WY)

1988 £345.00 (BEN) £352.50 (WY)
1988 IB £3,400.00 (FA)
1988 magnum £685.42 (WY)
1987 £225.00 (ROB)
1987 magnum IB £1,730.00 (FA)
£1,850.00 (BUT)
1986 £279.06 (WY)
1986 IB £2,750.00 (FA)
1986 magnum £558.12 (WY)
1986 magnum IB £2,450.00 (FA)
1985 £401.46 (WY)
1985 IB £3,600.00 (FA) £3,950.00 (BUT)
1983 £271.72 (WY) £395.00 (RES)
1983 IB £2,600.00 (FA) £2,650.00 (BIB)
1982 £1,223.96 (WAT)
1982 IB £8,500.00 (GOE) £9,400.00 (FA)
1981 £235.00 (WAT) £270.25 (WY)
1981 magnum IB £2,500.00 (FA)
£2,630.00 (WY)
1980 IB £1,650.00 (FA)
1979 £380.00 (ROB)
1979 IB £2,600.00 (FA)
1979 magnum £532.66 (WY)
1978 £250.00 (REI) £293.75 (WY)
1978 IB £2,600.00 (FA)
1978 magnum £538.54 (WY) £675.00
(REI)
1978 magnum IB £2,450.00 (FA)
1976 IB £2,395.00 (BIB) £2,400.00 (FA)
1976 magnum IB £2,300.00 (FA)
1975 £575.75 (WY) £775.00 (ROB)
1971 IB £6,200.00 (FA)
1970 £768.64 (WY) £990.00 (ROB)
1967 £299.63 (FA)
1966 £595.00 (RES) £616.87 (WY)
1952 £350.00 (REI)

Peybonhomme-les-Tours *l ères Côtes de Blaye*
1994 £7.99 (NA)

Peyrabon *cru grand bourgeois Haut-Médoc*
1976 £11.75 (BU)

du Peyrat *l ères Côtes de Bordeaux*
1994 £4.95 (SAI)

de Pez *cru bourgeois supérieur St-Estèphe*
1994 £14.95 (AD)
1992 £10.52 (BY)
1989 £16.62 (HOG) £19.95 (RES) £32.00 (UB)
1988 £13.60 (WRI) £20.00 (BU)
1986 £22.50 (BU)
1982 £35.00 (REI)
1966 £35.00 (VIG)

Phélan-Ségur *cru grand bourgeois exceptionnel St-Estèphe*
1994 £17.50 (DI)
1994 EC £96.00 (MV)
1993 £18.93 (PLA)
1990 £19.85 (HOG)
1961 £47.00 (WY)
1959 £45.00 (ROB)

Pibran *cru bourgeois Pauillac*
1993 IB £135.00 (BUT)
1989 IB £145.00 (BUT) £180.00 (GOE)

Pichon-Longueville (called Pichon-Baron until 1988) *2ème cru classé Pauillac*
1995 IB £300.00 (GOE) £310.20 (LEA)
1995 EC £240.00 (BUT)
1994 £20.00 (REI)
1994 EC £215.00 (BUT)
1993 £22.25 (NI)
1992 £24.99 (BOT) £24.99 (WR)
1991 £38.75 (ROB)
1990 £76.50 (REI)
1990 IB £660.00 (FA) £663.00 (BIB)
£670.00 (WY) £680.00 (BUT)
1989 £62.18 (WAT) £70.00 (REI)
1989 IB £620.00 (FA) £650.00 (BIB)
1988 £36.00 (REI)
1988 IB £330.00 (FA)
1987 £24.26 (BY)
1986 £47.00 (WY)
1985 £43.00 (BER)
1964 £30.00 (REI)
1947 £150.00 (VIG)

Pichon-Longueville-Lalande (called Pichon-Lalande until 1993) *2ème cru classé Pauillac*
1995 EC £495.00 (WAT) £500.00 (BUT)
1994 IB £305.00 (FA) £310.00 (BIB)
1994 EC £320.00 (BUT)
1994 magnum £59.53 (WAT)
1993 £21.75 (DI) £22.25 (NI) £23.20 (BER)
1993 IB £235.00 (FA)
1992 £20.36 (WAT)
1992 IB £203.00 (BIB)
1991 £38.75 (ROB)
1990 £49.45 (WAT)
1990 IB £475.00 (FA) £480.00 (BIB)
1989 £45.75 (LAY) £47.00 (WY) £55.32 (WAT) £57.50 (BEN) £60.00 (BER)
1989 IB £520.00 (BIB) £580.00 (BUT) £580.00 (FA)
1989 magnum IB £585.00 (BUT)
1989 imperial £452.38 (FA)
1988 £58.95 (STA) £60.00 (RES)
1988 IB £380.00 (FA) £470.00 (WY)
1986 £54.05 (WAT) £81.50 (ROB) £82.25 (WY) £92.50 (TAN)
1986 IB £820.00 (FA) £870.00 (BIB)
1986 magnum IB £820.00 (FA)
1985 £45.00 (RES) £49.50 (LAY) £58.75 (WY) £62.50 (BEN) £68.00 (WS)
1985 IB £580.00 (GOE) £585.00 (BIB) £620.00 (FA) £650.00 (BUT)
1985 jeroboam £364.25 (FA)
1983 £45.00 (LAY) £76.37 (WY)
1983 magnum £164.50 (WY)
1982 £181.50 (JON) £184.57 (WAT) £193.87 (WY) £250.00 (RES)
1982 IB £1,750.00 (FA) £1,850.00 (GOE)
1982 magnum £375.00 (REI)
1981 £33.00 (CRO) £44.50 (REI) £47.00 (WS) £54.95 (STA) £55.95 (LEA)
1979 £44.00 (CRO)
1978 £63.00 (CRO) £78.99 (JON)
1978 IB £600.00 (FA)
1976 £41.12 (WY)
1975 £53.50 (REI) £76.37 (WY) £77.49 (JON)
1975 IB £430.00 (FA)
1971 £26.50 (REI)
1970 £52.87 (WY) £82.00 (CRO)
1970 IB £820.00 (FA)
1967 £52.87 (WY)
1966 £75.00 (REI) £129.25 (WY)
1959 £120.00 (REI) £193.38 (WY)
1959 IB £1,800.00 (FA)
1956 £94.00 (WY) £175.00 (RES)
1952 £92.50 (REI)

le Pin *Pomerol*
1995 IB £4,950.00 (BIB) £5,400.00 (GOE) £5,600.00 (FA)
1995 EC £6,100.00 (WAT)
1994 £430.35 (WAT)
1994 IB £3,200.00 (GOE) £3,700.00 (FA)
1994 EC £4,000.00 (BUT)
1993 £269.27 (WY) £395.00 (RES)
1993 IB £2,500.00 (GOE) £3,200.00 (BIB) £3,500.00 (BUT)
1992 £212.97 (WY)
1991 £298.64 (WY)
1991 IB £2,850.00 (FA)
1990 IB £7,000.00 (GOE) £8,750.00 (BIB) £9,200.00 (FA) £9,500.00 (BUT)
1989 £705.00 (FA) £745.00 (REI)
1989 IB £7,000.00 (GOE)
1988 £481.75 (FA) £485.00 (REI)
1988 IB £6,100.00 (BIB)
1986 £634.50 (FA)
1986 IB £6,500.00 (BUT)
1985 IB £7,000.00 (GOE) £8,475.00 (BIB) £8,550.00 (WY)
1984 £405.37 (WY)
1983 £822.50 (FA)
1983 IB £8,000.00 (GOE) £10,440.00 (BIB)
1982 IB £1,900.00 (FA) £21,000.00 (GOE)

Pitray *Bordeaux Supérieur Côtes de Castillon*
1995 EC £43.00 (WAT)
1994 £6.95 (BU)
1993 £5.73 (WAT)
1990 £5.95 (REI) £8.32 (WAT) £8.52 (NO)
1988 £8.32 (WAT)

Plagnac *cru bourgeois Médoc*
1993 £9.99 (UN)
1992 £8.59 (WHI) £9.39 (PLA)

Plince *Pomerol*
1995 EC £115.00 (BUT)
1988 £13.99 (SAT)

la Pointe *Pomerol*
1995 EC £134.00 (NEW)
1994 IB £110.00 (FA)
1970 £25.00 (BU)

Pontet-Canet *5ème cru classé Pauillac*
1995 IB £220.00 (GOE)
1995 EC £175.00 (WAT)
1994 £19.95 (DI)
1994 IB £138.00 (RAE)
1994 magnum £41.91 (WAT)
1992 £15.95 (LEA)
1990 £24.95 (BER)
1989 £18.60 (HIG) £38.20 (UB)
1989 magnum £38.00 (HIG)
1988 £16.99 (HIG) £23.25 (STA)
1986 £26.95 (LEA) £29.77 (BY)
1985 £29.95 (ROB)
1981 magnum £29.50 (REI)
1979 £16.50 (BU)
1961 £60.00 (REI)
1957 £50.00 (VIG)
1953 £41.12 (WY)

Potensac *cru grand bourgeois Médoc*
1995 EC £85.00 (BUT) £88.00 (WAT)
£111.67 (CHA)
1994 IB £95.00 (GOE)
1994 EC £62.00 (MV) £80.00 (BUT)
1993 £9.01 (WAT) £9.50 (HIG)
1992 £10.63 (CHA)
1991 £8.48 (HOG)
1990 £23.50 (SOM)
1990 IB £145.00 (BUT)
1989 £17.95 (RES) £18.20 (PIP) £24.50
(STA)
1988 £18.21 (PLA)
1987 £11.55 (COU) £11.95 (ROB)
1986 £14.92 (FA)
1986 IB £145.00 (GOE)
1985 £19.90 (CRO) £19.95 (RES)
1983 £17.50 (REI) £22.50 (ROB)
1978 £24.00 (CRO)

Pouget *4ème cru classé Margaux*
1981 £17.50 (BU)

Poujeaux *cru grand bourgeois exceptionnel*
Moulis
1995 IB £150.00 (GOE)
1995 EC £120.00 (BUT) £133.00 (COU)
1993 £13.95 (BER) £15.20 (DI)
1990 £18.50 (WS) £33.50 (STA)
1989 £8.75 (REI) £15.00 (TAN)

Pouyanne *Graves*
1993 £5.83 (SOM)

Prieur de Meyney *St-Estèphe*
1992 £8.75 (WHI)

le Prieuré *grand cru classé St-Émilion*
1990 £19.85 (AD)
1985 £18.93 (BY) £19.95 (AD)

Prieuré-Lichine *4ème cru classé*
Margaux
1995 IB £140.00 (GOE)
1995 EC £190.00 (HIG)
1989 £25.00 (HOG)
1988 £16.99 (HIG)
1986 £20.00 (CRO)

Puy-Blanquet *grand cru St-Émilion*
1990 £11.99 (JON)

Puy-Castéra *cru bourgeois Haut-Médoc*
1995 EC £66.00 (COU)
1994 £7.93 (COU)
1993 £6.87 (SOM)

Puygueraud *Côtes de Francs*
1993 £8.50 (DI)
1988 £10.70 (TAN)

Puylazat *Côtes de Castillon*
1994 £5.40 (TAN)

Rahoul *Graves*
1992 £11.75 (NI)

Ramage-la-Bâtisse *cru bourgeois Haut-*
Médoc
1992 £7.95 (WR) £7.95 (BOT) £7.95 (THR)
1990 £9.70 (FOR) £10.99 (POR) £11.99
(AME)

Rauzan-Gassies *2ème cru classé*
Margaux
1983 £29.50 (ROB)
1982 £25.00 (BU) £85.00 (UB)
1970 £18.50 (REI)
1961 £100.00 (RES)
1959 £85.19 (WY)
1949 £145.00 (REI)

Rauzan-Ségla *2ème cru classé Margaux*
1995 EC £285.00 (WAT)
1994 £19.27 (LAY)
1994 EC £195.00 (BUT)
1993 £23.30 (WAT)
1993 IB £170.00 (FA)
1990 £38.31 (PEN) £42.10 (WY) £45.00
(RES)
1990 IB £430.00 (FA)
1989 IB £383.00 (BIB)

1986 £46.51 (WAT) £58.75 (WY)
1985 £34.50 (ROB) £34.66 (TW)
1982 £32.50 (REI) £48.50 (ROB)
1970 £28.88 (WY)
1962 £32.50 (REI) £40.00 (VIG)
1955 magnum £275.00 (REI)
1949 £95.00 (VIG)

Réserve de la Comtesse *Pauillac*
1994 IB £143.00 (BIB)
1993 £14.25 (REI) £14.95 (WS) £15.75 (EL) £16.99 (VIC)
1992 £10.50 (TAN)
1990 £39.95 (NI)
1988 £20.00 (WS)
1984 £13.51 (BY)
1982 £40.00 (REI)

Respide-Médeville *Graves*
1986 £15.16 (TW)

Reynier *Bordeaux Supérieur*
1994 £6.49 (NA)

Reynon *1ères Côtes de Bordeaux*
1994 £8.74 (BY)

Reysson *cru bourgeois Haut-Médoc*
1994 £7.84 (HA)
1990 £10.95 (LEA)
1988 £8.49 (NEW)

Richotey *Fronsac*
1994 £5.95 (WS)
1993 £5.50 (WS)
1989 £7.99 (SAT)

la Rivière *Fronsac*
1992 £5.99 (WR) £5.99 (THR) £5.99 (BOT)
1991 £9.95 (AME)
1990 £12.95 (SAT) £14.95 (VIG)
1989 £14.29 (SAT)
1988 £13.99 (SAT) £14.95 (VIG)
1986 £13.49 (SAT)

de Roquetaillade-la-Grange *Graves*
1994 £7.95 (STA)
1988 £10.75 (BU)

Roquevieille *Côtes de Castillon*
1994 £5.95 (STA)
1988 £5.58 (PEN)

la Rose-Figeac *Pomerol*
1962 £27.50 (BU)

Rouget *Pomerol*
1989 £19.99 (JON)
1988 £21.95 (STA)

Rousset *Côtes de Bourg*
1993 £5.95 (AD)
1990 £6.59 (JON)

St-Georges *St-Georges-St-Émilion*
1990 £22.09 (PLA)

St-Pierre *Lussac-St-Émilion*
1992 £15.95 (LEA)
1989 £28.50 (ROB)

St-Pierre *4ème cru classé St-Julien*
1994 EC £145.00 (BUT)
1983 £17.00 (CRO)
1982 £34.50 (AD) £45.00 (REI)
1979 £23.55 (WRI)
1978 £24.00 (CRO)

de Sales *Pomerol*
1992 £12.95 (BY)
1981 £21.58 (BY)
1975 £35.45 (UB)
1970 £30.00 (VIG)

Sarget de Gruaud-Larose *St-Julien*
1993 £15.85 (HIC) £15.95 (STA) £15.95 (POR)
1992 £11.50 (CRO) £11.75 (WHI) £12.99 (SAF)
1989 £17.92 (PLA)
1983 £16.50 (CRO)

Sauman *Côtes de Bourg*
1993 £5.95 (DI)

Segonzac *1ères Côtes de Blaye*
1994 £5.25 (WAI) £5.60 (AS) £5.85 (DI) £6.25 (SAI)

Sénéjac *cru bourgeois supérieur Haut-Médoc*
1993 £8.45 (WAI) £9.81 (ROS)
1991 £9.40 (TAN)
1989 £16.00 (MV) £17.86 (SOM)

Sestignan *cru bourgeois Médoc*
1990 £9.75 (BU)

Siaurac *Lalande-de-Pomerol*
1993 £11.99 (BO)
1990 £9.99 (FUL)

Siran *cru bourgeois supérieur Margaux*
1993 £12.25 (BER) £17.40 (PIP)
1990 £29.00 (STA)
1990 magnum £55.00 (RES)
1985 £25.20 (PIP)

Sirius *Bordeaux*
1993 £5.99 (WR) £5.99 (THR) £5.99 (BOT)

Smith-Haut-Lafitte *cru classé Pessac-Léognan*
1995 IB £240.00 (GOE)
1995 EC £255.00 (BUT)
1994 EC £125.00 (BUT)
1993 £19.60 (BY)
1982 £32.31 (TW)
1978 £19.95 (VIG)

Sociando-Mallet *cru grand bourgeois Haut-Médoc*
1994 £15.86 (SOM) £19.88 (PLA)
1992 £14.38 (PLA) £19.60 (BY)
1991 £10.99 (RAE)
1989 £18.80 (ROS) £25.51 (PLA)
1989 IB £200.00 (GOE) £205.00 (BIB)
1988 £29.00 (RES)
1988 IB £180.00 (GOE)
1986 £27.50 (RES)
1986 IB £220.00 (GOE)
1982 £31.72 (FA)

Soutard *grand cru classé St-Émilion*
1986 £26.44 (PLA)

de Tabuteau *Lussac-St-Émilion*
1993 £7.91 (VIN)

du Tailhas *Pomerol*
1992 £11.84 (BY)
Taillefer *Pomerol*
1978 £18.50 (BU)

Talbot *4ème cru classé St-Julien*
1995 IB £150.00 (FA)
1994 £23.50 (PEN) £24.95 (STA)
1994 EC £165.00 (BUT)
1994 ½ bottle £8.52 (WAT)
1994 magnum £34.07 (WAT)
1990 IB £260.00 (BIB) £315.00 (WY)
1989 £26.95 (LAY) £28.99 (OD) £35.25 (WY)
  £37.50 (WR) £37.50 (BOT) £38.95 (ROB)
1989 IB £260.00 (FA)
1989 ½ bottle £18.80 (WY)
1988 £19.99 (FUL) £27.90 (WAT) £29.37
  (WY) £29.95 (RES) £31.73 (TAN)

1986 £29.95 (DI) £39.50 (GAL) £39.50
  (CRO) £45.82 (WAT) £50.52 (WY)
1986 IB £400.00 (FA)
1985 £30.83 (LON) £38.50 (REI) £38.97
  (WAT) £43.08 (WY) £58.00 (VIN)
1985 IB £285.00 (BIB) £375.00 (FA)
1983 £17.69 (JON) £25.00 (BU) £38.77
  (WY) £41.42 (FA) £45.82 (PLA)
1982 £65.11 (WAT) £70.50 (WY)
1981 IB £260.00 (BIB)
1978 £38.77 (WY) £46.95 (ROB)

1978 IB £350.00 (GOE)
1975 £27.50 (BU) £29.37 (WY)
1970 £38.77 (WY) £42.50 (REI)
1970 ½ bottle £17.50 (REI)
1970 magnum £76.37 (WY)
1966 £58.75 (WY)
1961 £95.00 (CRO)
1952 £75.00 (REI)

la Terrasse *Bordeaux Supérieur Côtes de Castillon*
1975 £9.75 (BU)

Terre Rouge *Médoc*
1993 £7.40 (HAH) £7.65 (LAY) £7.95 (POR)
1988 IB £71.00 (BUT)

de Terrefort-Quancard *Bordeaux Supérieur*
1992 £6.49 (POR)

Terrey-Gros-Cailloux *cru bourgeois St-Julien*
1989 £12.49 (JON)
1988 £15.30 (PIP)
1988 IB £115.00 (GOE)

du Tertre *5ème cru classé Margaux*
1995 EC £150.00 (HIG)
1986 £28.95 (ROB)
1985 £24.50 (ROB)
1970 £20.00 (VIG)

Tertre-Daugay *grand cru classé St-Émilion*
1924 £88.12 (WY)

Tertre Rôteboeuf *St-Émilion*
1995 EC £550.00 (COU) £620.00 (BUT) £625.00 (WAT)
1994 £44.06 (COU) £57.28 (WAT)
1994 EC £650.00 (BUT)
1992 £25.95 (COU)
1990 £59.90 (CRO)
1989 £56.00 (CRO) £66.00 (COU)
1988 £49.00 (CRO)
1986 £48.00 (CRO)
1985 £46.00 (CRO)
1983 £31.73 (FA)

Thibaud-Bellevue *Bordeaux Supérieur Côtes de Castillon*
1990 £6.95 (WS)

la Tonnelle *St-Émilion*
1990 £7.48 (NO)

Toumalin *Canon-Fronsac*
1988 £8.49 (JON)

Tour-Bellegarde *Bordeaux Supérieur*
1971 £9.75 (BU)

la Tour-Carnet *4ème cru classé Haut-Médoc*
1985 £14.11 (FLE)
1978 £14.60 (CRO)
1975 £17.95 (WRI)

la Tour-de-By *cru grand bourgeois Médoc*
1994 £8.99 (AME)
1993 £8.90 (PIP) £9.20 (TAN) £9.99 (HIG) £10.25 (WHI)
1991 £9.55 (JON)
1989 £11.50 (REI) £15.95 (ROB)
1985 £14.95 (ROB)

la Tour-de-Grenet *Lussac-St-Émilion*
1993 £7.75 (BU)

Tour de l'Espérance *Bordeaux Supérieur*
1993 £5.09 (BY)

la Tour-de-Mons *cru bourgeois supérieur Margaux*
1991 £11.45 (BER)
1924 £115.00 (CRO)
1906 £111.62 (WY)

Tour-des-Combes *grand cru St-Émilion*
1990 £9.00 (WAT)

Tour-du-Haut-Moulin *cru grand bourgeois Haut-Médoc*
1994 £12.50 (DI)
1990 £12.95 (WS)
1990 IB £125.00 (GOE)

Tour-du-Pas-St-Georges *St-Georges-St-Émilion*
1995 EC £57.00 (MV) £63.72 (TAN)
1994 £8.60 (TAN)
1994 EC £54.00 (MV)
1993 £9.95 (AD) £11.00 (MV)
1989 £11.50 (REI)

la Tour-du-Pin-Figeac *grand cru classé St-Émilion*
1994 £16.41 (LON)
1986 £19.95 (SAT)
1970 £22.50 (REI)

la Tour-Figeac *grand cru classé St-Émilion*
1989 £19.95 (NA) £25.99 (BOT) £25.99 (WR)

la Tour-Haut-Brion *cru classé Pessac-Léognan*
1982 £161.56 (WY)
1970 IB £490.00 (FA)

la Tour-Martillac *cru classé Pessac-Léognan*
1994 £16.95 (DI)

la Tour-St-Bonnet *cru bourgeois Médoc*
1995 EC £54.00 (NEW)
1994 £6.87 (FLE) £6.99 (HOG) £7.33 (FOR)
1990 £13.95 (ROB) £16.92 (SOM)
1990 IB £130.00 (BUT)
1970 £16.50 (REI)

les Tourelles de Longueville *Pauillac*
1993 £15.95 (LEA)
1991 £15.83 (BY)

Tourteau-Chollet *Graves*
1990 £8.99 (BO)

Tronquoy-Lalande *cru grand bourgeois St-Estèphe*
1994 £9.99 (PEN)

Troplong-Mondot *grand cru classé St-Émilion*
1995 IB £390.00 (GOE)
1995 EC £325.00 (WAT)
1994 IB £320.00 (GOE)
1993 £38.99 (WR) £38.99 (BOT)
1993 IB £248.00 (BIB) £290.00 (BUT)
1971 £14.50 (REI) £18.80 (FA)

Trotanoy *Pomerol*
1994 £38.97 (WAT)
1994 EC £330.00 (BUT)
1993 £36.03 (WAT)
1993 IB £460.00 (BUT)
1990 £56.40 (AV)
1990 IB £470.00 (BIB)
1988 £39.00 (BO)
1986 £43.57 (WY)
1983 £61.00 (STA)
1982 £230.10 (WAT) £315.00 (ROB)
1982 IB £2,300.00 (BIB) £2,450.00 (FA)
1981 £46.02 (WY) £57.50 (ROB)
1980 £35.25 (WY)
1980 IB £190.00 (FA)
1978 £70.00 (REI)
1977 £32.50 (BU)
1976 £42.50 (REI) £83.75 (UB)
1975 £137.00 (WAT)
1971 £205.63 (FA)

Trottevieille *1er grand cru classé St-Émilion*
1994 £23.95 (DI)
1993 £8.50 (REI)
1989 £21.54 (HIG)
1988 £35.51 (PLA)
1982 £25.00 (BU)
1979 £27.50 (RES)
1947 £125.00 (ROB)

la Valade *Fronsac*
1992 £7.30 (UB)
1990 £10.99 (SAT)

Verdignan *cru grand bourgeois Haut-Médoc*
1989 £15.50 (PIP)
1985 £14.50 (ROB)

Victoria *cru bourgeois Haut-Médoc*
1990 £8.54 (ROS)

Vieux-Château-Bourgneuf *Pomerol*
1975 £8.50 (REI)
1964 £35.00 (VIG)

Vieux-Château-Certan *Pomerol*
1995 EC £375.00 (TAN) £398.00 (WAT)
1994 £31.60 (TAN)
1994 IB £294.96 (RAE) £295.00 (BIB)
1994 EC £295.00 (BUT)
1993 £27.30 (BER) £35.90 (DI)
1993 IB £210.00 (RAE) £240.00 (BUT)
1992 £17.95 (RAE) £24.95 (VIC)
1992 IB £185.00 (GOE) £235.00 (BIB)
1990 £52.00 (DI) £75.00 (ROB)
1989 £40.14 (WY) £48.00 (BER)
1989 IB £390.00 (BIB) £400.00 (BUT)
1988 £41.30 (TAN)
1988 IB £450.00 (GOE)
1988 magnum £115.00 (RES)
1986 £69.45 (UB)
1986 IB £490.00 (FA) £490.00 (BIB) £500.00 (BUT) £600.00 (GOE)
1986 magnum IB £500.00 (FA)
1985 £55.00 (PIP)
1985 IB £350.00 (BIB)
1983 IB £370.00 (GOE)
1982 £75.00 (RES)
1982 IB £560.00 (FA)
1981 £41.50 (ROB)

Villegeorge *cru bourgeois supérieur exceptionnel Haut-Médoc*
1992 £9.49 (VIC)
1982 £15.95 (RAE)
1981 £13.99 (RAE) £24.95 (UB)
1978 £14.99 (RAE)
1975 £15.95 (RAE)

Villemaurine *grand cru classé St-Émilion*
1991 £17.89 (AV)

Villeneuve de Cantemerle *Haut-Médoc*
1993 £11.29 (WHI)

Vraye-Croix-de-Gay *Pomerol*
1994 EC £130.00 (BUT)
1985 £27.55 (AD)
1983 £23.81 (BY)

EC *(ex-cellar) price per dozen, excl shipping, duty and VAT.* **IB** *(in bond) price per dozen, excl duty and VAT.*
All other prices, per bottle incl VAT.

WHITE BORDEAUX

DRY

Under £5.00

1995
les Bouhets £4.49 (SAI)
la Dame de Maucaillou £4.99 (OD)
Moulin de Launay £4.95 (AD)
l'Ortelan £4.25 (SAI)
Tertre du Moulin £3.99 (SAI)
1994
Moulin de Launay ½ bottle £4.89 (JON)

£5.00 → £6.99

1996
Bel Air £5.25 (WS)
Haut Rian £5.10 (PIP) £5.19 (ELL)
★ Pierrail £5.47 (CHA)
Thieuley £5.65 (WS) £6.55 (AD)
1995
Barton & Guestier 1725 £5.49 (FUL)
Bauduc £5.16 (LON)
Bonnet £5.65 (NI) £6.39 (EL)
Carsin £5.95 (SAI)
de l'Étoile £6.55 (AD) £6.70 (TAN)
Maitre d'Estournel £5.99 (OD)
Marjosse £5.65 (WS)
Moulin de Launay £5.10 (TAN)
Mouton-Cadet £5.45 (GRE) £5.49 (SAI)
   £5.49 (SAF) £5.99 (FUL)
de Pic £5.95 (AD)
Roquetaillade-la-Grange £6.95 (STA)
Sirius £5.95 (WS)
1994
Bauduc les Trois Hectares £5.72 (LON)
de l'Étoile £6.45 (JON)
1993
Bonnet £5.69 (WR) £5.69 (THR) £5.69 (BOT)
Domaine la Grave £6.99 (HIG)
1992
Coucheroy £6.59 (THR) £6.59 (BOT)
1990
Loudenne £6.94 (FLE)
1988
de l'Étoile £6.95 (BER)

£7.00 → £8.99

1995
le Chec £7.55 (AD)
de l'Hospital £8.99 (OD)
Thieuley Cuvée Francis Courselle £7.99
   (OD)

1994
Cruzeau £8.99 (EL)
Loudenne £7.49 (NA)
Reynon £7.95 (WS)
Thieuley Cuvée Francis Courselle £7.25
   (SOM)
Tour de Mirambeau Cuvée Passion £7.99
   (OD)
1993
Coutet Sec £8.99 (WR) £8.99 (BOT)
Michel Lynch £7.64 (BUT)
1992
de Rochemorin £8.59 (NI)
1991
de Landiras £8.95 (LEA)
1990
Cabannieux £7.99 (POR)
1989
Guiraud 'G' £8.32 (BUT)

CHATEAU GUIRAUD

1985
la Tour Martillac £8.95 (RAE)

£9.00 → £11.99

1995
Cabannieux £11.49 (NA)
1994
Rieussec 'R' £11.75 (STA)
1993
Fonreaud 'Le Cygne' £11.95 (AD)
Rieussec 'R' £9.95 (VIG)
1992
Doisy-Daëne Grand Vin Sec £10.59 (TAN)
Haut Lagrange £9.59 (NI)
1990
Domaine la Grave £9.60 (HIG)
Sirius £9.11 (BUT)

> *Stars (★) indicate wines
> selected by Oz Clarke in the
> Best Buys section which begins
> on page 12.*

£12.00 → £14.99

1995
Couhins-Lurton £14.95 (NI)
1993
L'Esprit de Chevalier £13.51 (FA)
Olivier £12.95 (BER)
1992
Couhins-Lurton £12.69 (YOU) £13.10
(TAN) £14.95 (ROB)
1991
Couhins-Lurton £13.50 (RAE) £13.65 (AD)
£14.95 (NI)
1990
Couhins-Lurton £12.95 (POR)
1988
Domaine la Grave £13.51 (BUT)
1987
Laville-Haut-Brion £12.80 (NEZ)
1980
la Louvière £12.50 (BU)

£15.00 → £19.99

1995
Couhins-Lurton £16.94 (BUT)
1992
Carbonnieux £16.35 (HAH)
L'Esprit de Chevalier £16.50 (RAE) £18.95
(AD)
1990
la Tour Martillac £16.50 (NI)
1989
Carbonnieux £18.47 (AV)
la Tour Martillac £16.95 (GRE)

£20.00 → £29.99

1995
de Fieuzal £26.73 (BUT)
Smith-Haut-Lafitte £21.84 (BUT)
1994
de Fieuzal £25.75 (BUT)
Pavillon Blanc du Château Margaux
£28.40 (HAH)
1992
la Louvière £20.10 (FOR)
Pavillon Blanc du Château Margaux
£26.48 (FOR)
1990
L'Esprit de Chevalier £22.99 (UB)
1989
la Louvière £22.81 (BUT)
1985
Larrivet-Haut-Brion £28.69 (BUT)
1967
Bouscaut £29.50 (RAE)

£30.00 → £39.99

1994
Domaine de Chevalier £34.56 (FA) £34.56
(BUT) £35.74 (WATT)
1993
de Fieuzal £37.40 (TAN)
1992
Domaine de Chevalier £31.63 (RAE)
£37.50 (FA)
1991
Domaine de Chevalier £38.97 (RAE)
1990
de Fieuzal £32.50 (BEN)
Pavillon Blanc du Château Margaux
£30.00 (VIG)
1988
Laville-Haut-Brion £37.99 (BUT)
1984
Haut-Brion Blanc £37.50 (BU)
1976
Domaine de Chevalier £37.60 (FA)

£40.00 → £49.99

1995
Domaine de Chevalier £40.05 (RAE)
1989
Domaine de Chevalier £48.27 (BUT)
1988
Haut-Brion Blanc £48.27 (BUT) £49.50
(RAE)
1986
Domaine de Chevalier £42.89 (BUT)
Pavillon Blanc du Château Margaux
£49.00 (UB)
1976
Roumieu £47.00 (WY)
1965
'Y' d'Yquem £45.00 (BU)
1963
Laville-Haut-Brion £42.50 (BU)

£50.00 → £69.99

1995
Laville-Haut-Brion £52.19 (BUT)
1990
de Fieuzal £55.13 (BUT)
1988
Domaine de Chevalier £52.88 (WY)
Laville-Haut-Brion £50.00 (ROB)
Pavillon Blanc du Château Margaux
£58.75 (TW)
'Y' d'Yquem £55.50 (UB)
1978
'Y' d'Yquem £58.75 (WY)

1967
Roumieu £64.63 (WY)
1926
Pavillon Blanc du Château Margaux
  £62.28 (WY)

£70.00 → £89.99

1994
Haut-Brion Blanc £84.80 (BUT)
1989
Laville-Haut-Brion £77.16 (BUT)
1981
Haut-Brion Blanc £76.38 (WY)
1967
Laville-Haut-Brion £70.50 (WY)
1960
'Y' d'Yquem £80.00 (BEN)
1949
Carbonnieux £82.25 (WY)

£110.00 → £160.00

1990
Haut-Brion Blanc £148.15 (BUT)
1989
Haut-Brion Blanc £113.88 (BUT)

SWEET

Under £7.00

1993
Marquis de Beausoleil Ste-Croix-du-Mont
  £6.99 (UN)
1990
Beausite Monprimblanc £6.75 (GRE)
de Berbec £6.49 (OD) £6.75 (VIC) £6.99
  (THR) £6.99 (BOT) £6.99 (WR)
1984
Coutet ½ bottle £6.49 (NI)

£7.00 → £8.99

1994
la Caussade £7.75 (WAI)
la Grave £7.30 (WS)
des Tours £8.50 (AD)
1993
des Arroucats £7.99 (QUE)
Domaine du Noble £8.32 (ELL)
1989
la Chartreuse ½ bottle £8.95 (WS)
Liot ½ bottle £7.69 (HAL)
1988
Liot ½ bottle £8.14 (HAL) £8.95 (WS)
1967
Domaine du Noble £8.99 (RAE)

£9.00 → £11.99

1994
la Chartreuse ½ bottle £9.75 (WAI)
Rabaud-Promis ½ bottle £9.95 (SAI)
1993
Domaine du Noble £9.15 (PLA)
Fayau £11.25 (GRE)
la Rame £9.99 (MAJ) £10.35 (NI)
des Tours £9.75 (LAY) £9.95 (JON)
1992
Fayau £9.80 (MV)
1990
de Cérons £9.95 (SAI)
Rabaud-Promis ½ bottle £11.99 (BIB)
Rayne-Vigneau ½ bottle £10.43 (BUT)
la Tour Blanche ½ bottle £10.92 (BUT)
1989
d'Arche ½ bottle £11.95 (WS)
Broustet ½ bottle £10.43 (BUT)
la Chartreuse ½ bottle £11.30 (HAH)
Coutet ½ bottle £10.98 (QUE) £11.65 (BUT)
1988
Filhot ½ bottle £9.45 (QUE)
les Justices ½ bottle £11.63 (TW)
Rayne-Vigneau ½ bottle £9.45 (QUE)
1986
Coutet ½ bottle £9.45 (NI)
1983
Rayne-Vigneau ½ bottle £10.58 (WY)
la Tour Blanche ½ bottle £11.75 (WY)
1981
Filhot ½ bottle £9.98 (SAT)
1978
Doisy-Daëne £11.75 (WY)
1975
d'Arricaud £9.95 (RAE)

£12.00 → £14.99

1992
Cyprès de Climens £12.50 (RAE)
la Rame £13.50 (VIG)
1991
Fayau £12.15 (UB)
1990
Filhot ½ bottle £14.99 (OD)
Guiraud ½ bottle £13.50 (MV)
1989
la Chartreuse £14.99 (FUL)
Coutet ½ bottle £13.75 (GRE)
1988
Broustet ½ bottle £12.50 (STA) £14.95 (ROB)
Filhot £13.00 (BIB)
Liot £14.00 (JON)
Rayne-Vigneau ½ bottle £13.49 (NO)

1986
Coutet ½ bottle £12.25 (GRE)
Rayne-Vigneau ½ bottle £12.25 (GRE)
1984
Rieussec ½ bottle £13.95 (RES) £14.95 (VIG)
1983
Loupiac Gaudiet £12.95 (SAT)
de Malle £14.15 (SAT)
Rayne-Vigneau ½ bottle £12.95 (VIG)
1982
Climens ½ bottle £14.50 (RAE)
1979
Coutet ½ bottle £14.10 (WY)
1973
Coutet £12.93 (WY)

£15.00 → £19.99

1991
Climens ½ bottle £18.95 (RES)
1990
la Chartreuse £19.50 (WS)
Climens ½ bottle £17.77 (BUT)
Coutet £16.10 (NO)
Guiraud ½ bottle £17.95 (VIG)
Loubens £15.20 (LAY)
Rieussec ½ bottle £17.63 (WY)
Suduiraut £18.95 (RES)
Suduiraut ½ bottle £19.90 (TAN)
1989
la Chartreuse £16.74 (HA) £19.60 (TAN)
Coutet £18.49 (BO)
Coutet ½ bottle £19.95 (UB)
Doisy-Daëne £19.39 (COU)
Filhot £18.90 (FA) £19.23 (HA)
Liot £15.99 (JON) £18.99 (BIB)
de Malle £16.95 (BO)
Suduiraut ½ bottle £17.63 (WY) £18.49
   (BO) £18.76 (NO)
1988
Cantegril £15.94 (TAN)
la Chartreuse £19.00 (TAN)
Climens ½ bottle £17.63 (WY) £18.75 (BUT)
Filhot £16.95 (RAE)
Guiraud ½ bottle £17.97 (NO)
Lamothe-Guignard £18.95 (AD) £19.39
   (COU)
Liot £15.50 (WS)
Rabaud-Promis £17.50 (RAE)
Rayne-Vigneau £15.28 (WY)
1986
Coutet ½ bottle £15.00 (HOG) £19.00 (TAN)
Filhot £17.95 (DI)
Filhot ½ bottle £15.95 (RES)
1985
Suduiraut ½ bottle £15.00 (HOG)

1983
la Chartreuse £16.25 (JON)
Filhot £18.76 (SAT)
Nairac £18.90 (FA)
Rabaud-Promis ½ bottle £15.95 (RES)
Rayne-Vigneau £18.80 (WY) £19.50 (HOG)
Suduiraut ½ bottle £19.95 (ROB)

£20.00 → £29.99

1992
Coutet £26.90 (UN) £26.95 (WR)
1991
Climens £27.01 (PLA) £28.50 (WAI)
1990
Bastor-Lamontagne ½ bottle £21.20 (BUT)
la Chartreuse £20.30 (HAH)
Coutet £25.00 (WS) £26.36 (HOG)
Doisy-Védrines £27.50 (BER)
Filhot £23.85 (NI)
Guiraud £27.80 (TAN)
Nairac £24.00 (MV)
Rabaud-Promis £22.99 (BIB)
Rieussec £27.50 (NI)
Sigalas-Rabaud £29.99 (OD)
la Tour Blanche £21.25 (NI)
1989
d'Arche £26.79 (PLA)
Broustet £20.50 (PIP)
Climens ½ bottle £23.95 (VIG)
Coutet £22.81 (BUT) £25.95 (ELL)
Doisy-Daëne £26.50 (BER) £29.95 (RES)
Guiraud ½ bottle £20.00 (WS)
Lamothe-Guignard £25.00 (RES)
Rayne-Vigneau £22.80 (FOR) £25.00 (GRE)
   £27.00 (AD)
Romer du Hayot £22.30 (AD)
Suduiraut £21.95 (ROB) £26.95 (BEN)
1988
Broustet £24.50 (PIP)
Cantegril £20.60 (AD)
Climens ½ bottle £24.50 (TAN)
Coutet £24.95 (NI) £25.85 (WY) £27.95
   (RES) £29.50 (GRE)
Lafaurie-Peyraguey £26.73 (BUT)
de Malle £24.95 (DI)
Rayne-Vigneau £21.29 (PIP)
Suduiraut £23.49 (BO)
la Tour Blanche £20.86 (BUT) £27.72 (PIP)
1987
Rabaud-Promis £25.30 (AD)
1986
Coutet £22.50 (BEN)
Doisy-Védrines £23.89 (BIB)
les Justices £22.91 (TW)
Sigalas-Rabaud £21.29 (PIP)

1985
Climens ½ bottle £26.50 (JON)
Lafaurie-Peyraguey £20.37 (FA)
1984
Rieussec £26.95 (BEN)
1983
Climens ½ bottle £24.95 (BEN) £25.85 (WY)
Coutet £26.50 (RES)
Coutet ½ bottle £21.50 (ROB)
Filhot £25.85 (WY) £27.50 (RES)
de Malle £24.63 (NO)
Suduiraut £29.95 (TAN)
Suduiraut ½ bottle £22.50 (STA)
la Tour Blanche £23.45 (JON) £28.91 (NO)
1981
Climens £26.35 (JON)
1980
Climens £24.95 (RAE) £27.20 (TAN)
1978
Guiraud £20.37 (FA)
1975
Filhot £27.50 (BEN) £29.95 (POR)

£30.00 → £39.99

1990
Climens £35.00 (RAE)
Guiraud £30.00 (MV) £32.17 (HA)
Lafaurie-Peyraguey £32.00 (HOG) £36.50
(STA) £37.51 (NO) £38.50 (VIG)
1989
Climens £36.00 (RAE) £36.00 (WS)
Coutet £30.00 (WS)
Lafaurie-Peyraguey £33.59 (BUT) £38.00
(BER)
Rieussec £35.00 (RAE) £38.10 (AD)
Rieussec ½ bottle £32.00 (STA)
Sigalas-Rabaud £36.52 (BUT)
Suduiraut £32.00 (PIP) £33.49 (ROS) £34.59
(BO)
la Tour Blanche £33.25 (AD)
1988
Climens £37.50 (BUT) £38.78 (WY)
Coutet £31.01 (TAN) £32.50 (EL) £34.95
(LAY) £37.50 (ROB)
Lafaurie-Peyraguey £37.50 (RES)
Rayne-Vigneau £37.50 (RES)
Rieussec £34.99 (OD)
Rieussec ½ bottle £32.08 (NO)
Suduiraut £30.65 (BUT)
1986
Climens £32.52 (HA) £35.25 (BUT)
de Fargues £36.52 (FA)
Rieussec £34.50 (PIP) £38.78 (WY)
1985
Suduiraut £32.90 (AV)

1983
Coutet £31.68 (TAN) £32.99 (HA) £35.00
(ROB)
Lafaurie-Peyraguey £32.50 (BEN)
Rieussec £36.52 (FA)
Rieussec ½ bottle £30.95 (UB)
Sigalas-Rabaud £35.00 (VIG)
1982
Suduiraut £38.50 (ROB)
1981
Climens £32.50 (RES)
1980
Climens £36.40 (UB)
1975
Coutet £30.65 (FA) £33.70 (TAN)
1970
la Tour Blanche £35.00 (VIG)
1966
Guiraud £33.78 (BIB)
1935
la Tour Blanche £38.78 (WY)
1924
Guiraud ½ bottle £31.73 (WY)

£40.00 → £59.99

1990
Bastor-Lamontagne £40.44 (BUT)
de Fargues £56.95 (LAY) £59.00 (VIG)
Rieussec £42.50 (LAY) £46.00 (BER)
la Tour Blanche £45.00 (BER)
d'Yquem ½ bottle £56.30 (WATT) £57.92
(FA)
1989
Climens £52.00 (BER)
de Fargues £59.00 (VIG)
Sigalas-Rabaud £46.50 (BER)
Suduiraut £47.20 (FOR)
1988
Climens £46.08 (TAN)
de Fargues £59.00 (VIG)
Rieussec £45.00 (POR) £49.50 (NA)
Suduiraut £49.00 (BER)
1986
Climens £47.00 (WY)
Rieussec £40.80 (TAN) £46.50 (BER) £46.50
(WR) £46.50 (BOT) £48.94 (NO)
1985
de Fargues £52.68 (BUT)

> *In each price band wines
> are listed in vintage order.
> Within each vintage they
> are listed in A–Z order.*

1983
Climens £43.95 (LAY) £46.50 (BEN) £47.00 (WY) £48.00 (LEA)
Guiraud £43.00 (BER)
Lafaurie-Peyraguey £45.00 (RES)
Rieussec £42.70 (NI) £47.00 (WY) £50.24 (TAN) £57.50 (RES)
Rieussec ½ bottle £53.00 (JON)
1982
Suduiraut £47.25 (UB)
1976
Rieussec £59.50 (RES)
1975
Coutet £40.00 (RES)
Filhot £56.40 (WY)
Rieussec £45.50 (JON)
1971
Suduiraut £44.65 (WY)
1956
Gilette £47.29 (FA)
1949
la Tour Blanche £52.75 (FA)
1924
Guiraud ½ bottle £52.88 (WY)
1923
la Tour Blanche £58.75 (WY)

£60.00 → £89.99

1990
d'Yquem ½ bottle £69.99 (OD) £72.85 (BUT)
1989
d'Yquem ½ bottle £60.37 (FA) £62.57 (WATT) £74.99 (OD) £76.00 (MV) £76.38 (WY) £85.00 (RES) £85.09 (BUT)
1988
Rieussec £61.00 (STA)
d'Yquem ½ bottle £65.26 (FA) £69.99 (OD) £70.16 (BUT) £77.55 (WY) £85.00 (MV)
1985
d'Yquem ½ bottle £81.42 (BUT)
1983
Raymond-Lafon £82.25 (WY)
1967
Climens £68.50 (RAE) £77.55 (WY)
1962
Sigalas-Rabaud £76.38 (WY)
1961
Coutet £64.63 (WY)
1939
Filhot £88.13 (WY)
Rayne-Vigneau £70.50 (WY)
1934
Filhot £88.13 (WY)
1926
Lafaurie-Peyraguey £64.63 (WY)

1924
Coutet £78.73 (WY)
1919
Sigalas-Rabaud £88.13 (WY)

£90.00 → £119.99

1990
d'Yquem £102.81 (WATT) £108.49 (FA)
1989
d'Yquem £110.94 (FA) £117.50 (HA)
d'Yquem ½ bottle £90.00 (VIG) £95.00 (ROB) £105.16 (TW)
1986
d'Yquem ½ bottle £99.50 (ROB)
1982
d'Yquem ½ bottle £113.60 (UB)
1968
d'Yquem £105.75 (WY)
1966
Climens £99.88 (WY)
1962
Gilette £99.88 (WY)
1943
Rieussec £111.63 (WY)
1941
Rayne-Vigneau £111.63 (WY)
1928
Climens £94.00 (WY)

£120.00 → £149.99

1990
d'Yquem £125.00 (WS) £126.12 (BUT) £135.00 (OD) £145.00 (LEA) £149.50 (LAY)
1989
d'Yquem £129.00 (OD) £135.13 (WY) £145.00 (LAY) £147.50 (TAN)
1988
d'Yquem £128.56 (FA) £137.00 (BIB) £138.36 (BUT) £141.00 (WY) £145.00 (LAY)
1981
d'Yquem £120.00 (BEN) £141.00 (WY) £145.00 (LEA)
1978
d'Yquem £129.00 (YOU)
1945
Rayne-Vigneau £135.13 (WY)

£150.00 → £199.99

1990
d'Yquem £155.00 (TAN) £160.00 (VIG)
1989
d'Yquem £165.00 (RES) £169.20 (BUT) £197.99 (TW)

1988
d'Yquem £165.00 (RES) £185.00 (DI)
1986
d'Yquem £165.00 (LAY) £165.00 (OD)
1983
d'Yquem £167.73 (BUT) £190.00 (ROB)
1982
d'Yquem £175.00 (BER)
1981
d'Yquem £159.50 (RES)
1980
d'Yquem £180.00 (ROB)
1971
de Fargues £152.75 (WY)
1968
d'Yquem £179.00 (POR)
1960
d'Yquem £176.25 (FA)
1959
Rieussec £150.00 (BEN)
1953
Climens £170.00 (BEN)
1934
Filhot £160.00 (ROB)
1924
Climens £152.75 (WY)
1919
Climens £158.63 (WY)

£200.00 → £299.99

1986
d'Yquem £205.00 (BER) £211.50 (TW)
1983
d'Yquem £260.00 (RES)
1976
d'Yquem £202.00 (FA) £229.13 (WY)
  £230.00 (BEN) £295.00 (RES)
1971
d'Yquem £266.00 (BEN)
1966
d'Yquem £246.75 (WY)
1962
d'Yquem £252.63 (FA)
1959
d'Yquem ½ bottle £246.75 (WY)
1934
Gilette Crème de Tête £235.00 (TW)
1921
Filhot £235.00 (WY)

£300.00 → £399.99

1976
d'Yquem £325.00 (ROB)
1962
d'Yquem £345.00 (POR) £350.00 (RES)

1956
d'Yquem £346.63 (WY)
1950
d'Yquem £335.00 (BEN)
1929
Climens £364.25 (FA)

£400.00 → £499.99

1967
d'Yquem £423.00 (FA) £495.00 (RES)
1962
d'Yquem £410.00 (ROB)
1959
d'Yquem £400.00 (NO) £452.38 (FA)
1955
d'Yquem £495.00 (BEN)
1953
d'Yquem £470.00 (POR) £499.38 (WY)

c. £506.00

1933
d'Yquem £505.25 (WY)

£560.00 → £565.00

1967
d'Yquem £560.00 (BEN) £564.00 (WY)

c. £635.00

1959
d'Yquem £635.00 (BEN)

£700.00 → £750.00

1949
d'Yquem £728.50 (WY)
1945
d'Yquem £750.00 (ROB)

c. £852.00

1928
d'Yquem £851.88 (WY)

ROSÉ

Under £5.00

1996
Bel Air £4.95 (WS)
1995
Thieuley Clairet £4.65 (SOM)

£5.00 → £6.50

1996
de Sours Rosé £5.99 (MAJ)
1995
Thieuley Clairet £6.34 (ROS)

BURGUNDY

All the world wants Burgundy, and large parts of the world can pay high prices for it. This means the rest of us have to be cunning to find affordable wines

There are times I wish I was a millionaire. Look at these prices: £475.50 for just six bottles of Sauzet Bâtard-Montrachet. £600 for a full case of Sauzet Puligny-Montrachet Les Combettes. £792 for a case of Jean-Noël Gagnard's Bâtard-Montrachet. Yes, the 1995 Burgundies are on offer, and demand is strong.

So strong that by the time you read this all the above wines will have been snapped up. Yes, even at those prices. If you're still hoping to buy top Burgundy from the 1995 vintage, you may have to think again.

This is where buying Burgundy differs from buying Bordeaux. You certainly *can* buy claret when the first en primeur offers appear – but you don't have to. Except in the case of the tiniest Pomerol châteaux, the wines will almost always be available later. In Burgundy quantities are just too small: Justerini & Brooks had only ten cases of Sauzet's Bâtard-Montrachet.

Non-millionaires like me have to find other ways of buying Burgundy. And opening offers aren't such a bad idea at my level, either: there were some lovely basic Bourgogne Blancs around from the likes of Jean-Yves Devevey and Jean-Philippe Fichet for around £100 a case. If that seems a lot to pay for basic Burgundy, remember that no Burgundy is cheap, and you'll get better value from a good grower in a simple appellation than vice versa.

And yes, you can still find certain wines later, when they've got some bottle age. Waitrose and Oddbins are particularly good hunting grounds for fairly priced village wines made with style and flair.

GRAPE VARIETIES

ALIGOTÉ (white) Not planted in the best sites – though there are a few vines in Corton-Charlemagne. Aligoté from old vines can produce a lovely, refreshing wine, scented like buttermilk soap yet as sharp and palate-cleansing as a squeeze of lemon juice. *Dujac* and a few others barrique-ferment Aligoté with surprising success.

CHARDONNAY (white) In a world panting for Chardonnay, Burgundy makes the most famous Chardonnay of all. Even in the decidedly dicky Burgundian climate, it produces good to excellent wine almost every year. Its flavour depends on where it is grown, and how the wine is made. Chardonnays made without the use of oak barrels for aging will taste very different from barrel-aged wines. A Mâcon produced in stainless steel will have appley fruit; Côte Chalonnaise Chardonnay is generally rather taut and chalky-dry, but given some oak, it can become delicately nutty. In the North of the Beaujolais region Chardonnay has a stony dryness; in the South it is nearer to the fatter, softer, wines of southern Burgundy. Chablis generally produces lean wine, but in riper years and with some oak aging it can get much rounder. The Côte d'Or is the peak of achievement for Chardonnay, and a top wine from the Côte de Beaune manages to be luscious, creamy and honeyed yet totally dry, the rich, ripe fruit entwined with the scents of new oak in a surprisingly powerful wine – from the right producer, the world's greatest dry white. It is this that has so enticed wineries elsewhere to mimic Burgundian Chardonnay.

GAMAY (red) The Gamay has no pretensions: in Beaujolais it can simply make one of the juiciest, most gulpable, gurgling

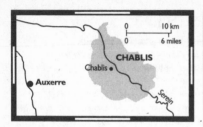

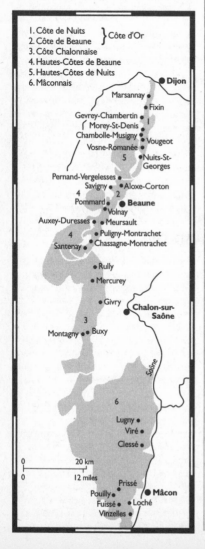

1. Côte de Nuits ⎫
2. Côte de Beaune ⎬ Côte d'Or
3. Côte Chalonnaise ⎭
4. Hautes-Côtes de Beaune
5. Hautes-Côtes de Nuits
6. Mâconnais

CLASSIFICATIONS

Burgundy has five different levels of classification:

Non-specific regional appellations with no geographical definition, e.g. Bourgogne, which may come from inferior land or young vines.

Specific regional appellations, e.g. Côte de Beaune-Villages, generally a blend from one or more villages. Côte de Nuits-Villages is usually better.

Village commune wines Each village has its vineyards legally defined. Vineyards with no special reputation are usually blended together under the village name. But there is a growing move towards even relatively unknown vineyards appearing on the label. These unclassified vineyards are called *lieux-dits* or 'stated places'. They can only appear on the label in letters half the size of the village name.

Premier cru It's typical of Burgundy that *premier cru* or 'First Growth' actually means 'Second Growth', because these are the second-best vineyard sites. Even so, they contain some of Burgundy's finest wines. They are classified by both village and vineyard names, e.g. Gevrey-Chambertin, Combe-aux-Moines. The vineyard name must follow the village name on the label, and it may be in the same size print. Confusingly, some growers use smaller print, but the appellation should make it clear whether it is a *premier cru* or a *lieu-dit*.

Grand cru These are the real top growths. Not every village has one. The reds are mostly in the Côte de Nuits, the whites in the Côte de Beaune. A *grand cru* vineyard name can stand alone on the label without the village – for example, Chambertin from the village of Gevrey-Chambertin. (Note that by tradition, a Burgundy village is allowed to tack on the name of its *grand cru* vineyard, and use the compound name for wines that have nothing to do with the *grand cru*, for instance Puligny-Montrachet.)

wines the world has to offer. Can, I stress: not all Beaujolais is like this. Ideally it is simple, cherry-sharp, with candy-like fruit, sometimes with hints of raspberry or strawberry. The wines from the *crus* go further, but in the main their similarity from the grape is greater than the differences in the places they come from. All but the wines of the top villages should be drunk as young as you can find them.

PINOT BEUROT (white) Known elsewhere as Pinot Gris. Very rare in Burgundy, but it produces rich, buttery wine usually used to soften Chardonnay. There is a little unblended Pinot Beurot in the Hautes-Côtes and Aloxe-Corton.

PINOT BLANC (white) There is a little of this in the Côte d'Or – in Aloxe-Corton, for instance, where it makes a soft, quick-maturing wine. Rully in the Côte Chalonnaise has some and it ripens well in the Hautes-Côtes. There is also an odd white mutation of Pinot Noir – as in Nuits-St-Georges where the *premier cru* la Perrière makes a savoury white, and in the Monts Luisants vineyard in Morey-St-Denis.

PINOT NOIR (red) The sulkiest, trickiest fine wine grape in the world is the exclusive grape in almost all red Burgundies. It needs a more delicate balance of spring, summer and autumn climate than any other variety to achieve greatness.

It used to be true to say that no other part of the world could produce a Pinot Noir to match those of Burgundy. But isolated growers in Oregon, California, New Zealand, Australia and South Africa are now making very fine examples. Even so, Burgundy is still the only place on earth where fine Pinot Noirs are made in any great quantity. The problem is, there are still some awful Pinot Noirs, too: heavy, chewy and sweet-fruited or thin and pallid. But there are fewer of these now, as standards have risen to help to justify Burgundy prices. From a good producer Burgundian Pinot Noir should be light, elegant, intense, and perfumed with raspberry or strawberry fruit and a hint of violets. Oak will add spicier, complex notes. Except for wine from the very top vineyards, Burgundy can be drunk young with pleasure. But a great *cru* from a great vintage undoubtedly benefits from a decade or more in bottle.

WINE REGIONS

ALOXE-CORTON, AC (Côte de Beaune; red, white) Overwhelmingly a red-wine village, and it has the only red *grand cru* in the Côte de Beaune, le Corton, also sold under various subdivisions like Corton-Bressandes and Corton Clos du Roi and more widely available than the other *grands crus* of Burgundy. If we're talking about village wines, then the reds of Savigny are at least as good, and you're not paying a premium there for the hyphenated Corton. Go for *Jadot, Drouhin, Jaffelin, Chandon de Briailles, Daniel Senard,* and *Tollot-Beaut.* Also good: *Faiveley, Dubreuil-Fontaine, Juillot, Michel Voarick, Bouzereau-Gruère.*

The village also has one of the Côte's most famous white *grands crus,* Corton-Charlemagne. This can be a magnificent,

blasting wall of flavour, not big on nuance, but strong, buttery and ripe, traditionally supposed to require long aging to show its full potential. Except from a handful of producers, Corton-Charlemagne rarely matches the quality of Burgundy's other white *grands crus.* Some argue that the *cru* is simply too large; others that the temptation to overproduce is not always resisted.

AUXEY-DURESSES, AC (Côte de Beaune; red, white) A village with a deservedly high reputation for full, but fairly gentle, nicely fruity reds. Excellent wines have been made recently by a handful of good growers. Look for *Ampeau, Diconne, Alain Gras, Duc de Magenta, Leroy, Roy, Pascal Prunier, Thévenin.*

Too many of the whites recently have been disappointingly soft and flabby, but producers like *Ampeau, Diconne, Duc de Magenta, Jadot, Leroy* and *Pascal Prunier* are still making pretty decent stuff.

BÂTARD-MONTRACHET, AC

(Côte de Beaune; white) *Grand cru* of Chassagne and Puligny lying just below le Montrachet and, from a good producer, displaying a good deal of its dramatic flavour, almost thick in the mouth, all roast nuts, butter, toast and honey. Can be exciting, if inevitably expensive. Good names: *Blain-Gagnard, Jean-Noël Gagnard, Leflaive, Bernard Morey, Pierre Morey, Michel Niellon, Pernot, Poirier, Ramonet* and *Sauzet*.

BEAUJOLAIS, AC

(red) This covers all the basic wines, the produce of the flatter, southern part of Beaujolais. Most of the best is now sold as Nouveau. Run-of-the-mill Beaujolais, apart from Nouveau, is likely to be pretty thin stuff, or beefed up illegally with something altogether different. But since you're allowed to re-label Nouveau as 'Beaujolais', some of the best wine in the new year (much appreciated by those who scoff at Nouveau) will be none other than re-labelled Nouveau. Best: *Blaise, Carron, Charmet, Ch. de la Plume,* co-op at *Bully, Duboeuf Bouteille Cristal, Garlon, Labruyère, Loron, Paul Sapin, Domaine des Vissoux.*

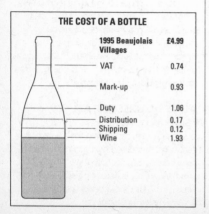

THE COST OF A BOTTLE

1995 Beaujolais Villages		£4.99
VAT		0.74
Mark-up		0.93
Duty		1.06
Distribution		0.17
Shipping		0.12
Wine		1.93

BEAUJOLAIS BLANC, AC (white)

Usually quite expensive and in its rather firm, stony-dry way is rarely as enjoyable as a good Mâcon-Villages. I'd plant Gamay instead if I lived there. *Charmet* is the most interesting producer, and *Tête* is good.

BEAUJOLAIS NOUVEAU (or PRIMEUR)

(red) The new vintage wine of Beaujolais, released in the same year as the grapes are gathered, at midnight on the third Thursday in November. It will normally improve for several months in bottle, and even longer in good Nouveau vintages – a couple of years, maybe.

BEAUJOLAIS ROSÉ, AC (rosé)

Usually an apology for a wine, although the co-op at *Bois d'Oingt* can make good stuff. But it's usually too expensive.

BEAUJOLAIS SUPÉRIEUR, AC (red)

Supérieur means that the basic alcoholic content is higher. It doesn't ensure a better wine, and is rarely seen on the label.

BEAUJOLAIS-VILLAGES, AC (red)

Thirty-nine villages can use this title. The wines are certainly better than basic Beaujolais, a little fuller and deeper, and the cherry-sharp fruit of the Gamay is usually more marked. However, always look for a wine bottled in the region, and preferably one from a single vineyard, because an anonymous blend of Beaujolais-Villages may simply mean a heftier version of an ordinary Beaujolais. *Noël Aucoeur, Domaine de la Brasse, Domaine de la Chapelle de Vatre (Sarrau), Jacques Dépagneux, de Flammerécourt, Château Gaillard, Gutty Père et Fils, André Large, Château des Loges, Jean-Charles Pivot, Jean-Luc Tissier, Trichard* and *Château des Vergers* are good and local, but most domaines are bottled by one of the merchants in the region. Labelling by the domaine is on the increase.

BEAUNE, AC

(Côte de Beaune; red, white) One of the few reliable commune wines, usually quite light, with a soft, 'red fruits' sweetness and a flicker of something minerally to smarten it up nicely. The wines are nearly all red. Beaune has the largest acreage of vines of any Côte d'Or commune, and they are mostly owned by merchants. It has no *grands crus* but many excellent *premiers crus*, for example Grèves, Marconnets, Teurons, Boucherottes, Vignes Franches and Cent Vignes. Prices tend to be reasonable, as Beaune is less fashionable than many. The best producers here are *Morot, Drouhin, Jadot* and *Tollot-Beaut,* but reliable wines are also made by *Lafarge, Besancenot-Mathouillet, Bouley, Germain, Jaffelin* and *Morey.*

BIENVENUES-BÂTARD-MONTRACHET, AC (Côte de Beaune; white)
A tiny *grand cru* situated in Puligny below le Montrachet, and within the larger Bâtard-Montrachet AC, whose wines are similar. The Bienvenues wines, however, are often lighter and more elegant, although they may lack a tiny bit of Bâtard's drive. Best producers: *Carillon, Clerc, Leflaive, Pernot, Ramonet.*

BLAGNY, AC (Côte de Beaune; red)
The red wines from this village are usually a bit fierce, but then this is the white wine heartland of Burgundy, so I'm a bit surprised they grow any red at all. Best producers: *Leflaive, Matrot.*

BONNES-MARES, AC (Côte de Nuits; red)
Usually one of the most – or should I say one of the very few – reliable *grands crus,* which ages extremely well over ten to 20 years to a lovely smoky, chocolate-and-prunes richness. Best names: *Domaine des Varoilles, Drouhin, Dujac, Groffier, Jadot, Roumier, de Vogüé.*

BOURGOGNE ALIGOTÉ, AC
(white) Usually rather sharp and green except where old vines make exciting wine, but the locals add crème de cassis to it to make kir – which tells you quite a lot about

it. Best: *Coche-Dury, Confuron, Devevey, Diconne, Jobard, Rion, Rollin.*

BOURGOGNE ALIGOTÉ DE BOUZERON, AC (Côte Chalonnaise; white)
The white wine pride of the Côte Chalonnaise is made from the Aligoté grape in the village of Bouzeron. The vines are frequently old – this seems to be more crucial for Aligoté than for most other wines – and the buttermilk soap nose is followed by a very dry, slightly lemony, pepper-sharp wine, too good to mix with cassis. The best of all Aligotés, rich and oaky, comes from *de Villaine. Chanzy* and *Bouchard Père et Fils* are also good.

BOURGOGNE BLANC, AC (white)
Anything from a basic Burgundy grown in the less good spots anywhere between Chablis and the Mâconnais to a carefully matured wine from a serious producer, either from young vines or from parts of his vineyard that just miss a superior AC, especially on the borders of Meursault. Best: *Boisson-Vadot, Michel Bouzereau, Boyer-Martenot, Boisson-Morey, Coche-Dury, J Deverey, Dussort, Jadot, Javillier, Jobard, Labouré-Roi, René Manuel, Millot-Battault* and the *Buxy* co-op (look for *Clos de Chenoves*).

BOURGOGNE GRAND ORDINAIRE, AC (red)
Très ordinaire. Pas très grand. The bottom of the Burgundy barrel, rarely seen outside Burgundy. It may be made from Pinot Noir and Gamay, and even a couple of obscure grapes, the Tressot and César, as well.

BOURGOGNE PASSE-TOUT-GRAINS, AC (red)
Often decent, lightish wine made usually in the Côte d'Or or the Côte Chalonnaise from Gamay blended with a minimum of one-third Pinot Noir. In some years it may be mostly Pinot. *Rodet* and *Chanson* make it well, but *Rion, Léni-Volpato, Henri Jayer, Thomas, Chaley* or *Cornu* are also good. But even at its absolute best, true Burgundy it ain't.

BOURGOGNE ROUGE, AC (red) The basic red AC, stretching from Chablis in the North to the Beaujolais *crus* in the South. Unknown Bourgogne Rouge is best avoided – much of it is very basic indeed. Domaine-bottled Bourgogne Rouge from good growers – and a handful of merchants – can be excellent value. The best wines come from vineyards just outside the village appellations. Look for *Bourgeon, Coche-Dury, Germain, d'Heuilly-Huberdeau, Henri Jayer, Juillot, Lafarge, Mortet, Parent, Pousse d'Or, Rion* and *Rossignol*. Good merchants include *Drouhin, Faiveley, Jadot, Jaffelin, Labouré-Roi, Latour, Olivier Leflaive, Leroy, Rodet, Vallet*. The co-ops at *Buxy* and *Igé* are also good as is the *Caves des Hautes-Côtes*. Most wines should be drunk quite young.

BROUILLY, AC (Beaujolais; red) Brouilly usually makes one of the lightest *cru* wines, and in general rarely improves much with keeping. In fact, it makes a very good Nouveau. A few properties make a bigger wine to age – but even then, nine months to a year is quite enough. Good names include *Château de la Chaize, Domaine Crêt des Garanches, Château de Fouilloux, Hospices de Belleville, Château de Pierreux, Domaine de Combillaty (Duboeuf), Domaine de Garanches, André Large* and *Château de Nevers. Château des Tours*, although lovely young, can age longer.

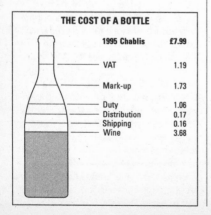

THE COST OF A BOTTLE

	1995 Chablis	£7.99
VAT		1.19
Mark-up		1.73
Duty		1.06
Distribution		0.17
Shipping		0.16
Wine		3.68

CHABLIS, AC (white) Simple Chablis, mostly soft, sometimes acidic, covers the widest area of the appellation. So it covers a multitude of sins, with a lot of wine going under négociants' labels, and a lot being sold by the local co-op, *la Chablisienne* – they make most of the négociants' stuff too. Some of the co-op's best *cuvées* are outstandingly good, but many are too bland and soft. New oak, which is lavishly used by growers such as Fèvre and Droin, often smothers the steely and minerally qualities that make top Chablis so exciting. Best: *Adhémar-Boudin, Christian Adine, Pascal Bouchard, Jean-Marc Brocard, la Chablisienne co-op, Jean Collet, René Dauvissat, Defaix, Jean-Paul Droin, Joseph Drouhin, William Fèvre, Alain Geoffroy, Jean-Pierre Grossot, Michel Laroche, Bernard Légland, Long Depaquit, Louis Michel, Dom. des Milandes, Moreau, Guy Mothe, Raveneau, Regnard, Savary, Simmonet-Fèbvre, Robert Vocoret*.

CHABLIS GRAND CRU, AC (white) The seven *grands crus* (Blanchots, Preuses, Bougros, Grenouilles, Valmur, Vaudésir and les Clos) *can* be outstanding, though they seldom rival the *grands crus* of the Côte de Beaune. To get the best out of them, you need to age them, preferably after oaking, although *Louis Michel's* oak-free wines age superbly. Recent vintages have seen a growing use of oak, sometimes giving deeper, richer wines which will benefit from bottle-aging, but some wines are marred by clumsy or excessive use of new oak.

CHABLIS PREMIER CRU, AC (white) There are some 30 vineyard names in this category, but they have been rationalized into 12 main plots. Expansion mania has meant that many hardly suitable pieces of vineyard are now accorded *premier cru* status, so the difference in quality between basic Chablis and *premier cru* isn't always all that it should be. However, in recent years there has been a definite move towards quality by the better growers and *la Chablisienne* co-operative.

CHAMBERTIN, AC (Côte de Nuits; red) Most famous of the eight *grands crus* of Gevrey-Chambertin, this vineyard should and can make wines that are big, strong and intense in their youth, mellowing to a complex, perfumed, plummy richness as they mature. Good ones need ten to 15 years' aging. Best producers: *Drouhin, Faiveley, Leroy, Denis Mortet, Ponsot, Rebourseau, Rousseau, Tortochot.*

CHAMBERTIN CLOS-DE-BÈZE, AC (Côte de Nuits; red) *Grand cru* in the village of Gevrey-Chambertin next to Chambertin both geographically and in quality. It needs seven to ten years in bottle. May be sold as Chambertin. Best: *Drouhin, Bruno Clair, Faiveley, Gelin, Mugneret-Gibourg, Rousseau, Thomas-Moillard* and *Damoy* since 1992.

CHAMBOLLE-MUSIGNY, AC (Côte de Nuits; red) This village can make light, cherry-sweet, intensely perfumed Burgundy, but sadly most commercial Chambolle will be too sweet and gooey to retain much perfume. The best producer is *Georges Roumier*, with wonderful wines in every vintage from 1985. The best *premier cru* is les Amoureuses, which deserves to be *grand cru* and is priced accordingly. Best producers: *Barthod-Noëllat, Château de Chambolle-Musigny, Drouhin, Dujac, Groffier, Hudelot-Noëllat, Rion, Serveau, de Vogüé.*

CHAPELLE-CHAMBERTIN, AC (Côte de Nuits; red) The wines of this *grand cru* are typically lighter and more delicate than the other *grands crus*. But over-lightness – resulting from over-production – is their curse. The best producers are *Damoy* (since 1993), *Louis Jadot* and *Rossignol-Trapet.*

CHARMES-CHAMBERTIN, AC (Côte de Nuits; red) This is the biggest of the *grands crus* of Gevrey-Chambertin. It can be fine, strong, sensuous wine, but as with all of them, it can also be disgracefully light. Best producers: *Bachelet, Charlopin-*

CHABLIS VINEYARDS

Grands Crus
Blanchots, Bougros, les Clos, Grenouilles, Preuses, Valmur, Vaudésir. la Moutonne, considered a *grand cru*, is from a parcel in Preuses and Vaudésir.

Premiers Crus
Fourchaume (including Fourchaume, Vaupulent, Côte de Fontenay, Vaulorent, l'Homme Mort); Montée de Tonnerre (including Montée de Tonnerre, Chapelot, Pied d'Aloup); Monts de Milieu; Vaucoupin; les Fourneaux (including les Fourneaux, Morein, Côte des Prés-Girots); Beauroy (including Beauroy, Troesmes); Côte de Léchet; Vaillons (including Vaillons, Châtains, Séché, Beugnons, les Lys); Mélinots (including Mélinots, Roncières, les Épinottes); Montmains (including Montmains, Forêts, Butteaux); Vosgros (including Vosgros and Vaugiraut); Vaudevey.

Parisot, Drouhin, Dugat, Dujac, Rebourseau, Roty, Rousseau, Tortochot.

CHASSAGNE-MONTRACHET, AC (Côte de Beaune; red, white) Its fame lies in its large share of the white *grand cru* vineyard of le Montrachet. The reds are a puzzle. At their best they're good value, if a bit heavy, plummy and earthy. The best names for red are *Amiot-Bonfils, Carillon, Colin, Jean-Noël Gagnard, Duc de Magenta, Gagnard-Delagrange, René Lamy, Albert Morey, Moreau, Jean Pillot, Ramonet.* Of the whites, the *grands crus* are excellent, but the *premiers crus* rarely dazzle quite like those of nearby Puligny-Montrachet. The Chassagne '86s are mostly at their best now, and should be drunk; the '89s are wonderfully ripe and concentrated and can be drunk now or kept for years. The '90s and '92s will be magic. Best producers of white in Chassagne include: *Blain-Gagnard, Carillon, Colin, Duc de Magenta, Fontaine-Gagnard, Jean-Noël Gagnard, Gagnard-Delagrange, Lamy-Pillot, Laguiche, Château de* la Maltroye, Moreau, Albert Morey, Bernard Morey, Niellon, Fernand Pillot and Ramonet. Jaffelin is the best merchant here.

CHÉNAS, AC (Beaujolais; red) This is the second-smallest Beaujolais cru, making strong, dark wines, sometimes a bit tough, that can be drunk a year after the harvest, or aged to take on a Pinot Noir-like flavour. Ultra-fashionable in France at the moment. Look out for Louis Champagnon, Charvet, Château de Chénas, Domaines des Brureaux, Domaine Chassignon, Domaine de la Combe Remont (Duboeuf), Pierre Perrachon and Émile Robin.

CHEVALIER-MONTRACHET, AC (Côte de Beaune; white) A grand cru vineyard of the village of Puligny, giving a leaner wine than le Montrachet, but one with a deep flavour as rich and satisfying as a dry white wine can get. Good examples will last for 20 years. Best: Bouchard Père et Fils, Clerc, Jadot, Latour, Leflaive, Niellon.

CHIROUBLES, AC (Beaujolais; red) A cru for early drinking: naturally light, similar to Beaujolais-Villages in weight, but with a cherry scent that makes it France's favourite Beaujolais cru. Look for Georges Boulon, René Brouillard, Cheysson, Château Javernand, Château de Raousset, Jean-Pierre Desvignes, Duboeuf, Méziat and Georges Passot.

CHOREY-LÈS-BEAUNE, AC (Côte de Beaune; red) A source of good value, soft, fruity reds. Because the village isn't popular or hyped, these are some of the few affordable Burgundies. Drouhin, Germain and Tollot-Beaut are the best producers.

CLOS DES LAMBRAYS, AC (Côte de Nuits; red) This grand cru in Morey-St-Denis belongs to a single owner, and has recently been sold. The estate had become very run down and the wines were not only very rare but also not very tasty. Let's hope the new owner can change things.

CLOS DE LA ROCHE, AC (Côte de Nuits; red) Largest and finest grand cru of Morey-St-Denis. When not made too lightweight, this can be splendid wine, full of redcurrant-and-strawberry richness when young, but coming to resemble pretty good Chambertin after ten years or so. Best names: Amiot, Dujac, Leroy, both Hubert and Georges Lignier, Ponsot, Rousseau.

CLOS ST-DENIS, AC (Côte de Nuits; red) This small vineyard has rarely achieved great heights and is probably the least famous of all the grands crus. Dujac's is the best known, but look out for Charlopin-Parisot, Georges or Hubert Lignier, Ponsot.

CLOS DE TART, AC (Côte de Nuits; red) Grand cru of Morey-St-Denis owned by Beaujolais merchants Mommessin. At best it is light but intense wine which lasts.

CLOS DE VOUGEOT, AC (Côte de Nuits; red) Over 80 growers share this grand cru and, while the land at the top of the slope is very fine, the land by the road is not. That rare thing, a good bottle of Clos de Vougeot, is fat, rich, strong and thick with the sweetness of perfumed plums and honey, unsubtle but exciting. It is only found in top vintages, like 1988 and '90, and then only from the best producers. Best names: Arnoux, Ch. de la Tour, Jacky Confuron, Drouhin-Laroze, Engel, Grivot, Gros, Hudelot-Noëllat, Jadot, Lamarche, Leroy, Meo-Camuzet, Mugneret, Raphet.

CORTON, AC (Côte de Beaune; red, white) The only red grand cru vineyard in the Côte de Beaune. Ideally, red Corton should have something of the richness and strength of Clos de Vougeot, but it tends to be four-square and unrewarding until it is mature, and then only the top wines are good. Best producers include: Chandon de Briailles, Dubreuil-Fontaine, Faiveley, Gaunoux, Laleur-Piot, Maldant, Prince de Mérode, Rapet, Daniel Senard, Tollot-Beaut. The finest white is the Hospices de Beaune's Corton-

Vergennes, and *Chandon de Briailles* makes Corton-Bressandes that is half Pinot Blanc.

CORTON-CHARLEMAGNE, AC

(Côte de Beaune; white) This famous *grand cru* of Aloxe-Corton and Pernand-Vergelesses occupies the upper half of the dome-shaped hill of Corton. It is planted almost entirely with Chardonnay, but a little Pinot Blanc or Pinot Beurot can add intriguing fatness to the wine. Good names: *Bitouzet, Bonneau du Martray, Chandon de Briailles, Chapuis, Dubreuil-Fontaine, M Juillot, Hospices de Beaune, Jadot, Laleure-Piot, Latour, Rapet.*

CÔTE CHALONNAISE, AC (red,

white) Light, usually clean-tasting Chardonnay predominates among the whites – although at long last the idea of oak-aging is catching on. But the Côte Chalonnaise has one star that cannot be overshadowed by the famous Côte d'Or: the village of Bouzeron makes the finest and the most famous Aligoté in all France. The top three villages of Rully, Mercurey and Givry all produce good reds, too, with a lovely, simple strawberry-and-cherry fruit.

CÔTE DE BEAUNE (red, white) The

southern part of the Côte d'Or, fairly evenly divided between red and white wines. The tiny AC Côte de Beaune can produce light but tasty reds in warm years. Best producers: *Bouchard Père et Fils, René Manuel, J Allexant.*

CÔTE DE BEAUNE-VILLAGES, AC

(red) Catch-all red wine appellation for 16 villages on the Côte de Beaune. Only Aloxe-Corton, Beaune, Volnay and Pommard cannot use the appellation. Rarely seen nowadays and rarely exciting. Still, it *is* worth checking out the wines of *Jaffelin, Lequin-Roussot* and *Bachelet.*

CÔTE DE BROUILLY, AC (Beaujolais;

red) The Mont de Brouilly, a pyramid-shaped hill in the middle of the *cru* of Brouilly, makes quite different wine to Brouilly itself. The soil is of volcanic origin, and the slopes lap up the sun. Best: *Château Thivin, Conroy, Domaine de la Pierre Bleue, Jean Sanvers, Lucien Verger, Chanrion.*

CÔTE DE NUITS (red, white) The

northern part of the Côte d'Or, in theory producing the biggest wines. Frequently it doesn't and many of Burgundy's most disappointing bottles come from the top Côte de Nuits communes. It is almost entirely devoted to Pinot Noir.

CÔTE DE NUITS-VILLAGES, AC

(red) Covers the three southernmost villages of Prissey, Comblanchien and Corgoloin, plus Fixin and Brochon in the North. Usually fairly light and dry, it can have good cherry fruit and the delicious vegetal decay flavour of good Côte de Nuits red. Often good value. Look out for *Durand, Rion, Rossignol* and *Tollot-Voarick,* and especially *Chopin-Groffier* and *Domaine de l'Arlot.*

CÔTE D'OR (red, white) The source of

Burgundy's fame – a thin sliver of land worth its weight in gold. It has two halves, the Côte de Nuits in the North and the Côte de Beaune in the South. There is a fine crop of illustrious whites in the southern portion.

CRÉMANT DE BOURGOGNE, AC

(white, rosé) Excellent, eminently affordable sparkling wine, made by the Champagne method, from Chardonnay and Pinot Noir. Try *Caves de Lugny* for white and *Caves de Bailly* for lovely fresh, strawberryish pink.

CRIOTS-BÂTARD-MONTRACHET,

AC (Côte de Beaune; white) Tiny *grand cru* in Chassagne-Montrachet nuzzled up against Bâtard-Montrachet. In fact it's hardly ever seen; the wines resemble Bâtard in power and concentration but are leaner, more minerally. Best: *Blain-Gagnard, Fontaine-Gagnard.*

CRU The ten Beaujolais *crus* or growths (Fleurie, Moulin-à-Vent, Brouilly, Chénas, Côte de Brouilly, Chiroubles, Juliénas, St-Amour, Morgon, Régnié) are the top villages in the steeply hilly, northern part of Beaujolais. All *should* have definable characteristics, but the produce of different vineyards and growers is all too often blended to a mean by merchants elsewhere. Always buy either a single-estate wine, or one from a good local merchant like *Chanut Frères, Duboeuf, Dépagneux, Ferraud, Loron, Sarrau, Thomas la Chevalière, Louis Tête,* and *Trenel*. Elsewhere in Burgundy the best vineyards are labelled *grand cru*, and the second-best *premier cru*.

ÉCHÉZEAUX, AC (Côte de Nuits; red) This is a large, slightly second-line *grand cru* vineyard in the village of Vosne-Romanée. Best producers: *Domaine de la Romanée-Conti, Engel, Faiveley, Forey, Louis Gouroux, Grivot, Henri Jayer, Mongeard-Mugneret, Mugneret-Gibourg.*

EPINEUIL, AC (red) Tiny region in the North of Burgundy, producing light but fragrant styles of Pinot Noir.

FIXIN, AC (Côte de Nuits; red) A suburb of Dijon, Fixin can make some of Burgundy's sturdiest reds: deep, strong, tough but plummy when young, but capable of mellowing with age. Such wines are slowly reappearing. If you want to feel you're drinking Gevrey-Chambertin without shouldering the cost, Fixin from the following producers could fit the bill: *Bordet, Charlopin-Parizot, Bruno Clair, Fougeray, Roger Fournier, Gelin, Guyard, Joliet, Jadot, Moillard, Philippe Rossignol.*

FLAGEY-ÉCHÉZEAUX, AC (Côte de Nuits; red) A commune that sells its basic wines as Vosne-Romanée but, in Échézeaux and Grands-Échézeaux, has two *grands crus.*

FLEURIE, AC (Beaujolais; red) Often the most delicious of the *crus*, gentle and round,

its sweet cherry-and-chocolate fruit just held firm by a touch of tannin and acid. Its deserved popularity in Britain and the US has led to high prices. Try *Château de Fleurie (Loron), Chauvet, Chignard, Colonge, Domaine de la Grand, Grand Pré (Sarrau), Domaine de la Presle, Domaine des Quatre Vents, Duboeuf's la Madone, Bernard Paul, Verpoix,* the *Fleurie* co-op's *cuvées, Cuvée Presidente Marguerite* and *Cuvée Cardinale.*

GEVREY-CHAMBERTIN, AC (Côte de Nuits; red) This village has eight *grands crus*, and two of them, Chambertin and Chambertin Clos-de-Bèze can be some of the world's greatest wines. They should have rough, plumskins and damson strength, fierce when young, but assuming a brilliant, wafting perfume and intense, plummy richness when mature. *Bachelet, Boillot, Burguet, Dugat, Michel Esmonin, Philippe Leclerc, Mortet, Naddef* and *Rossignol-Trapet* are names to look out for among younger producers. Of the old estates, *Rousseau* is best but *Domaine des Varoilles* is also good. Also look out for *Frédéric Esmonin, René Leclerc, Maume* and *Roty*, and for the merchants' bottlings from *Drouhin, Jadot, Faiveley* and *Jaffelin*. Be aware that there are still some overpriced horrors bearing the sacred name.

GIVRY, AC (Côte Chalonnaise; red) Small but important red wine village. At their best, the wines are deliciously warm and cherry-chewy with a slightly smoky fragrance to them, but there are too many mediocre bottles around, especially from négociants. *Baron Thénard* is the best estate, but *Chofflet, Clos Salomon, Joblot, Laborbe, Lespinasse, Mouton* and *Ragot* are also worth investigating.

LA GRANDE RUE, AC (Côte de Nuits; red) This vineyard is wholly owned by the Lamarche family. Elevated to *grand cru* status in 1990, more because of its potential, than because of the wines it has recently produced.

GRANDS-ÉCHÉZEAUX, AC (Côte de Nuits; red) A *grand cru* capable of delicately scented, plum-and-woodsmoke wine which goes rich and chocolaty with age. Best names: *Domaine de la Romanée-Conti, Drouhin, Engel, Mongeard-Mugneret.*

GRIOTTE-CHAMBERTIN, AC (Côte de Nuits; red) One of the smallest *grands crus* of Gevrey-Chambertin. Best: *Drouhin, Claude Dugat, F Esmonin, Ponsot, Roty.*

HAUTES-CÔTES DE BEAUNE and HAUTES-CÔTES DE NUITS (red, white) A hilly backwater consisting of 28 villages which make fairly good, light, strawberry-like Pinot and a lot of reasonably good, light, dry Chardonnay at a decent price. The red grapes do not always ripen fully every year, but they had no problems in 1989 or '90. Look out for the red Hautes-Côtes de Nuits wines of *Cornu, Domaine des Mouchottes, Jayer-Gilles, Thévenet* and *Verdet* and the red Hautes-Côtes de Beaunes of *Bouley, Capron Manieux, Chalet, Guillemard, Joliot, Mazilly* and *Plait*. The *Caves des Hautes-Côtes* is beginning to produce some of the best value wines in the whole of Burgundy. Good whites come from *Chaley, Cornu, Devevey, Goubard, Jayer-Gilles, Thévenot-le-Brun, Alain Verdet* (organic).

IRANCY, AC (red) Mostly Pinot Noir from vineyards just to the south-west of Chablis, sometimes with a little of the darker, tougher local grape, the César. Rarely deep in colour, but always perfumed, slightly plummy and attractive. Cool years can provide disappointingly thin wines. Best drunk while young and fresh. It must legally be labelled 'Bourgogne Irancy'. Good producers: *Léon & Serge Bienvenu, Bernard Cantin, André & Roger Delaloge, Gabriel Delaloge, Jean Renaud, Simmonet-Fèbvre.*

JULIÉNAS, AC (Beaujolais; red) Juliénas can be big wine, with tannin and acidity, but many of the best more closely resemble the mixture of fresh red fruit and soft, chocolaty warmth that makes for good Fleurie. Good ones include *Château du Bois de la Salle, Domaine des Bucherats, Château des Capitans, Château de Juliénas, Domaine de la Dîme, René Monnet, Domaine de la Vieille Église, Pelletier, Duboeuf.*

LADOIX-SERRIGNY, AC (Côte de Beaune; red) Overshadowed by the more famous Aloxe-Corton next door. It's worth looking out for though, as *Capitain, Cornu, Prince de Mérode, Chevalier* and *Ravaut* all make decent, crisp wines at fair prices.

LATRICIÈRES-CHAMBERTIN, AC (Côte de Nuits; red) Small *grand cru* vineyard in Gevrey-Chambertin and very similar in style to Chambertin though without the power. So long as the producer hasn't pushed the yields too high, it is at its best at ten to 15 years. Best producers: *Ponsot, Leroy, Rossignol-Trapet.*

MÂCON BLANC, AC (Mâconnais; white) This should be good value, light Chardonnay, but too often it's not. Most Mâcon simply cannot compete with the best-value New World wines.

MÂCON BLANC-VILLAGES, AC (Mâconnais; white) One step up from basic Mâcon Blanc, this must come from the 43 Mâcon communes with the best land. The rare good ones show the signs of honey and fresh apples and some of the nutty, yeasty depth associated with fine Chardonnay. These come from those villages, notably Viré, Clessé, Prissé and Lugny, that add their own village names (Mâcon-Viré, etc). Full, buttery yet fresh, sometimes spicy. There is a handful of growers making serious, oak-aged wine from low-yielding vines. *Merlin, Guffens Heynen* and *Jean Thévenet* are names to look for. Others include: *Bicheron, Bonhomme, Danauchet, Goyard, Guillemot-Michel, Josserand, Lassarat, Manciat-Poncet, Signoret, Talmard* and *Thévenet-Wicart.*

MÂCON ROUGE, AC (Mâconnais; red)
There's a lot of red wine made in the
Mâconnais but it's usually fairly lean, earthy
Gamay without the spark of Beaujolais' fruit.
If it appeals, try wines from Igé and Mancey,
or *Lafarge*'s wine from Bray. *Lassarat* is
improving things by using new oak.

MARANGES, AC (Côte de Beaune; red)
An AC created in 1989; previously the
wines were sold as Côte de Beaune-Villages
but now these sturdy, rustic reds are
coming into their own. *Drouhin*'s is good.

MARSANNAY, AC (Côte de Nuits; red,
rosé) Used to produce mostly rosé under
the name Bourgogne Rosé de Marsannay,
but the introduction of an appellation for
reds in 1987 has encouraged growers to
switch. The first results of this new
seriousness are most encouraging and some
lovely wines are already emerging, usually
quite dry and cherry-perfumed, sometimes
more full-blown and exciting. One to
watch. Best: *Bouvier, Charlopin-Parizot, Roty,
Bruno Clair, Collotte, Fougeray, Fournier,
Geantet-Pansiot, Huguenot, Jadot, Naddef.*

MAZIS-CHAMBERTIN, AC (Côte de
Nuits; red) This *grand cru* in Gevrey-
Chambertin is far more reliable than most
of the neighbouring *grands crus*. Mazis can
have a superb deep blackberry-pip, damson-
skin and blackcurrant fruit which gets more
exciting after six to 12 years. Best: *Faiveley,
Gelin, Hospices de Beaune, Maume,
Rebourseau, Roty, Rousseau, Tortochot.*

MAZOYÈRES-CHAMBERTIN, AC
(Côte de Nuits; red) *Grand cru* of Gevrey-
Chambertin, rarely seen since producers
generally take up the option of using the
grand cru Charmes-Chambertin instead.
Perrot-Minot produces a fine example.

MERCUREY, AC (Côte Chalonnaise;
red, white) The biggest Chalonnais village,
producing half the region's wines. Indeed
many call the Côte Chalonnaise the 'Région

de Mercurey'. It's mostly red wine, often
fairly full, with attractive strawberry fruit and
a little smoky fragrance. As with the other
Chalonnais reds, Mercurey's problems are
infuriating inconsistency of quality, allied to
callous exploitation of the name by some
négociants. *Faiveley* and *Juillot* make a fine
range of red Mercureys, but look out also
for *Ch. de Chamirey, Chandesais, Chanzy,
Domaine la Marche, Dufouleur, Jacqueson, de
Launay, Meix-Foulot, Monette, Saier* and *de
Suremain*. Whites have been improving, as
rising prices have spurred producers to
greater efforts. Good examples come from
*Château de Chamirey, Faiveley, M Juillot,
Protheau, Rodet.*

MEURSAULT, AC (Côte de Beaune;
white) It has by far the largest white
production of any commune in the Côte
d'Or, and this is one of several reasons why
its traditionally high overall standard is
gradually being eroded. The wines should
be big and nutty and have a delicious, gentle
lusciousness, and sometimes even peachy,
honeyed flavours. But there are too many
bland, flabby wines that don't come even
close. Meursault has more producers
bottling their own wine than any other
village. Try *Ampeau, Pierre Boillot, Boisson-
Vadot, Boyer-Martenot, Michel Bouzereau,
Buisson-Battault, Coche-Debord, Coche-Dury,
Comtes Lafon, Fichet, Gauffroy, Henry
Germain, Jean Germain, Grivault, Patrick
Javillier, François Jobard, René Manuel, Matrot,
Michelot-Buisson, Millot-Battault, Pierre Morey,
Prieur, Roulot.*

MONTAGNY, AC (Côte Chalonnaise;
white) In general the wines are a bit lean
and chalky-dry, but now that the use of new
oak barrels for aging the wine is creeping in,
much more interesting wines are appearing.
Best: *Arnoux*, co-op at *Buxy, Latour, B Michel,
de Montorge, Alain Roy, Vachet*. Merchants:
Olivier Leflaive and *Rodet.*

MONTHELIE, AC (Côte de Beaune;
red) These wines deserve recognition,

because they're full, dry, rather herby or piney, but with a satisfying rough fruit. They're often a good buy but stick to growers, not négociants. **Best producers:** *Boussey, Caves des Hautes-Côtes, Deschamps, Doreau, Garaudet, Château de Monthelie, Monthelie-Douhairet, Potinet-Ampeau, de Suremain, Thévenin-Monthelie.*

LE MONTRACHET, AC (Côte de Beaune; white) This is white Burgundy at its absolute greatest, the finest of fine white *grands crus* in the villages of Puligny and Chassagne. Does it mean most enjoyable, most happy-making? Not really. In fact the flavours can be so intense it's difficult sometimes to know if you're having fun drinking it or merely giving your wine vocabulary an end-of-term examination. So be brave if someone opens a bottle and let the incredible blend of spice and smoke, honey and ripeness flow over you. **Good producers:** *Amiot-Bonfils Père et Fils, Domaine de la Romanée-Conti, Jadot, Comtes Lafon, Drouhin Laguiche, Pierre Morey, Prieur, Thénard* and, since 1991, *Leflaive.*

MOREY-ST-DENIS, AC (Côte de Nuits; red) These wines are expensive and often suffer from overproduction. At their best they blend the perfume of Chambolle-Musigny with the body of Gevrey-Chambertin, and exhibit a slight savouriness that mellows into a rich chocolaty mouthful. Many are too light to be successful, but you'll find sound and sometimes exciting bottles from *Pierre Amiot, Bryczek, Dujac, Georges* and *Hubert Lignier, Marchand, Ponsot, Serveau, Charloppin, Perrot-Minot* and *Vadey-Castagnier.*

MORGON, AC (Beaujolais; red) The wines of this *cru* can be glorious. They can start thick and dark, and age to a chocolaty, plummy depth with an amazing cherries smell. A sort of reserve category called Morgon Age has to be kept for at least 18 months before release. *Jacky Janodet's* Morgon is intense. Look also for *Aucoeur, Château de Pizay, Château de Raousset, Descombes, Desvignes, Domaine de la Chanaise, Domaine Roche-St-Jean, Domaine de Ruyère, Drouhin, Gobet, Lapierre, Félix Longepierre* and *Georges Vincent.*

MOULIN-À-VENT, AC (Beaujolais; red) Enter the heavy brigade. These *cru* wines should be solid, and should age for three to five years and more from good years like 1991. The best of them have a big, plummy, Burgundian style, and their toughness doesn't give you much option but to wait for them to mellow. At the opposite end of the spectrum to straight Beaujolais, this is one of the few *crus* that can respond well to discreet oak aging. *Louis Champagnon's* is good, as is *Brugne, Charvet, Duboeuf, Château des Jacques, Château du Moulin-à-Vent, Château Portier, Domaine de la Tour de Bief, Jacky Janodet, Raymond Siffert* and *Héritiers Maillard* (formerly *Héritiers Tagent*).

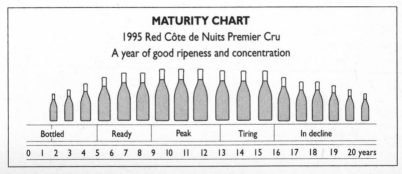

MATURITY CHART
1995 Red Côte de Nuits Premier Cru
A year of good ripeness and concentration

Bottled	Ready	Peak	Tiring	In decline

0 1 2 3 4 5 6 7 8 9 10 11 12 13 14 15 16 17 18 19 20 years

MUSIGNY, AC (Côte de Nuits; red, white) Extremely fine *grand cru* which gave its name to Chambolle-Musigny. All but a third of a hectare is planted to the red Pinot Noir, capable of producing Burgundy's most heavenly scented wine, and there have been some great recent offerings: 1989 and 1993 from *Château de Chambolle-Musigny*, all vintages since 1990 from *de Vogüé* (which also makes white) as well as tiny amounts from *Roumier*. Best names include: *Château de Chambolle-Musigny, Jadot, Leroy, Jacques Prieur, Georges Roumier, de Vogüé*.

NUITS-ST-GEORGES, AC (Côte de Nuits; red) When it's good, this has an enthralling decayed – rotting even – brown richness of chocolate and prunes rising out of a fairly light, plum-sweet fruit – gorgeous, whatever it sounds like. It is expensive but increasingly reliable. *Labouré-Roi* is the most consistent merchant for Nuits, although *Moillard, Jaffelin* and *Jadot* are increasingly good particularly at *premier cru* level. The most famous growers are *Robert Chevillon, Gouges, Michelot* and *Daniel Rion*, but excellent wines are also made by *Domaine de l'Arlot, Ambroise, Jean Chauvenet, Chicotot, Jean-Jacques Confuron* and there's the amazingly deep (and amazingly expensive) *Leroy*.

PERNAND-VERGELESSES, AC (Côte de Beaune; red, white) The village whites are generally fairly lean and need time to soften, but can be gently nutty and very enjoyable from a good producer. They can also be very good value. Best names in white: *Dubreuil-Fontaine, Germain, Laleure-Piot, Pavelot, Rapet, Rollin*. Some quite attractive, softly earthy reds are made. Look for the *premier cru* Île de Vergelesses. Best reds: *Besancenot-Mathouillet, Caves des Hautes-Côtes, Chandon des Briailles, Delarche, Dubreuil-Fontaine, Laleure-Piot, Pavelot, Rapet* and *Rollin*.

PETIT CHABLIS, AC (Chablis; white) There used to be lots of this grown on the least-good slopes. But the growers objected that it made it sound as though their wine was a lesser form of Chablis. Nowadays pretty well the whole lot is called 'Chablis' – so we can't tell what's what, *they're* all richer, they're happy, we're not... I give up.

POMMARD, AC (Côte de Beaune; red) From good producers, Pommard can have a strong, meaty sturdiness, backed by slightly jammy but attractively plummy fruit. Not subtle, but many people's idea of what red Burgundy should be. They need ten years to show their class. The most consistently fine wines are made by *de Courcel, Comte Armand* and *de Montille*, but also look out for the wines of *Boillot, Château de Pommard, Girardin, Lahaye, Lejeune, Jean Monnier, Parent, Pothier* and *Pousse d'Or*.

POUILLY-FUISSÉ, AC (Mâconnais; white) Like Chablis, this is an appellation whose price yo-yos unacceptably according

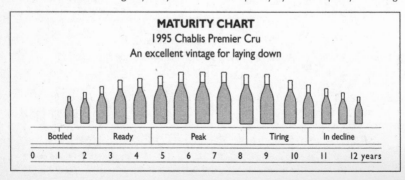

MATURITY CHART
1995 Chablis Premier Cru
An excellent vintage for laying down

Bottled	Ready	Peak	Tiring	In decline

0   1   2   3   4   5   6   7   8   9   10   11   12 years

to supply and demand. It is sometimes best in years which are not too rich. Best producers: *Barraud, Béranger, Cordier, Corsin, Duboeuf*'s top selections, *Ferret, M Forest, Guffens-Heynen, Leger-Plumet, Loron's les Vieux Murs, Manciat-Poncet, Noblet, Roger Saumaize, Valette, Vincent* at *Château Fuissé*. Adjoining villages Pouilly-Loché, AC and Pouilly-Vinzelles, AC make similar wines at half the price.

PULIGNY-MONTRACHET, AC

(Côte de Beaune; white) The peak of great white pleasure is to be found in the various Montrachet *grands crus*. Le Montrachet is peerless, showing how humble words like honey, nuts, cream, smoke, perfume and all the rest do no honest service to a wine that seems to combine every memory of ripe fruit and scent with a dry, penetrating savouriness. There are several other *grands crus* less intense, but which offer the same unrivalled mix. There are *premiers crus* as well. It's always worth buying a single-vineyard wine, as much of the village wine that's produced is sold in bulk to négociants whose offerings vary between the delicious and the disgraceful. Look for *Amiot-Bonfils, Jean-Marc Boillot, Boyer-Devèze, Carillon, Gérard Chavy, Drouhin, Jadot, Labouré-Roi, Laguiche*, both *Domaine Leflaive* and *Olivier Leflaive, Pernot, Ramonet-Prudhon, Antonin Rodet, Sauzet, Thénard*.

RÉGNIÉ, AC

(Beaujolais; red) Beaujolais' tenth *cru*. Makes wine quite similar to Brouilly in ripe vintages but a bit weedy when the sun doesn't shine. *Duboeuf Bouteille Cristal* is the best from this village.

RICHEBOURG, AC

(Côte de Nuits; red) Exceptional *grand cru* of Vosne-Romanée. It's a wonderful name for a wine – Richebourg – and, at its best, it manages to be fleshy yet filled with spice and perfume and the clinging richness of chocolate and figs. Best producers: *Grivot, Domaine de la Romanée-Conti, Gros, Henri Jayer, Leroy, Méo-Camuzet*.

LA ROMANÉE, AC

(Côte de Nuits; red) This *grand cru* is the smallest AC in France, solely owned by the Liger-Belair family and sold by *Bouchard Père et Fils*. Now that Bouchard is under new and more rigorous ownership, we may see whether Romanée, solid but never sensational hitherto, deserves its status.

LA ROMANÉE-CONTI, AC

(Côte de Nuits; red) This tiny *grand cru* is capable of a more startling brilliance than any other Burgundy. The 7000 or so bottles it produces per year are instantly seized on by the super-rich before we mortals can even get our tasting sheets out. Wholly owned by the *Domaine de la Romanée-Conti*.

LA ROMANÉE-ST-VIVANT, AC

(Côte de Nuits; red) *Grand cru* in the village of Vosne-Romanée. It is far less easy to taste young than its neighbouring *grands crus* and needs a good 12 years to show what can be a delicious, savoury yet sweet personality. Best names: *Arnoux, Domaine de la Romanée-Conti, Latour, Leroy*.

RUCHOTTES-CHAMBERTIN, AC

(Côte de Nuits; red) This is the smallest Gevrey-Chambertin *grand cru*, with wines of deeper colour and longer-lasting perfumed richness than most of the village's other *grands crus*. Best producers: *F Esmonin, Georges Mugneret, Roumier, Rousseau*.

RULLY, AC

(Côte Chalonnaise; red white) This village gets my vote for the most improved white AC in Burgundy. The use of new oak to ferment and age the wine is producing wonderfully soft, spicy Burgundies of good quality – and, surprisingly, still relatively low prices. Best producers for white: *Bêtes, Chanzy, Cogny, Delorme, Drouhin, Dury, Duvernay, Domaine de la Folie, Jacqueson, Jaffelin, Olivier Leflaive,*

The Price Guides for this section begin on page 183.

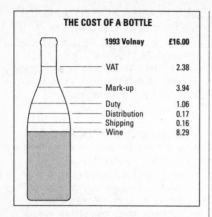

THE COST OF A BOTTLE

	1993 Volnay	£16.00
	VAT	2.38
	Mark-up	3.94
	Duty	1.06
	Distribution	0.17
	Shipping	0.16
	Wine	8.29

Rodet. Best for red: *Chanzy, Ch. de Rully, Delorme, Domaine de la Folie, Duvernay, Faiveley, Jacqueson, Jaffelin.*

ST-AMOUR, AC (Beaujolais; red)
Among the most perfect Beaujolais, this pink-red wine usually has freshness and peachy perfume and good, ripe fruit all at once. It isn't that common here (though the French love it), and yet it is frequently the most reliable and most enjoyable *cru*. Look for *Château de St-Amour, Domaine des Billards (Loron), Buis, Domaine des Ducs, Domaine du Paradis, Patissier, André Poitevin, Francis Saillant, Paul Spay.*

ST-AUBIN, AC (Côte de Beaune; red, white) Some of Burgundy's best-value wines, though the reds are a touch earthy. They are reliable, and give real pleasure after a few years of aging. Best: *Bachelet, Clergy, Lamy, Prudhon, Gérard Thomas* and *Roux,* but wines from négociants *Jadot* and *Olivier Leflaive* are their equal. Good whites come from *Bachelet, Clerget, Lamy, Olivier Leflaive, Prudhon, Thomas* and *Roux.*

ST-ROMAIN, AC (Côte de Beaune; red, white) Full, rather broad-flavoured, cherry-stone dry reds, that perform best in very warm years. On the whole sold cheaper than they deserve. Look for *Bazenet, Buisson, Gras, Thévenin* and *Thévenin-*

Monthelie. The flinty, dry whites are often of decent quality and pretty good value. Beware cooler vintages, when the grapes sometimes don't ripen properly. Best are: *Bazenet, Buisson, Germain, Gras, Thévenin, Thévenin-Monthelie.*

ST-VÉRAN, AC (Mâconnais; white) Pouilly-Fuissé's understudy, capable of simple, soft, quick-maturing but attractive, rather honeyed white Burgundy. Best producers: *Corsin, Dépardon, Dom. des Deux Roches, Duboeuf, Grégoire, Lassarat, de Montferrand, Saumaize, Thibert, Vincent –* and, above all, *Drouhin.*

SANTENAY, AC (Côte de Beaune; red) Rough and ready red. At its best, with a strong, savoury flavour and good strawberry fruit, though nowadays frequently rather lean and mean. Best: *Belland, Drouhin, Girardin, Lequin-Roussot, Morey, Pousse d'Or, Prieur-Bonnet, Roux.* Even here, there can be variation.

SAVIGNY-LÈS-BEAUNE, AC (Côte de Beaune; red) Gaining in reputation at the expense of Beaune. Light, attractive earthiness and strawberry fruit. Try *Bize, Camus-Bruchon, Capron-Manieux, Chandon de Briailles, Écard-Guyot, Girard-Vollot, Guillemot, Pavelot, Tollot-Beaut.*

SAUVIGNON DE ST-BRIS, VDQS
(white) Wine of AC quality grown south-west of Chablis that languishes as a VDQS because Sauvignon Blanc is not an AC grape in the area. Often one of the most nettly, most greeny-gooseberryish of all, but recent ones have been more expensive and less exciting. It has not really faced up to the competition from New Zealand – and Bordeaux. Best: *Louis Bersan, Jean-Marc Brocard, Robert & Philippe Defrance, Michel Esclavy, Goisot, André Sorin.*

LA TÂCHE, AC (Côte de Nuits; red) Another *grand cru* monopoly of the *Domaine de la Romanée-Conti.* The wine is heavenly, so rich and heady that the perfumes are sometimes closer to age-old brandy than table wine and the flavour loaded with spice and dark fruits and the acrid richness of chocolate.

VOLNAY, AC (Côte de Beaune; red) One of the most perfumed red Burgundies, with a memorable cherry-and-strawberry spice, but also, in its *premiers crus*, able to turn on a big, meaty style without losing the perfume. The best are *Lafarge, Comte Lafon, Marquis d'Angerville, de Montille* and *Pousse d'Or,* Other good names: *Ampeau, Blain-Gagnard, Boillot, Bouley, Clerget, Delagrange, Vaudoisey-Mutin, Voillot.* Volnay did very well in 1989, '90, '91 and '93.

VOSNE-ROMANÉE, AC (Côte de Nuits; red) The greatest Côte de Nuits village. Its *grands crus* cost more than any red on earth, and, remarkably for Burgundy, they are dominated by a single estate, *Domaine de la Romanée Conti.* These

vineyards make wines capable of more startling brilliance than any other, with flavours as disparate yet as intense as the overpowering, creamy savouriness of fresh *foie gras* and the deep, sweet scent of ripe plums and prunes in brandy. There are also fine *premiers crus,* and the village wines, though not as reliable as they were, can sometimes reflect their leaders. The 1987s and '89s are good; the '85s, '88s and '90s unutterably great. Apart from the DRC, look for *Arnoux, Sylvain Cathiard, Confuron-Coteditot, Engel, Grivot, Jean Gros, Hudelot-Noëllat, Georges Jayer, Henri Jayer, Henri Lamarche, Leroy, Méo-Camuzet, Mongeard-Mugneret, Georges Mugneret, Pernin-Rossin, Rouget, Daniel Rion* and *Jean Tardy.*

VOUGEOT, AC (Côte de Nuits; red) A village famous only because of its *grand cru,* Clos de Vougeot, which at its best is plummy and broad. However, there are some decent wines made outside the Clos – most notably from *Bertagna* and *Clerget.*

BURGUNDY AND BEAUJOLAIS VINTAGES

Red Burgundy is more subject to vintage fluctuation than white; with the latter, most years can produce a fair amount of pretty good wine. The rule for Beaujolais, drink as young as possible. Only top wines from the best villages will benefit much from aging, although Nouveau may improve with a month or two's rest.

1996 Excellent, concentrated, classic Chablis; the Côte d'Or whites and reds are also ripe, with good acidity, and should age well. Whites may not be as concentrated as in 1995. Beaujolais looks promising.

1995 A year of low yields, ripe tannins and good concentration in the reds, and good quality but not greatness in the whites. For once, there is little to choose in quality between the Côte de Beaune and the Côte de Nuits. In Chablis quality is first-rate. A very good rather than an exceptional year for Beaujolais, with soft, fruity wines. Some of the *cru* wines could prove well-structured and, like the 1991s, suitable for aging.

1994 Light wines with attractive, reasonable colours and lowish acidity. However, some reds are over-extracted and show harsh tannins without sufficient fruit to support them. Buy cautiously. The best whites are showing a raciness and vigour that contrasts nicely with the plumper, richer 1992s, which have always overshadowed them. Beaujolais made some very attractive wines, although quality varies.

1993 The reds from the best producers have good depth of colour, power of fruit and well-constructed tannins, though some are a little too tannic or underripe. The whites have turned out far better than at first seemed likely. They have plumped up nicely and have plenty of fruit, but don't count on them making old Beaunes. In Beaujolais there are some good wines among the *crus*.

1992   Acidity is low among the reds, but it's a good year to choose in restaurants, as the wines are fast developers. The whites were far better, with masses of exuberant fruit and seemingly better acidity than their 1991 counterparts. Beaujolais was below average in quality, with thin, light wines. Buy only from quality-conscious producers.

1991   There were some very good concentrated reds made, but it's a very patchy vintage. The whites are also patchy in quality, though without the reds' occasional brilliance. Beaujolais was excellent, with good colour and relatively high tannin levels.

1990   The 1990 reds are brilliantly fruity, naturally high in sugars. Most producers now consider this the best of the great trio of 1988, 1989 and 1990. Lesser wines will be ready early; the best are sumptuously rich. The whites are proving to be inferior to the reds. A good rather than a great vintage for white Burgundy. In Beaujolais it was a corker of a vintage – very good quality and plenty of it. The *crus* are drinking beautifully now.

1989   A lot of good reds, but only a few exceptional ones. They are softer than the 1988s, though some are superbly concentrated, particularly in the Côte de Beaune. Some may prove better than the '88s. it was an outstanding year for white Burgundy, at least in the hands of competent winemakers. Almost all the best growers' wines are beautifully balanced, despite their richness, though some are ageing fast. Beaujolais had wonderful colour and pungent fruit, and prices shot up.

1988   Many growers produced firm, concentrated reds, now beginning to emerge from their shells. Some superb wines, but quite a few dour ones, too. Among the whites, Mâconnais wines had a bright, fresh fruit not seen down that way for a few years. Beaujolais was exceptional, with marvellous luscious, clear, ripe fruit, and even the best should be drunk up now.

1987   The best 1987 reds are very good indeed, Côte de Beaune having the edge over Côte de Nuits. The lesser wines aren't as good as those of 1985, but are better than those of 1986. Drink now.

1986   The reds are showing good perfume but need drinking soon, as do most whites. Chablis *grands crus* are drinking well, but there's no hurry to drink up.

1985   The reds have turned out unevenly, though the best are still good. The whites have proper acid balance and an outstanding concentration of fruit. Pity nobody waited to find out because most '85s were consumed long ago. If you do see one from a good producer, go for it – well, perhaps not, I've just remembered the price it'll be. Chablis started out with a lesser reputation, but top wines from good producers can still be good.

1983   The best reds display impressive flavour. If you can wait another few years you may have the most impressive old-style Burgundies made in the last two decades, but I'd avoid Vosne-Romanée, Chambolle-Musigny and Morey-Saint-Denis. The whites are frequently heavy, rather unrefreshing, soggy-flavoured wines (made, all too often, from overripe, rot-affected grapes) which rapidly lost their fruit. Some rare examples may turn out to be wonderful, but if that is the case I have yet to discover them. Even the best should be ready by now, though.

1982   The best reds are from the Côte de Beaune and are delicate, perfumed, nicely balanced and need drinking up.

BASIC BURGUNDY

RED

Under £7.00

1995
Bourgogne Coteaux de St-Bris, Brocard
£6.95 (AD)
1994
Bourgogne Rouge Fûts de Chêne, Cave
de Buxy £5.25 (NA)
Bourgogne Rouge, Labouré-Roi £6.92 (ROS)
1992
Bourgogne Passe-Tout-Grains, Rion £6.75
(MV)
1987
Bourgogne Passe-Tout-Grains, Lejeune
£6.99 (RAE)

£7.00 → £7.99

1995
Bourgogne Rouge, Faiveley £7.95 (DI)
Bourgogne Rouge, Roger et Joël Remy
£7.96 (LEA)
1994
Bourgogne Rouge, Cave de Buxy £7.69
(AUR)
1993
Bourgogne Rouge, Parent £7.50 (GAL)
Bourgogne Rouge Tasteviné, Bichot £7.49
(UN)
1988
Bourgogne Passe-Tout-Grains, Henri
Jayer £7.95 (RAE)

£8.00 → £9.99

1995
Bourgogne Rouge, Philippe Charlopin
£9.50 (LEA)

1994
Bourgogne Rouge, Georges Roumier
£8.50 (WS) £9.10 (TAN)
Bourgogne Rouge, Mortet £9.95 (LEA)
Bourgogne Rouge, Philippe Charlopin
£9.95 (LEA)
1993
Bourgogne Rouge Cave Privée, Rodet
£8.95 (LEA)

£10.00 → £12.99

1995
Bourgogne la Digoine, Villaine £10.95
(AD)
Bourgogne Rouge, Dugat-Py £10.95 (LEA)
Bourgogne Rouge, Mugneret-Gibourg
£11.95 (LEA)
Bourgogne Rouge, Georges Roumier
£11.00 (TAN)
1994
Bourgogne la Digoine, Villaine £11.26
(COU)
Bourgogne Rouge, Coche-Dury £10.28
(DOM)
Bourgogne Rouge, Michel Lafarge £11.25
(GAU)
1993
Bourgogne Rouge, Michel Lafarge £11.50
(HAH)
Bourgogne Rouge, Mortet £10.95 (LEA)

£19.00 → £25.99

1995
Bourgogne Rouge, Coche-Dury £25.75
(BUT)
1988
Bourgogne Rouge, Henri Jayer £20.86
(BUT) £24.50 (REI)

MERCHANTS SPECIALIZING IN BURGUNDY
see Merchant Directory (page 413) for details

All the following merchants are exceptionally good. Adnams (AD), Averys (AV), Bennetts (BEN), Berry Bros. & Rudd (BER), Bibendum (BIB), Bute Wines (BUT), Butlers Wine Cellar (BU), Anthony Byrne (BY), Châteaux Wines (CHA), Corney & Barrow (CB), Direct Wine (DI), Eldridge Pope (EL), Farr Vintners (FA), Goedhuis (GOE), Roger Harris (HAW), John Harvey & Sons (HAR), Haynes Hanson & Clark (HAH), Hicks & Don (HIC), Justerini & Brooks, Lay & Wheeler (LAY), Lea & Sandeman (LEA), Morris & Verdin (MV), Le Nez Rouge (NEZ), James Nicholson (NI), Oddbins (OD), Thos. Peatling , Raeburn (RAE), Reid Wines (1992) Ltd (REI), T&W Wines (TW), Tanners (TAN), Howard Ripley (RIP), Wine Society (WS), Peter Wylie (WY)

WHITE

Under £6.00

1996
Bourgogne Aligoté, Cave de Buxy £5.99 (NA)
1993
Bourgogne Chardonnay, A Bichot £5.99 (UN)

£6.00 → £7.99

1995
Bourgogne Aligoté de Bouzeron, Villaine £7.65 (REI)
Bourgogne Aligoté, Duboeuf £7.50 (STA)
Bourgogne Aligoté, Mouton £6.59 (TAN)
Bourgogne Blanc, Cave de Buxy £6.30 (AUR)
Bourgogne Blanc, Latour £6.59 (MAJ)
1994
Bourgogne Aligoté, Rollin £7.99 (BIB)
Bourgogne Chardonnay, Jadot £7.79 (VIC)

£8.00 → £9.99

1995
Bourgogne Aligoté, Verget £8.50 (LAY)

Bourgogne Chardonnay les Champs Perriers, Clerc £8.99 (VIN)
1994
Bourgogne Aligoté, Rion £9.00 (MV)
Bourgogne Blanc, Leroy £9.99 (MAJ)

£10.00 → £12.99

1994
Bourgogne Blanc, Charles et Remi Jobard £10.58 (COU) £10.95 (LEA) £12.44 (RAE)
Bourgogne Blanc Cuvée des Forgets, Patrick Javillier £10.25 (SOM) £12.95 (VIG)
1993
Bourgogne Blanc, Domaine Leflaive £12.04 (BUT)
1992
Bourgogne Blanc, Leroy £10.50 (WS)

SPARKLING

Under £8.50

Non-vintage
Crémant de Bourgogne Cave de Lugny £5.70 (SOM) £6.75 (WAI) £6.99 (OD)
Crémant de Bourgogne Rosé Cave de Lugny £6.95 (WAI) £8.30 (HAH)

BEAUJOLAIS

RED

Under £5.00

1995
Beaujolais-Villages Château du Bluizard
£4.99 (TES)
Beaujolais-Villages Domaine de la Ronze
£4.69 (ASD)
1994
Beaujolais-Villages Duboeuf £4.99 (THR)
£4.99 (WR) £4.99 (FUL) £4.99 (TES)

£5.00 → £5.99

1996
Beaujolais Duboeuf £5.95 (STA)
Beaujolais-Villages les Champs Bouthier,
Sapin £5.95 (STA)
Beaujolais-Villages Pivot £5.90 (PIP)
1995
Beaujolais Cave Beaujolais de St-Verand
£5.75 (HAW)
Beaujolais Loron £5.95 (DI)
Beaujolais-Villages Château de Lacarelle
£5.35 (WS)
Beaujolais-Villages Château de Néty £5.65
(EL)
Beaujolais-Villages Château des Vierres,
Duboeuf £5.99 (NI)
Beaujolais-Villages Château du Basty
£5.49 (OD)
Beaujolais-Villages Jaffre £5.69 (WHI)
Beaujolais-Villages Pivot £5.58 (DOM)
Beaujolais-Villages St Ennemond £5.99 (OD)
Morgon Jambon £5.99 (ASD)
Régnié Duboeuf £5.99 (SAF)
1994
Beaujolais Loron £5.70 (TAN)
Beaujolais-Villages Loron £5.69 (UN)

£6.00 → £6.49

1995
Beaujolais Blaise Carron £6.35 (HAW)
Beaujolais Garlon £6.35 (HAW)
Beaujolais-Villages Cave des Producteurs
Juliénas £6.10 (HAW)
Beaujolais-Villages Colonge £6.19 (AME)
£6.22 (ELL)
Beaujolais-Villages Domaine Aucoeur
£6.20 (RSJ)
1994
Chénas Château de Chénas £6.49 (NEW)

£6.50 → £6.99

1996
Beaujolais Lantignié, Domaine Joubert
£6.75 (AD)
Beaujolais-Villages Duboeuf £6.75 (STA)
Beaujolais-Villages Roux £6.55 (HAW)
Brouilly Domaine de Combillaty, Duboeuf
£6.95 (NEZ)
Brouilly Large £6.66 (CHA)
Juliénas les Envaux, Pelletier £6.66 (CHA)
Morgon le Clachet, Brun £6.66 (CHA)
1995
Brouilly de Pierreux, Duboeuf £6.99 (FUL)
Chénas Benon £6.75 (HAW)
Chénas Château de Chénas £6.65 (HAW)
Fleurie Clos de la Chapelle des Bois,
Verpoix £6.85 (ASD)
Juliénas Château des Capitans, Sarrau
£6.95 (SAI)
Juliénas Domaine de la Seigneurie £6.60
(NEZ)
Morgon Domaine des Arcades £6.50 (AS)
Morgon Domaine Jean Descombes,
Duboeuf £6.50 (NI) £6.95 (NEZ) £6.99
(BOT) £6.99 (WR) £6.99 (THR)
Régnié Franc Cinquin £6.99 (OD)
1994
Chénas Domaine de Mongrin, Gaec des
Ducs £6.85 (REI)
Chiroubles Méziat £6.99 (OD)
Juliénas Benon £6.75 (HAW)
Juliénas Loron £6.99 (UN)

£7.00 → £7.49

1996
Juliénas Domaine Joubert £7.20 (AD)
Moulin-à-Vent Brugne £7.20 (CHA)
1995
Beaujolais Cuvée Centenaire, Charmet
£7.05 (HAW)
Brouilly Duboeuf £7.49 (POR)
Brouilly Large £7.22 (PLA)
Chénas Léspinasse £7.05 (HAW)
Côte de Brouilly Domaine de Chavannes
£7.25 (EL)
Côte de Brouilly Domaine de la Voûte
des Crozes, Chanrion £7.15 (RSJ)
Fleurie Château du Grand Pré £7.49 (MAJ)
Juliénas Domaine Joubert £7.00 (TAN)
Juliénas Pelletier £7.04 (PLA) £7.25 (EL)
Morgon Aucoeur £7.15 (RSJ)

Morgon Jambon £7.39 (AUR)
Morgon le Clachet, Brun £7.04 (PLA)
£7.25 (EL)
Régnié Château Chassantour, Perroud
£7.30 (TAN)
Régnié Noël £7.05 (HAW)
Régnié Roux £7.15 (HAW)
St-Amour Domaine du Paradis £7.30 (NEZ)
1994
Juliénas Léspinasse £7.05 (HAW)
Morgon Domaine des Vieux Cèdres,
Loron £7.04 (PEN)
Moulin-à-Vent Domaine de la Tour du
Bief, Duboeuf £7.49 (BOT) £7.49 (THR)

£7.50 → £7.99

1996
Brouilly Château des Tours £7.80 (PIP)
Fleurie Dénojean-Burtin £7.50 (WS)
Fleurie Duboeuf £7.99 (THR) £7.99 (WR)
£7.99 (VIC) £7.99 (BOT)
Fleurie Sélection Éventail, Domaine de
Montgénas £7.50 (CHA)
1995
Beaujolais-Villages Dumas £7.50 (LEA)
Brouilly de Pierreux, Duboeuf £7.65 (WS)
Brouilly Duboeuf £7.99 (QUE)
Brouilly Geoffray £7.65 (HAW)
Brouilly Jean Lathuilière £7.85 (HAW)
Brouilly Latour £7.72 (HOG)
Chénas Domaine de la Combe Remont,
Duboeuf £7.50 (STA)
Chénas Domaine Louis Champagnon
£7.50 (PIP)
Chiroubles Château de Raousset £7.90
(PIP)
Chiroubles Domaine de la Grosse Pierre
£7.95 (HAH)
Chiroubles Duboeuf £7.95 (STA) £7.99 (QUE)
Chiroubles la Maison des Vignerons £7.60
(HAW) £7.95 (AD)
Chiroubles Loron £7.70 (TAN)
Côte de Brouilly Château Thivin £7.95
(GRE)
Côte de Brouilly Joubert £7.70 (TAN)
Fleurie Cave Co-op. de Fleurie £7.70 (HAW)
Fleurie Château de Fleurie, Loron £7.76
(FLE)
Fleurie Domaine des Quatre Vents,
Duboeuf £7.95 (NEZ)
Fleurie Domaine Paul Bernard £7.99 (OD)
Fleurie Duboeuf £7.99 (TES)
Fleurie la Madone, Celliers des Samsons
£7.75 (SAI)
Fleurie la Madone, Duboeuf £7.95 (NEZ)

Fleurie Sapin £7.99 (WAI)
Juliénas Clos des Poulettes, Loron £7.99
(GRE)
Juliénas Domaine de la Seigneurie £7.95
(STA)
Juliénas Domaine de la Vieille Église,
Loron £7.90 (DI)
Juliénas Duboeuf £7.99 (QUE)
Juliénas Loron £7.64 (PEN)
Morgon Duboeuf £7.95 (STA) £7.99 (QUE)

★ Morgon les Versauds, Perrachon £7.72
(PIP)
Moulin-à-Vent Duboeuf £7.65 (NI)
Moulin-à-Vent le Vivier, Brugne £7.85
(WHI) £7.99 (EL)
Moulin-à-Vent Loron £7.99 (UN)
1994
Chénas Domaine de Mongrin, Gaec des
Ducs £7.90 (WRI)
Côte de Brouilly Joubert £7.85 (JON)
Fleurie Château de Fleurie, Loron £7.99
(FUL)
Juliénas Aujas £7.95 (HAW)
Juliénas les Capitans, Louis Tête £7.73
(HOG)
Morgon Aucoeur £7.60 (HAW)
Morgon Fontcraine, Loron £7.99 (GRE)
Moulin-à-Vent Domaine Lemonon, Loron
£7.95 (WRI)
St-Amour les Bonnets, Bernard Patissier
£7.98 (PLA)

£8.00 → £8.99

1996
Brouilly Château Thivin £8.55 (AD)
Côte de Brouilly Château Thivin £8.05
(HAW)
Fleurie Clos de la Chapelle des Bois,
Verpoix £8.00 (PIP)
1995
Brouilly de Pierreux, Duboeuf £8.65 (STA)
Chénas Domaine Louis Champagnon
£8.50 (MV)
Côte de Brouilly Château Thivin £8.05
(HAW) £8.99 (DI)

Fleurie Berrod £8.30 (GAL)
Fleurie Château de Fleurie, Loron £8.00
(WRI) £8.30 (TAN) £8.37 (PEN) £8.59 (EL)
Fleurie Château des Deduits, Duboeuf
£8.66 (NI)
Fleurie Colonge £8.30 (WS) £8.49 (AME)
£8.57 (ELL) £8.80 (TAN)
Fleurie Domaine des Quatre Vents,
Duboeuf £8.65 (NI)
Fleurie Duboeuf £8.99 (QUE)
Fleurie la Roilette, Coudert £8.81 (COU)
Fleurie les Garans, Latour £8.54 (HOG)
£8.99 (NEW)
Fleurie Sélection Éventail, Domaine de
Montgénas £8.21 (PLA)
Morgon Côte de Py, Savoye £8.59 (GN)
Moulin-à-Vent Domaine de la Tour du
Bief, Duboeuf £8.90 (STA)
Moulin-à-Vent Domaine Lemonon, Loron
£8.85 (GRE)
St-Amour Domaine des Pins, Echallier
£8.08 (ELL)
St-Amour Domaine du Paradis £8.65 (STA)
1994
Chiroubles Louis Tête £8.18 (HOG)
Fleurie Grill Midi, Duboeuf £8.51 (ROS)
Juliénas Condemine £8.15 (HAW)
Moulin-à-Vent Caves Kuhnel £8.25 (SAI)
Moulin-à-Vent Château des Jacques £8.25
(AS)
Moulin-à-Vent Janin £8.10 (PIP) £8.52 (DOM)

£9.00 → £11.49

1996
Brouilly Château des Tours £10.20 (GN)
1995
Brouilly Château des Tours £9.75 (BEN)
£10.03 (NO)
Brouilly Michaud £9.80 (MV)
Fleurie Château de Fleurie, Loron £9.45
(GRE) £9.50 (DI)
Fleurie Château du Grand Pré £9.50 (STA)
Fleurie Clos de la Chapelle des Bois,
Verpoix £9.85 (NO)
Fleurie Colonge £9.95 (BER)
Fleurie Grill Midi, Duboeuf £9.60 (GN)
Fleurie la Madone, Louis Tête £9.10 (HOG)
Fleurie les Garans, Latour £9.40 (WY)
Fleurie Verpoix £9.95 (BEN)
Morgon Duboeuf £9.55 (UB)
Moulin-à-Vent Domaine Berrod £9.95 (AD)
Moulin-à-Vent Domaine Charvet £9.00
(TAN)
Moulin-à-Vent Drouhin £9.75 (REI)
Moulin-à-Vent Duboeuf £9.99 (QUE)

1994
Beaujolais-Villages Château des Vergers
£9.30 (UB)
Chiroubles Loron £9.95 (ROB)
Fleurie Colonge £11.45 (ROB)
Fleurie Dumas £9.95 (LEA)
Morgon Marcel Lapierre £10.00 (BIB)
1993
Brouilly Château des Tours £11.45 (ROB)
Moulin-à-Vent Château du Moulin-à-Vent
£9.95 (HAW)
Moulin-à-Vent les Hospices, Collin &
Bourisset £9.95 (POR)

£11.50 → £19.99

1995
Fleurie Michel Chignard £11.50 (MV)
Juliénas Domaine du Clos du Fief, Michel
Tête £11.60 (UB)
1966
Moulin-à-Vent Château des Jacques
£18.50 (REI)

WHITE

Under £6.00

1995
Beaujolais Blanc Bully £4.29 (TES)
Beaujolais Blanc Duboeuf £5.99 (MAJ)

£6.00 → £7.50

1996
Beaujolais Blanc Cave des Grands Crus
Blancs £6.70 (HAW) £6.95 (LEA)
Beaujolais Blanc Château des Tours £7.30
(PIP)
Beaujolais Blanc Domaine des Terres
Dorées £7.20 (AD)
1994
Beaujolais-Villages Blanc Château des
Jacques £7.45 (AS)

c. £10.00

1995
Beaujolais Blanc Château des Tours
£10.00 (NO)

ROSÉ

c. £6.00

1995
Beaujolais Supérieur Rosé, Cave
Beaujolais du Bois d'Oingt £6.00 (HAW)

CHABLIS

WHITE

Under £6.00

1995
Sauvignon de St-Bris, Domaine des
  Remparts £5.90 (TAN)
Sauvignon de St-Bris, Goisot £5.75 (GAL)
1993
Sauvignon de St-Bris, Sorin-Defrance
  £5.35 (SOM)

£6.00 → £6.99

1996
Sauvignon de St-Bris, Brocard £6.45 (AD)
1995
Chablis la Chablisienne £6.99 (SO)
Chablis Tricon £6.99 (UN)
1994
Chablis Domaine des Manants, Brocard
  £6.95 (POR)
Sauvignon de St-Bris, Fèvre £6.19 (ROS)
Sauvignon de St-Bris, Sorin-Defrance
  £6.75 (WRI)
1993
Sauvignon de St-Bris, Defrance £6.85 (EL)

£7.00 → £7.99

1995
Chablis Domaine de l'Églantière £7.78 (ELL)
Chablis J Moreau £7.25 (WHI) £7.92 (HA)
Chablis la Chablisienne £7.99 (WAI) £7.99
  (VIC)
Chablis Simonnet-Febvre £7.72 (CHA)
Chablis Vocoret £7.99 (MAJ)
Chardonnay Domaine des Remparts,
  Sorin £7.44 (HIG)
1994
Chablis Domaine de Vauroux £7.99 (FUL)
Chablis la Chablisienne £7.99 (MAR)
Chablis Vaillons, Droin ½ bottle £7.32 (DOM)

£8.00 → £9.99

1996
Chablis Fourchaume, J Moreau £9.65 (FOR)
Chablis la Chablisienne £8.49 (AUR)
1995
Chablis Bouchard Père £8.25 (BY)
Chablis Domaine des Manants, Brocard
  £8.75 (AD)
Chablis Domaine du Valéry, Durup £8.80
  (TAN)

Chablis Durup £8.17 (DOM)
Chablis Fèvre £8.50 (REI)
Chablis Hamelin £9.30 (ELL)
Chablis Montée de Tonnerre, Durup
  £9.99 (EL)
Chablis Pautré £9.99 (HIG)
Chablis Régnard £9.29 (HOG)
Chablis Vaillons, J Moreau £9.65 (FOR)
Chablis Vau-Ligneau, Alain Geoffroy £9.99
  (OD)
★ Chablis Vieilles Vignes, Emmanuel Dampt
  £9.99 (SUN)
1994
Chablis Daniel Defaix £9.99 (WR)
Chablis Domaine de l'Églantière £8.99
  (AME)
Chablis Drouhin £9.60 (NI)
Chablis Durup £8.45 (EL) £8.65 (HAH)
Chablis Fourchaume, Durup £9.99 (EL)
Chablis Grossot £9.95 (LAY)
Chablis Mont de Milieu, Moreau £9.99
  (HOG)
Chablis Vaillons, J Moreau £9.95 (WS)
  £9.99 (THR) £9.99 (WR) £9.99 (BOT)
1993
Chablis Château de Maligny, Durup £8.14
  (BY)
Chablis Domaine de Vauroux £8.69 (NI)
  £8.86 (ROS)
Chablis Légland £8.75 (BIB)
1992
Chablis Château de Maligny, Durup £8.99
  (WR) £8.99 (BOT) £8.99 (THR)
Chablis Montée de Tonnerre, Durup
  £9.79 (BY)
1986
Chablis Simonnet-Febvre £8.50 (REI)

£10.00 → £11.99

1996
Chablis Drouhin £10.50 (STA)
1995
Chablis 1er Cru, Drouhin £10.75 (GRE)
Chablis 1er Cru, Laroche £11.75 (PLA)
Chablis Adhémar Boudin £10.95 (LEA)
Chablis Beauroy, la Chablisienne £10.99
  (AUR)
Chablis Drouhin £10.62 (WATT)
Chablis Fourchaume Domaine de
  Colombier, Mothe £10.99 (ASD)
Chablis Fourchaume, Domaine de Valéry
  £10.50 (TAN)

Chablis Fûts de Chêne, Grossot £10.65 (LAY)

Chablis la Forêt, Pinson £11.00 (PIP)

Chablis Laroche £10.90 (DI)

Chablis Long-Depaquit £10.10 (PEN)

Chablis Mont de Milieu, Pinson £11.00 (PIP)

Chablis Montée de Tonnerre, Louis Michel £11.99 (OD)

Chablis Montmains, Louis Michel £10.50 (REI) £11.49 (OD) £11.95 (WS)

Chablis Vaillons, Simonnet-Febvre £10.67 (CHA)

Chablis Vau Ligneau, Hamelin £11.10 (NEZ)

Chablis Vaudevey, Laroche £10.75 (WHI) £11.99 (GRE)

1994

Chablis Alain Geoffroy £10.49 (BOT) £10.49 (THR) £10.49 (WR)

Chablis Daniel Defaix £11.95 (LAY)

Chablis Fourchaume, Durup £10.87 (DOM)

Chablis Gautheron £10.49 (UN)

Chablis Montée de Tonnerre, Durup £10.87 (DOM)

Chablis Montmains, Brocard £11.50 (FLE) £11.95 (AD)

Chablis Montmains, Légland £11.00 (BIB)

Chablis Tribut £11.50 (LEA)

Chablis Vaillons, J Moreau £10.70 (HA)

Chablis Vaulorent, Fèvre £10.85 (REI)

1993

Chablis Fourchaume, la Chablisienne £10.95 (HOG)

Chablis Long-Depaquit £10.79 (VIN) ^

Chablis Montmains, Domaine de la Tour Vaubourg £11.55 (NI)

Chablis Vaillons, Simonnet-Febvre £10.67 (CHA)

Chablis Vaudésir, Droin ½ bottle £11.17 (DOM)

Chablis Vaudevey, Laroche £11.75 (PLA)

1992

Chablis la Forêt, Pinson £11.00 (BIB)

Chablis Mont de Milieu, Pinson £11.00 (BIB)

1990

Chablis 1er Cru Grand Cuvée, la Chablisienne £11.19 (SO)

£12.00 → £13.99

1995

Chablis Côte de Léchet, Tribut £13.95 (LEA)

Chablis Fourchaume, Boudin £13.95 (LEA)

Chablis Fourchaume, la Chablisienne £12.95 (GN) £12.99 (NA)

Chablis Fourchaume, Laroche £12.87 (PLA)

Chablis Séchet, René Dauvissat £13.16 (TAN)

Chablis Vaillons, Long-Depaquit £13.22 (PEN)

1994

Chablis Côte de Léchet, Tribut £13.95 (LEA)

Chablis Montmains, Laroche £12.75 (GRE) £12.91 (PLA)

Chablis Vau Ligneau, Hamelin £13.95 (BEN)

1993

Chablis 1er Cru, Drouhin £12.30 (NI)

Chablis Beauroy, Tribut £13.81 (DOM)

Chablis Mont de Milieu, Grossot £13.85 (LAY)

Chablis Montée de Tonnerre, Droin £13.50 (BIB)

Chablis Vaillons, Droin £13.50 (BIB)

Chablis Vaillons, Fèvre £12.75 (ROS)

Chablis Vaillons, Laroche £12.32 (PLA)

Chablis Vaulorent, Fèvre £13.23 (ROS)

Chablis Vosgros, Droin £13.51 (DOM)

1990

Chablis 1er Cru Grand Cuvée, la Chablisienne £12.99 (MAR)

£14.00 → £16.99

1995

Chablis 1er Cru, Drouhin £14.95 (STA)

Chablis Côte de Léchet, Tribut £14.98 (BUT)

Chablis Séchet, René Dauvissat £15.95 (LEA)

1994

Chablis Beauroy, Tribut £14.95 (LEA)

Chablis Côte de Léchet, Tribut £14.04 (DOM)

Chablis la Forêt, René Dauvissat £14.69 (DOM)

Chablis Montmains, Droin £14.04 (DOM)

Chablis Séchet, René Dauvissat £14.69 (DOM)

Chablis Vaillons, Droin £14.04 (DOM)

Chablis Vaillons, René Dauvissat £14.69 (DOM)

1993

Chablis Fourchaume, Laroche £16.55 (DI)
Chablis la Forêt, René Dauvissat £15.47 (BUT)
Chablis Vaillons, Raveneau £16.55 (HAH)
Chablis Vaudésir, J Moreau £16.94 (HOG)

1992

Chablis Côte de Léchet, Etienne et Daniel Defaix £16.95 (VIG)
Chablis les Lys, Daniel Defaix £16.95 (VIG)
Chablis Vaillons, Daniel Defaix £16.95 (VIG)

1991

Chablis Côte de Léchet, Etienne et Daniel Defaix £14.99 (BO)
Chablis les Lys, Daniel Defaix £15.80 (TAN)
Chablis Vaillons, Daniel Defaix £14.99 (BO)

1990

Chablis 1er Cru Grand Cuvée, la Chablisienne £14.94 (GN)
Chablis Côte de Léchet, Etienne et Daniel Defaix £16.95 (VIG)
Chablis les Lys, Daniel Defaix £16.94 (LAY)

£17.00 → £19.99

1995

Chablis les Clos, René Dauvissat £19.75 (TAN)
Chablis Montée de Tonnerre, Droin £17.45 (BER)
Chablis Montée de Tonnerre, Verget £17.50 (LAY)

1994

Chablis les Clos, Brocard £18.50 (GAL)
Chablis les Clos, Pinson £17.90 (PIP)
Chablis Vaudésir, Louis Michel £17.50 (REI) £18.49 (OD)
Chablis Vocoret £18.90 (BUT)

1993

Chablis Bougros, Domaine de Colombier, Mothe £17.95 (POR)
Chablis Grenouilles, Domaine de Château Grenouille £19.98 (RIP)
Chablis Vaudésir, Long-Depaquit £19.54 (PEN)

1992

Chablis Bougros, Fèvre £18.45 (ROS)
Chablis les Clos des Hospices, Moreau £19.50 (HOG)
Chablis les Preuses, la Chablisienne £19.93 (FLE)
Chablis Vaudésir, J Moreau £18.00 (HOG)

1991

Chablis les Clos, Pinson £19.00 (BIB)
Chablis les Lys, Daniel Defaix £18.10 (YOU)

1990

Chablis Côte de Léchet, Etienne et Daniel Defaix £17.50 (WS) £18.50 (ROB)
Chablis Grenouilles, Domaine de Château Grenouille £19.99 (MAR)
Chablis les Preuses, la Chablisienne £17.99 (AUR)

£20.00 → £24.99

1994

Chablis Grenouilles, Droin £23.30 (RAE)
Chablis les Clos, Brocard £21.50 (AD)
Chablis les Clos, Droin £22.33 (DOM)
Chablis les Clos, René Dauvissat £22.91 (DOM)
Chablis les Preuses, René Dauvissat £22.91 (DOM)
Chablis Valmur, Droin £20.66 (RAE) £24.49 (JON)

1993

Chablis Blanchots, Laroche £23.50 (GRE)
Chablis Grenouilles, Droin £23.50 (DOM)
Chablis la Moutonne, Long-Depaquit £22.82 (PEN)
Chablis les Clos, René Dauvissat £22.91 (DOM) £23.30 (BUT)
Chablis les Preuses, René Dauvissat £22.81 (BUT)
Chablis Vaudésir, Droin £21.74 (DOM) £23.00 (JON)

1992

Chablis les Clos, Brocard £22.87 (FLE)
Chablis les Clos, Drouhin £24.66 (NO)
Chablis les Clos, Pinson £24.87 (NO)
Chablis les Clos, Vocoret £20.25 (VIN)
Chablis Séchet, René Dauvissat £22.81 (BUT)

1991

Chablis Valmur, Droin £20.00 (BIB)
Chablis Vaudésir, Droin £20.00 (BIB)

1990

Chablis Vaillons, Daniel Defaix £20.27 (TW)

1988

Chablis Bougerots, Laroche £22.64 (NO)

£25.00 → £30.00

1995

Chablis les Clos, Laroche £28.14 (PLA)
Chablis les Clos, René Dauvissat £25.95 (LEA)
Chablis Vaudésir, Drouhin £28.50 (BEN)

1993

Chablis Grenouilles, Droin £25.50 (JON)

1984

Chablis les Lys, Daniel Defaix £29.95 (VIG)

CÔTE CHALONNAISE

RED

Under £9.00

1995
Mercurey la Framboisière, Faiveley £8.65 (REI)
Rully Drouhin £8.99 (OD)
1994
Givry Clos du Cellier aux Moines, Delorme £8.09 (WAT)

£9.00 → £10.99

1994
Givry le Pied de Clou, Lummp £10.95 (LEA)
Givry Remmoissenet £9.89 (AV)
Mercurey les Mauvarennes, Faiveley £9.75 (DI)
1993
Givry Ier Cru Clos Salomon, du Gardin £10.95 (WS)
Givry Clos Jus, Mouton £9.50 (SOM) £10.60 (TAN)
Mercurey Château de Chamirey £10.75 (WHI) £10.99 (EL)
Mercurey Domaine de la Croix Jacquelet, Faiveley £10.60 (BEN)
Mercurey Latour £9.35 (PEN)
1992
Mercurey Maréchal £9.90 (PIP)

£11.00 → £14.99

1995
Givry Clos Jus, Lummp £11.95 (LEA)
Mercurey Carillon £12.35 (AD)
Rully Clos de Bellecroix, Domaine de la Folie £11.49 (NA)
1994
Mercurey Juillot £11.46 (DOM)
Rully Château de Rully Rodet £11.69 (WHI)
Rully Domaine de la Renarde, Delorme £12.67 (GN)
Rully les Chaponnières, Jacqueson £12.00 (TAN) £14.50 (STA)
1993
Mercurey Clos du Roy, Faiveley £13.85 (HAH) £14.80 (BEN)
Mercurey Domaine du Meix-Foulot £11.27 (PLA) £11.99 (JON) £13.95 (ROB)
1992
Mercurey Clos des Barraults, Juillot £14.69 (DOM)

WHITE

Under £6.50

1995
Givry Clos des Vignes Rondes, Lumpp ½ bottle £6.20 (LEA)
Montagny Ier Cru, Cave de Buxy £6.29 (CO)

£6.50 → £7.99

1994
Montagny Château de Davenay, Picard £7.75 (SAI)
Montagny Latour £7.99 (NEW)

£8.00 → £10.99

1995
Montagny Ier Cru les Coères, Bernard Michel £9.34 (DOM)
Montagny Ier Cru Mont les Cuchots, Cave de Buxy £9.75 (AD)
1994
Mercurey Château de Chamirey, Rodet £9.99 (MAJ)
Montagny Roy £10.45 (PLA) £10.55 (WRI)
Rully Ier Cru Meix Cadot, Dury £9.95 (RAE)
Rully Château de Rully Rodet £9.95 (SAI)
Rully Faiveley £10.95 (DI)
1993
Givry Clos des Vignes Rondes, Lumpp £8.95 (LEA)
Rully Château de Rully Rodet £9.59 (WHI)
Rully Faiveley £10.50 (GRE)
Rully la Chaume, Dury £9.89 (JON)

£11.00 → £12.99

1995
Mercurey les Velay, Domaine de la Monette £11.95 (LEA)
1994
Mercurey Juillot £12.87 (DOM)
Rully Grésigny, Jacqueson £12.45 (NEZ) £12.50 (TAN)
Rully les St Jacques, Villaine £11.26 (COU)

£13.00 to £13.99

1994
Mercurey Clos Rochette, Faiveley £13.95 (GRE)
1993
Montagny Château de Davenay, Moillard £13.22 (VIN)

CÔTE D'OR

RED

Under £7.00

1995
Hautes-Côtes de Beaune Tête de Cuvée,
Caves des Hautes Côtes £6.99 (WAI)
1994
Hautes-Côtes de Nuits, Caves des
Hautes-Côtes £5.99 (TES)
1992
Gevrey-Chambertin Remoissenet £6.30
(MV)

£7.00 → £8.99

1995
Chorey-lès-Beaune Labouré-Roi £8.60
(PIP)
Côte de Nuits-Villages Chopin-Groffier
£7.95 (BAN)
1994
Savigny-lès-Beaune Latour £8.61 (FOR)
£8.99 (NEW)
1993
Côte de Beaune-Villages Drouhin £8.70 (NI)

£9.00 → £9.99

1995
Chorey-lès-Beaune Roger et Joël Remy
£9.95 (LEA)
Nuits-St-Georges Paul Dugenais £9.95 (SAI)
Savigny-lès-Beaune Latour £9.39 (WHI)
1994
Côte de Beaune-Villages Drouhin £9.99
(GRE)
Santenay Bouchard Père £9.21 (BY)
Savigny-lès-Beaune Latour £9.20 (TAN)
£9.34 (PEN) £9.86 (PLA)
1992
Nuits-St-Georges Caves des Hautes
Côtes £9.99 (FUL)
Savigny les Bourgeots, Bize £9.95 (WS)

£10.00 → £10.99

1995
Chorey-lès-Beaune Château de Chorey-
lès-Beaune, Jacques Germain £10.99
(WHI)
1994
Chassagne-Montrachet Latour £10.98
(PLA)
Savigny-lès-Beaune Pavelot £10.87 (DOM)

1993
Côte de Beaune Drouhin £10.49 (OD)
£10.85 (REI)
Pommard les Épenots, Domaine Mussy
£10.85 (RAE)
St-Aubin les Frionnes, Prudhon £10.30
(TAN)
St-Aubin Thomas Père et Fils £10.80 (GN)
Volnay Domaine Boillot £10.75 (BU)
1991
St-Aubin Sentier du Clou, Prudhon
£10.50 (BIB)

£11.00 → £11.99

1995
Gevrey-Chambertin Labouré-Roi £11.35
(EL)
Monthélie Garaudet £11.60 (PIP)
1994
Chassagne-Montrachet Vieilles Vignes,
Amiot £11.95 (LEA)
Chorey-lès-Beaune Tollot-Beaut £11.49
(THR) £11.50 (TAN) £11.99 (DI)
Côte de Beaune Drouhin £11.86 (ROS)
1993
Santenay Drouhin £11.59 (NI)

1992
Aloxe-Corton Latour £11.45 (FOR)
Fixin Fougeray £11.40 (BER)
Fixin Gelin £11.69 (PLA)
Santenay Remoissenet £11.75 (GRE)
1990
St-Aubin Sentier du Clou, Prudhon
£11.69 (JON)
1988
Côte de Nuits-Villages Rion £11.59 (FLE)

£12.00 → £12.99

1995
Chassagne-Montrachet Vieilles Vignes,
Amiot £12.95 (LEA)
Côte de Beaune Drouhin £12.50 (GRE)
Vosne-Romanée Engel £12.95 (GAU)

1994
Auxey-Duresses Michel Prunier £12.40
(TAN)
Beaune Épenottes, Parent £12.99 (SAF)
Chassagne-Montrachet Louis Carillon
£12.39 (NA)
Nuits-St-Georges Domaine de l'Arlot
£12.99 (WR)
1993
Chassagne-Montrachet Henri Germain
£12.50 (TAN)
Gevrey-Chambertin Rossignol-Trapet
£12.99 (SAF)
Santenay la Maladière, Prieur £12.15 (EL)
1991
Savigny-lès-Beaune les Lavières, Camus-
Bruchon £12.50 (WRI)

£13.00 ➜ £13.99

1995
Aloxe-Corton Chandon de Briailles
£13.25 (REI)
Gevrey-Chambertin Trapet £13.99 (OD)
Marsannay Monchenevoy, Philippe
Charlopin-Parizot £13.95 (LEA)
1994
Gevrey-Chambertin Rodet £13.95 (SAI)
£13.99 (WHI)
Maranges Clos des Loyères Vieilles
Vignes, Girardin £13.95 (STA)
Santenay la Maladière, Girardin £13.60
(NEZ)
1993
Beaune Teurons, Bouchard Père £13.08
(BY)
Chorey-lès-Beaune Maillard £13.75 (GRE)
Nuits-St-Georges Labouré-Roi £13.55
(ROS)
Pommard les Cras, Belland £13.79 (WAT)
1992
Aloxe-Corton les Chaillots, Latour
£13.26 (FOR)
Beaune Blanches Fleurs, Tollot-Beaut
£13.85 (RAE)
Beaune Marconnets, Remoissenet £13.95
(WS)
Beaune Vignes Franches, Latour £13.30
(FOR)
Côte de Nuits-Villages Clos du Chapeau,
Domaine de l'Arlot £13.17 (BY)
Monthélie Château de Monthélie,
Suremain £13.40 (NEZ)
1991
Savigny-lès-Beaune les Guettes, Doudet-
Naudin £13.60 (BER)

£14.00 ➜ £14.99

1995
Pernand-Vergelesses Île de Vergelesses,
Chandon de Briailles £14.50 (REI)
1994
Chassagne-Montrachet Henri Germain
£14.50 (LEA) £14.75 (AD)
Marsannay Longeroies, Denis Mortet
£14.04 (DOM)
Nuits-St-Georges Rodet £14.35 (WHI)
Pommard Clos des Épeneaux, Armand ½
bottle £14.95 (LEA)
1993
Aloxe-Corton Latour £14.49 (NEW)
£14.95 (QUE)
Chambolle-Musigny Hudelot-Noëllat
£14.00 (RIP)
Marsannay Longeroies, Denis Mortet
£14.60 (WS)
Nuits-St-Georges Domaine de l'Arlot
£14.39 (BY)
Vosne-Romanée les Violettes, Georges
Clerget £14.30 (LON)
1992
Beaune Vignes Franches, Latour £14.10
(WY)
Volnay Michel Lafarge £14.99 (SAF)
1991
Chassagne-Montrachet Gagnard-
Delagrange £14.28 (BY)
Gevrey-Chambertin Chanson £14.95
(POR) £14.99 (JON)
Nuits-St-Georges Domaine de l'Arlot
£14.00 (BUT)
1989
Beaune Teurons, Domaines du Château
de Beaune £14.30 (HOG)
1986
Corton les Renardes, Michel Voarick
£14.95 (LEA)

£15.00 ➜ £15.99

1995
Gevrey-Chambertin Rossignol-Trapet
£15.30 (PIP)
Savigny-lès-Beaune les Lavières, Chandon
de Briailles £15.95 (LEA)

---

*Stars (★) indicate wines
selected by Oz Clarke in the
Best Buys section which begins
on page 12.*

1994

Aloxe-Corton Chandon de Briailles £15.90 (HAH)

Aloxe-Corton Tollot-Beaut £15.86 (DOM)

Nuits-St-Georges Jean Chauvenet £15.99 (VIC)

Nuits-St-Georges les Fleurières, Jean-Jacques Confuron £15.75 (HIC)

Savigny-lès-Beaune les Lavières, Chandon de Briailles £15.18 (COU)

1993

Aloxe-Corton Rollin £15.37 (RAE)

Beaune Teurons, Rossignol-Trapet £15.90 (PIP)

Beaune Toussaints, Albert Morot £15.50 (SOM)

Morey-St-Denis en la Rue de Vergy, Domaine Henri Perrot-Minot £15.65 (WAT)

Santenay les Gravières, Domaine de la Pousse d'Or £15.95 (DI)

1992

Beaune Bressandes, Henri Germain £15.32 (TAN)

Nuits-St-Georges Faiveley £15.75 (DI) £15.99 (GRE)

1990

Aloxe-Corton Champy £15.93 (HOG)

£16.00 → £16.99

1995

Beaune Clos des Ursules, Jadot £16.94 (FA)

1994

Chambolle-Musigny Georges Roumier £16.92 (MV)

Fixin Charlopin-Parizot £16.95 (LEA)

Gevrey-Chambertin Clos Prieur, Marc Roy £16.99 (OD)

Gevrey-Chambertin Latour £16.54 (FOR)

Gevrey-Chambertin Mortet £16.44 (PLA)

Savigny-lès-Beaune Marconnets, Bize £16.75 (LAY)

1993

Aloxe-Corton Roger et Joël Remy £16.95 (LEA)

Beaune Bressandes, Henri Germain £16.00 (TAN)

Beaune Vignes Franches, Latour £16.95 (VIG)

Chambolle-Musigny la Combe d'Orvaux, Grivot £16.75 (REI)

Nuits-St-Georges Jean Chauvenet £16.95 (POR)

Nuits-St-Georges Domaine de l'Arlot £16.95 (AD)

Savigny-lès-Beaune les Peuillets, Pavelot £16.45 (DOM) £16.95 (LEA)

Vosne-Romanée Engel £16.75 (GAU)

Vosne-Romanée les Suchots, Alain Hudelot-Noëllat £16.75 (RIP)

1992

Gevrey-Chambertin Denis Mortet £16.50 (WS)

Gevrey-Chambertin Mortet £16.95 (LEA)

Volnay de Montille £16.20 (HAH)

1991

Corton Latour £16.65 (WY)

Gevrey-Chambertin Denis Mortet £16.50 (WS)

Morey-St-Denis Bruno Clair £16.99 (ROS)

£17.00 → £17.99

1995

Beaune Clos des Ursules, Jadot £17.50 (REI)

Pernand-Vergelesses Île de Vergelesses, Chandon de Briailles £17.50 (LEA)

1994

Gevrey-Chambertin Armand Rousseau £17.46 (TAN) £17.59 (EL)

Morey-St-Denis Georges Roumier £17.63 (DOM)

Volnay Domaine Boillot £17.45 (BER)

1993

Aloxe-Corton les Chaillots, Latour £17.95 (STA)

Beaune Clos du Roi, Camus-Bruchon £17.99 (RAE)

Morey-St-Denis Dujac £17.50 (RIP)

1992

Beaune Clos du Roi, Tollot-Beaut £17.99 (VIC)

Chambolle-Musigny Georges Roumier £17.55 (MV)

Savigny-lès-Beaune Marconnets, Bize £17.20 (HAH)

1991

Aloxe-Corton Rollin £17.50 (BIB)

Gevrey-Chambertin Faiveley £17.50 (GRE)

Savigny-lès-Beaune les Lavières, Chandon de Briailles £17.11 (ROS)

1989

Chambolle-Musigny Ghislaine Barthod £17.95 (RAE)

Nuits-St-Georges Faiveley £17.95 (DI)

£18.00 → £19.99

1995

Beaune Montrevenots, Jean-Marc Boillot £18.95 (LEA)

Volnay Domaine Boillot £18.95 (LEA)

1994

Beaune Grèves, Tollot-Beaut £18.21 (DOM)

Chambolle-Musigny Dujac £19.88 (BUT)

Gevrey-Chambertin Armand Rousseau £18.95 (STA)

Gevrey-Chambertin Vieilles Vignes, Dugat-Py £18.30 (HAH) £18.95 (LEA)

Morey-St-Denis Clos de la Bussière, Georges Roumier £18.00 (MV) £18.10 (TAN)

Morey-St-Denis Dujac £19.39 (BUT)

Pommard les Épenots, Domaine Mussy £18.60 (SOM)

1993

Aloxe-Corton Drouhin £18.95 (STA)

Chassagne-Montrachet Champs-Gains, Jean Marc Morey £18.30 (PIP)

Chassagne-Montrachet les Vergers, Amiot £18.95 (LEA)

Gevrey-Chambertin Bachelet £18.80 (RIP)

Gevrey-Chambertin Domaine Boillot £19.45 (BER)

Gevrey-Chambertin Drouhin £18.35 (NI)

Morey-St-Denis Clos de la Bussière, Georges Roumier £19.20 (RIP)

Nuits-St-Georges Jean Chauvenet £18.99 (RAE)

Nuits-St-Georges Michelot £18.20 (NEZ)

Pommard les Bertins, Lescure £19.20 (PIP)

Savigny-lès-Beaune la Dominode, Pavelot £18.95 (LEA)

Volnay Domaine Boillot £19.95 (LEA)

Vosne-Romanée Domaine Mugneret-Gibourg £19.19 (COU)

Vosne-Romanée Engel £19.95 (BER)

1992

Nuits-St-Georges les Perrières, Jean Chauvenet £19.35 (SOM)

1991

Beaune Teurons, Jadot £18.14 (HA)

Nuits-St-Georges les Porets St-Georges, Gouges £19.50 (REJ)

Pernand-Vergelesses Île de Vergelesses, Chandon de Briailles £18.10 (HAH)

Volnay les Caillerets, Clos des 60 Ouvrées, Domaine de la Pousse d'Or £19.88 (FA)

Volnay Santenots Matrot £19.09 (ELL)

Vosne-Romanée Remoissenet £19.61 (AV)

Vosne-Romanée Rion £19.80 (MV)

1989

Beaune Teurons, Bouchard Père £18.75 (GRE)

Savigny-lès-Beaune la Dominode, Bruno Clair £19.95 (BEN)

1988

Beaune les Montrevenots, Jean-Marc Boillot £18.80 (RIP)

Beaune Vignes Franches, Latour £19.95 (VIG)

Gevrey-Chambertin Bachelet £18.10 (GAU)

1987

Clos de Vougeot Noëllat £18.95 (NEZ)

Gevrey-Chambertin Vieilles Vignes, Alain Burguet £18.25 (RIP)

Savigny-lès-Beaune les Lavières, Ampeau £18.50 (LEA)

£20.00 → £22.49

1994

Gevrey-Chambertin Clos Prieur, Mortet £21.50 (LEA)

Nuits-St-Georges les Pruliers, Grivot £20.66 (RAE)

Vosne-Romanée Méo-Camuzet £21.99 (BO)

1993

Aloxe-Corton Tollot-Beaut £20.49 (JON)

Beaune Teurons, Rossignol-Trapet £20.05 (HAH)

Gevrey-Chambertin Lignier £21.75 (LAY)

Nuits-St-Georges Jean Chauvenet £21.90 (BER)

Nuits-St-Georges Clos des Forets St-Georges, Domaine de l'Arlot £22.40 (RIP)

Nuits-St-Georges Drouhin £21.95 (STA)

Pommard les Chaponniers, Parent £20.00 (GAL)

Pommard les Saucilles, Jean-Marc Boillot £20.95 (RAE)

Volnay les Caillerets, Domaine de la Pousse d'Or £21.95 (LAY)

Volnay Michel Lafarge £20.30 (HAH)

1992

Beaune Clos des Mouches, Drouhin £21.85 (GRE)

Beaune Grèves Vigne de l'Enfant Jesus, Bouchard Père £20.84 (BY) £22.32 (WATT)

Gevrey-Chambertin Cazetiers, Armand Rousseau £20.21 (RIP)

Morey-St-Denis Clos de la Bussière, Georges Roumier £20.25 (MV)

> Please remember that **Webster's** is a price guide and not a price list. It is not meant to replace up-to-date merchants' lists.

Nuits-St-Georges les Chaignots, Michelot
£21.74 (DOM)
Nuits-St-Georges Rion £21.59 (YOU)
Volnay Champans, Marquis d'Angerville
£21.50 (RES)
Volnay Santenots Prieur £21.15 (WHI)
1991
Beaune Teurons, Jadot £21.97 (QUE)
Morey-St-Denis Clos de la Bussière,
Georges Roumier £21.80 (HAH)
1990
Beaune Cent Vignes, Lois Dufouleur
£22.27 (VIN)
Gevrey-Chambertin Dujac £20.86 (BUT)
Nuits-St-Georges Faiveley £21.50 (GRE)
Volnay les Angles, Domaine Boillot
£21.74 (FLE)
1989
Corton Clos de la Vigne au Saint, Latour
£21.54 (WY)
Corton Latour £21.27 (QUE)
Gevrey-Chambertin Vieilles Vignes, Alain
Burguet £20.90 (GAU)
Nuits-St-Georges Faiveley £20.95 (WRI)
Pommard les Saucilles, Jean-Marc Boillot
£22.32 (RIP)
Vosne-Romanée Rion £21.50 (FLE)
1985
Auxey-Duresses les Ecusseaux, Ampeau
£20.50 (REI)
1982
Beaune Dames Hospitalières, Hospices de
Beaune £20.00 (VIG)
1979
Chambolle-Musigny Latour £20.20 (FOR)

£22.50 ➝ £24.99

1995
Beaune Grèves, Tollot-Beaut £22.95 (DI)
Corton Maréchaudes, Chandon de
Briailles £22.75 (REI)
Gevrey-Chambertin Vieilles Vignes,
Philippe Charlopin £23.50 (LEA)
1994
Chassagne-Montrachet Clos St Jean,
Amiot £22.50 (LEA)
Gevrey-Chambertin Mortet £22.50 (RES)
Gevrey-Chambertin Vieilles Vignes,
Philippe Charlopin £22.95 (LEA)
Nuits-St-Georges les Perrières, Jean
Chauvenet £24.50 (POR)
Volnay les Caillerets, Clos des 60 Ouvrées,
Domaine de la Pousse d'Or £22.50 (LAY)
Vosne-Romanée les Beaux Monts,
Domaine Jean Grivot £22.90 (BER)

1993
Corton Clos de la Vigne au Saint, Latour
£23.16 (HA)
Gevrey-Chambertin Armand Rousseau
£23.50 (RES) £24.50 (REI)
Gevrey-Chambertin Vieilles Vignes, Alain
Burguet £24.00 (RIP)
Pommard Rugiens, Domaine Courcel
£23.50 (RIP)
Vosne-Romanée les Chaumes, Jean Tardy
£24.77 (RES)
1992
Gevrey-Chambertin Cazetiers, Armand
Rousseau £22.50 (WS)
Latricières-Chambertin Trapet £24.99 (OD)
Pommard Domaine de la Pousse d'Or
£24.90 (AD)
Volnay Michel Lafarge £23.85 (HAH)
1991
Chambolle-Musigny les Veroilles,
Ghislaine Barthod £23.25 (WRI)
Nuits-St-Georges les Pruliers, Gouges
£24.00 (JON)
Volnay les Angles, Domaine Boillot
£24.95 (BER)
1990
Chambolle-Musigny Dujac £24.87 (RIP)
Morey-St-Denis Dujac £22.99 (DI)
Nuits-St-Georges Faiveley £23.10 (TAN)
Volnay Clos d'Audignac, Domaine de la
Pousse d'Or £23.99 (YOU)
1989
Beaune Bressandes, Morot £22.95 (RES)
Chambolle-Musigny Ghislaine Barthod
£23.95 (STA)
Corton Latour £23.50 (PEN)
Gevrey-Chambertin Combottes, Dujac
£23.30 (BUT)
Morey-St-Denis Clos des Ormes, Faiveley
£22.50 (REI)
Nuits-St-Georges Clos de la Maréchale,
Faiveley £22.50 (GRE)
Nuits-St-Georges Jadot £24.86 (QUE)
Volnay de Montille £24.10 (HAH)
1988
Aloxe-Corton Drouhin £23.50 (WY)
Corton Maréchaudes, Chandon de
Briailles £23.50 (LEA)
Nuits-St-Georges Méo-Camuzet £22.99
(RAE)
Pommard les Épenots, Château de
Meursault £22.50 (GRE)
Savigny-lès-Beaune les Lavières, Tollot-
Beaut £23.10 (UB)
Volnay Santenots Latour £23.50 (STA)

1986
Beaune Grèves Vigne de l'Enfant Jesus,
Bouchard Père £22.50 (REI)
Vosne-Romanée les Beaumonts, Domaine
Rion £24.90 (GAU)
1985
Savigny-lès-Beaune Ampeau £24.18 (CHA)
1984
Pommard Ampeau £24.50 (LEA)

£25.00 → £27.49

1995
Beaune Clos des Mouches, Drouhin
£25.50 (BEN)
Gevrey-Chambertin Coeur du Roy,
Dugat-Py £25.50 (LEA)
1994
Nuits-St-Georges Chaignots, Mugneret-
Gibourg £26.93 (COU)
Pommard les Jarollières, Domaine de la
Pousse d'Or £26.95 (DI)
Volnay Santenots Lafon £26.95 (AD)
1993
Beaune Clos des Mouches, Drouhin
£26.95 (NI)
Chassagne-Montrachet Clos de la
Boudriotte, Ramonet-Prudhon £26.50
(RIP)
Nuits-St-Georges Clos des Forets St-
Georges, Domaine de l'Arlot £25.66 (BY)
Nuits-St-Georges les Pruliers, Gouges
£26.99 (JON)
Pommard les Épenots, Armand £25.75
(BUT)
1992
Gevrey-Chambertin Champeaux, Mortet
£25.50 (RAE) £25.85 (DOM)
Pommard les Épenots, Mme de Courcel
£25.00 (RES)
1991
Clos de la Roche Armand Rousseau
£25.75 (BUT)
Gevrey-Chambertin Cuvée de l'Abeille,
Ponsot £27.45 (ROB)
Nuits-St-Georges les Chaignots, Georges
Mugneret £25.50 (LEA)
Volnay Santenots Lafon £25.20 (MV)
£26.55 (AD)
Volnay Vendanges Selectionées, Lafarge
£25.35 (BER)
1990
Corton Clos de la Vigne au Saint, Latour
£25.50 (WRI)
Nuits-St-Georges Clos de la Maréchale,
Faiveley £26.50 (GRE)

£27.50 → £29.99

1995
Chambolle-Musigny de Vogüé £27.55 (REI)
Corton Clos du Roi, Chandon de Briailles
£28.50 (REI)
Nuits-St-Georges Clos des Forets St-
Georges, Domaine de l'Arlot £29.67
(BUT)
1994
Chambolle-Musigny de Vogüé £27.50 (RES)
Gevrey-Chambertin Lavaux-St-Jacques,
Dugat-Py £29.00 (LEA)
1993
Chambolle-Musigny Ghislaine Barthod
£29.30 (BER)
Corton Grancey, Latour £29.26 (PEN)
Échézeaux Engel £27.75 (GAU)
Mazis-Chambertin Armand Rousseau
£29.37 (RIP)
Nuits-St-Georges Chaignots, Mugneret-
Gibourg £29.50 (LAY)
Nuits-St-Georges les Pruliers, Gouges
£27.50 (RES)
Pommard les Épenots, Latour £28.50 (GN)
Pommard Pezerolles, Domaine de
Montille £28.95 (HAH)
1992
Chambolle-Musigny les Feusselottes,
Georges Mugneret £27.50 (LEA)
Clos de la Roche Armand Rousseau
£28.73 (BY)
Mazis-Chambertin Armand Rousseau
£28.45 (TAN)
1991
Clos de la Roche Armand Rousseau
£28.00 (RIP)
Corton-Bressandes Tollot-Beaut £29.50
(DI)
Pommard Clos des Épeneaux, Armand
£29.70 (MV)

Volnay Clos d'Audignac, Domaine de la
  Pousse d'Or £28.50 (ROB)
Volnay les Caillerets, Clos des 60
  Ouvrées, Domaine de la Pousse d'Or
  £28.20 (GAU)

1990
Corton Clos de la Vigne au Saint, Latour
  £29.38 (WY)
Corton Grancey, Latour £28.20 (PEN)
Gevrey-Chambertin Faiveley £29.00 (BER)
Pommard les Saucilles, Jean-Marc Boillot
  £29.20 (RIP)
Volnay les Caillerets, Clos des 60 Ouvrées,
  Domaine de la Pousse d'Or £29.90 (DI)

1988
Clos de Vougeot Noëllat £28.10 (NEZ)
Corton Grancey, Latour £29.50 (STA)
Nuits-St-Georges Clos de la Maréchale,
  Faiveley £27.75 (GRE)
Volnay les Caillerets, Domaine de la
  Pousse d'Or £29.00 (RES)

1986
Chambolle-Musigny de Vogüé £29.38 (WY)
Clos St-Denis Dujac £29.31 (RIP)

1985
Beaune Perrières, Latour £27.50 (VIG)
Gevrey-Chambertin Clos des Varoilles,
  Domaine des Varoilles £27.50 (REI)

£30.00 → £34.99

1995
Corton-Bressandes Chandon de Briailles
  £33.00 (LEA)

1994
Échézeaux Mugneret £31.95 (LAY)
Gevrey-Chambertin Clos des Ruchottes,
  Armand Rousseau £31.63 (BUT)
Pommard Clos des Épeneaux, Armand
  £34.42 (TW)

1993
Chambolle-Musigny les Feusselottes,
  Georges Mugneret £31.00 (LEA)
Clos de la Roche Armand Rousseau
  £30.50 (RIP) £30.77 (BY) £33.99 (TAN)
Corton-Bressandes Chandon de Briailles
  £33.60 (HAH)
Pommard Clos des Épeneaux, Armand
  £30.60 (MV) £34.99 (YOU)
Pommard les Épenots, Armand £33.75 (LAY)
Volnay les Caillerets, Domaine de la
  Pousse d'Or £30.95 (BER)
Vosne-Romanée les Beaumonts, Domaine
  Rion £30.60 (MV)
Vosne-Romanée les Chaumes, Méo-
  Camuzet £31.24 (RAE)

1992
Chambolle-Musigny de Vogüé £34.50 (ROB)
Corton Perrières, Juillot £30.55 (DOM)
Ruchottes-Chambertin Clos des
  Ruchottes Monopole, Armand
  Rousseau £30.77 (BY)

1991
Charmes-Chambertin Armand Rousseau
  £32.50 (ROB) £32.50 (RES)
Pommard les Vignots, Leroy £33.59 (FA)
Volnay Clos des Chênes, Michel Lafarge
  £34.07 (RIP) £34.35 (HAH) £34.50 (RAE)
Volnay les Caillerets, Clos des 60
  Ouvrées, Domaine de la Pousse d'Or
  £33.90 (TW)

1990
Clos de Vougeot Mongeard-Mugneret
  £33.78 (WATT)
Corton Bouchard Père £30.00 (HOG)
Nuits-St-Georges Clos des Forets St-
  Georges, Domaine de l'Arlot £33.10 (BY)
Nuits-St-Georges les Pruliers, Gouges
  £34.00 (UB)

1989
Beaune Clos des Mouches, Drouhin
  £31.26 (NO) £31.50 (GRE)

Corton Clos du Roi, Dubreuil-Fontaine
  £30.89 (BY)
Nuits-St-Georges Vignes Rondes, Rion
  £30.60 (MV)
Volnay les Caillerets, Clos des 60 Ouvrées,
  Domaine de la Pousse d'Or £33.95 (BER)

1988
Beaune Clos des Mouches, Drouhin
  £32.90 (TW)
Charmes-Chambertin Armand Rousseau
  £34.61 (RIP)
Corton Perrières, Juillot £30.55 (DOM)
Latricières-Chambertin Trapet £30.75 (BY)
Mazis-Chambertin Armand Rousseau
  £32.50 (GAU)

1987
Charmes-Chambertin Dujac £30.65 (BUT)
Corton Clos des Cortons, Faiveley
  £33.95 (DI)

1985
Pommard Ampeau £32.50 (REI)
Pommard Clos Blanc, Machard de
  Gramont £32.00 (LEA)
1982
Musigny Drouhin £34.50 (REI)
Volnay Santenots Ampeau £33.50 (LEA)

£35.00 → £39.99

1995
Corton Clos du Roi, Chandon de Briailles
  £35.00 (LEA)
Échézeaux Drouhin £38.90 (BEN)
1994
Bonnes-Mares Roumier £38.78 (DOM)
Chambolle-Musigny les Amoureuses,
  Roumier £36.00 (MV)
Clos de Vougeot Méo-Camuzet £36.52
  (RAE)
Gevrey-Chambertin Clos St-Jacques,
  Armand Rousseau £38.95 (LAY)
Nuits-St-Georges Méo-Camuzet £37.00
  (BO)
1993
Chambolle-Musigny de Vogüé £35.00 (RES)
Chapelle-Chambertin Trapet £35.54 (FA)
Clos de Vougeot Grivot £39.75 (LAY)
Clos St-Denis Dujac £38.00 (RIP)
Gevrey-Chambertin Combottes, Dujac
  £35.25 (RIP)
Nuits-St-Georges les St-Georges, Gouges
  £35.00 (RES)
Volnay Clos des Chênes, Michel Lafarge
  £37.65 (GAU)
Volnay Santenots Lafon £37.75 (BEN)
1992
Bonnes-Mares de Vogüé £39.50 (REI)
Bonnes-Mares Roumier £38.77 (RIP)
Clos de la Roche Armand Rousseau
  £37.50 (BUT)
Clos de la Roche Dujac £39.50 (LAY)
Clos de Vougeot Méo-Camuzet £36.99
  (OD)
Échézeaux Henri Jayer £39.60 (RAE)
Nuits-St-Georges aux Allots, Leroy
  £39.75 (LAY)
Ruchottes-Chambertin Domaine
  Mugneret £36.50 (LEA)

---

*In each price band wines
are listed in vintage order.
Within each vintage they
are listed in A–Z order.*

1991
Charmes-Chambertin Armand Rousseau
  £37.65 (BER)
Clos de la Roche Armand Rousseau
  £35.00 (RES) £35.00 (ROB)
Clos de la Roche Dujac £37.60 (RIP)
  £37.95 (DI)
Ruchottes-Chambertin Domaine
  Mugneret £37.50 (LEA)
Volnay Clos de la Bousse d'Or, Domaine
  de la Pousse d'Or £36.52 (BER)
1990
Beaune Clos des Mouches, Drouhin
  £37.50 (UB)
Clos de Vougeot Drouhin £39.95 (REI)
Pommard les Épenots, Mme de Courcel
  £35.00 (RES)
Ruchottes-Chambertin Armand Rousseau
  £36.43 (FA)
1989
Clos de la Roche Armand Rousseau
  £35.75 (BEN)
Corton-Bressandes Tollot-Beaut £38.78
  (WY)
Mazis-Chambertin Faiveley £39.90 (DI)
1988
Corton-Bressandes Tollot-Beaut £39.85
  (AD)
Gevrey-Chambertin Combottes, Dujac
  £35.54 (BUT)
Gevrey-Chambertin Jadot £36.00 (BER)
Nuits-St-Georges les Damodes, Jean
  Chauvenet £35.00 (WS)
Nuits-St-Georges aux Allots, Leroy
  £35.54 (FA)
1987
Clos de Vougeot Arnoux £35.00 (WHI)
Échézeaux Drouhin £35.00 (RES)
Pommard les Épenots, Mme de Courcel
  £35.75 (UB)
1985
Volnay Champans, Marquis d'Angerville
  £37.95 (UB)
Volnay les Caillerets, Clerget £35.00 (RES)
1982
Clos de Vougeot Drouhin £35.00 (VIG)
Volnay Santenots Ampeau £35.29 (YOU)
1978
Auxey-Duresses les Ecusseaux, Ampeau
  £35.00 (LEA)
Nuits-St-Georges Viénot £35.25 (TW)
Volnay Santenots Ampeau £39.50 (REI)
1969
Gevrey-Chambertin Clos des Varoilles,
  Domaine des Varoilles £35.00 (REI)

£40.00 → £49.99

1994
Bonnes-Mares Roumier £44.10 (MV)
Chambertin Armand Rousseau £45.82
  (BUT) £47.50 (LAY)
Chambertin Clos-de-Bèze, Armand
  Rousseau £45.82 (BUT) £47.19 (TAN)
Chambolle-Musigny les Amoureuses, de
  Vogüé £49.00 (DI)
Clos de Vougeot Georges Mugneret
  £42.00 (LEA)
Échézeaux Dujac £45.34 (BUT)
Échézeaux Henri Jayer £40.44 (RAE)

1993
Bonnes-Mares Jadot £40.93 (FA)
Chambertin Clos-de-Bèze, Damoy £44.85
  (RES)
Chambertin Trapet £42.10 (PIP)
Charmes-Chambertin Bachelet £43.47 (RIP)
Charmes-Chambertin Dujac £45.34 (BUT)
Latricières-Chambertin Faiveley £41.65 (REI)
Mazis-Chambertin Faiveley £41.00 (RIP)
  £47.00 (LEA)

1992
Bonnes-Mares de Vogüé £49.23 (PLA)
Bonnes-Mares Roumier £41.13 (DOM)
  £45.00 (RES)
Clos de la Roche Vieilles Vignes, Ponsot
  £48.75 (LAY)
Clos de Vougeot Georges Mugneret
  £45.00 (LEA)
Clos St-Denis Dujac £44.17 (BY)
Griotte-Chambertin Ponsot £42.30 (MV)
Latricières-Chambertin Ponsot £42.30 (MV)
Nuits-St-Georges aux Boudots, Leroy
  £45.34 (FA)

1991
Clos de Vougeot Georges Mugneret
  £45.00 (LEA)
Clos de Vougeot Méo-Camuzet £42.50
  (RES)
Corton Bonneau du Martray £40.07 (PLA)

1990
Clos de la Roche Armand Rousseau
  £40.44 (BUT)
Clos de Vougeot Grivot £42.00 (LEA)
Corton-Bressandes Drouhin £41.61 (WY)

1989
Chambolle-Musigny les Amoureuses, de
  Vogüé £48.92 (NO)
Charmes-Chambertin Armand Rousseau
  £49.50 (UB)
Clos de Vougeot Drouhin £48.95 (STA)
Pommard les Vignots, Leroy £40.44 (FA)

1988
Clos St-Denis Dujac £41.12 (RIP)

1987
Clos de la Roche Vieilles Vignes, Ponsot
  £48.99 (YOU)

1985
Morey-St-Denis Clos des Lambrays, Saier
  £49.25 (BUT)
Nuits-St-Georges les Boudots, Grivot
  £49.50 (RES)
Pommard Ampeau £42.50 (LEA)
Pommard Domaine de la Pousse d'Or
  £49.95 (RES)

1982
Chambertin Clos-de-Bèze, Armand
  Rousseau £43.08 (WY)
Latricières-Chambertin Faiveley £47.00
  (TW)

£50.00 → £59.99

1995
Chambertin Clos-de-Bèze, Drouhin
  £58.50 (BEN)
Clos de Vougeot Georges Mugneret
  £50.00 (LEA)
Musigny Jadot £54.64 (FA)

1993
Chambertin Clos-de-Bèze, Damoy £51.99
  (TW)
Chapelle-Chambertin Ponsot £54.15 (BUT)
Charmes-Chambertin Dujac £54.00 (BER)
Clos de la Roche Dujac £51.21 (BUT)
Corton Clos des Cortons, Faiveley
  £52.90 (HAH)

1992
Échézeaux Domaine de la Romanée-
  Conti £52.87 (WY)
Musigny Vieilles Vignes, de Vogüé £50.00
  (REI)
Romanée-St-Vivant Domaine de la
  Romanée-Conti £59.99 (EL)
Vosne-Romanée aux Brulées, Méo-
  Camuzet £55.00 (RES)

1991
Chambertin Clos-de-Bèze, Armand
  Rousseau £55.00 (RES)
Échézeaux Domaine de la Romanée-
  Conti £57.09 (FA)
Griotte-Chambertin Ponsot £50.23 (BUT)

1989
Ruchottes-Chambertin Clos des
  Ruchottes Monopole, Armand
  Rousseau £59.50 (REI)
Vosne-Romanée les Beaumonts, Leroy
  £58.07 (FA)

1985
Beaune Grèves Vigne de l'Enfant Jesus,
Bouchard Père £58.26 (WATT)
Gevrey-Chambertin Clos St-Jacques,
Armand Rousseau £50.00 (WS)
1979
Mazis-Chambertin Faiveley £52.86 (TW)
Pommard Pezerolles, Domaine de
Montille £55.00 (RES)
1976
Chambertin Trapet £54.36 (BY)
Musigny Vieilles Vignes, de Vogüé £54.15
(FA)
Pommard Ampeau £54.00 (LEA)
1971
Nuits-St-Georges aux Boudots, Leroy
£54.15 (FA)
1956
Grands-Échézeaux Domaine de la
Romanée-Conti £55.50 (REI)
1934
Beaune Grèves, Chanson £55.00 (REI)

£60.00 ➜ £79.99

1995
Bonnes-Mares de Vogüé £72.50 (REI)
1993
Bonnes-Mares de Vogüé £69.81 (FA)
Chambertin Armand Rousseau £70.50
(RIP) £77.65 (BUT)
Chambertin Clos-de-Bèze, Armand
Rousseau £62.25 (REI) £70.50 (RIP)
Chambertin Clos-de-Bèze, Faiveley
£62.00 (RIP) £77.60 (HAH)
Échézeaux Domaine de la Romanée-
Conti £71.28 (FA)
Pommard les Vignots, Leroy £73.73 (FA)
Vosne-Romanée aux Brulées, Méo-
Camuzet £61.98 (RES)
1992
Chambertin Clos-de-Bèze, Armand
Rousseau £60.00 (RES)
Clos de Vougeot Leroy £64.92 (FA)
Grands-Échézeaux Domaine de la
Romanée-Conti £75.00 (BER)
Richebourg Domaine de la Romanée-
Conti £77.75 (LAY)
Romanée-St-Vivant les Quatres Journaux,
Latour £61.20 (WY)
1991
Musigny Vieilles Vignes, de Vogüé £64.97
(NO)
Richebourg Domaine Gros £68.50 (DI)
Romanée-St-Vivant Domaine de la
Romanée-Conti £77.35 (WY)

1990
Chambertin Vieilles Vignes, Trapet £64.63
(TW)
Chambolle-Musigny les Amoureuses,
Joseph Drouhin £69.52 (WY)
1989
Richebourg Domaine Gros £74.06 (BY)
Vosne-Romanée les Beaumonts, Leroy
£60.02 (BUT)
1985
Chambertin Clos-de-Bèze, Armand
Rousseau £70.00 (WS)
Mazis-Chambertin Armand Rousseau
£68.50 (REI)
1979
Latricières-Chambertin Faiveley £64.63
(TW)
1969
Volnay Santenots Prieur £60.00 (RES)
1955
Pommard Clos de la Commaraine,
Jaboulet-Vercherre £75.00 (ROB)

£80.00 ➜ £99.99

1993
Corton Clos du Roi, Chandon de Briailles
£89.00 (LEA)
Échézeaux Domaine de la Romanée-
Conti £87.50 (LAY)
1992
Richebourg Domaine de la Romanée-
Conti £98.75 (BU)
1989
Musigny de Vogüé £97.42 (ELL)
Musigny Vieilles Vignes, de Vogüé £82.25
(WY)
La Romanée Domaines du Château de
Vosne-Romanée, Bouchard Père £95.60
(HOG)
1986
Échézeaux Henri Jayer £93.31 (BUT)
Grands-Échézeaux Domaine de la
Romanée-Conti £99.00 (UB)
1983
Échézeaux Domaine de la Romanée-
Conti £80.00 (RES)
Grands-Échézeaux Domaine de la
Romanée-Conti £88.12 (TW)

£100.00 ➜ £149.99

1993
Échézeaux Domaine de la Romanée-
Conti £104.77 (WATT) £120.00 (BEN)
Romanée-St-Vivant Domaine de la
Romanée-Conti £145.00 (REI)

1992
Latricières-Chambertin Leroy £106.04 (FA)
Richebourg Domaine de la Romanée-
    Conti £108.98 (BUT) £120.00 (BER)
Romanée-St-Vivant Leroy £120.73 (FA)
La Tâche Domaine de la Romanée-Conti
    £127.29 (WY)
1991
Grands-Échézeaux Domaine de la
    Romanée-Conti £105.00 (BER)
Richebourg Domaine de la Romanée-
    Conti £103.11 (FA) £112.11 (WY)
1989
Clos de la Roche Leroy £110.94 (FA)
Musigny Vieilles Vignes, de Vogüé £101.95
    (BEN)
Romanée-St-Vivant Domaine de la
    Romanée-Conti £115.00 (RES)
1988
Grands-Échézeaux Domaine de la
    Romanée-Conti £115.00 (BO)
1987
Échézeaux Domaine de la Romanée-
    Conti £128.56 (BUT)
Richebourg Domaine de la Romanée-
    Conti £141.00 (TW)
Vosne-Romanée Méo-Camuzet £115.00
    (NA)
1985
Chambertin Armand Rousseau £141.98
    (WATT)
Échézeaux Domaine de la Romanée-
    Conti £145.00 (REI)
1979
Grands-Échézeaux Domaine de la
    Romanée-Conti £135.00 (RES)
Vosne-Romanée Cros Parantoux, Henri
    Jayer £123.38 (FA)
1949
Beaune Grèves Vigne de l'Enfant Jesus,
    Bouchard Père £125.00 (REI)

£150.00 → £199.99

1993
Grands-Échézeaux Domaine de la
    Romanée-Conti £150.60 (WATT)

> Please remember that
> **Webster's** is a price
> guide and not a price list. It
> is not meant to replace up-
> to-date
> merchants' lists.

Richebourg Domaine de la Romanée-
    Conti £153.73 (WY) £195.00 (BEN)
Richebourg Méo-Camuzet £158.92 (FA)
Romanée-St-Vivant Domaine de la
    Romanée-Conti £150.00 (BEN) £156.18
    (WATT)
1992
La Tâche Domaine de la Romanée-Conti
    £182.73 (VIN)
1990
Romanée-St-Vivant Domaine de la
    Romanée-Conti £153.04 (FA) £164.50
    (WY)
1989
Romanée-St-Vivant Domaine de la
    Romanée-Conti £180.00 (BER)
1988
La Tâche Domaine de la Romanée-Conti
    £185.00 (BO)
1986
Richebourg Domaine de la Romanée-
    Conti £195.00 (STA)
1969
Échézeaux Domaine de la Romanée-
    Conti £195.00 (RES)
Grands-Échézeaux Domaine de la
    Romanée-Conti £150.00 (BEN)
1928
Grands-Échézeaux Barolet £150.00 (REI)

£200.00 → £299.99

1993
Richebourg Domaine de la Romanée-
    Conti £205.62 (WATT)
La Tâche Domaine de la Romanée-Conti
    £211.79 (FA) £223.74 (WY) £225.00 (EL)
1991
La Tâche Domaine de la Romanée-Conti
    £245.00 (BER)
1990
Richebourg Domaine de la Romanée-
    Conti £216.69 (FA) £235.00 (WY)
Vosne-Romanée les Beaumonts, Leroy
    £241.17 (FA)
1988
Richebourg Domaine de la Romanée-
    Conti £219.69 (NO)
1986
La Tâche Domaine de la Romanée-Conti
    £205.00 (STA)
1971
Échézeaux Domaine de la Romanée-
    Conti £205.00 (STA)
1969
Chambertin Ponsot £225.00 (RES)

£300.00 → £549.99

1993
Clos de Vougeot Leroy £540.50 (FA)
Latricières-Chambertin Leroy £540.50 (FA)
Nuits-St-Georges aux Boudots, Leroy
£363.57 (FA)
1990
Richebourg Domaine de la Romanée-
Conti £331.94 (WATT) £360.00 (BER)
La Tâche Domaine de la Romanée-Conti
£353.77 (BUT) £381.87 (WATT)
1985
La Tâche Domaine de la Romanée-Conti
£422.50 (REI)
1978
La Tâche Domaine de la Romanée-Conti
£495.00 (BEN) £525.00 (RES)
1971
Romanée-St-Vivant Domaine de la
Romanée-Conti £360.00 (ROB)
1962
La Tâche Domaine de la Romanée-Conti
£378.98 (WY)

c. £922.00

1993
Romanée-Conti Domaine de la Romanée-
Conti £921.69 (FA)

£1,000.00 → £2,999.00

1993
Romanée-Conti Domaine de la Romanée-
Conti £1,150.00 (BEN) £1,752.71 (WATT)
1990
Romanée-Conti Domaine de la Romanée-
Conti £2,008.56 (BUT)
1978
Romanée-Conti Domaine de la Romanée-
Conti £2,878.75 (FA)

c. £3,320.00

1990
Romanée-Conti Domaine de la Romanée-
Conti £3,319.37 (WATT)

WHITE

Under £10.00

1994
Hautes-Côtes de Nuits Chaley £7.95 (NA)
Pernand-Vergelesses Olivier Leflaive
£9.85 (HAH)
1993
St-Aubin la Pucelle, Roux Père et Fils
£8.95 (WS)
St-Romain Domaine Leflaive £8.99 (DI)
Savigny-lès-Beaune Pavelot £9.95 (LEA)

£10.00 → £11.99

1995
Auxey-Duresses Labouré-Roi £10.20 (PIP)
Auxey-Duresses Olivier Leflaive £11.00
(WS)
Pernand-Vergelesses Jacques Germain
£10.99 (WHI)
Savigny-lès-Beaune Montchenevoy,
Javillier £11.95 (BAN)
1994
Marsannay Jadot £10.49 (WR) £10.49 (BOT)
1993
Puligny-Montrachet Carillon £10.50 (REI)
St-Aubin la Pucelle, Lamy-Pillot £11.75 (BY)
St-Aubin Prudhon £11.50 (JON)

£12.00 → £13.99

1995
Monthélie le Champ Fulliot, Garaudet
£13.80 (PIP)
Santenay Blanc le St-Jean, Girardin £13.80
(NI)
1994
Auxey-Duresses Olivier Leflaive £12.99 (DI)
Meursault Boisson-Vadot £13.37 (BY)
Meursault Michelot-Buisson £13.99 (OD)
Pernand-Vergelesses Dubreuil-Fontaine
£13.95 (RES)
Pernand-Vergelesses Rollin £13.02 (RAE)
St-Aubin Jadot £13.22 (HA)
St-Aubin la Chatenière, Roux Père et Fils
£12.89 (EL)
Savigny-lès-Beaune les Vermots Dessus,
Girardin £13.61 (ELL) £13.80 (NI)
1993
Chassagne-Montrachet Lamy-Pillot
£13.38 (BY)
Hautes-Côtes de Beaune Jayer-Gilles
£13.95 (WS)
Meursault Clos du Château, Château de
Meursault £12.75 (POR)

1991
Pernand-Vergelesses Rollin £13.99 (RAE)
Puligny-Montrachet Latour £13.70 (HOG)
Savigny-lès-Beaune Camus-Bruchon
£13.45 (JON)

£14.00 → £15.99

1996
Chassagne-Montrachet Pillot £15.95 (LEA)
1995
Meursault Bouchard Père £15.37 (BY)
Meursault Michelot £15.00 (TAN)
Puligny-Montrachet Domaine Gérard
Chavy £15.20 (PIP)
St-Aubin le Charmois, Olivier Leflaive
£14.50 (LAY)
1994
Chassagne-Montrachet Domaine Leflaive
£14.90 (WS)
Meursault-Blagny, Latour £15.47 (FA)
Meursault Cuvée Charles Maxime,
Latour-Giraud £14.99 (SAF)
Puligny-Montrachet Clerc £14.95 (BAN)
Puligny-Montrachet Drouhin £15.89 (NI)
Savigny-lès-Beaune Pavelot £15.22 (DOM)
1993
Chassagne-Montrachet Sauzet £14.49 (FA)
Meursault Latour £14.92 (HOG) £15.99
(MAJ)
Puligny-Montrachet Domaine Gérard
Chavy £15.75 (SOM)
Puligny-Montrachet Sauzet £15.47 (FA)
1992
Pernand-Vergelesses Rollin £15.00 (BIB)

£16.00 → £17.99

1996
Puligny-Montrachet Pillot £16.95 (LEA)
1995
Meursault Michelot £16.95 (AD)
Meursault sous la Velle, Charles et Remi
Jobard £16.95 (LEA)
Savigny-lès-Beaune Montchenevoy,
Javillier £16.50 (LAY)
1994
Chassagne-Montrachet Bachelet £16.99
(RAE)
Chassagne-Montrachet Verget £16.94 (FA)
Corton-Charlemagne, Verget £17.29 (YOU)
Meursault Bouchard Père £16.07 (BY)
Meursault Charmes, Brunet £17.25 (EL)
Meursault Charmes, Latour £16.94 (FA)
Meursault Jadot £17.99 (MAR)
Meursault Latour £17.86 (HA)
Meursault Remoissenet £17.50 (WS)

Pernand-Vergelesses Domaine Chandon
de Briailles £16.50 (LEA)
Puligny-Montrachet Clerc £17.99 (FUL)
Puligny-Montrachet Labouré-Roi £17.65
(EL)
1993
Chassagne-Montrachet Lamy-Pillot
£16.37 (BY)
Chassagne-Montrachet Latour £16.99 (MAJ)
Meursault-Blagny, Latour £17.12 (HOG)
Meursault Latour £16.84 (WATT) £16.99
(NEW)
Meursault Matrot £17.14 (ELL)
Meursault Michelot-Buisson £17.55 (NEZ)
Meursault sous la Velle, Charles et Remi
Jobard £16.95 (LEA)
1990
Meursault l'Ormeau, Coche £16.99 (RAE)
1989
Puligny-Montrachet la Garenne, Thomas
£17.00 (YOU)
1987
Puligny-Montrachet Domaine Leflaive
£16.50 (BU)

£18.00 → £19.99

1995
Chassagne-Montrachet Verget £19.95 (LEA)
Meursault Drouhin £19.50 (GRE)
Meursault Verget £19.88 (FA)
Puligny-Montrachet Carillon £19.50 (POR)
£19.95 (LAY) £19.99 (BOT)
Puligny-Montrachet Drouhin £18.46 (WATT)
Puligny-Montrachet les Enseignères,
Chavy-Chouet £18.95 (LEA)
1994
Chassagne-Montrachet Labouré-Roi
£18.08 (ROS)
Chassagne-Montrachet Latour £19.98
(QUE)
Chassagne-Montrachet Vide-Bourse,
Pillot £19.95 (LEA)
Meursault Charmes, Michelot £18.00 (BER)
Meursault Chevalières, Charles et Remi
Jobard £18.49 (COU) £19.50 (LEA)
Meursault Genevrières, Latour £18.90 (FA)
Meursault les Tillets, Javillier £18.48 (BY)
£18.80 (SOM)
Puligny-Montrachet Carillon £18.95 (NI)
£19.55 (LAY)
Puligny-Montrachet Latour £18.00 (HIG)
Puligny-Montrachet les Folatières, Chavy
£19.90 (PIP)
Puligny-Montrachet Sous les Puits,
Bachelet £19.99 (RAE)

1993

Chassagne-Montrachet Morgeot, Gagnard
Delagrange £19.90 (HAH)
Meursault-Blagny, Latour £18.99 (MAJ)
£19.95 (VIG)
Meursault l'Ormeau, Coche £19.89 (JON)
Puligny-Montrachet Domaine Gérard
Chavy £18.00 (MV)
Puligny-Montrachet Latour £19.95 (VIG)
Puligny-Montrachet les Folatières,
Boisson-Vadot £18.48 (BY)
St-Aubin 1er Cru, Bachelet £18.40 (UB)

1992

Chassagne-Montrachet Latour £19.39
(WATT)
Meursault Matrot £18.69 (ROS)
Meursault sous la Velle, Charles et Remi
Jobard £19.95 (LEA)
Puligny-Montrachet Domaine Gérard
Chavy £18.35 (NO)

1991

Chassagne-Montrachet la Boudriotte,
Gagnard-Delagrange £19.70 (HAH)

1990

Puligny-Montrachet Bouchard Père
£18.42 (BY)
Puligny-Montrachet Latour £18.80 (PEN)

£20.00 → £24.99

1996

Chassagne-Montrachet Grandes, Pillot
£24.95 (LEA)
Chassagne-Montrachet Vide-Bourse,
Pillot £21.50 (LEA)

1995

Chassagne-Montrachet Chaumées, Colin-
Deleger £22.50 (EL)
Chassagne-Montrachet Colin-Deleger
£21.50 (LAY)
Chassagne-Montrachet Grandes, Pillot
£24.95 (LEA)
Meursault Genevrières, Charles et Remi
Jobard £24.50 (LEA)
Meursault Poruzots, Jobard £24.50 (LEA)
Puligny-Montrachet Boillot £23.95 (LEA)
Puligny-Montrachet Carillon £20.95 (AD)
£21.99 (NA)
Puligny-Montrachet les Enseignères,
Olivier Leflaive £21.95 (GN)

1994

Chassagne-Montrachet Drouhin £20.35
(STA)
Chassagne-Montrachet Grandes, Pillot
£24.50 (LEA)
Chassagne-Montrachet Jadot £23.99 (WR)

Chassagne-Montrachet la Boudriotte,
Gagnard-Delagrange £21.95 (HAH)
Chassagne-Montrachet les Chenevottes,
Colin-Deleger £24.95 (LAY)
Chassagne-Montrachet les Vergers, Colin
£22.72 (RAE)
Chassagne-Montrachet Marquis de
Laguiche £24.50 (REI)
Chassagne-Montrachet Sauzet £20.30
(TAN)
Chassagne-Montrachet Vide-Bourse,
Pillot £22.81 (COU)
Meursault-Blagny, Latour £20.76 (PEN)
Meursault Genevrières, Charles et Remi
Jobard £23.95 (LEA) £23.99 (COU)
Meursault Goutte d'Or, Latour £21.85
(REI)
Meursault les Luchets, Roulot £22.91 (DOM)
Meursault les Meix Chavaux, Roulot
£22.91 (DOM)
Meursault les Tillets, Javillier £23.95 (VIG)
Meursault les Vireuils, Dupont Fahn
£20.95 (NI)
Meursault Poruzots, Jobard £23.95 (LEA)
Meursault Rougeots, Verget £21.84 (FA)
Puligny-Montrachet Boillot £23.95 (LEA)
Puligny-Montrachet Clos de la Mouchère,
Henri Boillot £23.99 (VIC)
Puligny-Montrachet Drouhin £21.25 (STA)
Puligny-Montrachet Domaine Leflaive
£22.81 (FA) £24.70 (UB) £24.77 (BUT)
Puligny-Montrachet les Chalumeaux,
Chavy-Chouet £21.50 (LEA)
Puligny-Montrachet les Champs Gains,
Clerc £24.99 (FUL)
Puligny-Montrachet les Pucelles, Domaine
Leflaive £22.50 (WS)
Puligny-Montrachet Sauzet £20.54 (BY)
£21.40 (TAN) £21.50 (AD) £22.91 (DOM)

1993

Chassagne-Montrachet Colin-Deleger
£21.35 (BER)
Chassagne-Montrachet les Chaumes,
Jean-Marc Morey £23.90 (PIP)
Chassagne-Montrachet les Vergers, Colin
£23.99 (JON)
Chassagne-Montrachet Morgeot, Henri
Germain £22.40 (TAN)

*Stars (★) indicate wines
selected by Oz Clarke in the
Best Buys section which begins
on page 12.*

Chassagne-Montrachet Niellon £20.86
(BUT)
Chassagne-Montrachet Pillot £21.50 (BER)
£22.77 (GN)
Meursault Charmes, Charles et Remi
Jobard £24.95 (LEA)
Meursault Charmes, Henri Germain
£24.65 (AD)
Meursault Jobard £22.72 (RAE)
Meursault Santenots, Marquis d'Angerville
£21.95 (REI)
Puligny-Montrachet Carillon £22.00 (YOU)
Puligny-Montrachet la Garenne, Thomas
£22.38 (GN) £23.50 (ROB)
Puligny-Montrachet Olivier Leflaive
£22.27 (TW)
Puligny-Montrachet les Folatières, Latour
£24.09 (JON)
Puligny-Montrachet les Perrières, Sauzet
£23.79 (FA)
1992
Chassagne-Montrachet Morgeot, Henri
Germain £23.85 (AD) £24.67 (RIP)
Meursault-Blagny, Latour £21.50 (QUE)
Meursault-Blagny, Matrot £21.50 (GAU)
Meursault Chevalières, Charles et Remi
Jobard £21.50 (LEA)
Meursault Genevrières, Latour £20.07
(WATT)
Meursault Jobard £24.95 (RAE)
Meursault l'Ormeau, Coche £20.39 (JON)
Puligny-Montrachet Latour £21.50 (WHI)
Puligny-Montrachet les Chalumeaux,
Matrot £23.65 (GAU)
1991
Puligny-Montrachet Boillot £20.99 (YOU)
Puligny-Montrachet Domaine Leflaive
£21.50 (REI)
Puligny-Montrachet Olivier Leflaive
£24.75 (AD)
Puligny-Montrachet les Referts, Sauzet
£24.77 (FA)
1989
Chassagne-Montrachet Morgeot, Henri
Germain £24.67 (RIP)
Puligny-Montrachet les Referts, Bouchard
Père £23.96 (BY)
1988
Morey-St-Denis Clos de Monts Luisants,
Ponsot £21.99 (YOU)
Puligny-Montrachet Latour £21.11 (PEN)
Puligny-Montrachet les Folatières,
Bouchard Père £23.96 (BY)
1987
Puligny-Montrachet Clerc £22.20 (TW)

1986
Meursault Genevrières, Latour-Giraud
£20.56 (FA)
Meursault Jobard £22.81 (BUT)
1972
Chassagne-Montrachet les Caillerets,
Bachelet-Ramonet £22.50 (BU)

£25.00 → £29.99

1995
Beaune Clos des Mouches, Drouhin
£29.18 (FA)
Chassagne-Montrachet Drouhin £26.93
(WATT)
Chassagne-Montrachet les Champs Gains,
Amiot £29.50 (LEA)
Chassagne-Montrachet Marquis de
Laguiche £29.00 (LEA)
Meursault Rougeots, Verget £25.75 (FA)
Puligny-Montrachet Champ Canet,
Carillon £28.95 (LAY)
Puligny-Montrachet les Folatières,
Drouhin £26.24 (WATT)
Puligny-Montrachet Sous le Puits, Verget
£29.18 (FA)
1994
Chassagne-Montrachet Clos St Jean,
Amiot £27.95 (LEA)
Chassagne-Montrachet les Vergers, Colin
£26.99 (JON) £29.95 (ROB)
Chassagne-Montrachet Morgeot, Henri
Germain £25.20 (TAN) £26.50 (LEA)
Meursault Charmes, Henri Germain
£25.20 (TAN) £26.50 (LEA)
Meursault Charmes, Lafon £29.59 (YOU)
Meursault les Tessons Clos de Mon
Plaisir, Roulot £27.61 (DOM)
Puligny-Montrachet Boillot £25.99 (RAE)
Puligny-Montrachet Clavoillon, Domaine
Leflaive £27.71 (FA) £28.95 (LAY)
Puligny-Montrachet Domaine Leflaive
£25.50 (LAY)
Puligny-Montrachet les Folatières, Chavy
£25.00 (MV)
Puligny-Montrachet les Perrières, Sauzet
£28.69 (FA)
1993
Chassagne-Montrachet Chaumées, Colin-
Deleger £26.99 (JON)
Chassagne-Montrachet les Caillerets,
Jean-Marc Morey £27.50 (RES)
Chassagne-Montrachet Marquis de
Laguiche £27.50 (BU)
Meursault Poruzots, Jobard £28.69 (BUT)
£29.77 (RAE)

Nuits-St-Georges Clos de l'Arlot,
Domaine de l'Arlot £28.32 (BY) £29.18
(BUT)

Puligny-Montrachet Clavoillon, Domaine
Leflaive £28.40 (TAN)

Puligny-Montrachet la Garenne, Thomas
£27.94 (BY)

Puligny-Montrachet les Folatières, Sauzet
£25.75 (FA)

Puligny-Montrachet les Perrières, Carillon
£29.50 (LAY)

Puligny-Montrachet les Referts, Sauzet
£28.45 (TAN)

1992

Chassagne-Montrachet Niellon £25.75
(BUT)

Meursault Charmes, Brunet £29.95 (GAU)

Meursault Charmes, Henri Germain
£25.00 (RIP)

Meursault Charmes, Matrot £25.20 (GAU)

1991

Meursault Genevrières, Jobard £27.90 (AD)

Meursault Jobard £25.90 (UB)

Puligny-Montrachet les Champs Gains,
Clerc £27.71 (BY)

1990

Meursault-Blagny, Jadot £27.99 (WR)
£27.99 (BOT)

Meursault Clos de la Barre, Lafon £29.90
(GAU)

Meursault Jobard £27.45 (AD)

1989

Meursault Charmes, Michelot £25.00 (RIP)

Puligny-Montrachet Domaine Leflaive
£29.60 (AD)

1988

Corton-Charlemagne Olivier Leflaive
£26.44 (FA)

Puligny-Montrachet Clos de la Garenne,
Drouhin £29.37 (WY)

1986

Puligny-Montrachet Domaine Leflaive
£26.73 (BUT)

Puligny-Montrachet les Folatières,
Bouchard Père £26.00 (PEN)

Puligny-Montrachet les Folatières,
Drouhin £28.20 (FA)

1983

Meursault Ampeau £28.68 (CHA)

1981

Bienvenues-Bâtard-Montrachet Bachelet-
Ramonet £25.00 (RIP)

1980

Meursault la Pièce sous le Bois, Ampeau
£28.20 (CHA) £29.00 (LEA)

£30.00 → £39.99

1995

Beaune Clos des Mouches, Drouhin
£30.35 (WATT) £33.00 (LEA) £35.00 (GRE)
£37.95 (BEN)

Chassagne-Montrachet en Remilly, Verget
£32.95 (LAY)

Chassagne-Montrachet les Caillerets,
Amiot £32.50 (LEA)

Corton-Charlemagne Jadot £35.00 (REI)
£36.52 (FA)

Meursault Genevrières, Jobard £30.65 (BUT)

Meursault Poruzots, Jobard £30.65 (BUT)

Puligny-Montrachet Boillot £37.99 (BUT)

Puligny-Montrachet Clavoillon, Domaine
Leflaive £32.50 (LAY) £37.50 (BUT)

Puligny-Montrachet les Combettes, Prieur
£35.00 (LEA)

Puligny-Montrachet les Truffières, Colin-
Deleger £34.95 (LAY)

1994

Chassagne-Montrachet les Ruchottes,
Bachelet-Ramonet £36.25 (BER)

Chassagne-Montrachet Morgeot,
Bachelet-Ramonet £34.95 (ROB)

Corton-Charlemagne Bonneau du
Martray £36.52 (FA)

Corton-Charlemagne Dubreuil-Fontaine
£31.80 (BY)

Corton-Charlemagne Latour £32.61 (FA)
£39.95 (VIG)

Corton-Charlemagne Olivier Leflaive
£30.15 (HAH)

Corton-Charlemagne Rollin £36.52 (RAE)

Corton Domaine Chandon de Briailles
£39.50 (LEA)

Meursault Clos de la Barre, Lafon £35.99
(YOU)

Meursault Genevrières, Jobard £30.16
(BUT) £30.65 (RAE)

Meursault Lafon £36.50 (BEN) £37.50 (FA)

Meursault le Poruzot Dessus, Charles et
Remi Jobard £38.60 (BER)

Meursault Poruzots, Jobard £30.65 (RAE)

Puligny-Montrachet Boillot £35.64 (BUT)

Puligny-Montrachet Champ Canet,
Carillon £30.00 (NA)

---

*In each price band wines
are listed in vintage order.
Within each vintage they
are listed in A–Z order.*

Puligny-Montrachet Champ Canet, Sauzet
£33.59 (FA) £34.38 (BY) £35.25 (DOM)
Puligny-Montrachet la Garenne, Sauzet
£32.90 (DOM)
Puligny-Montrachet la Garenne, Thomas
£30.09 (BY)
Puligny-Montrachet les Combettes,
Domaine Leflaive £39.95 (FA)
Puligny-Montrachet les Perrières, Boillot
£39.00 (LEA)
Puligny-Montrachet les Perrières, Carillon
£31.82 (ELL)
Puligny-Montrachet les Referts, Sauzet
£30.09 (BY) £33.50 (LAY) £34.08 (DOM)
1993
Beaune Clos des Mouches, Drouhin
£33.60 (BEN) £35.25 (WY) £35.75 (BER)
Chassagne-Montrachet Niellon £32.00
(BER)
Corton-Charlemagne Jadot £35.54 (BUT)
Corton-Charlemagne Latour £33.78 (WY)
£36.99 (MAJ)
Meursault Lafon £30.00 (REI) £34.57 (FA)
Meursault Poruzots, Jobard £34.00 (BIB)
Nuits-St-Georges Clos de l'Arlot,
Domaine de l'Arlot £33.95 (LAY)
Puligny-Montrachet Boillot £30.00 (BER)
£33.59 (BUT)
Puligny-Montrachet Champ Canet, Sauzet
£32.23 (BY) £32.90 (DOM)
Puligny-Montrachet Clavoillon, Domaine
Leflaive £34.50 (JON)
Puligny-Montrachet la Garenne, Sauzet
£32.31 (DOM) £35.00 (RES)
Puligny-Montrachet la Truffière, Boillot
£33.65 (BER)
Puligny-Montrachet Domaine Leflaive
£38.19 (PLA)
Puligny-Montrachet les Combettes,
Sauzet £33.59 (FA) £35.25 (DOM) £36.00
(WS)
Puligny-Montrachet les Perrières, Sauzet
£32.31 (DOM) £33.00 (JON) £36.50 (RES)
1992
Bienvenues-Bâtard-Montrachet Bachelet
£39.00 (RAE)
Chassagne-Montrachet Marquis de
Laguiche £38.78 (WY) £38.97 (WATT)
Corton-Charlemagne Bonneau du
Martray £37.00 (RIP) £37.50 (FA)
Corton-Charlemagne Drouhin £32.89 (NI)
Corton-Charlemagne Rollin £36.80 (RAE)
Meursault Charmes, Michelot £32.50 (WS)
Meursault les Vireuils, Roulot £37.48 (NO)
Meursault Perrières, Michelot £37.50 (RES)

Nuits-St-Georges Clos de l'Arlot,
Domaine de l'Arlot £30.36 (BY) £30.65
(BUT)
Puligny-Montrachet Champ Canet, Sauzet
£31.63 (FA)
Puligny-Montrachet Clavoillon, Domaine
Leflaive £36.52 (FA)
Puligny-Montrachet les Perrières, Sauzet
£30.65 (FA)
1991
Corton-Charlemagne Bouchard Père
£31.90 (BY)
Corton-Charlemagne Latour £32.31 (WY)
£33.50 (QUE) £34.50 (REI) £37.95 (VIG)
£39.60 (GN)
Puligny-Montrachet la Garenne, Sauzet
£30.00 (ROB)
1990
Corton-Charlemagne Bouchard Père
£35.07 (BY) £36.39 (HOG)
Corton-Charlemagne Drouhin £30.35 (FA)
Meursault Charmes, Matrot £34.37 (TW)
Puligny-Montrachet les Combettes,
Domaine Leflaive £38.48 (FA)
1989
Chassagne-Montrachet Latour £35.25 (WY)
Nuits-St-Georges Clos de l'Arlot,
Domaine de l'Arlot £31.63 (BUT)
Puligny-Montrachet Clos de la Garenne,
Drouhin £32.90 (WY)
1988
Beaune Clos des Mouches, Drouhin
£37.50 (GRE)
Chassagne-Montrachet Marquis de
Laguiche £30.65 (BUT)
Chassagne-Montrachet Sauzet £31.67 (PLA)
Corton-Charlemagne Michel Voarick
£39.95 (BEN)
Corton-Charlemagne Rollin £32.95 (RAE)
1987
Bâtard-Montrachet Domaine Leflaive
£36.23 (FA)
Corton-Charlemagne Jadot £32.50 (REI)
1986
Corton-Charlemagne Bonneau du
Martray £39.50 (RIP)
Corton-Charlemagne Bouchard Père
£37.31 (PEN)
Corton-Charlemagne Drouhin £38.19 (FA)
Meursault Genevrières, Latour £35.54
(BUT)
Meursault Poruzots, Jobard £32.61 (BUT)
1984
Bienvenues-Bâtard-Montrachet Domaine
Leflaive £38.00 (RIP)

Meursault la Pièce sous le Bois, Ampeau
£31.00 (LEA)
Meursault Perrières, Ampeau £33.50 (LEA)
Puligny-Montrachet les Combettes,
Ampeau £36.00 (LEA)
1983
Corton-Charlemagne Bonneau du
Martray £38.19 (FA)
Meursault Perrières, Ampeau £35.00 (RES)
1982
Corton-Charlemagne Rapet £32.50 (REI)
Meursault la Pièce sous le Bois, Ampeau
£39.00 (LEA)
1980
Meursault Perrières, Ampeau £30.00 (YOU)
Puligny-Montrachet les Combettes,
Ampeau £32.67 (CHA) £33.00 (LEA)
1976
Meursault Jadot £30.00 (REI)

£40.00 → £49.99

1996
Corton-Charlemagne Bonneau du
Martray £47.50 (LEA)
1995
Corton-Charlemagne Drouhin £44.50
(BEN)
Corton-Charlemagne Latour £41.42 (BUT)
Corton-Charlemagne, Verget £49.00 (LEA)
1994
Bâtard-Montrachet Latour £46.32 (FA)
Beaune Clos des Mouches, Drouhin
£45.00 (ROB)
Bienvenues-Bâtard-Montrachet Clerc
£46.00 (FUL)
Chevalier-Montrachet Bouchard Père
£47.73 (BY)
Corton-Charlemagne Georges Roumier
£49.00 (MV)
Corton-Charlemagne Juillot £45.83 (DOM)
Corton-Charlemagne Latour £41.13 (PEN)
Meursault Clos de la Barre, Lafon £43.38
(FA)
Meursault Perrières, Roulot £41.13 (DOM)
Puligny-Montrachet Champ Canet, Sauzet
£45.00 (RES)
Puligny-Montrachet la Garenne, Sauzet
£40.00 (RES)
Puligny-Montrachet les Combettes,
Sauzet £41.13 (DOM)
Puligny-Montrachet les Perrières, Sauzet
£40.00 (RES)
Puligny-Montrachet les Pucelles, Domaine
Leflaive £44.36 (FA) £46.31 (BUT) £47.95
(LAY)

1993
Bâtard-Montrachet Latour £48.96 (WY)
Bâtard-Montrachet Sauzet £49.25 (FA)
Chevalier-Montrachet Bouchard Père
£41.41 (BY)
Corton-Charlemagne Bonneau du
Martray £46.95 (LAY) £49.00 (MV)
Corton-Charlemagne Juillot £41.13 (DOM)
Corton-Charlemagne Latour £42.00 (STA)
Corton Domaine Chandon de Briailles
£43.50 (LEA) £45.00 (RES)
Meursault Clos de la Barre, Lafon £43.38
(FA) £44.75 (BEN)
Meursault Perrières, Michelot £42.50 (RES)
Puligny-Montrachet les Pucelles, Domaine
Leflaive £42.40 (FA) £47.95 (LAY)
1992
Beaune Clos des Mouches, Drouhin
£48.47 (WATT)
Chevalier-Montrachet Bouchard Père
£46.15 (BY)
Corton-Charlemagne Bonneau du
Martray £43.70 (HAH) £49.50 (RES)
Corton-Charlemagne Drouhin £47.00 (WY)
Corton-Charlemagne Michel Voarick
£46.00 (LEA)
Meursault Lafon £46.32 (FA)
Puligny-Montrachet la Garenne, Sauzet
£49.50 (RES)
Puligny-Montrachet les Perrières, Sauzet
£49.50 (RES)
Puligny-Montrachet Sous le Puits, Verget
£42.40 (FA)
1991
Bâtard-Montrachet Latour £42.10 (WY)
Bienvenues-Bâtard-Montrachet Domaine
Ramonet £48.50 (RIP)
Bienvenues-Bâtard-Montrachet Sauzet
£48.50 (REI)
Corton-Charlemagne Rollin £42.00 (BIB)
1990
Chevalier-Montrachet Bouchard Père
£47.91 (HOG)
Corton-Charlemagne Bonneau du
Martray £40.44 (FA) £49.50 (LAY)
Corton-Charlemagne Rapet £42.48 (ROS)
1889
Corton-Charlemagne Drouhin £40.95 (BO)
Chassagne-Montrachet Marquis de
Laguiche £41.13 (WY)
Puligny-Montrachet les Pucelles, Domaine
Leflaive £42.00 (DI)
1988
Bienvenues-Bâtard-Montrachet Clerc
£49.21 (BY)

Chassagne-Montrachet Marquis de
Laguiche £41.13 (WY)
Chevalier-Montrachet Bouchard Père
£46.15 (BY)
1987
Corton-Charlemagne Bonneau du
Martray £44.00 (MV)
1986
Bâtard-Montrachet Bouchard Père £40.36
(BY)
Puligny-Montrachet Clavoillon, Domaine
Leflaive £40.44 (BUT)
1985
Chassagne-Montrachet Marquis de
Laguiche £43.48 (WY)
Corton Domaine Chandon de Briailles
£47.50 (LEA)
Puligny-Montrachet Clavoillon, Domaine
Leflaive £48.50 (REI)
Puligny-Montrachet les Folatières, Clerc
£42.50 (RES) £45.00 (RES)
1983
Meursault la Pièce sous le Bois, Ampeau
£42.50 (LEA)
Meursault Perrières, Ampeau £45.50 (LEA)
1982
Meursault Perrières, Ampeau £41.00 (LEA)
Puligny-Montrachet les Combettes,
Ampeau £43.50 (LEA)
Puligny-Montrachet les Folatières,
Drouhin £45.53 (WY)
1979
Corton-Charlemagne Latour £42.50 (REI)
Meursault Charmes, Ampeau £44.50 (LEA)
Meursault la Pièce sous le Bois, Ampeau
£42.50 (LEA)

£50.00 ➡ £69.99

1995
Corton-Charlemagne Bonneau du
Martray £55.00 (LEA) £55.13 (BUT)
Corton-Charlemagne Jadot £50.23 (BUT)
Puligny-Montrachet les Pucelles, Domaine
Leflaive £51.95 (LAY) £58.06 (BUT)
1994
Bâtard-Montrachet Domaine Leflaive
£63.75 (LAY) £64.92 (FA) £66.39 (BUT)
Bâtard-Montrachet Gagnard £57.08 (FA)
£58.55 (BUT)
Bâtard-Montrachet Sauzet £63.94 (FA)
£64.63 (DOM)
Bâtard-Montrachet Domaine Ramonet
£67.86 (FA)
Bienvenues-Bâtard-Montrachet Domaine
Leflaive £55.75 (LAY) £56.11 (FA)

Bienvenues-Bâtard-Montrachet Sauzet
£63.94 (FA) £68.15 (DOM)
Chevalier-Montrachet les Desmoiselles,
Latour £50.72 (FA) £67.50 (VIG)
Chevalier-Montrachet Niellon £60.02 (BUT)
Corton-Charlemagne Bonneau du
Martray £52.29 (PLA)
Meursault Charmes, Lafon £54.99 (YOU)
Meursault Perrières, Lafon £58.99 (YOU)
Puligny-Montrachet les Pucelles, Domaine
Leflaive £50.00 (RES)
1993
Bâtard-Montrachet Drouhin £57.28 (WY)
Bâtard-Montrachet Sauzet £65.00 (RES)
Bienvenues-Bâtard-Montrachet Domaine
Ramonet £54.15 (FA)
Chevalier-Montrachet les Desmoiselles,
Latour £58.75 (WY)
Meursault Charmes, Lafon £59.04 (FA)
Meursault Perrières, Lafon £68.84 (FA)
le Montrachet Thénard £69.88 (AV)
1992
Bâtard-Montrachet Latour £66.00 (STA)
Chevalier-Montrachet Bouchard Père
£57.00 (BER)
Corton-Charlemagne Bonneau du
Martray £51.00 (MV) £51.23 (NO)
Corton-Charlemagne Jadot £52.68 (BUT)
Corton-Charlemagne Latour £51.70 (WY)
£57.57 (WATT)
Corton-Charlemagne Michel Voarick
£64.63 (WY)
Meursault Clos de la Barre, Lafon £67.50
(REI)
Puligny-Montrachet les Combettes,
Sauzet £65.00 (RES)
1991
Bâtard-Montrachet Domaine Leflaive
£55.13 (BUT)
Bâtard-Montrachet Latour £52.88 (PEN)
Bâtard-Montrachet Domaine Ramonet
£57.09 (FA)
Bienvenues-Bâtard-Montrachet Domaine
Ramonet £52.50 (REI)
Chevalier-Montrachet Domaine Leflaive
£61.00 (FA)
Criots-Bâtard-Montrachet Blain-Gagnard
£54.00 (BIB)
Meursault Genevrières, Lafon £52.19 (FA)
le Montrachet Thénard £60.00 (WS)
1990
Corton-Charlemagne Latour £59.53 (FA)
£67.07 (WATT)
Meursault Clos de la Barre, Lafon £52.00
(YOU)

1989
Bâtard-Montrachet Olivier Leflaive £66.50 (DI)
Corton-Charlemagne Bonneau du Martray £50.23 (BUT)
Corton-Charlemagne Latour £62.50 (BEN)
Puligny-Montrachet les Pucelles, Domaine Leflaive £52.19 (FA) £67.37 (BUT)
1988
Bâtard-Montrachet Blain-Gagnard £52.88 (DOM)
Beaune Clos des Mouches, Drouhin £57.95 (RES)
Corton-Charlemagne Drouhin £55.23 (WY)
Puligny-Montrachet les Combettes, Sauzet £65.00 (RES)
1987
Bienvenues-Bâtard-Montrachet Domaine Leflaive £54.50 (REI)
le Montrachet Marquis de Laguiche £68.50 (REI)
1986
Bienvenues-Bâtard-Montrachet Domaine Leflaive £65.60 (FA)
Chevalier-Montrachet Bouchard Père £53.03 (PEN)
Corton-Charlemagne Latour £63.94 (FA)
Puligny-Montrachet les Pucelles, Domaine Leflaive £54.15 (FA)
1983
Puligny-Montrachet Domaine Leflaive £56.40 (WY)
1981
Bâtard-Montrachet Domaine Leflaive £64.63 (FA)

£70.00 → £99.99

1995
Bâtard-Montrachet Domaine Leflaive £79.12 (BUT)
Bâtard-Montrachet Sauzet £77.65 (FA)
Chevalier-Montrachet les Desmoiselles, Latour £71.31 (BUT)
1994
Chevalier-Montrachet Domaine Leflaive £76.67 (FA) £79.75 (LAY) £84.50 (BUT)
Corton-Charlemagne Latour £80.00 (VIG)
le Montrachet Latour £83.23 (FA)
1993
Bâtard-Montrachet Pierre Morey £75.00 (RES)
Chevalier-Montrachet Domaine Leflaive £74.71 (BUT) £79.50 (RES) £79.75 (LAY)
le Montrachet Bouchard Père £78.25 (HOG) £79.39 (BY)

le Montrachet Jadot £77.65 (RAE) £85.00 (VIG) £87.64 (ELL)
le Montrachet Latour £87.15 (WY)
le Montrachet Marquis de Laguiche £99.88 (WY)
le Montrachet Sauzet £81.56 (FA)
1992
Bâtard-Montrachet Gagnard £76.67 (BUT)
Bâtard-Montrachet Sauzet £70.50 (DOM)
Bâtard-Montrachet Domaine Ramonet £97.23 (FA)
Bienvenues-Bâtard-Montrachet Domaine Leflaive £75.69 (FA) £79.61 (BUT)
Chevalier-Montrachet Domaine Leflaive £72.26 (TW)

Chevalier-Montrachet les Desmoiselles, Latour £79.50 (STA)
Meursault Clos de la Barre, Lafon £95.00 (RES)
Musigny Comte de Vogüé £78.33 (WY)
1991
Bâtard-Montrachet Sauzet £80.00 (BER)
Meursault Charmes, Lafon £83.00 (RES)
Meursault Genevrières, Lafon £85.00 (RES)
Meursault Rougeots, Coche-Dury £71.77 (BUT)
le Montrachet Marquis de Laguiche £82.70 (NI)
Musigny Comte de Vogüé £82.25 (WY)
1990
Bâtard-Montrachet Remoissenet £75.00 (WS)
Chevalier-Montrachet les Desmoiselles, Latour £82.25 (WY)
le Montrachet Marquis de Laguiche £91.50 (NI)
Puligny-Montrachet les Pucelles, Domaine Leflaive £75.00 (RES)

> **Webster's** *is an annual publication. We welcome your suggestions for next year's edition.*

1989
Bienvenues-Bâtard-Montrachet Domaine
   Leflaive £95.00 (RES)
Bienvenues-Bâtard-Montrachet Sauzet
   £75.00 (REI)
Chevalier-Montrachet Domaine Leflaive
   £75.00 (DI)
1988
Bâtard-Montrachet Latour £72.26 (VIN)
Chevalier-Montrachet Domaine Henri
   Clerc £95.00 (RES)
1986
Bâtard-Montrachet Latour £74.03 (WY)
   £74.71 (BUT)
Chevalier-Montrachet Domaine Leflaive
   £75.00 (REI)
Meursault Charmes, Lafon £88.13 (FA)
le Montrachet Bouchard Père £76.59 (PEN)
le Montrachet Thénard £72.46 (FA)
1985
Corton-Charlemagne Latour £74.71 (BUT)
   £76.67 (FA) £85.78 (WY)
1984
Bâtard-Montrachet Domaine Leflaive
   £95.00 (ROB)
1983
Corton-Charlemagne Bonneau du
   Martray £70.50 (WY)
Puligny-Montrachet les Pucelles, Domaine
   Leflaive £75.00 (REI)
1978
Corton-Charlemagne Bonneau du
   Martray £75.40 (FA)
1970
Puligny-Montrachet les Combettes,
   Sauzet £89.00 (RES)

£100.00 → £199.99

1995
le Montrachet Amiot £159.00 (LEA)
le Montrachet Latour £127.59 (BUT)
le Montrachet Prieur £155.00 (LEA)
1993
le Montrachet Jadot £118.77 (BUT)
le Montrachet Prieur £131.50 (BER)
Musigny Comte de Vogüé £123.67 (BUT)
   £125.00 (RES)
1992
Bâtard-Montrachet Sauzet £130.00 (RES)
le Montrachet Latour £117.01 (WATT)
le Montrachet Marquis de Laguiche
   £117.50 (WY) £120.00 (RIP) £126.80
   (WATT) £145.50 (BEN)
1991
Meursault Perrières, Lafon £105.00 (RES)

1990
Bâtard-Montrachet Domaine Ramonet
   £111.63 (FA)
le Montrachet Bouchard Père £100.71
   (HOG)
1989
le Montrachet Bouchard Père £106.29 (BY)
1986
le Montrachet Jadot £126.70 (NO)
le Montrachet Marquis de Laguiche
   £164.50 (WY)
1985
Chevalier-Montrachet les Desmoiselles,
   Latour £105.75 (TW)
le Montrachet Latour £158.63 (WY)
le Montrachet Thénard £125.00 (WS)
1978
Bâtard-Montrachet Latour £125.00 (REI)
Chevalier-Montrachet les Desmoiselles,
   Latour £145.00 (REI)
Corton-Charlemagne Latour £117.50 (WY)
le Montrachet Latour £175.00 (REI)
1970
Bâtard-Montrachet Domaine Leflaive
   £165.00 (RES)

£200.00 → £499.99

1994
le Montrachet Lafon £304.82 (FA)
1993
le Montrachet Domaine de la Romanée-
   Conti £392.94 (FA)
le Montrachet Lafon £220.00 (YOU)
   £330.00 (BEN)
le Montrachet Leflaive £352.50 (FA)
1988
le Montrachet Domaine de la Romanée-
   Conti £352.50 (WY)
1986
Chassagne-Montrachet Clos de Chapelle,
   Duc de Magenta £323.10 (BUT)
1982
le Montrachet Domaine de la Romanée-
   Conti £358.38 (FA) £446.50 (TW)
1977
le Montrachet Domaine de la Romanée-
   Conti £229.13 (FA)
1971
le Montrachet Marquis de Laguiche
   £250.00 (REI)

c. £885.00

1994
le Montrachet Domaine de la Romanée-
   Conti £883.80 (BUT)

MÂCONNAIS

WHITE

Under £5.00

1996
Mâcon-Villages Cave Co-op. de Viré £4.59 (CO)
1995
Mâcon-Lugny Eugène Blanc, Cave de Lugny £4.95 (SOM)
1991
Mâcon Monbellet, Goyard ½ bottle £4.55 (REI)

£5.00 → £5.99

1996
Mâcon-Villages Rodet £5.50 (MAR)
1995
Mâcon-Lugny Duboeuf £5.85 (NEZ)
Mâcon-Lugny les Charmes, Cave de Lugny £5.95 (WAI)
Mâcon-Lugny les Charmes, Producteurs St-Gengoux £5.75 (GAL)
Mâcon-Prissé Cave Co-op. Prissé £5.85 (HAH)
St-Véran en Crèches, Daniel Barraud ½ bottle £5.00 (LEA)
1994
Mâcon-Villages Loron £5.90 (TAN)
1993
Mâcon-Villages Duboeuf £5.59 (NI)

£6.00 → £6.99

1996
Mâcon-Lugny les Genièvres, Latour £6.95 (STA)
Mâcon-Villages Duboeuf £6.60 (STA)
Mâcon-Vinzelles Cave des Grands Crus Blancs £6.95 (LEA)
St-Véran Domaine St-Martin, Duboeuf £6.25 (NEZ)
St-Véran Sapin £6.45 (HAW)
1995
Mâcon Chardonnay les Ecuyers £6.95 (SAI)
Mâcon Chardonnay Talmard £6.75 (HAH) £6.95 (POR)
Mâcon-Lugny les Genièvres, Latour £6.29 (HOG) £6.49 (NEW) £6.95 (POR)
Mâcon-Uchizy Raphael Sallet £6.70 (HAH)
Mâcon-Vinzelles Cave des Grands Crus Blancs £6.70 (HAW)
St-Véran Latour £6.87 (HOG)

£7.00 → £7.99

1996
St-Véran Domaine Deux Roches £7.49 (POR)
St-Véran Duboeuf £7.50 (STA)
1995
Mâcon-Charnay Blanc Manciat-Poncet £7.35 (HAW)
Mâcon-Lugny les Genièvres, Latour £7.04 (PEN) £7.20 (TAN) £7.27 (PLA) £7.35 (QUE)
Pouilly-Fuissé la Verchère, Daniel Barraud ½ bottle £7.00 (LEA)
St-Véran en Creches, Jacques Saumaize £7.75 (WS)
1994
Mâcon-Clessé Signoret £7.55 (HAW)
Mâcon-Fuissé Paquet £7.95 (LEA)
St-Véran Domaine Deux Roches £7.49 (FUL)
1993
Mâcon la Roche Vineuse, Merlin £7.50 (BIB)
1992
Mâcon-Viré Clos du Chapitre, Dépagneux £7.95 (WS)

£8.00 → £9.99

1996
Mâcon-Vinzelles Cave des Grands Crus Blancs £8.25 (HAW)
Pouilly-Vinzelles Mathias £8.30 (PIP)
St-Véran Vieilles Vignes Domaine des Deux Roches £9.95 (POR)
1995
Mâcon-Clessé Guillemot £9.60 (TAN)
Mâcon la Roche Vineuse, Merlin £9.00 (MV)
Mâcon-Villages Tête de Cuvée, Verget £8.62 (FA) £9.50 (LEA)
Mâcon-Viré Cuvée Spéciale, Bonhomme £9.34 (DOM)
Pouilly-Fuissé Domaine Béranger, Duboeuf £9.95 (NEZ)
Pouilly-Loché Cave des Crus Blancs £8.25 (HAW)
Pouilly-Vinzelles Bouchard Père et Fils £8.53 (HOG)
St-Véran Château Fuissé, Vincent £8.10 (TAN) £8.45 (AD) £8.52 (DOM) £9.35 (EL)
St-Véran Corsin £8.99 (NA)
St-Véran Domaine des Valanges, Paquet £9.60 (BER)
St-Véran Domaine Deux Roches £8.30 (HAH)

St-Véran les Chailloux Domaine des Deux
Roches £8.75 (HIC)
St-Véran Verget £9.60 (FA)
St-Véran en Crèches, Daniel Barraud
£9.50 (LEA)

1994
Mâcon-Lugny les Genièvres, Latour £8.23
(WY)
Mâcon-Viré Cuvée Spéciale, Bonhomme
£8.81 (DOM)
St-Véran Château Fuissé, Vincent £8.10
(TAN)
St-Véran Domaine des Valanges, Paquet ½
bottle £8.95 (RAE)
St-Véran Latour £8.80 (GN)

1993
Mâcon-Viré Goyard £9.95 (WS)
Pouilly-Loché Cave des Crus Blancs £8.21
(PLA)
St-Véran Château Fuissé, Vincent £8.50
(DI)

1990
St-Véran Latour £8.23 (WY)

£10.00 → £12.49

1995
Pouilly-Fuissé Château Fuissé, Vincent
£11.99 (DI)
Pouilly-Fuissé Latour £10.88 (HOG)
Pouilly-Fuissé les Crays, Forest £12.25 (BAN)
Pouilly-Fuissé les Vieux Murs, Loron
£10.95 (POR)
Pouilly-Fuissé Vessigaud £10.65 (ROS)

1994
Mâcon-Clessé Guillemot £10.15 (HAH)
St-Véran Cuvée Prestige Lassarat £10.95
(STA)

1993
Mâcon Monbellet, Goyard £11.50 (BIB)
£11.59 (JON)
Mâcon-Viré Domaine Emilian Gillet,
Thevenet £11.55 (COU)
Mâcon-Viré Goyard £10.99 (RAE)
Pouilly-Fuissé Manciat-Poncet £10.75
(HAW)

1992
Mâcon-Clessé Domaine Emilian Gillet,
Thévenet £11.55 (COU)

£12.50 → £15.99

1996
Pouilly-Fuissé Latour £13.25 (STA)
1995
Pouilly-Fuissé Château Fuissé, Vincent
£14.69 (DOM)

Pouilly-Fuissé la Roche, Daniel Barraud
£13.95 (LEA)
Pouilly-Fuissé la Verchère, Daniel Barraud
£12.95 (LEA)
Pouilly-Fuissé Verget £13.02 (FA) £15.95
(LEA)
Pouilly-Fuissé Vieilles Vignes, Daniel
Barraud £15.95 (LEA)

1994
Mâcon-Clessé Domaine de la Bon Gran,
Thévenet £14.29 (YOU)
Mâcon-Viré Domaine Emilian Gillet,
Thevenet £12.95 (LEA)
Pouilly-Fuissé Château Fuissé, Vincent
£13.30 (TAN) £13.50 (WS) £14.69 (DOM)
Pouilly-Fuissé Corsin £12.50 (REI) £12.95
(NA) £14.95 (AD)
Pouilly-Fuissé les Crays, Forest £15.95 (NI)
Pouilly-Fuissé Tête de Cuvée, Verget
£13.51 (FA)
Pouilly-Fuissé Vieilles Vignes, Melin £13.99
(RAE)

1993
Mâcon-Clessé Domaine de la Bon Gran,
Thévenet £13.90 (TAN) £14.65 (BEN)

£16.00 → £19.99

1995
Pouilly-Fuissé Château Fuissé Vieilles
Vignes, Vincent £19.39 (DOM) £19.75
(HIC) £19.95 (AD)
Pouilly-Fuissé les Crays, Forest £17.99
(YOU)

1993
Pouilly-Fuissé Château Fuissé, Vincent
£17.50 (DI)

1988
Pouilly-Fuissé Château Fuissé, Vincent
£16.50 (RAE)

£20.00 → £29.99

1994
Pouilly-Fuissé Château Fuissé Vieilles
Vignes, Vincent £21.80 (TAN) £26.50
(RES)
Pouilly-Fuissé les Combettes, Château
Fuissé £22.95 (RES)

1986
Pouilly-Fuissé Château Fuissé, Vincent
£25.75 (BUT)

c. £37.50

1992
Mâcon-Clessé Domaine de la Bon Gran,
Thévenet £37.50 (LEA)

CHAMPAGNE

**There's cheap Champagne, and there's inexpensive Champagne.
The stuff I want tastes as though it costs at least £5 a bottle more than
it does – and yes, such wines do exist**

Okay, we're all drinking Champagne again. Britain is once more the top export market for Champagne, and in 1996 we drank nearly as much as we did at the height of the '80s boom.

This may or may not be a good omen for the future. The trade reckons we're all piling off to expensive restaurants and drinking it by the (expensive) glass; well, maybe we are. It's certainly true that the quality of Champagne on offer in restaurants has risen – and if we're going to pay a lot anyway we want quality for our money.

And because I want quality for my money, I can't be bothered with the very cheapest Champagnes. There's such good stuff around at the moment for £15 – less, probably, if you wait for the Christmas offers – that it's pointless to pay £10 and congratulate yourself on getting a bargain.

You're not getting a bargain; you're getting indigestion. Because although the general quality is so high this year, it is still perfectly possible to find wines that are green, characterless and oversweetened. (They have to be oversweetened, to compensate for the lack of ripeness and age.) And the wa o find these wines is to be stingy.

If I decide to pay £15–£20 then there are wonderful, classic non-vintage wines to be had. There are even a few good vintages, but to my mind vintage Champagne is a special occasion wine, and I'd rather have a top non-vintage wine with plenty of bottle age than a second-rate vintage.

Another thing: don't drink Champagne too young. Any decent non-vintage will improve with six-months' to a year's bottle age – it will round out and gain complexity. And that's what you're paying for.

GRAPE VARIETIES

CHARDONNAY The grape of white Burgundy fame here tends to produce lighter, fresher juice, and the resulting Champagnes are the most perfumed and honeyed of all. Good Blanc de Blancs have a superb, exciting flavour that is improved by aging, especially those from the southern end of the Côte de Blancs.

PINOT MEUNIER Champagne's second black grape, making a softer, fruitier style of wine, important for producing simple wines for drinking young, and useful for lightening the assertive weight of Pinot Noir. That being said, Krug uses some Pinot Meunier in its very long-lived Grande Cuvée.

PINOT NOIR The grape that makes all the finest red Burgundies also makes white Champagne. Pinot Noir has enough

difficulty ripening in Burgundy, and further north in Champagne it almost never attains any great depth and strength of colour or alcohol, which is fair enough since the general idea here is to produce a *white* wine. Very careful pressing of the grapes is the best way to draw off the juice with as little colour from the skins as possible, and what reddish tinge there is (and there's always some) generally precipitates out naturally during fermentation. Even so, the juice does feel quite big: a Champagne relying largely on Pinot Noir is certain to be heavier and take longer to mature than those made from the other grapes. It can also go with food rather better. And yes, Champagne does make a very little still red wine from Pinot Noir, but it takes a hot year to make it attractive. Most Pinot made as red wine is used to colour rosé.

WINE STYLES AND LABELLING

BLANC DE BLANCS Champagne made only from Chardonnay; it has become more fashionable as drinkers look for a lighter style. Should not only be fresh but creamy and bright as well, and should get deeper and richer as it ages. Some firms, notably *Henriot, Mumm, Joseph Perrier* and *Bruno Paillard* make excellent NV (non-vintage) Blanc de Blancs, and the *Union* co-operatives at Avize and le Mesnil make the most of their positions at the heart of the Côte des Blancs. Most firms sell vintage Blanc de Blancs (watch out for *Billecart-Salmon, Drappier, Jacquesson, Pol Roger, Roederer*) and a couple also make luxury cuvées. *Taittinger's Comtes de Champagne, Dom Ruinart, Salon* and *Krug's Clos de Mesnil* are the benchmarks.

BLANC DE NOIRS This white style is made from black grapes only. Few have the quality and longevity of *Bollinger's Vieilles Vignes*, but none is even half as expensive. Most are rather solid. *Pierre Vaudon* is an elegant exception, and tremendous value for money; *H Billiot* is fine, and *de Venoge* is rich and ripe. *Sainsbury's* version is good value. *Serge Mathieu* does not indicate on the label that it is Blanc de Noirs, and you would never guess it from its fresh, light, zesty style.

BRUT Very dry – more so than either 'Sec' or 'Extra Dry'.

BUYER'S OWN BRAND (BOB) A wine blended to a buyer's specification, or more probably, to a price limit. The grapes are of lesser quality, the wines usually younger, and cheaper. However, *Sainsbury* and *Waitrose* Champagnes are consistent and good value.

CM This means *co-opérative-manipulant* and shows that the wine comes from a co-operative, whatever the brand name implies.

COTEAUX CHAMPENOIS Still wines, red, rosé or white. Overpriced and generally rather acid. A village name, such as Cramant (white) or Bouzy (red) may appear. *Alain Vesselle's* Bouzy and *René Geoffroy's* Cumières have produced exciting reds, but all producers are as variable as the climate.

DE LUXE/CUVÉE DE PRESTIGE/ CUVÉE DE LUXE A special highly prized blend, mostly vintage. Some undeniably great wines and some gaudy coat-tailers. At these prices one's looking for immense complexity and refinement. In general these wines are drunk *far* too young. Most need a good ten years to shine. Some of the best: *Bollinger RD, Charles Heidsieck Cuvée de Millenaires, Dom Pérignon, Dom Ruinart, Krug Grande Cuvée, Laurent Perrier Grand Siècle, Pol Roger Cuvée Sir Winston Churchill, Roederer*

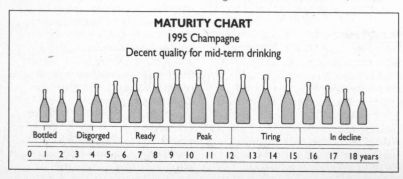

MATURITY CHART
1995 Champagne
Decent quality for mid-term drinking

| Bottled | Disgorged | Ready | Peak | Tiring | In decline |

0 1 2 3 4 5 6 7 8 9 10 11 12 13 14 15 16 17 18 years

*Cristal, Taittinger Comtes de Champagne,
Cuvée NF Billecart, Cattier Clos du Moulin,
Philipponnat Clos des Goisses, Perrier-Jouët
Belle Epoque, Veuve Clicquot la Grande
Dame.*

DEMI-SEC Medium-sweet. Rarely very nice, but *Louis Roederer* can be outstanding, and *Veuve Clicquot* is usually the most consistent.

DOUX Sweet. *Louis Roederer*'s is an excellent example.

EXTRA DRY Confusingly, this is less dry than 'Brut', but drier than 'Sec'.

GRAND CRU In Champagne it is communes that are classified, not individual vineyards, and the 17 *grand cru* communes in the region are the best. The next best are the *premiers crus*.

GRANDE MARQUE Ambiguous term meaning 'great brand'. It is a self-styled group of 24 houses, including the 15 or so best known. The term *should* be synonymous with quality – better grapes, older reserve wines and more rigid selection. It might be in future, if they ever get around to agreeing anything.

NM In the code on the label, this means *négociant-manipulant* (merchant-handler) and shows that the producer is one of the 265 Champagne houses operating in the region.

NON-DOSAGE Most Champagne has a little sweetness – a 'dosage' – added just before the final cork is put in. A few are sold absolutely bone-dry and will have names like Brut Zero. Best are *Laurent-Perrier, Piper-Heidsieck*. They're designed to show that it's the wine, not the dosage that provides the quality. Do they prove their point? Well, they're uncompromising. And I'm not sure that I'd choose to drink one for pure pleasure.

NON-VINTAGE (NV) The flagship of most houses, and the one by which a producer should be judged. The wines are generally based on one vintage and usually aged for three years. But many of the best provide greater depth and age, and ensure consistency by using up to 40 per cent of *vins de réserve*, wines from previous years, thus giving more depth and maturity to the blend. At the moment quality is generally excellent, and of the major names only *Mercier, Moët* and *Canard-Duchêne* are seriously disappointing. Best: *Besserat de Bellefon, Gosset, Alfred Gratien, Henriot, Jacquart, Bruno Paillard, Pol Roger, Pommery, Billecart-Salmon, Mailly Grand Cru, Joseph Perrier, Krug, Roederer, Taittinger* (superb), *Pierre Vaudon, Veuve Clicquot, Vilmart* and *Bollinger*. All gain from a few months in bottle after purchase.

PREMIER CRU The 38 *premier cru* communes are those just below *grand cru* in quality. All the other communes are unclassified.

RC A new designation of *récoltant-co-opérateur* – for a grower selling wine made at a co-op. It should stop growers who've carted their grapes along to the co-op and collected the bottles afterwards from pretending they've made it themselves. Should. Somehow it doesn't seem to appear on labels that often.

RECENTLY DISGORGED A term for Champagnes that have been left in the cellars, drawing flavour from their yeast deposits, for much longer than usual before disgorging. The wines can rest for 20 or perhaps even 30 years on the lees but are usually released after seven to ten. *Bollinger RD* is the most famous and still the best; also good are *Deutz, Alfred Gratien* and *Laurent-Perrier*.

RICH The sweetest Champagne. *Roederer* can be superbly balanced. *Veuve Clicquot* has a great vintage version.

RM Indicates that a grower, a *récoltant-manipulant*, made it himself, rather than taking it to the co-op. Try: *Bara, Billiot, Bonnaire, Clouet, René Geoffroy, Michel Gonet, André Jacquart, Lassalle, Legras, Vesselle, Vilmart.*

ROSÉ Traditionally, the pink colour is gained by a short maceration of the black grapeskins with the juice, as practised by *Laurent-Perrier*. But most producers are not so traditional and make their rosé by adding a little still red Bouzy to white wine before bottling. Ideally rosés are aromatic, fruity wines, with a delicious strawberry or cherry flavour. Sadly, many of these are indistinguishable from white. Most should be drunk young. Best producers are: *Billecart-Salmon, Bollinger, Dom Ruinart, Alfred Gratien, Jacquart Mosaïque, Lassalle, Laurent-Perrier, Pol Roger, Louise Pommery, Roederer*

and *Roederer Cristal. Krug rosé* is way ahead in a class of its own, and at that price so it should be.

SEC Literally 'dry', but any Champagne so labelled will actually be medium dry. 'Extra Dry' and 'Brut' are drier.

SR Société de Récoltants. Label code for a family company of growers.

VINTAGE The wine produced from the grapes of a single, good year. Vintage Champagne is fuller and deeper than non-vintage, but almost always released too young. Best names: *Billecart-Salmon, Bollinger, Gosset Grande Millésime, Henriot, Krug, Mailly Grand Cru, Bruno Paillard, Joseph Perrier, Laurent-Perrier, Perrier-Jouët, Pol Roger, Louis Roederer, Ruinart, Taittinger, Pierre Vaudon, Veuve Devaux* and *Veuve Clicquot.*

CHAMPAGNE HOUSES WHO'S WHO

BESSERAT DE BELLEFON ★★★★
Makes, elegant, restrained Champagnes of good depth.

BILLECART-SALMON ★★★★(★)
Terrifically elegant Champagne from a family-owned house. Very refined, mature wines and a delicate rosé. Its vintage, Cuvée NF Billecart, is also excellent.

BOLLINGER ★★★★(★) Like Krug, Bollinger makes 'English-style' Champagnes: rich, oaky, but more steely and almost half the price. The NV is currently excellent. RD, its luxury cuvée, is kept on its lees until just before sale.

F BONNET ★★ Inexpensive offshoot of Piper Heidsieck and Charles Heidsieck, with mature and biscuity non-vintage.

DEUTZ ★★★ This house is back on form again with creamy-rich, biscuity non-vintage and an excellent quality prestige cuvée called William Deutz.

DRAPPIER ★★(★) Consistent quality, although the style bounces between ultra-fruity and rich and biscuity according to how much bottle age the wine has.

DUVAL-LEROY ★★ Fresh, fragrant style in a Chardonnay-dominated Champagne. Good value and consistent.

ALFRED GRATIEN ★★★★ Serious, oak-fermented wine at a much lower price than Krug. Very long-lived vintage. Even the non-vintage needs extra bottle age.

CHARLES HEIDSIECK ★★★
Probably the best value Grande Marque NV around at the moment; rich, full style and good vanilla finesse.

HENRIOT ★★★★ Good bottle age and unrelenting quality. Very rich; lovely depth.

The Price Guides for this section begin on page 221.

KRUG ★★★★★ Classic, mellow, rich. Oak-fermented Grande Cuvée is outstanding. The expensive rosé has incomparable Pinot Noir cherry fruit. Even more expensive Clos de Mesnil is a rich, single-vineyard Blanc de Blancs.

JACQUESSON ★★★ Always good quality and finesse, whether the elegant, flowery non-vintage or the rich, well-extracted vintage.

LANSON ★★★ Classic, long-maturing vintage. The NV is seductively drinkable.

LAURENT-PERRIER ★★★★ One of the most reliable of non-vintages, with excellent rosé. Prestige brand Grand Siècle is (sensibly) a blend of several vintages, but there is now also a much more expensive vintage version.

MOËT & CHANDON ★★★ Brut Imperial currently seems undistinguished and not worthy of its fame. Vintages usually show better but are released too young.

MUMM ★★ All too frequently unimpressive, although at the moment it seems better than usual. A lot of mothers get it for Mother's Day; not mine. Delicate, creamy Mumm de Cramant, when you catch it freshly disgorged.

BRUNO PAILLARD ★★★ Fresh, elegant and satisfying Champagne from one of the most consistent producers.

JOSEPH PERRIER ★★★★ The non-vintage is extremely rich and well aged, with biscuity complexity and wonderfully high acidity.

PERRIER-JOUËT ★★★ Able to make light, classic Champagne. Best known for Belle Époque in a pretty bottle, all flowery elegance, echoed in the fresh, slightly unripe-cherry feel of the wine, which always mellows with age.

POL ROGER ★★★★ Model family firm, producer of Churchill's favourite fizz. Delicious, delicate Blanc de Blancs. NV, vintage and Cuvée Sir Winston Churchill are all top class. New are vintage Blanc de Chardonnay, vintage rosé and a Demi-sec.

POMMERY ★★★ This house is currently on good form, with wines of light, flowery elegance. The prestige cuvée, Louise Pommery, is superb.

LOUIS ROEDERER ★★★★★ Famous for Cristal, invented for sweet-toothed Russian Tsars. Now the most natural of all the prestige cuvées, reflecting the quality of each vintage. The subtle, ripe NV can be one of the best. Good Demi-sec.

RUINART ★★★★ The non-vintage ' R' de Ruinart has lots of bottle age and a distinctive style closer to the traditional 'goût anglais' than many. Not for those who like their Champagne light, young and delicate. The vintage is rich.

TAITTINGER ★★★★(★) Splendidly light, modern, Chardonnayish style of great excitement, though its Blanc de Blancs Comtes de Champagne goes sumptuously rich with age.

PIERRE VAUDON ★★★(★) This stands up extremely well against the top Grandes Marques, and it's not expensive. Good weighty, ripe stuff.

VEUVE CLICQUOT ★★★★ For a century and a half greatly loved by the British. The NV can still have the rich, warm style first made famous by the formidable Madame Veuve Clicquot-Ponsardin. Prestige cuvée la Grande Dame is almost chocolate-rich – its 1985 was a classic.

VILMART ★★★(★) Rich, full Champagne, more in the Bollinger than the Pommery mode. Plenty of flavour, weight and ripeness. Good vintage.

CHAMPAGNE VINTAGES

In theory Champagne firms only make single-vintage wines in especially fine years. But only a few firms, like Bollinger and Laurent-Perrier, follow the theory. Most either opt too readily for vintage wines in marginal years or, increasingly, release wines after only five years in bottle, which may be okay for French tastes but leaves the average Brit with an acid stomach. Nevertheless, most firms come up with decent vintage.

1996   Splendidly ripe, balanced wines that are likely to be widely declared. The non-vintage wines should be good, as well, when they start coming on stream.

1995   The wines are significantly superior to those of the previous four years, and this will be the first widely declared vintage since the outstanding 1990.

1994   Of the few reputable producers likely to declare this a vintage, Vilmart's Grand Cellier d'Or will probably be the best.

1993   Roederer managed to produce a vintage Champagne after rejecting no less than half its own crop. Others who will declare this year include A Bonnet, Vilmart, Jacquesson, Gosset and Gardet, with Cattier, Drappier and Jacquart also possible.

1992   No-one seriously expected any house to declare 1992 a vintage. But after the drenching debacle of 1993 all hopes were pinned on 1994, and when that suffered the same damp fate, the Champagne trade suddenly found itself staring at a four year gap between vintage years. It is hard not to be cynical, but even as the 1994 crop was being harvested, a number of houses had already re-evaluated 1992 and – surprise, surprise – they decided that 1992 would be the vintage to follow 1990. Well, it has the edge over 1991, 1993 and 1994, but whether the quality is really good enough is another matter.

1991   Possibly a dark horse of a vintage. Alain de Polignac of Pommery rates this year as better than 1989 and 1988. Generally speaking it is the second-worst year between 1991 and 1994, but individual wines can have great potential: try Philipponnat's Clos des Goisses, Vilmart's Coeur de Cuvée, Henri Mandois and De Nauroy. Roederer declared a rosé.

1990   The year most commonly available at the moment. It was widely declared and many of the wines are superb. Try Jacquart, Lanson, Laurent-Perrier, Perrier-Jouët, Pommery, Roederer, Ruinart, Taittinger, Pierre Vaudon. But they're not at their best yet: give them several years in the cellar.

1989   Drink these before the 1990s, but give them a few years yet. Look for Joseph Perrier, Mailly, Bruno Paillard, Veuve Clicquot.

1988   The wines have bite, backbone and fruit, but will be drunk too young. Try and buck the trend and put some aside for a few more years. Henriot and Pol Roger are tops, of those currently available.

1987   A lot of wine, but even the Champenois are not enthusiastic about its quality. Only Pommery declared a vintage. Why, we ask ourselves?

1986   Would have made a decent, if slightly hard vintage, but got sold far too young.

1985   Fine wines, without any of the hardness of some vintages. There's very little still available, but if you've got any it should be delicious now.

1983   Still high-grade, if a little lean.

CHAMPAGNE PRICE GUIDES

SPARKLING WHITE

Under £12.00

Non-vintage
Bruno Paillard ½ bottle £10.94 (HAL)
Moët & Chandon Brut Impérial ½ bottle
£10.50 (TAN) £10.75 (GRE) £10.99 (BOT)
£10.99 (THR) £10.99 (BO) £10.99 (WR)
£11.00 (FOR) £11.22 (PLA) £11.25 (WHI)
£11.40 (STA) £11.49 (POR) £11.49 (CO)
£11.49 (TES) £11.95 (ROB) £11.99 (FUL)
'R' de Ruinart ½ bottle £11.60 (STA)
£11.95 (VIG)
Veuve Clicquot ½ bottle £10.41 (WY)
£11.75 (BO) £11.80 (FOR) £11.85 (GRE)
1989
Bollinger ½ bottle £11.00 (REI)
Veuve Clicquot ½ bottle £11.50 (REI)

£12.00 → £13.99

Non-vintage
Baron de Beaupré £13.95 (POR)
Bauget-Jouette £13.50 (HIG)
Benedick £12.95 (LEA)
Billecart-Salmon ½ bottle £13.56 (HAL)
Bollinger ½ bottle £12.95 (GRE) £13.50 (DI)
£13.70 (FOR) £13.81 (PLA) £13.95 (VIG)
£13.95 (BEN)
Camuset Réserve £13.00 (BIB)
Canard-Duchêne £12.99 (HOG) £13.99
(NEW)
Duchâtel £12.49 (UN)
George Goulet £13.81 (LON)
Georges Gardet £13.25 (NO)
Heidsieck Dry Monopole £13.49 (JON)
£13.49 (NEW) £13.51 (FLE)
Pierre Vaudon 1er Cru £13.95 (HAH)
de Telmont £13.99 (MAJ)

£14.00 → £15.99

Non-vintage
Bauget-Jouette £14.99 (AME) £15.50 (NA)
Beerens £15.00 (BIB)
Blin £14.99 (OD)
Bonnet £14.99 (OD)
Canard-Duchêne £14.95 (GRE) £15.45
(WAI) £15.49 (MAJ) £15.49 (BO) £15.49
(UN) £15.95 (ROB)
★ Drappier Carte d'Or £14.72 (BY) £14.99
(THR) £14.99 (WR) £14.99 (BOT)
Duval Leroy Fleur de Champagne £15.26
(PLA) £15.49 (AUR)
Ellner £14.50 (LAY)
Georges Gardet £14.99 (VIN)
Joseph Perrier £15.99 (FUL)
Mercier £15.95 (WAI) £15.95 (GRE) £15.99
(SAI) £15.99 (WR) £15.99 (TES)
Mercier Demi-Sec £15.85 (GRE) £15.99
(BOT) £15.99 (WR) £15.99 (THR)
Michel Gonet £14.99 (BU)
Pannier £15.87 (ROS)
Piper Heidsieck £15.95 (GRE) £15.99 (SAI)
Pol Roger £14.90 (SOM)
Pol Roger White Foil £15.95 (SOM)
Salon £15.99 (JON)
Salon Blanc de Blancs £14.75 (THR)
1990
George Goulet £15.97 (LON)

£16.00 → £17.99

Non-vintage
Ayala £16.49 (MAJ) £17.50 (QUE)
Billecart-Salmon £17.95 (LEA) £17.99 (NI)
Deutz Brut Cuvée Classic £17.60 (FOR)
Duval Leroy Fleur de Champagne £17.86
(ROS)
Henriot Souverain £16.07 (BY)

MERCHANTS SPECIALIZING IN CHAMPAGNE
see Merchant Directory (page 413) for details

Most good merchants have a fair variety of Champagnes, and generally list the most popular of the Grandes Marques, plus one or two cheaper ones. Most, too, have a pretty varied list of sparkling wines from other countries, and it is quite hard to single out merchants with exceptionally good lists of Champagne. Nevertheless, for a wider than average choice, try especially: Adnams (AD), Averys of Bristol (AV), Bennetts (BEN), Bibendum (BIB), Eldridge Pope (EL), Farr Vintners (FA), Justerini & Brooks, Lea & Sandeman (LEA), Majestic (MAJ), Oddbins (OD), Roberson (ROB), T&W Wines (TW), Tanners (TAN), Peter Wylie (WY) – a few old vintages

Jacquart Séléction £17.95 (POR) £17.99 (EL)
Joseph Perrier Cuvée Royal £16.95 (ROB)
£17.00 (TAN) £17.50 (BU)
Lanson £17.49 (SAI) £17.95 (POR) £17.99
(SAT)
Laurent-Perrier £17.50 (BIB) £17.96 (PLA)
Legras Grand Cru Blanc de Blancs £16.95
(LEA)
Mercier £16.34 (FOR) £16.49 (FUL) £16.49
(UN) £16.49 (VIC) £17.20 (LAY) £17.45
(ROB)
Mercier Demi-Sec £16.49 (VIC) £16.99 (JON)
Moët & Chandon Brut Impérial £17.94
(HOG)
Piper Heidsieck £16.99 (BO) £16.99 (CO)
£16.99 (TES) £16.99 (BOT) £16.99 (SAF)
£16.99 (THR) £16.99 (WR) £16.99 (SO)
£17.90 (FOR)
Pommery Royale £16.50 (GRE)
de Venoge Cordon Bleu £16.95 (EL)
1990
Bauget-Jouette Grande Réserve £17.50
(HIG)
Pierre Vaudon 1er Cru £17.60 (HAH)
1989
Canard-Duchêne £16.99 (NEW)
Drappier Carte d'Or £16.23 (BY)
Louis Roederer Brut Premier £17.85 (REI)
1988
Alfred Gratien ½ bottle £16.50 (WS)
Duval Leroy Fleur de Champagne £17.04
(PLA)

£18.00 → £19.99

Non-vintage
Alfred Gratien £19.95 (SAI) £19.99 (OD)
Bollinger £19.95 (HIC)
Bruno Paillard £18.50 (WHI)
Charles Heidsieck £18.99 (GRE) £19.95
(UB) £19.99 (BOT) £19.99 (WR) £19.99
(TES)
Deutz £18.50 (GRE)
George Goulet £18.30 (PIP)
Joseph Perrier Cuvée Royal £18.50 (HAH)
£18.70 (GN) £19.95 (NA)
Lanson £18.45 (WAI) £18.49 (TES) £18.49
(FUL) £18.49 (ASD) £18.49 (SO) £18.49
(CO) £18.49 (UN) £18.49 (SAF) £18.75
(WRI) £18.79 (PLA)
Laurent-Perrier £18.15 (EL) £18.50 (LEA)
£19.20 (LAY) £19.27 (CHA) £19.29 (WHI)
£19.49 (THR) £19.49 (WR) £19.49 (BOT)
£19.49 (MAJ) £19.49 (UN) £19.95 (ROB)
£19.95 (AD) £19.99 (OD)
Louis Roederer £19.90 (NI)

Moët & Chandon Brut Impérial £18.79
(PLA) £18.99 (GRE) £18.99 (BO) £19.49
(SAI) £19.49 (FUL) £19.49 (ASD) £19.50
(TAN) £19.75 (WRI) £19.95 (TES) £19.95
(POR) £19.99 (CO) £19.99 (BOT) £19.99
(SAF) £19.99 (WR) £19.99 (THR) £19.99
(UN) £19.99 (VIC) £19.99 (MAJ)
Mumm Cordon Rouge £18.49 (UN)
£18.49 (VIC) £18.49 (THR) £18.49 (BOT)
£18.49 (OD) £18.49 (WR) £18.50 (ROB)
Perrier-Jouët £18.49 (OD) £18.49 (WR)
£18.49 (BOT) £18.49 (MAJ) £18.49 (THR)
Pol Roger White Foil £19.55 (HOG)
Pommery £18.45 (EL) £18.95 (ROB) £18.99
(MAJ) £19.00 (BIB)
'R' de Ruinart £19.95 (LEA) £19.99 (GRE)
Taittinger £19.09 (PLA)
Veuve Clicquot £19.75 (HOG)
1995
Billecart-Salmon £19.49 (ELL)
1990
Canard-Duchêne £19.95 (ROB)
Massé £18.50 (VIG)
Mercier £19.76 (FOR)
1988
Georges Gardet £19.95 (VIG)
Salon Blanc de Blancs £19.99 (THR)

£20.00 → £21.99

Non-vintage
Bruno Paillard Blanc de Blancs £20.75
(NEZ) £21.90 (GAU)
Charles Heidsieck £20.12 (FOR) £20.30
(PIP) £20.49 (UN)
Louis Roederer £21.21 (HOG)
Moët & Chandon Brut Impérial £20.75
(LAY) £21.25 (STA) £21.50 (QUE)
Pol Roger £20.99 (GRE) £21.00 (WS)
£21.95 (ROB)

Pol Roger White Foil £20.99 (UN) £21.30
(TAN) £21.50 (BER) £21.95 (LEA) £21.97
(PEN) £21.99 (MAJ) £21.99 (VIC) £21.99
(WR) £21.99 (THR) £21.99 (OD)
'R' de Ruinart £21.50 (VIG) £21.50 (STA)
Taittinger £20.85 (GRE) £21.95 (LEA)
£21.95 (LAY) £21.95 (POR) £21.99 (UN)

Taittinger Brut Réserve £21.99 (WHI)
£21.99 (NA) £21.99 (FUL)
Veuve Clicquot £20.50 (GRE) £20.90 (PLA)
£20.94 (FLE) £20.99 (NEW) £21.15 (WY)
£21.49 (BO) £21.50 (TAN) £21.50 (GAL)
£21.95 (WAI) £21.95 (LEA) £21.95 (LAY)
£21.99 (ASD) £21.99 (FUL) £21.99 (SAT)
£21.99 (VIC) £21.99 (TES) £21.99 (WHI)
£21.99 (SAI)
Veuve Clicquot White Label Demi-Sec
£20.50 (GRE)
1990
Jacquesson Blanc de Blancs £21.75 (YAP)
1989
Bruno Paillard £21.00 (NEZ)
Joseph Perrier £21.59 (GN)
Joseph Perrier Cuvée Royal £20.95 (NEW)
1988
Perrier-Jouët £21.99 (FUL)

£22.00 → £23.99

Non-vintage
Bollinger £22.70 (TAN) £22.90 (PLA)
£22.95 (GRE) £23.11 (WATT) £23.38
(PEN) £23.40 (PIP) £23.45 (UB) £23.50
(BER) £23.50 (WY) £23.56 (VIN) £23.58
(SAT) £23.95 (DI) £23.95 (WAI) £23.99
(NA) £23.99 (UN) £23.99 (SAI) £23.99
(ASD) £23.99 (TES)
Louis Roederer £22.26 (PLA) £22.95
(GRE) £22.99 (EL) £23.00 (WAI) £23.25
(TES) £23.50 (LAY) £23.50 (BIB) £23.60
(TAN) £23.75 (WRI) £23.95 (ROB) £23.95
(UN) £23.99 (MAJ) £23.99 (BO) £23.99
(OD)
Louis Roederer Brut Premier £22.91
(WATT) £22.95 (LEA) £23.00 (WS) £23.25
(BER) £23.99 (WR) £23.99 (THR)
Louis Roederer Rich £22.41 (PEN) £23.20
(PLA) £23.95 (ROB) £23.99 (MAJ)
Perrier-Jouët £22.90 (PIP)
Pol Roger £22.56 (FOR)
Pol Roger White Foil £22.79 (ROS) £22.95
(UB) £22.95 (WRI) £23.50 (POR) £23.50
(QUE) £23.75 (BEN) £23.95 (LAY) £23.95
(STA)
Taittinger £22.36 (FOR) £22.99 (OD)
£22.99 (MAJ) £23.50 (ROB)

> Stars (★) indicate wines
> selected by Oz Clarke in the
> Best Buys section which begins
> on page 12.

Veuve Clicquot £22.25 (WRI) £22.35 (STA)
£22.50 (FOR) £22.60 (GAU) £22.91 (PEN)
£22.95 (BIB) £22.95 (ROB) £22.99 (OD)
£22.99 (CO) £22.99 (MAJ) £22.99 (FUL)
£22.99 (WR) £22.99 (AUR) £22.99 (THR)
£22.99 (BOT) £22.99 (UN) £22.99 (SAF)
£23.50 (QUE) £23.50 (BEN) £23.60 (HAH)
£23.68 (GN) £23.95 (VIG)
Veuve Clicquot White Label Demi-Sec
£22.35 (STA) £22.99 (FUL) £23.95 (THR)
£23.95 (BOT) £23.95 (WR)
1990
Moët & Chandon Brut Impérial £22.95
(HOG)
Perrier-Jouët £23.95 (ROB) £23.99 (BOT)
£23.99 (OD) £23.99 (WR) £23.99 (THR)
Pommery £22.50 (GRE)
1989
Deutz Blanc de Blancs £23.70 (FOR)
Jacquart Sélection £23.50 (MV)
Joseph Perrier Cuvée Royal £22.50
(BU)
Lanson £22.49 (VIC) £23.99 (THR) £23.99
(WR) £23.99 (BOT)
1988
Drappier £22.95 (SAT)
Laurent-Perrier £23.99 (WHI)
Pol Roger Blanc de Chardonnay £22.35
(SOM)
Salon Blanc de Blancs £22.50 (AD)

£24.00 → £25.99

Non-vintage
Bollinger £24.00 (WS) £24.00 (WHI) £24.00
(WRI) £24.39 (WAT) £24.49 (BO) £24.50
(LEA) £24.56 (FOR) £24.65 (LAY) £24.75
(QUE) £24.77 (BUT) £24.78 (ROS) £24.95
(BEN) £24.95 (ROB) £24.95 (POR) £24.95
(VIG) £24.95 (STA) £24.99 (SAF) £24.99
(THR) £24.99 (OD) £24.99 (FUL) £24.99
(WR) £24.99 (AUR) £24.99 (MAJ) £24.99
(EL) £24.99 (VIC) £24.99 (BOT) £24.99 (CO)
Gosset Grande Reserve £25.50 (DI)
Louis Roederer £24.95 (AD) £24.95 (BEN)
£24.96 (QUE) £25.65 (HAH)
Louis Roederer Brut Premier £24.29
(ROS) £24.95 (STA) £24.95 (VIG)
Taittinger Brut Réserve £24.50 (STA)
1990
Charles Heidsieck £25.00 (PIP)
Moët & Chandon Brut Impérial £24.75
(ROB) £24.75 (POR) £24.76 (FOR) £24.80
(TAN) £24.99 (WAT) £24.99 (BOT) £24.99
(FUL) £24.99 (WR)
Pommery £25.99 (OD)

1989
Billecart-Salmon Cuvée N.F. Billecart
£25.95 (LEA)
Pommery £25.99 (FUL)
1988
Lanson £24.99 (JON)
Laurent-Perrier £24.99 (NEW) £25.50
(LEA) £25.95 (ROB)
Moët & Chandon Brut Impérial £24.85
(QUE) £24.99 (TES) £24.99 (UN)
Pol Roger £25.50 (HOG)

Veuve Clicquot Gold Label £25.79 (PLA)

£26.00 → £29.99

Non-vintage
Duval Leroy Fleur de Champagne £27.95
(SAI)
Gosset Brut Reserve £29.70 (GN)
Gosset Grande Reserve £26.99 (YOU)
£27.94 (HA) £27.95 (LEA) £29.95 (ROB)
Perrier-Jouët Blason de France £26.70 (PIP)
Veuve Clicquot Gold Label £26.15 (BO)
1990
Taittinger £27.50 (LEA) £29.99 (OD)
1989
Billecart-Salmon £26.50 (NI) £29.99 (OD)
Billecart-Salmon Cuvée N.F. Billecart
£29.38 (ELL)
Louis Roederer £29.99 (FUL)
Taittinger £27.95 (POR) £27.99 (FUL)
Veuve Clicquot £27.50 (FOR) £28.50 (GRE)
£28.50 (HAH) £28.90 (WRI) £28.95 (LEA)
£28.99 (NEW) £28.99 (EL) £29.95 (ROB)
Veuve Clicquot Gold Label £28.80 (PIP)
Veuve Clicquot Rich Reserve £28.00 (GRE)
Veuve Clicquot Vintage Reserve £28.95
(WS)
1988
Alfred Gratien £26.00 (WS)
Billecart-Salmon Cuvée N.F. Billecart
£28.49 (COU)
Laurent-Perrier £26.65 (LAY) £27.36 (CHA)
Pol Roger £27.75 (GRE) £27.95 (VIG)
£28.00 (BER) £28.80 (TAN) £29.38 (PEN)
Veuve Clicquot £26.40 (HOG) £28.50
(WHI) £28.99 (FUL) £28.99 (SAI)

1986
Duval Leroy Cuvée des Roys £28.80 (TAN)
Louis Roederer Blanc de Blancs £26.30 (NI)
Pol Roger £29.69 (ROS)
Pol Roger Blanc de Chardonnay £29.50
(REI)
1985
Gosset Grande Millésime £29.50 (POR)
1982
Drappier Carte d'Or £26.46 (GN)

£30.00 → £39.99

Non-vintage
Krug Grande Cuvée ½ bottle £32.99 (WR)
£32.99 (THR) £32.99 (BOT) £34.50 (BEN)
£34.50 (STA)
Lanson magnum £36.95 (BOT) £36.95 (WR)
Laurent-Perrier magnum £38.99 (MAJ)
£39.72 (CHA)
Moët & Chandon Brut Impérial magnum
£37.40 (TAN) £39.95 (POR) £39.99 (CO)
£39.99 (BOT) £39.99 (WR) £39.99 (TES)
£39.99 (THR) £39.99 (BO)
Perrier-Jouët magnum £39.95 (ROB)
Pommery Royale magnum £33.00 (GRE)
Veuve Clicquot magnum £39.90 (GRE)
1990
Louis Roederer £32.99 (JON) £39.75 (STA)
£39.95 (LEA)
Louis Roederer Blanc de Blancs £34.20
(LAY) £35.19 (PLA) £39.95 (STA) £39.95
(BEN)
1989
Bollinger £35.00 (PIP) £35.49 (TES) £36.50
(POR) £37.30 (BEN) £38.40 (EL) £38.50
(LEA) £38.55 (HAH) £38.95 (VIG) £39.95
(AD)
Bollinger Grande Année Vintage £32.50
(HIC) £34.00 (DI) £34.27 (WATT) £35.00
(WS) £35.75 (BER) £38.45 (LAY) £38.99
(VIC) £39.42 (GN)
Louis Roederer £36.80 (TAN)
Pol Roger White Foil magnum £38.00 (REI)
Veuve Clicquot Rich Reserve £32.99 (UN)
Veuve Clicquot Vintage Reserve £31.45
(HAH) £31.50 (LAY)
1988
Bollinger £31.33 (WY) £32.25 (HOG)
£35.09 (WAT) £35.49 (BOT) £35.49 (WR)
£35.49 (THR) £35.95 (WRI)
Bollinger Grande Année Vintage £30.29
(SAI) £33.75 (GRE) £35.74 (ROS) £37.50
(QUE) £37.99 (FUL) £38.99 (MAJ)
Deutz Cuvée de William Deutz £31.20
(FOR)

Pol Roger £31.50 (ROB) £31.90 (BEN) £31.95 (LEA) £32.55 (UB) £32.90 (HAH) £33.00 (MV) £33.61 (VIN)
Pol Roger Blanc de Chardonnay £37.50 (GRE) £37.60 (PEN) £38.50 (WRI)
Veuve Clicquot £31.99 (THR) £31.99 (BOT)
Veuve Clicquot Rich £32.05 (HAH)
Veuve Clicquot Rich Reserve £32.00 (LEA) £33.99 (WR) £33.99 (BOT)
1986
Pol Roger Cuvée Sir Winston Churchill £39.95 (SOM)
1985
Bollinger Grande Année Vintage £39.66 (WATT)
Dom Ruinart Blanc de Blancs £34.95 (GRE)
Gosset Grande Millésime £35.99 (YOU) £36.00 (WRI) £39.00 (LEA)
Heidsieck Diamant Bleu £34.99 (OD)
1983
Gosset Grande Millésime £38.59 (YOU)
Louis Roederer £35.25 (PEN)

£40.00 → £49.99

Non-vintage
Bollinger magnum £45.90 (GRE) £48.17 (PLA) £49.57 (LAY) £49.95 (DI)
Laurent-Perrier Cuvée Grande Siècle £49.50 (WS)
Moët & Chandon Brut Impérial magnum £40.30 (WRI) £41.00 (WHI) £41.25 (JON) £41.78 (LAY) £42.99 (FUL) £43.95 (ROB)
Perrier-Jouët Belle Époque £44.99 (BOT) £44.99 (WR) £44.99 (THR)
Pol Roger magnum £41.75 (GRE)
Pol Roger White Foil magnum £41.10 (UB) £44.50 (ROB) £44.50 (ROB) £47.00 (PEN) £47.50 (WRI) £49.35 (QUE)
'R' de Ruinart magnum £45.00 (VIG)
Veuve Clicquot magnum £45.95 (THR) £45.95 (WR) £45.95 (BOT) £47.50 (ROB) £49.95 (VIG)
1989
Bollinger £42.00 (MV)
Perrier-Jouët Belle Époque £46.99 (OD) £48.75 (PIP)
Veuve Clicquot la Grande Dame £49.94 (WY)
1988
Billecart-Salmon Grande Cuvée £42.50 (LEA)
Bollinger £42.99 (VIN)
Dom Ruinart £49.95 (VIG)
Dom Ruinart Blanc de Blancs £45.00 (BER) £45.00 (LEA)

1986
Pol Roger Blanc de Chardonnay £40.00 (MV)
1985
Perrier-Jouët Belle Époque £44.95 (GRE)
Taittinger Comtes de Champagne Blanc de Blancs £49.35 (FA)
1982
Bollinger RD £45.04 (WY) £46.33 (HOG) £47.45 (DI) £48.50 (GRE) £49.50 (WRI) £49.95 (PLA)
1966
Bollinger ½ bottle £44.50 (REI)

£50.00 → £59.99

Non-vintage
Bollinger magnum £51.90 (TAN) £53.25 (BEN) £55.00 (VIG)
Krug Grande Cuvée £56.30 (FA)
Laurent-Perrier Cuvée Grande Siècle £52.29 (PEN) £55.50 (AD) £55.63 (CHA)
1990
Dom Pérignon £51.42 (HOG) £56.60 (PIP) £57.57 (PLA) £59.95 (STA) £59.99 (BO)
1989
Louis Roederer Cristal £59.00 (REI)
Veuve Clicquot la Grande Dame £55.00 (RES) £55.00 (GRE) £55.80 (HAH) £59.95 (AD)
1988
Alfred Gratien magnum £55.00 (WS)
Dom Pérignon £51.90 (WY) £52.19 (FA) £55.99 (FUL) £56.00 (WHI) £56.20 (WAT) £56.95 (WRI) £59.50 (FOR) £59.95 (SAI)
Moët & Chandon Brut Impérial magnum £52.10 (UN) £59.50 (ROB)
Taittinger Comtes de Champagne Blanc de Blancs £55.50 (WRI) £59.99 (MAJ) £59.99 (NA)
Veuve Clicquot la Grande Dame £55.99 (FUL)
1986
Dom Pérignon £56.00 (BIB)
Pol Roger Cuvée Sir Winston Churchill £54.89 (HOG) £57.75 (GRE) £59.50 (TAN)
Taittinger Comtes de Champagne Blanc de Blancs £59.95 (ROB)

Please remember that **Webster's** *is a price guide and not a price list. It is not meant to replace up-to-date merchants' lists.*

1985
Bollinger RD £52.50 (PIP)
Dom Pérignon £52.87 (WY) £54.50 (GRE)
£54.64 (PEN) £55.99 (VIN) £55.99 (FUL)
£58.00 (TAN) £59.99 (TES) £59.99 (JON)
1982
Bollinger RD £50.99 (YOU) £51.40 (BEN)
£51.66 (ROS) £52.00 (LEA) £54.45 (THR)
£54.45 (BOT) £54.99 (FUL) £55.50 (VIN)
£58.75 (PEN) £58.85 (UB)
1976
Bollinger RD £50.23 (BUT)
1966
Charles Heidsieck la Royale £52.50 (REI)

£60.00 → £74.99

Non-vintage
Dom Pérignon £61.99 (MAJ)
Krug Grande Cuvée £60.75 (WHI) £60.98
(HOG) £61.71 (PEN) £63.75 (PIP) £63.95
(GRE) £64.00 (WAT) £64.00 (BIB) £64.15
(UB) £64.70 (TAN) £65.95 (LAY) £65.95
(BOT) £65.95 (WR) £66.50
(BER) £66.99 (VIC) £67.50 £67.75
(BEN) £68.00 (LEA) £68.61 (VIN) £68.95 (EL)
£68.95 (ROB) £69.00 (JON) £69.75 (QUE)

Laurent-Perrier Cuvée Grande Siècle
£69.90 (EL)
1990
Dom Pérignon £61.50 (LAY) £61.99 (OD)
Louis Roederer Cristal £68.50 (WHI)
£73.88 (ROS)
1989
Louis Roederer Cristal £69.82 (FA) £70.50
(PLA) £71.48 (WATT) £71.67 (AV) £73.50
(JON) £74.50 (LAY)
Veuve Clicquot la Grande Dame £62.00
(LEA) £65.00 (UN) £65.00 (VIC)
1988
Laurent-Perrier Cuvée Grande Siècle
£73.97 (AV)
Louis Roederer Cristal £68.74 (NO)
£71.80 (HOG) £73.42 (FOR)
Pol Roger magnum £62.00 (WS)
Veuve Clicquot ½ bottle £62.50 (ROB)

1986
Dom Pérignon £60.95 (POR)
Pol Roger Cuvée Sir Winston Churchill
£61.75 (WRI) £63.40 (HAH) £65.00 (ROB)
1985
Bollinger RD £64.50 (AD)
Dom Pérignon £61.95 (THR) £61.95 (BOT)
£61.95 (WR) £62.28 (QUE) £66.88 (FA)
Krug £66.97 (HOG) £70.00 (BIB) £71.77 (FA)
Pol Roger Cuvée Sir Winston Churchill
£60.60 (UB) £64.63 (PEN) £65.79 (VIN)
1982
Salon £69.82 (FA)
Taittinger Comtes de Champagne Blanc
de Blancs £65.90 (BUT)
1971
Charles Heidsieck £60.02 (BUT)
Dom Ruinart Blanc de Blancs £64.63 (WY)
1969
Bollinger £60.00 (YOU)

£75.00 → £99.99

1990
Louis Roederer Cristal £80.95 (STA)
£82.90 (HAH) £89.99 (MAJ)
1989
Bollinger magnum £77.50 (BEN) £80.00 (VIG)
Bollinger Grande Année magnum £77.55
(PEN)
Louis Roederer Cristal £75.00 (BIB)
£75.50 (BEN) £76.00 (GRE) £76.34 (NO)
£77.65 (PEN) £77.70 (TAN) £77.95 (WRI)
£79.65 (EL) £85.00 (RES) £85.00 (VIG)
1988
Louis Roederer Cristal £79.95 (WR)
1985
Krug £76.49 (THR) £76.49 (BOT) £76.49
(WR) £76.99 (OD) £77.35 (HAH) £78.95
(STA) £79.00 (AD) £79.00 (LEA) £79.99
(VIN) £82.50 (ROB) £85.00 (RES)
1982
Bollinger Vieilles Vignes Françaises, Blanc
de Noirs £75.00 (GRE)
Krug £95.00 (REI) £97.92 (FA)
1979
Bollinger £85.00 (MV)
Bollinger RD £75.00 (RES) £79.95 (THR)
Krug £85.02 (NO)
Taittinger Comtes de Champagne Blanc
de Blancs £75.00 (REI)
1975
Bollinger RD £95.00 (WS) £98.00 (YOU)
Krug £82.25 (PEN)
1953
Alfred Gratien £85.00 (REI)

£100.00 → £129.99

Non-vintage
Bollinger jeroboam £108.00 (NA)
Laurent-Perrier Cuvée Grande Siècle
 magnum £112.44 (CHA)
Moët & Chandon Brut Impérial jeroboam
 £115.00 (ROB)
Pol Roger White Foil jeroboam £105.00
 (GRE) £123.90 (WRI) £126.00 (QUE)
Veuve Clicquot jeroboam £115.00 (MAJ)
 £120.00 (VIG) £120.00 (WR) £120.00 (BOT)
1989
Bollinger Vieilles Vignes Françaises, Blanc
 de Noirs £115.55 (BEN)
1988
Bollinger magnum £129.25 (WY)
Louis Roederer Cristal magnum £120.00
 (REI)
1986
Bollinger Vieilles Vignes Françaises, Blanc
 de Noirs £129.00 (RES)
Pol Roger Cuvée Sir Winston Churchill
 magnum £129.00 (RES)
1976
Dom Pérignon £115.00 (YOU)
1964
Moët & Chandon Brut Impérial magnum
 £123.96 (FA)

£130.00 → £199.99

Non-vintage
Moët & Chandon Brut Impérial
 methuselah £191.70 (HOG)
1989
Louis Roederer Cristal magnum £180.00
 (ROB)
1988
Dom Pérignon magnum £140.00 (VIG)
1985
Dom Pérignon magnum £137.50 (ROB)
Krug magnum £188.00 (WY)
Krug Clos du Mesnil Blanc de Blancs
 £142.96 (FA) £146.45 (HAH) £156.50
 (BEN) £165.00 (RES) £175.00 (ROB)
1983
Louis Roederer Cristal magnum £152.75
 (FA)
1982
Krug magnum £199.75 (FA)
Krug Clos du Mesnil Blanc de Blancs
 £150.00 (REI)
1976
Krug £139.95 (BO)
Krug Collection £147.00 (REI) £151.77 (FA)

1973
Krug £150.00 (RES) £195.00 (ROB)
1969
Perrier-Jouët Belle Époque £150.00 (VIG)
1947
Perrier-Jouët £145.00 (REI)
1929
Pommery £196.50 (REI)

£200.00 → £299.99

Non-vintage
Pol Roger White Foil methuselah £235.50
 (WRI) £244.40 (PEN) £253.00 (QUE)
Veuve Clicquot methuselah £230.00 (MAJ)
 £275.00 (RES)
1969
Dom Pérignon £225.00 (RES)
1961
Krug £210.00 (REI)
1947
Perrier-Jouët magnum £275.00 (REI)

£320.00 → £350.00

Non-vintage
Pol Roger White Foil salmanazar £350.00
 (WRI)
1966
Moët & Chandon Brut Impérial jeroboam
 £325.00 (REI)

SPARKLING ROSÉ

Under £15.00

Non-vintage
Bonnet £14.99 (OD)
Bruno Paillard ½ bottle £11.97 (HAL)
George Goulet £14.60 (LON)

£15.00 → £19.99

Non-vintage
Bauget-Jouette £17.50 (HIG) £17.99 (AME)
Bricout £19.95 (LEA)
Bruno Paillard £17.70 (NEZ)
Bruno Paillard 1er Cuvée £18.95 (YAP)
Canard-Duchêne £15.49 (NEW) £15.99
 (HOG) £16.95 (GRE)
Charbaut £19.55 (PEN)
Mercier £15.85 (GRE) £15.99 (FUL) £16.35
 (FOR) £16.49 (WR) £16.49 (BOT)
Joseph Perrier Cuvée Royale £19.78 (TAN)
1989
Laurent-Perrier £18.95 (REI)
1988
Pol Roger £19.95 (SOM)

£20.00 → £29.99

Non-vintage
Billecart-Salmon £23.50 (LEA) £24.50 (NI)
£25.95 (ROB) £26.75 (BER) £26.93 (ELL)
£26.99 (COU) £26.99 (OD)
Gosset Grande Rosé £24.04 (HA)
Joseph Perrier Rosé £27.50 (NA)
Lanson £21.99 (VIC) £21.99 (THR) £21.99
(WR) £21.99 (BOT) £22.49 (UN) £23.99
(WHI)
Laurent-Perrier £22.95 (NEW) £23.50 (BIB)
£23.55 (FUL) £23.79 (CHA) £23.99 (WHI)
£24.49 (UN) £24.50 (GRE) £24.50 (LEA)
£24.75 (EL) £24.80 (TAN) £24.95 (VIG)
£24.95 (STA) £24.99 (BOT) £24.99 (THR)
£24.99 (WR) £24.99 (MAJ) £24.99 (JON)
£25.00 (WS) £25.50 (LAY) £25.50 (ROB)
£25.50 (WRI) £25.60 (PLA) £25.99 (OD)
£26.20 (PIP) £26.75 (HAH) £26.91 (PEN)
Louis Roederer £26.50 (QUE) £28.50 (NI)
Joseph Perrier Cuvée Royale £21.95 (NEW)
Pommery £20.95 (ROB) £21.00 (BIB)
1990
Deutz £21.30 (FOR)
Gosset £29.95 (LEA)
Moët & Chandon £26.00 (FOR)
1988
Billecart-Salmon Cuvée Elisabeth Salmon
£29.96 (COU)
Moët & Chandon £29.95 (ROB) £29.99 (UN)
Pol Roger £26.35 (REI)
Veuve Clicquot £27.42 (WY) £29.00 (GRE)
£29.90 (FOR)
1985
Charles Heidsieck £26.99 (PIP)

£30.00 → £39.99

1990
Gosset Grande Rosé £36.95 (ROB) £38.49
(EL)
1989
Louis Roederer £32.55 (HAH) £36.50 (ROB)
1988
Bollinger £31.72 (WY) £38.25 (BEN)
Pol Roger £34.20 (HAH) £34.35 (WRI)
£34.70 (UB)
Veuve Clicquot £33.50 (ROB) £33.99 (WR)
£33.99 (BOT) £33.99 (THR)
1986
Pol Roger £31.50 (ROB) £31.78 (PEN)
1985
Bollinger £32.00 (DI) £32.31 (WY) £35.70
(TAN)
Pol Roger £35.25 (QUE)

£40.00 → £99.99

Non-vintage
Krug £49.95 (BO) £89.50 (LEA) £93.20
(HAH)
Laurent-Perrier magnum £48.76 (CHA)
£52.50 (ROB) £54.95 (VIG)
Perrier-Jouët Belle Époque £49.99 (BOT)
£49.99 (WR) £49.99 (THR)
1989
Perrier-Jouët Belle Époque £51.00 (PIP)
1988
Perrier-Jouët Belle Époque £49.95 (ROB)
1986
Dom Ruinart £44.50 (BIB) £54.00 (LEA)
£54.95 (VIG)
Taittinger Comtes de Champagne £47.98
(FA)
1981
Dom Ruinart £49.00 (DI)

£120.00 → £199.99

1988
Louis Roederer Cristal Rosé £150.00 (RES)
1982
Dom Pérignon £122.69 (FA) £135.00 (GRE)

c. £250.00

1966
Dom Pérignon £250.00 (VIG)

STILL WHITE

c. £17.00

Non-vintage
Coteaux Champenois Blanc de
Chardonnay, Laurent-Perrier £16.90
(CHA)

STILL RED

c. £17.50

Non-vintage
Coteaux Champenois Pinot Franc Cuvée
de Pinot Noir, Laurent-Perrier £17.15
(CHA)

> *In each price band wines
> are listed in vintage order.
> Within each vintage they
> are listed in A–Z order.*

JURA & SAVOIE

These are some of the most obscure wines in France – if you live outside the region, that is

You may have to go on holiday to taste these wines: few are exported, though if you look hard you might find some Seyssel and some *vin jaune*, and even the occasional bottle of Arbois lurking on merchants' lists.

The flavours are, shall we say, rather uncompromising. And the prices are not low. So why buy them? Just for the hell of it – and because if all anyone ever buys is Chardonnay and Cabernet I might as well start looking for another job.

WINES & WINE REGIONS

ARBOIS, AC (red, white, rosé) The reds are thuddingly full of flavour. The Savagnin grape weaves its demonic spell on the whites, though Chardonnay sometimes softens it. There are some attractive light reds and rosés made from Pinot Noir or Poulsard. Best: *Henri Maire, Pupillin co-op.*

BUGEY, VDQS (red, white) Look for the deliciously crisp Chardonnays; they're among the most refreshing in France.

CÔTES DU JURA, AC (red, white, rosé) Virtually indistinguishable in style and flavour (and grape varieties) from Arbois wines, though sometimes a little less weird.

CRÉPY, AC (white) The Chasselas grape here produces an even flimsier version of the already delicate Swiss Fendant, if that's possible. Drink young and fast, or not at all.

L'ÉTOILE, AC (white) Whites mostly from Savagnin and Chardonnay. Also Savagnin *vins jaunes.*

ROUSSETTE DE SAVOIE, AC (white) Fullest and softest of the Savoie whites.

SEYSSEL, AC and SEYSSEL MOUSSEUX, AC (white) The Roussette (blended with a little Molette) makes quite full, flower-scented but sharp-edged whites. The fizz is light but pepper-pungent. Best: *Varichon et Clerc.*

VIN JAUNE (white) This grows the same yeasty *flor* as dry sherry, and its startlingly, painfully intense flavours just get more and more evident as it matures. In fact it seems virtually indestructible, as long as the cork remains healthy. Château-Chalon AC is the most prized – and most pricy – and is difficult to find even in the region.

VIN DE SAVOIE, AC (red, white) These Alpine vineyards are some of the most beautiful in France and produce fresh, snappy wines. The white, from the Jacquère, Chardonnay or Chasselas, can be excellent, dry, biting, but with lots of tasty fruit. Drink young. The reds from Pinot Noir or Gamay are subtly delicious, while the Mondeuse produces some beefy beauties in hot years. A *cru* name may be on the best. Look for the villages of Abymes, Chignin, Apremont, Cruet, Montmélian, Chautagne and Arbin.

MERCHANTS SPECIALIZING IN JURA AND SAVOIE
see Merchant Directory (page 413) for details

Nobody exactly specialises in these areas, but the following merchants have some: Anthony Byrne (BY), S H Jones (JON), Longford Wines (LON), Terry Platt (PLA), Roberson (ROB), Tanners (TAN), Wine Society (WS)

JURA & SAVOIE PRICE GUIDES

JURA RED

Under £5.00

Non-vintage
Bonchalaz Maire £4.95 (ROB)

JURA WHITE

Under £7.00

1992
Côtes du Jura Blanc Bourdy £6.75 (WS)

£18.00 → £33.50

1990
Vin de Paille Bourdy, ½ bottle £18.00 (WS)
1989
Vin Jaune Château-Chalon, Bourdy £25.00 (WS)
1983
Vin Jaune Château-Chalon, Maire £33.50 (ROB)
Vin Jaune d'Arbois, Tissot £20.95 (PLA)

c. £41.00

1973
Vin Jaune Château-Chalon, Bourdy £41.00 (UB)

SAVOIE WHITE

Under £6.50

1995
Seyssel Tacounière, Mollex £6.35 (WS)
Non-vintage
Seyssel Varichon & Clerc £6.45 (REI)

SAVOIE SPARKLING

Under £8.00

Non-vintage
Blanc de Blancs, Varichon et Clerc £6.99 (JON) £7.79 (AUR)
Seyssel Blanc de Blancs Mousseux Varichon & Clerc £7.34 (ELL)

LOIRE

One of these days Loire wines will become fashionable. Start buying them now if you want to be able to say, 'Those of us who've been drinking them for years...'

Not a great deal happens in the Loire. Vintages come and go, prices rise and occasionally fall, and the wines become increasingly unfashionable. Vouvray, for example: who drinks Vouvray? Muscadet: why bother?

On the other hand, I could say: look how most wines chop and change with fashion. Look how some wines are hardly the same from one vintage to the next. And look at the Loire, doggedly sticking to indigenous styles that are just waiting for us to rediscover them.

You want an original flavour? You want to startle your friends? You can try Portugal, Italy or the Loire. Nobody else in the world is making anything that tastes like Vouvray. Nobody else in the world is making sweet Chenin Blanc with the intensity and the longevity of Quarts de Chaume – and that very longevity, the years of bottle age it needs to show at its best, is so hopelessly unfashionable that it's due for cult status.

Then there's the sheer inappropriateness of making red wines somewhere so far north that the grapes only really ripen in a hot year. Though come to think of it, Burgundy suffers from the same problem yet seems to survive. And Loire reds have improved so much in recent years – they've got more colour, more flavour and more weight – that if you want a good, wacky red that will demonstrate the breadth of your knowledge and the originality of your palate, don't look in Australia, look in Bourgueil.

Sauvignon, I grant you, can claim little of this status: it's positively commonplace. And of that other ubiquitous white I can still only say – Muscadet: why bother?

GRAPE VARIETIES

CABERNET FRANC (red) The great quality grape of Anjou and Touraine. All the best reds are based on Cabernet Franc, and the styles span the spectrum from the palest, most fleeting of reds to deep, strong and often austerely tannic wines of character and longevity.

CABERNET SAUVIGNON (red) This doesn't always ripen very well in the Loire, but even so it adds some backbone to the wines. It is really at its best in the warmest, ripest years.

CHARDONNAY (white) Increasingly widespread in the Loire and producing lean, light but tangy results in Haut-Poitou, in Anjou as Vin de Pays du Jardin de la France and in Orléans as Vin de l'Orléanais (where it's called Auvernat) – *Clos St-Fiacre* is terrific.

It also occurs in Muscadet (*le Chouan* and *Domaine Couillaud* are good) and adds character and softness to Anjou Blanc.

CHASSELAS (white) Makes adequate but dull wine at Pouilly-sur-Loire; it's actually best as a table grape, in a fruit salad.

CHENIN BLANC (white) A grape that cries out for sun and ripens (if that's the word) long after the other varieties.

It also performs superbly in the Loire in a few warm and misty mesoclimates (especially in Quarts de Chaume and Bonnezeaux), where noble rot strikes the Chenin with enough frequency to make it worthwhile going through all the pain and passion of producing great sweet wine, with steely acidity and the flavour of honeyed, ripe-apple fruit.

These wines can seem curiously disappointing when young, but fine sweet Chenin manages to put on weight and become sweeter for perhaps 20 years before bursting out into a richness as exciting as all but the very best from Germany or Bordeaux. And then it lasts and lasts…. Because Chenin Blanc is unfashionable, these wines can be remarkably undervalued; but you have to be prepared to tuck them away in the cellar for a long time.

GAMAY (red) In the Loire this rarely achieves the lovely, juicy glugginess of Beaujolais, but when made by a careful modern winemaker it can have a fair amount of fruit, though it always seems to have a tough edge.

MELON DE BOURGOGNE (white) The grape of Muscadet, light and neutral. It's good at producing fresh white, usually quite biting, and with a salty tang. It's usually for drinking young though a good domaine-bottled *sur lie* can mature surprisingly well.

PINOT NOIR (red) In and around Sancerre this can, in warm years, produce a lovely, light, cherry-fragrant wine that will be either a rosé or a light red. But really interesting examples are rare in the Loire, where it's usually too chilly to ripen the Pinot properly.

SAUVIGNON BLANC (white) The grape of Sancerre and Pouilly, and the main white grape of Touraine, with a whole range of fresh, green, tangy flavours that might remind you of anything from gooseberries to nettles and fresh-cut grass, and there's sometimes even a whiff of newly roasted coffee. The wines are usually quite tart – but thirst-quenching rather than gum-searing – and have loads of fruit. Sauvignon can age interestingly in bottle, but the odds are against it, except for the high-priced oak-aged cuvées.

WINE REGIONS

ANJOU BLANC SEC, AC (white) France's cheapest AC dry white made mostly from the hard-to-ripen Chenin Blanc, often tart, sulphured and sour. But it *can* be good, steely and honeyed, especially from Savennières with its two tiny special ACs, Coulée-de-Serrant and la Roche-aux-Moines, and from names such as *Domaine Richou* which mixes Chardonnay with the Chenin, for extra flavour and fruit. Other good names: *Mark Angeli (Cuvée Christine), Baranger, Château de Valliennes, Domaine de la Haute Perche, Jaudeau.*

ANJOU ROUGE CABERNET, AC (red) This ranges from mostly quite light when from the co-ops, and spicy, strong and capable of aging from the best estates. It can rival Bourgueil. Best: *Mark Angeli (Cuvée Martial), Ch. d'Avrille, Ch. de Chamboureau (Soulez), Clos de Coulaine, Dom. de la Petite Croix, Dom. du Petit Val, Dom. des Rochettes (Chauvin), Logis de la Giraudière (Baumard), Richou, Roussier.*

ANJOU ROUGE GAMAY, AC (red) Rarely more than adequate, but in the hands of someone like *Richou*, the 'rooty' character is replaced by a fresh, creamy fruit that is sharp and soft at once, and *very* good. *Domaine des Quarres* is also worth a try.

ANJOU-VILLAGES, AC (red) Cabernets Franc and Sauvignon from the 46 best villages in Anjou. Some are labelled Anjou-Villages Val-de-Loire. *Domaine de Montgilet, J-Y & H Lebreton, Domaine Ogereau* and *Richou* are good.

BONNEZEAUX, AC (white) One of the most unfairly forgotten great sweet wines of France. Prices for the lovely noble-rot-affected wines have risen, but are still low compared to Sauternes – which itself is cheap at the price. Look out for the outstanding wines of Mark Angeli (from old vines), Château de Fesles, Goizil, Renou and Denéchère.

BOURGUEIL, AC (red) Some of the best reds of the Loire come from this AC in Touraine. When they are young they can taste a bit harsh and edgy, but give them a few years and they will have a piercing blackcurrant fruit, sharp and thirst-quenching. They can age remarkably well, developing complex leathery, meaty flavours. Best: Audebert (estate wines), Pierre Breton, Caslot-Galbrun, J-F Demont, Domaine des Forges, Domaine des Ouches, Pierre-Jacques Druet, Lamé-Delille-Boucard.

CABERNET D'ANJOU, AC (rosé) There is a reasonable chance of a pleasant drink here, because the Cabernets – mostly Franc, but often with Cabernet Sauvignon too – do give pretty tasty wine, usually less sweet than simple Rosé d'Anjou. Best: Dom. Baranger, Dom. de Hardières, Dom. de Richou, Château de Valliennes.

CHEVERNY, AC (red, white) This Touraine region is improving fast. Its claim to fame is the teeth-grittingly dry white Romorantin grape, but there is also Chardonnay, Sauvignon Blanc and Chenin. Dom. des Huards is delicate and fine, and the confrérie at Oisly-et-Thésée is reliable. Others: Cazin, Gendrier, Gueritte and Tessier. Red Cheverny tends to be light and crisp, with a healthy dollop of Gamay perhaps beefed up with Cabernet Franc. Oisly-et-Thésée's is strawberryish with a fair bit of Pinot Noir in it.

CHINON, AC (red) In a ripe year (1990, '95 '96), Chinon can be delicious, exhibiting a great gush of blackcurrant and raspberry flavours. In poorer vintages it can be unpalatably bitter with surprising levels of green tannin. But winemaking standards have risen. Domaine wines are far better than négociant wines, which can be thin.

Best: Bernard Baudry, Jean Baudry, Domaine du Colombier, Couly-Dutheil, Druet, Gatien Ferrand, René Gouron, Charles Joguet, Alain Lorieux, Pierre Manzagol, Jean-François Olek, Jean-Maurice Raffault, Raymond Raffault, Domaine du Roncée, Domaine de la Tour.

COTEAUX DE L'AUBANCE, AC (white) Quite cheap, pleasant semi-sweet whites. Best: Dom. des Rochettes, Jean-Yves Lebreton and Dom. Richou.

COTEAUX DU LAYON, AC (white) A large AC producing varying qualities of sweet white wine, at its best rich and tasty with a taut acidity that allows the wine to age for a long time. Dom. Ambinois, Ch. du Breuil (from very old vines), Ch. de la Guimonière, Ogereau, Dom. du Petit Val, Dom. de la Pierre St-Maurille, Dom. des Quarres, Ch. de la Roulerie, Clos Ste-Catherine and Dom. de la Soucherie are worth trying. There are also six Coteaux du Layon-Villages ACs that usually offer higher quality. Some Anjou growers are now making sélection de grains nobles, very sweet, concentrated wines made from only botrytized grapes.

CRÉMANT DE LOIRE, AC (white) Sparkling wine AC intended to denote higher quality than basic sparkling Saumur but not much used. The wines are usually softer and nicer than the frequently harsh wines of Saumur. Best include the first-rate house of Gratien & Meyer, Langlois-Château, St-Cyr-en-Bourg co-op and the small Cave des Liards.

GROS PLANT, VDQS (white) Gros Plant rejoices in being one of the rawest wines in France, and the prosperity of dentists in Nantes is thanks in no small measure to the locals' predilection for the stuff. That said, it does go amazingly well with seafood and seems to suit oysters. Bossard's is soft and honeyed. Métaireau and Sauvion have also tamed its fury. Clos de la Sénaigerie and Clos de la Fine from Dom. d'Herbauges are good.

HAUT-POITOU, VDQS (red, white) Chardonnay and Sauvignon from the *Cave Co-opérative du Haut-Poitou* are good but tend to leaness, for the whites; the reds are fairly 'green' but reasonably enjoyable, and are usually made from Gamay.

MENETOU-SALON, AC (red, white, rosé) The Sauvignon is as good as that of Sancerre, and there are some fair reds and rosés. The *Vignerons Jacques Coeur* co-op produces about half the Sauvignon. *Henry Pellé* makes the best in Menetou, followed by *Jean-Max Roger* and *Dom. de Chatenoy*.

MONTLOUIS, AC (white) Chenin-based wines similar to Vouvray, but often more robust – which, when it comes to the Chenin grape, isn't always a good idea. *Dominique Moyer*, *Domaine des Liards* and *Jean-Pierre Trouvé* are good, but lots are short on fruit, long on sulphur.

MUSCADET, AC (white) Simple, light, neutral wine from near the coast. Straight Muscadet, without any further regional title, is usually flat and boring. But at least it's light – the Muscadet ACs are the only ones in France to impose a *maximum* alcohol level (12.3 per cent).

MUSCADET COTES DE GRAND-LIEU, AC (white) Demarcated in 1994, this latest Muscadet sub-region accounts for nearly half of the area that was basic Muscadet, and quality varies. The good news is that most is bottled *sur lie*.

MUSCADET DE SÈVRE-ET-MAINE, AC (white) The biggest Muscadet area, making the most but also the best wine. A good one may taste slightly nutty, peppery or salty, even honeyed, sometimes with creaminess from being left on the lees and sometimes with a slight prickle. It should always have a lemony acidity, and should feel light. Buy domaine-bottled wine only, and check the address, looking out for St-Fiacre and le Pallet, two of the best villages.

MUSCADET DES COTEAUX DE LA LOIRE, AC (white) Quality in this Muscadet sub-region isn't bad though the wines tend to lack the distinction of Muscadet de Sèvre-et-Maine. *Pierre Luneau* is good.

MUSCADET SUR LIE (white) This is the most important thing to look for on a Muscadet label. It indicates that the wine has been bottled straight off the lees (the yeast sediment from fermentation), thus having more depth than usual and a slight prickle. *Sauvion's Ch. du Cléray* and *Découvertes* range are very good. *Guy Bossard* makes good organic *sur lie*. Others: *Dom. de Coursay-Villages*, *Dom. du Grand Mouton*, *Pierre Luneau*, *Dom. de la Montaine*, *Ch. de Chasseloir*, *Clos de la Sénaigerie*, *Jean-Louis Hervouet*, *Dom. du 'Perd-son-pain'*, any from *Louis Métaireau* including *Dom. du Grand Mouton*, *Cuvée LM*, *Cuvée One*, unfiltered *Huissier*; both *Michel* and *Donatien Bahuaud's* single-domaine wines, *Bonhomme* and *Guilbaud*.

POUILLY-FUMÉ, AC (white) Just over the river from Sancerre and very similar. They can be fuller than Sancerre, and the best have a mineral complexity, but given the prices, there are still too many under-achievers. Best: *J C Châtelain*, *Didier Dagueneau* (Pouilly's most brilliant winemaker), *Serge Dagueneau*, *Château Favray*, *André Figeat* and the too-expensive *Baron de L.*

POUILLY-SUR-LOIRE, AC (white) Made from the dull Chasselas grape which makes good eating but not memorable drinking. *Serge Dagueneau* makes a good example.

QUARTS DE CHAUME, AC (white) A tiny AC with a perfect mesoclimate for nobly-rotten sweet wines. They are rare and expensive, not as sweet as Sauternes, but can be even more intense, with high acid stalking the rich apricot and honey fruit.

Jean Baumard is superb; also *Ch. de Bellerive* and *Ch. de l'Echarderie*.

QUINCY, AC (white) Crisp Sauvignon Blanc, usually lighter than Sancerre. *Dom. de Maison Blanche, Pierre Mardon, Jacques Rouzé* and *Jacques Coeur* co-op are good.

REUILLY, AC (white) Light, fragrant Sauvignon Blanc. *Gérard Cordier* and *Claude Lafond* are the main growers here. There is also some tasty red and rosé.

ROSÉ D'ANJOU, AC (rosé) The omnipresent and frequently omnihorrid French rosé. It is based on a pretty feeble grape, the Groslot, and suffers in the main from lack of fruit and excess of sulphur. A few, including the co-op at *Brissac*, can make it fresh.

ROSÉ DE LOIRE, AC (rosé) A little-made dry rosé from Anjou or Touraine.

ST-NICOLAS-DE-BOURGUEIL, AC (red) These Cabernet reds tend to be lighter and more forward than the reds of nearby Bourgueil. They can be very good, but stick to warm years. The wines of *Claude Ammeux, Caslot-Jamet, Jean-Paul Mabileau* and *Joël Taluau* seem best.

SANCERRE, AC (white) Green, smoky, tangy wine from the Sauvignon Blanc grape. At its best young, it should be super-fresh and fruity, tasting and smelling of gooseberries or cut grass, though it's seldom as assertively gooseberryish as New Zealand Sauvignon. Look for single-domaine wines – especially from *Archambault, Balland-Chapuis, Henri Bourgeois, Francis and Paul Cotat, Lucien Crochet, Pierre and Alain Dézat, Gitton, Dom. Laporte, Alphonse Mellot, Paul Millérioux, Henri Natter, Reverdy, Jean-Max Roger, Pierre Riffault, Vacheron* and *André Vatan*.

SANCERRE ROUGE, AC (red) Pinot Noir, and in general overrated, but the best

have a lovely cherry fragrance and sweetness of strawberries that can survive a year or two in bottle. Silly prices, though. *Henri Bourgeois, Domaine Vacheron, Pierre & André Dezat* are good and worth a try.

SAUMUR, AC (white) Champagne-method fizz from Chenin Blanc, perhaps with the welcome addition of Chardonnay, Sauvignon or even Cabernet Franc to round out the acid Chenin. Well-made sparkling Saumur (there is a little rosé) is lively and appley but too many are just too rough to revel with. Best: *Ackerman-Laurance, Bouvet-Ladubay, Gratien & Meyer, Langlois-Château*.

SAUMUR BLANC, AC (white) Usually ultra-dry Chenin Blanc, though it can occasionally be sweet, similar to Anjou Blanc.

SAUMUR-CHAMPIGNY, AC (red) Cabernet from the best villages in Saumur. It is way above other Loire reds thanks to a firm structure and velvety softness, fruit that is slightly raw and rasping, yet succulent and rich at the same time. Although the term 'vieilles vignes' is open to interpretation it is always the best bet for quality. *Domaine Filliatreau* makes an outstanding one, as well as *Primeur*, for immediate drinking. Also good: *Château de Chaintres, Château du Hureau, Château de Targé, Domaine Dubois, Domaine Lavigne, Domaine Sauzay-Legrand, Denis Duveau, Domaine de Nerleux, Domaine des Roches Neuves, Domaine du Val Brun*.

SAUMUR ROUGE, AC (red) Usually very light and dry Cabernet Franc from 38 villages round Saumur. Although it's light the fruit is often marked and attractively blackcurranty. The co-op at *St-Cyr-en-Bourg* is good, as is *Château Fouquet* from Paul Filliatreau.

SAVENNIÈRES, AC (white) Some of the world's steeliest, longest-living, diamond-dry white wines come from this tiny Anjou AC where the Chenin grape comes into its own. One vineyard, Savennières Coulée-de-Serrant, has its own AC within Savennières, and *Nicolas Joly's Clos de la Coulée-de-Serrant* is excellent. Also: *Yves Soulez* from the *Ch. de Chamboreau, Clos du Papillon, Jean Baumard (Clos Ste-Catherine), Dom. de la Bizolière* and the *Dom. aux Moines*.

TOURAINE, AC (red, white) Everybody sees Touraine Sauvignon, with some justification, as a Sancerre substitute. The *Confrérie des Vignerons de Oisly-et-Thésée* is good, as are *Paul Buisse, Ch. de l'Aulée, Dom. de la Charmoise (Marionnet), Ch. de Chenonceau, Dom. des Corbillières, Dom. Joël Delaunay* and *Dom. Octavie*. The reds are often less stalky than they were, but tend to be light. The *Domaine de la Charmoise (Marionnet)*, and the co-op of *Oisly-et-Thésée* produce fair Gamays. *Château de Chenonceau* is also good.

VIN DE PAYS DU JARDIN DE LA FRANCE (white) The general vin de pays of the Loire. Usually pleasant but unmemorable, but those based on

Sauvignon Blanc and Chardonnay can be considerably better. *Biotteau's Château d'Avrille* and *Domaine des Hauts de Saulière's* Chardonnays have lovely fruit.

VIN DE PAYS DES MARCHES DE BRETAGNE (red, white) These wines from the mouth of the Loire are usually fairly flimsy, lightweight numbers, but a good innovative grower can produce something unusual and exciting. *Guy Bossard*, for instance, a leading Muscadet producer, makes an amazingly fragrant and fruity red from Cabernet Franc.

VOUVRAY, AC (white) Sparkling and still whites from tangily dry to richly sweet, though usually caught in the middle. In fact, Vouvray is best at the off-dry demi-sec style, and from a good producer this Chenin wine, initially all searing acidity and rasping dryness, over many years develops a deep honey-and-cream flavour. Most commercial Vouvray is poor. Best: *Daniel Allias, Domaine des Aubuisières, Brédif, Chamalou, Château Gaudrelle, Pierre Mabille, Château Moncontour, Foreau, Huet, Prince Poniatowski* and *Domaine de Vaugoudy*.

LOIRE VINTAGES

Loire vintages are very important, and can be radically different along the river length. In poor vintages, Muscadet is most likely to be OK, while in hot vintages Sauvignon goes dull, but the Chenin finally ripens. The red grapes need the warm years.

1996 The reds and the Chenin had a bumper year and should age well, but there's enough acidity to keep the Sauvignon balanced, too.

1995 Some luscious dessert wines as well as fine reds, but quality is not even.

1994 Fair dry whites, but Coteaux du Layon should be best of all. Reds are lightweight.

1993 Good, flinty whites. Reds look capable of aging. The best Coteaux du Layon is botrytized and concentrated.

1992 A large crop of wines that generally lack concentration. The reds are very light.

1991 Sancerre and Pouilly-Fumé quantities were down by half. Quality was average.

1990 Sweet Chenins, built to last, may beat the '89s. Great reds too.

LOIRE PRICE GUIDES

DRY WHITE

Under £4.00

1996

Sauvignon de Touraine Bougrier £3.75 (WS)
Sauvignon de Touraine Confrérie d'Oisly et Thésée £2.99 (MAJ) £3.99 (OD)
VdP du Jardin de la France Chenin Blanc de Blanc, Bougrier £3.50 (WS)
VdP du Jardin de la France Chenin Blanc, Lurton £3.89 (SAI)
★ VdP du Jardin de la France Sauvignon Blanc, les Landiers £4.89 (SUN)

£4.00 ➜ £4.99

1996

Muscadet de Sèvre-et-Maine Fief de la Brie, Bonhomme £4.95 (AD)
Muscadet de Sèvre-et-Maine sur lie Domaine de la Bretonnière £4.85 (BAN)
Pouilly-Fumé Seguin ½ bottle £4.95 (LEA)
Saumur Blanc Château de Beauregard £4.70 (WS)
Saumur Cave des Vignerons de Saumur £4.75 (YAP)
Sauvignon de Touraine Domaine de la Bergerie £4.95 (AD)
Sauvignon de Touraine Domaine Guenault £4.10 (GAL)

1995

Coteaux du Giennois Balland-Chapuis £4.99 (OD)
Muscadet de Sèvre-et-Maine des Ducs, Chereau Carré £4.85 (BIB)
Muscadet de Sèvre-et-Maine Domaine de la Roche £4.99 (SAT)
Muscadet de Sèvre-et-Maine Moreau £4.72 (FOR)
Muscadet de Sèvre-et-Maine sur lie Fief de la Brie, Bonhomme £4.99 (JON)

£5.00 ➜ £5.99

1996

Cheverny Domaine Salvard £5.55 (AD)
Menetou-Salon Pellé £5.95 (SAI)
Muscadet de Sèvre-et-Maine sur lie Château de Cléray £5.80 (PIP)
Muscadet de Sèvre-et-Maine sur lie Château de l'Oiselinière de la Ramée £5.75 (WS)
Muscadet de Sèvre-et-Maine sur lie Domaine des Dorices £5.50 (GRE)
Muscadet de Sèvre-et-Maine sur lie Première, Jean Douillard £5.95 (SAI)
St-Pourçain Cuvée Printanière, Union des Vignerons £5.50 (YAP)
Sauvignon de Touraine Confrérie d'Oisly et Thésée £5.50 (STA)
Sauvignon de Touraine Domaine des Cabotières £5.95 (LEA)

1995

Muscadet de Sèvre-et-Maine sur lie Château de Chasseloir £5.50 (WS)
Muscadet de Sèvre-et-Maine sur lie Château de Cléray £5.75 (NEZ)
Muscadet de Sèvre-et-Maine sur lie Château de la Ferronière £5.25 (EL)
Muscadet de Sèvre-et-Maine sur lie Clos des Bourguignons £5.65 (HAH)
Muscadet de Sèvre-et-Maine sur lie Domaine de la Bretonnière £5.65 (NI)
Muscadet de Sèvre-et-Maine sur lie Domaine des Ratelles £5.50 (WS)
Muscadet sur lie Château de la Galissonière £5.99 (DI)
Reuilly Beurdin £5.50 (BAN) £5.69 (MAJ) £5.99 (NA)
Saumur Domaine des Hauts de Sanziers £5.20 (RSJ)

1994

Anjou Blanc Sec Château de la Genaiserie £5.25 (WS)

MERCHANTS SPECIALIZING IN THE LOIRE
see Merchant Directory (page 413) for details

Most merchants have some. Unusually imaginative lists can be found at: Adnams (AD), Averys of Bristol (AV), Bennetts (BEN), Anthony Byrne (BY), Eldridge Pope (EL), Justerini & Brooks, Lay & Wheeler (LAY), The Nobody Inn (NO), Terry Platt (PLA), Raeburn Fine Wines (RAE), The RSJ Wine Co (RSJ), T&W Wines (TW), Tanners (TAN), Ubiquitous Chip (UB), Waterloo Wine (WAT), Wine Society (WS)

£6.00 → £6.99

1996
Pouilly-Fumé les Loges, Saget £6.99 (MAJ)
Reuilly Beurdin £6.46 (ELL) £6.95 (AD)
Sauvignon de Touraine Domaine de la
    Preslé £6.40 (PIP)
Vouvray Jarry £6.95 (YAP)
1995
Anjou Blanc le Haut de la Garde, Château
    de Pierre Bise £6.30 (RSJ)
Menetou-Salon Morogues, Pellé £6.65 (WS)
Muscadet de Sèvre-et-Maine sur lie
    Château de la Ragotière £6.98 (VIN)
Muscadet de Sèvre-et-Maine sur lie Cuvée
    LM, Louis Métaireau £6.50 (NI)
Pouilly-Fumé Bailly £6.95 (WS)
Pouilly-Fumé Chatelain £6.70 (SOM)
Pouilly-Fumé Vieilles Vignes, Caves de
    Pouilly-sur-Loire £6.75 (SAT)
Quincy Rouze £6.77 (ROS) £6.90 (HAH)
Reuilly Beurdin £6.50 (GRE)
Saumur Blanc Château de Villeneuve
    £6.95 (LEA)
Sauvignon de Touraine Domaine de la
    Charmoise, Marionnet £6.00 (BIB)
1994
Coteaux du Giennois Balland-Chapuis
    £6.75 (LON)
Vouvray Château Moncontour £6.59 (NI)
    £6.59 (NA) £6.79 (UN)

£7.00 → £7.99

1996
Menetou-Salon la Charnivolle, Fournier
    £7.75 (STA)
Menetou-Salon Morogues, Pellé £7.85 (GRE)
Montlouis Sec, Berger Frères £7.25 (YAP)
Pouilly-Fumé Masson-Blondelet £7.49 (WAI)
Quincy Jaumier £7.25 (YAP)
Sancerre Laporte £7.80 (PIP)
Saumur Blanc Château de Villeneuve
    £7.20 (PIP)
Vouvray Domaine Peu de la Moriette
    £7.60 (PIP)
1995
Anjou Blanc le Haut de la Garde, Château
    de Pierre Bise £7.50 (LEA)
Pouilly-Fumé Domaine Coulbois £7.75
    (ASD)
Pouilly Fumé Fine Caillottes, Pabiot £7.75
    (AD)
Pouilly-Fumé Jean Pabiot £7.95 (POR)
Pouilly-Fumé les Bascoins, Masson-
    Blondelet £7.25 (BAN)

Sancerre Daulny £7.00 (GAL) £7.99 (WHI)
Savennières Clos de Coulaine £7.85 (RSJ)
Touraine Azay-le-Rideau la Basse
    Chevrière, Pavy £7.25 (YAP) £7.35 (WS)
VdP du Jardin de la France Chardonnay,
    Domaine Couillaud £7.19 (VIN)
Vouvray Domaine des Aubuisières £7.40
    (RSJ)
Vouvray le Haut Lieu, Huet £7.55 (REI)
1994
Menetou-Salon Pellé £7.59 (THR) £7.59
    (WR) £7.59 (BOT)
Pouilly-Fumé les Loges, Saget £7.95 (SAT)
Reuilly Beurdin £7.05 (BER)
Sancerre Domaine des Trois Piessons
    £7.99 (BOT) £7.99 (THR) £7.99 (WR)
Saumur Blanc Château de Villeneuve
    £7.89 (JON)
Savennières Château de Chamboureau,
    Soulez £7.85 (WS)
1993
Pouilly Fumé Fine Caillottes, Pabiot £7.99
    (JON)
Savennières Domaine du Closel, Mme de
    Jessey £7.35 (WAT)
Vouvray Brédif £7.95 (GRE)
Vouvray Château Moncontour £7.45 (GN)
    £7.55 (BEN)
1990
Vouvray Château de Vaudenuits £7.95
    (GRE)

£8.00 → £9.99

1996
Menetou-Salon Morogues, Pellé £9.25 (GN)
Menetou-Salon Teiller £8.25 (YAP)
Pouilly-Fumé Domaine des Berthiers,
    Jean-Claude Dagueneau £8.65 (REI)
Pouilly-Fumé les Berthiers, Claude Michot
    £8.50 (BIB)
Pouilly-Fumé Masson-Blondelet £8.90 (PIP)
Pouilly-Fumé Seguin £8.49 (VIC) £8.95 (LEA)
Sancerre Chavignol, Delaporte £9.95 (LEA)
Sancerre Chavignol le Manoir, André
    Neveu £9.75 (BIB)
Sancerre Clos des Roches, Vacheron
    £9.95 (NA)
Sancerre Jean Thomas £8.50 (BIB)

> *In each price band wines
> are listed in vintage order.
> Within each vintage they
> are listed in A–Z order.*

Sancerre le Croix au Garde, Pellé £8.75 (GRE)

Sancerre les Perriers, Vatan £9.50 (YAP)

Sancerre Michel Thomas £9.19 (BOD) £9.19 (SUN)

Sancerre Vacheron £9.95 (AD)

1995

Menetou-Salon Clos des Blanchais, Pellé £8.76 (ELL) £8.95 (POR)

Menetou-Salon Domaine de Chatenoy £8.35 (WRI) £8.50 (DI) £8.75 (BU)

Menetou-Salon Roger £8.20 (TAN)

Pouilly-Fumé André Dezat £8.40 (NI)

Pouilly-Fumé Château de Tracy £8.75 (GAL) £9.50 (WS) £9.90 (HAH) £9.95 (HIC) £9.99 (POR)

Pouilly-Fumé Chatelain £9.11 (DOM) £9.70 (BER)

Pouilly-Fumé Domaine des Berthiers, Jean-Claude Dagueneau £9.25 (WRI)

Pouilly-Fumé Domaine des Rabichattes £8.99 (RAE)

Pouilly-Fumé Domaine Thibault £9.55 (ELL) £9.99 (JON)

Pouilly-Fumé les Griottes, Bailly £8.50 (GRE) £8.55 (NA)

Pouilly-Fumé les Loges, Jean-Claude Guyot £8.75 (YAP)

Pouilly-Fumé les Loges, Saget £8.99 (VIN)

Pouilly-Fumé Seguin Père et Fils £9.50 (RAE)

Sancerre André Dézat £8.99 (NI) £9.40 (TAN) £9.75 (BER)

Sancerre Chavignol les Comtesses, Paul Thomas £9.65 (LAY)

Sancerre Clos de la Crêle, Lucien Thomas £8.40 (EL) £8.80 (COU)

Sancerre Clos des Roches, Vacheron £9.95 (GRE)

Sancerre Clos du Chaudenay Vieilles Vignes, Daulny £8.20 (GAL)

Sancerre Clos du Chêne Marchand, Roger £9.20 (TAN)

Sancerre Cuvée Flores, Vincent Pinard £9.49 (FUL)

Sancerre Daulny £8.10 (HAH)

Sancerre Domaine de Montigny, Natter £8.95 (LAY) £9.95 (VIG)

Sancerre les Perriers, Fournier £8.95 (STA)

Sancerre Paul Prieur £8.48 (HA) £9.11 (DOM)

Sancerre Roger £9.00 (MV)

Sancerre Vacheron £8.99 (MAJ)

Savennières Château de Chamboureau, Soulez £9.25 (YAP)

Savennières Château d'Epiré £8.75 (YAP)

Savennières Domaine de la Bizolière £8.50 (YAP)

Savennières Domaine du Closel, Mme de Jessey £8.75 (YAP)

Vouvray le Haut Lieu, Huet £8.49 (WAT) £8.80 (RSJ)

Vouvray le Mont, Huet £8.75 (REI)

1994

Chinon Blanc les Champs Chenin, Raffault £9.95 (WS)

Menetou-Salon Clos des Blanchais, Pellé £9.48 (NO)

Montlouis les Batisses, Délétang £8.15 (WS)

Pouilly-Fumé Domaine Thibault £9.60 (TAN)

Pouilly-Fumé Jean Pabiot £8.45 (HAH)

Sancerre Balland-Chapuis £9.85 (BER)

Sancerre Château de Thauvenay £8.68 (LON)

Sancerre Clos du Roy, Millérioux £9.30 (HOG)

Sancerre Domaine de Montigny, Natter £9.99 (RAE)

Sancerre Domaine de la Tonnelerie £8.49 (JON)

Vouvray Brédif £8.99 (UN)

Vouvray le Haut Lieu, Huet £8.35 (WS)

1993

Savennières Clos du Papillon, Baumard £8.35 (HOG) £8.65 (EL) £8.95 (GRE) £9.00 (REI)

Savennières Roche-aux-Moines, Domaine Aux Moines £9.85 (RSJ)

Vouvray Clos du Bourg, Huet £8.95 (WS) £9.70 (GAU)

Vouvray Clos Naudin, Foreau £9.81 (DI)

1990

Muscadet Vieilles Vignes, Château de Chasseloir £9.99 (WHI)

1989

Muscadet de Sèvre-et-Maine sur lie Château de Chasseloir £9.39 (PEN)

1988

Savennières Clos de Coulaine £8.50 (REI)

Savennières Roche-aux-Moines, Domaine Aux Moines £9.85 (RSJ)

£10.00 → £14.99

1996
Pouilly-Fumé Domaine Thibault £10.99 (GN)
1995
Pouilly-Fumé Château de Tracy £10.75
    (LAY) £10.95 (LEA) £10.95 (AD)
Pouilly-Fumé Chatelain £10.35 (BEN)
Pouilly-Fumé les Pechignolles £10.99 (HIG)
Pouilly-Fumé Masson-Blondelet £10.54 (NO)
Sancerre Clos des Roches, Vacheron
    £10.94 (GN) £11.45 (BEN) £12.50 (ROB)
Sancerre Laporte £10.85 (DI)
Sancerre les Belles Dames, Gitton £10.75
    (HIG)
Savennières Roche-aux-Moines, Soulez
    £11.25 (YAP)
1994
Pouilly-Fumé Cuvée Prestige, Châtelain
    £11.60 (SOM)
Pouilly-Fumé de Ladoucette, Château du
    Nozet £11.79 (HOG) £13.50 (FOR)
    £13.95 (STA) £13.99 (MAJ) £13.99 (QUE)
Sancerre Comte Lafond, Château du
    Nozet £11.26 (HOG) £11.75 (WY)
    £12.14 (WATT) £13.49 (MAJ)
Vouvray Clos du Bourg, Huet £12.50 (RAE)
Vouvray le Mont, Huet £10.80 (RAE)
1993
Pouilly-Fumé de Ladoucette, Château du
    Nozet £12.92 (WY) £14.55 (HAH)
Sancerre Chavignol la Grande Côte,
    Cotat £12.99 (RAE)
Sancerre les Romains, Gitton £10.99 (HIG)
Savennières Clos du Papillon, Baumard
    £10.50 (LAY) £10.60 (UB) £10.95 (ROB)
Vouvray Clos du Bourg, Huet £10.39 (JON)
Vouvray Clos Naudin, Foreau £10.89 (DI)
1990
Sancerre Comte Lafond, Château du
    Nozet £11.75 (WY)
1988
Vouvray le Haut Lieu, Huet £11.50 (JON)

£15.00 → £19.99

1995
Pouilly-Fumé Clos du Chailloux, Didier
    Dagueneau £16.45 (ROB) £16.50 (VIG)
Pouilly-Fumé Pur Sang, Didier Dagueneau
    £19.95 (VIG)
1994
Pouilly-Fumé Clos du Chailloux, Didier
    Dagueneau £15.10 (TAN) £16.50 (VIG)
Pouilly-Fumé du Buisson Menard, Didier
    Dagueneau £19.20 (TAN) £19.95 (VIG)

1993
Savennières Roche-aux-Moines, Clos de
    la Bergerie £15.50 (WS)
1991
Savennières Coulée-de-Serrant, Nicolas
    Joly £19.75 (REI)
1989
Vouvray le Haut Lieu, Huet £15.40 (AD)

£20.00 → £29.99

1994
Pouilly-Fumé Pur Sang, Didier Dagueneau
    £20.37 (FA) £20.50 (ROB) £20.95 (LAY)
Pouilly-Fumé Silex, Didier Dagueneau
    £27.71 (FA) £27.95 (ROB) £27.95 (VIG)
1992
Pouilly-Fumé Baron de L Château du
    Nozet £29.90 (WRI) £29.95 (STA)
Savennières Coulée-de-Serrant, Nicolas
    Joly £29.95 (VIG)
1991
Savennières Coulée-de-Serrant, Nicolas
    Joly £21.95 (UB) £22.00 (BIB) £28.50 (YAP)
1990
Savennières Coulée-de-Serrant, Nicolas
    Joly £21.99 (WAT) £26.63 (NO)
Vouvray Clos du Bourg, Huet £21.50 (REI)
1971
Vouvray Clos du Bourg, Huet £24.50 (RAE)
1964
Vouvray Brédif £29.50 (SAT)

£30.00 → £34.99

1992
Pouilly-Fumé Baron de L Château du
    Nozet £31.05 (HAH) £31.25 (BEN)
    £31.50 (VIG) £33.50 (ROB)

SPARKLING

Under £8.00

Non-vintage
Saumur Brut Bouvet-Ladubay £7.99 (MAJ)
1993
Saumur Brut La Grande Marque £7.25 (JON)
1992
Saumur Brut La Grande Marque £6.39 (POR)

£8.00 → £9.99

Non-vintage
Crémant de Loire Château Langlois £8.49
    (MAJ) £9.95 (BEN)
Montlouis Mousseux Brut Berger £8.75
    (YAP)

Montlouis Mousseux Demi-sec Berger
£8.75 (YAP)
Saphir Bouvet-Ladubay £9.95 (ROB)
Vouvray Brut Brédif £8.90 (GRE) £9.99 (JON)
Vouvray Brut Jarry £8.75 (YAP)
Vouvray Foreau £9.90 (AD)
1993
Saphir Bouvet-Ladubay £8.35 (NI)
Vouvray Pétillant, Huet £8.95 (WS)

£10.00 → £13.50

Non-vintage
Vouvray Foreau £10.90 (GAU)
Vouvray Méthode Champenoise, Huet
£10.85 (RAE)
1993
Vouvray Pétillant, Huet £10.85 (RAE)
1983
Vouvray Méthode Champenoise, Huet
£13.50 (GAU)
Vouvray Pétillant Demi-Sec Foreau
£11.50 (AD)

c. £22.00

1967
Vouvray Méthode Champenoise, Huet
£21.90 (GAU)

SWEET WHITE

Under £7.00

1993
Coteaux du Layon St Aubin de Luigné,
Domaine des Forges £5.95 (LEA)

£7.00 → £8.99

1996
Montlouis Vieilles Vignes, Berger Frères
£8.25 (YAP)
Vouvray Moelleux Jarry £8.95 (YAP)
1995
Coteaux de l'Aubance Domaine de Bablut
£8.50 (RSJ)
Coteaux du Layon Domaine Ogereau
£8.45 (RSJ)
Vouvray Domaine des Aubuisières Demi-
Sec £7.20 (RSJ)
Vouvray Plan de Jean Moelleux, Domaine
des Aubuisières £8.99 (OD)
1993
Vouvray Demi-Sec, Gilles Champion
£8.75 (LAY)
1985
Montlouis Moelleux Deletang £8.99 (RAE)

£9.00 → £12.99

1996
Montlouis Vendange Tardive, Berger
Frères £11.95 (YAP)
1995
Coteaux du Layon St Aubin de Luigné,
Domaine des Forges £11.40 (TAN)
Montlouis Moelleux, Dominique Moyer
£12.75 (LAY)
Montlouis Vendange Tardive, Berger
Frères £11.75 (YAP) £12.95 (LAY)
Vouvray Moelleux, Gilles Champion £9.95
(LAY)
1994
Coteaux du Layon Chaume les Aunis,
Château de la Roulerie £12.15 (NO)
Coteaux du Layon Clos de Ste-Catherine,
Baumard £10.20 (SOM) £10.50 (GRE)
Vouvray Clos Naudin Demi-sec, Foreau
£12.55 (AD)
Vouvray Moelleux Clos du Bourg, Huet
£12.50 (RAE)
1993
Coteaux du Layon Beaulieu l'Anclaie, Bise
£10.95 (LEA)
1990
Vouvray le Haut Lieu Moelleux, Huet ½
bottle £9.31 (NO)
Vouvray Moelleux Bourillon Dorléans
£12.50 (MV)
1989
Coteaux du Layon Leblanc £9.65 (RAE)
Vouvray le Haut Lieu Moelleux, Huet ½
bottle £9.50 (RAE)
Vouvray Moelleux Aigle Blanc,
Poniatowski £10.50 (GRE)
1985
Coteaux du Layon Chaume Château de
Bellevue, Tijou £9.40 (HIG)
Montlouis Moelleux Domaine des Liards,
Jean & Michel Berger £12.50 (VIG)
1983
Vouvray Clos de Bourg Demi-sec, Huet
£9.85 (REI)

£13.00 → £15.99

1995
Coteaux du Layon Chaume les Onnis,
Domaine des Forges £13.20 (TAN)
Coteaux du Layon Clos de Ste-Catherine,
Baumard £13.75 (GRE)
1994
Coteaux du Layon Beaulieu l'Anclaie, Bise
£14.95 (LEA)

1993
Quarts-de-Chaume Baumard £13.45
(SOM)
1990
Vouvray Moelleux le Bouchet, Domaine
des Aubuisières £14.50 (AD)
1989
Quarts-de-Chaume Château de Bellerive
£14.50 (WS)
Vouvray le Haut Lieu Demi-Sec, Huet
£13.20 (RSJ)
Vouvray Moelleux Bourillon Dorléans
£14.45 (VIG)
1988
Quarts-de-Chaume Baumard £14.50 (GRE)
Vouvray Moelleux Clos Naudin, Foreau
£14.99 (DI)
Vouvray Moelleux Huet £14.99 (RAE)
1985
Coteaux du Layon Chaume, Château de
la Guimonière £15.95 (VIG)
Vouvray le Haut Lieu Demi-Sec, Huet
£13.95 (WS)
1970
Coteaux du Layon Ravouin-Gesbron
£14.95 (WS)

£16.00 → £19.99

1995
Coteaux du Layon Beaulieu Vieilles
Vignes, Château du Breuil £17.20 (LAY)
Coteaux du Layon Domaine Sauveroy
£17.99 (OD)
1990
Bonnezeaux la Montagne Domaine du
Petit Val, Goizil £19.19 (NO)
Quarts-de-Chaume Baumard £19.74 (HOG)
Vouvray le Haut Lieu Moelleux, Huet
£16.75 (WS)
Vouvray le Mont, Huet £17.34 (NO)
Vouvray Moelleux Bourillon Dorléans
£19.09 (ELL)
1989
Montlouis Vendange Tardive, Berger
Frères £16.75 (YAP)
Quarts-de-Chaume Baumard £17.95 (GRE)
Quarts-de-Chaume Château de
l'Echarderie £19.50 (YAP)

> Stars (★) indicate wines
> selected by Oz Clarke in the
> Best Buys section which begins
> on page 12.

1988
Vouvray Moelleux Clos du Bourg, Huet
£17.50 (JON)
1986
Quarts-de-Chaume Château de Bellerive
£16.75 (WS)
Vouvray Moelleux Clos du Bourg, Huet
£16.99 (BIB)
1983
Anjou Moulin, Touchais £18.50 (ROB)

£20.00 → £29.99

1995
Quarts-de-Chaume Baumard £20.90 (EL)
£21.50 (GRE)
Quarts-de-Chaume Bise £20.40 (RSJ)
£23.95 (LEA)
Vouvray Moelleux Clos du Bourg, Huet
£20.25 (REI) £25.00 (VIG)
1993
Vouvray Cuvée Constance, Huet £29.00
(RAE) £29.90 (GAU)
1990
Bonnezeaux la Chapelle, Château de
Fesles £25.00 (WS) £29.97 (NO)
Quarts-de-Chaume Baumard £21.22 (NO)
Quarts-de-Chaume Château de Bellerive
£24.62 (NO)
Quarts-de-Chaume Château de
l'Echarderie £21.00 (YAP) £23.77 (NO)
Vouvray le Haut Lieu Moelleux, Huet
£26.50 (GAU) £28.50 (WAI)
Vouvray Moelleux Clos du Bourg, Huet
£21.55 (RSJ) £23.70 (GAU)
Vouvray Réserve Doux, Gilles Champion
£21.20 (AD)
1989
Bonnezeaux Château de Fesles £20.60 (NO)
Coteaux du Layon Clos de Ste-Catherine,
Baumard £20.43 (NO)
Quarts-de-Chaume Lalanne £22.96 (NO)
Vouvray le Haut Lieu Moelleux, Huet
£27.90 (RSJ)
Vouvray Moelleux Clos du Bourg, Huet
£29.95 (AD)
1985
Vouvray le Haut Lieu Moelleux, Huet
£22.91 (NO)
1978
Anjou Rablay, Maison Prunier £29.50 (REI)
1969
Anjou Moulin, Touchais £27.50 (WRI)
1962
Vouvray le Haut Lieu Demi-Sec, Huet
£28.50 (REI)

£30.00 → £49.99

1990
Vouvray le Mont, Huet £31.40 (GAU)
1989
Bonnezeaux la Chapelle, Château de
    Fesles £33.57 (NO)
Vouvray Moelleux Clos Naudin, Foreau
    £32.00 (HOG)
1985
Vouvray le Haut Lieu Moelleux, Huet
    £38.50 (REI)
1971
Vouvray Moelleux Clos du Bourg, Huet
    £42.35 (REI)

£50.00 → £79.99

1962
Vouvray Moelleux Clos du Bourg, Huet
    £54.00 (RAE)
1959
Vouvray Moelleux Clos du Bourg, Huet
    £76.07 (NO)
1957
Vouvray le Mont, Huet £75.00 (VIG)

£80.00 → £94.99

1947
Vouvray le Haut Lieu Moelleux, Huet
    £85.00 (REI) £93.00 (RAE)

£100.00 → £125.00

1947
Vouvray le Haut Lieu Moelleux, Huet
    £100.00 (VIG) £125.00 (WS)

ROSÉ

Under £8.00

1996
Reuilly Pinot Gris, Cordier £7.75 (YAP)
Sancerre Rosé Chavignol Domaine
    Delaporte ½ bottle £5.25 (LEA)
1995
Bourgueil Domaine Amirault £5.95 (LEA)
Cabernet d'Anjou Château de la
    Genaiserie £5.35 (WS)
Reuilly Pinot Noir, Beurdin £5.50 (BAN)
Sancerre Rosé les Cailleries, Vacheron
    £7.95 (WS)
Touraine Rosé Noble Jouée, Clos de la
    Dorée £5.55 (AD)
1993
Anjou Rosé Cellier de la Loire £3.99 (NI)

£8.00 → £9.99

1996
Sancerre Rosé Chavignol Domaine
    Delaporte £9.95 (LEA)
Sancerre Rosé les Romains, Vacheron
    £9.55 (NA)
1995
Sancerre Rosé Domaine de la Mercy
    Dieu, Bailly-Reverdy £9.95 (LAY)
Sancerre Rosé les Romains, Vacheron
    £9.75 (GRE)
1994
Sancerre Rosé André Dezat £8.99 (NI)

RED

Under £5.00

1995
Saumur Cave des Vignerons de Saumur
    £4.85 (AD)
Saumur Château de Beauregard £4.75
    (WS)

£5.00 → £6.99

1996
Chinon Couly-Dutheil £5.99 (MAJ)
Vin de Thouarsais, Gigon £5.95 (YAP)
1995
Anjou Rouge Logis de la Giraudière,
    Baumard £5.99 (EL)
Anjou-Villages Domaine Ogereau £6.30
    (RSJ)
Anjou-Villages Domaine des Rochelles,
    Lebreton £6.85 (RSJ)
★ Bourgueil Domaine de la Grive £6.30 (TAN)
Chinon les Aubuis, Caves des Vins de
    Rabelais £5.45 (AD)
Gamay du Haut Poitou Cave Co-op.
    £5.52 (FOR)
Menetou-Salon Rouge, Pellé £6.95 (WS)
Saumur-Champigny Château Villeneuve
    £6.80 (RSJ)
Saumur-Champigny Domaine de Nerleux
    £6.70 (RSJ)
1994
Gamay de Touraine Domaine de la
    Charmoise, Marionnet £6.00 (BIB)
Saumur-Champigny Château des
    Chaintres £6.95 (WS)
1993
Bourgueil la Hurolaie, Caslot-Galbrun
    £5.49 (TES)
Reuilly Pinot Noir, Beurdin £5.75 (BAN)

1992
Saumur Domaine du Langlois-Château
£6.25 (DI)

1991
Anjou Rouge Tijou £5.48 (HIG)

£7.00 ➜ £8.99

1996
Chinon Domaine Philippe Alliet £8.50
(LEA)
Chinon l'Arpenty, Desbourdes £7.75 (YAP)
Chinon Vieilles Vignes, Domaine Philippe
Alliet £8.95 (LEA)
Saumur-Champigny Domaine des Roches
Neuves £7.95 (LEA)
1995
Anjou-Villages Domaine des Rochelles,
Lebreton £7.20 (TAN)
Bourgueil les Cent Boisseles, Druet £7.99
(MAJ)
Bourgueil Domaine les Galichets £7.05 (RSJ)
St-Nicolas-de-Bourgueil la Source,
Domaine Amirault £8.95 (LEA)
Sancerre André Dezat £8.99 (NI)
Saumur Château Fouquet, Domaine
Filliatreau £7.25 (YAP)
1994
Saumur-Champigny Château Villeneuve
£8.25 (JON)
1993
Bourgueil Caslot Jamet £7.50 (WS)
Chinon Couly-Dutheil £8.75 (GRE)
St-Nicolas-de-Bourgueil Vieilles Vignes,
Taluau £7.95 (WS)
Sancerre les Cailleries, Vacheron £8.95
(WS)
Saumur-Champigny Château de Targé
£7.50 (SOM)
1990
Cabernet d'Anjou Clos de Coulaine £7.20
(GAU)
Chinon Clos de l'Echo, Couly-Dutheil
£8.65 (WAT)
1987
Bourgueil Beauvais, Druet £8.04 (BY)

£9.00 ➜ £10.99

1996
Bourgueil les Cent Boisseles, Druet £9.85
(AD)
1995
Bourgueil les Quartiers, Domaine
Amirault £9.50 (LEA)
St-Nicolas-de-Bourgueil les Malgagnes,
Domaine Amirault £9.95 (LEA)
Sancerre André Dezat £9.40 (TAN)
Sancerre Chavignol, Paul Thomas £9.95
(LAY)
Saumur-Champigny Terres Chauds,
Domaine des Roches Neuves £9.99 (MAJ)
Saumur-Champigny Vieilles Vignes,
Filliatreau £10.25 (YAP)
1994
Bourgueil Domaine des Ouches £9.30 (PIP)
Sancerre André Dezat £10.75 (LAY)
£10.99 (JON)
Sancerre les Cailleries, Vacheron £10.69
(NA) £10.85 (GRE)
1993
Bourgueil Beauvais, Druet £10.75 (YAP)
Saumur-Champigny Château du Hureau,
Vatan £9.68 (BER)
1991
Sancerre la Bourgeoise, Henri Bourgeois
£9.90 (SOM)
1990
Sancerre Domaine de Montigny, Natter
£10.95 (RAE)

£11.00 ➜ £12.99

1996
Sancerre André Dezat £11.00 (PIP)
Saumur-Champigny Terres Chauds,
Domaine des Roches Neuves £11.95
(LEA)
1989
Chinon Clos de l'Echo, Couly-Dutheil
£12.34 (NO)

£13.00 ➜ £18.99

1995
Bourgueil Grand Mont, Druet £13.25 (YAP)
Chinon Clos de la Dioterie, Joguet £14.70
(GAU) £14.95 (AD)
1994
Saumur-Champigny Domaine des Roches
Neuves £15.57 (PLA)
1988
Bourgueil Cuvée Vaumoreau, Druet
£18.75 (YAP)

RHÔNE

**Prices have risen in the Rhône, but should we stop buying?
Or is it just a question of being more canny than before?**

Where do you look to find good value in the Rhône? Actually, you don't have to look far. Much of the Rhône is pretty good value; it's just that there are fewer bargains about than there used to be.

The top wines are now expensive. But you can still get a Côte-Rôtie or Hermitage from a very good grower for less than the price of its equivalent in Burgundy; so in that respect, if French subtlety is what you seek, the Rhône can still look fairly priced. That Côte-Rôtie will also cost you less than a reasonable classed-growth claret (I'm not talking about the First or Second Growths here). So yes, in terms of comparable fine French wines, Rhônes are not overpriced. But they're getting close.

They can be quite tricky to understand, however. In the North, some growers favour using new oak; others eschew it altogether. Some make tannic monsters destined for the long term, others make more easily approachable wines. In the South things are still more complicated: Châteauneuf-du-Pape, with a few exceptions, is generally underperforming and Côtes du Rhône is so varied in style and quality as to be virtually meaningless as an appellation. The other wines of the South, like Gigondas, have often risen in price to a point where they don't look like terribly good value any more. Gigondas is aping fine wine prices these days. But is it a fine wine, or a superior country wine?

If you want a bargain, what should you buy? My advice would be to go for Côtes du Rhônes from top northern Rhône growers like Guigal; you'll get good winemaking, good grapes, and all the fascinating flavour of Syrah.

GRAPE VARIETIES

CARIGNAN (red) This grape is much maligned because in the far South it used to, and often still does, produce raw, fruitless wines that are the mainstay of the cheapest bulk wines. But old Carignan vines can produce strong, tasty, flavoursome wines that age well, and the variety's toughness is brilliantly moderated by the use of the carbonic maceration method of fermentation.

CINSAUT (red) This widely planted grape is now out of favour because of its inability to age. But it can add pepperiness and acidity to the blend, as at Château Rayas. Cinsaut often makes a successful contribution to rosé blends.

CLAIRETTE (white) Makes sparkling Crémant de Die, but is a bit dull unless livened up with the aromatic Muscat. In the South it makes big, strong whites that can be creamy, but more often dull and nutty. Needs careful handling and early drinking.

COUNOISE (red) Rich, spicy, floral flavours, and highly regarded at *Beaucastel* and *Durieu* in Châteauneuf-du-Pape. Could be promising.

GRENACHE (red) The most important red grape in the southern Rhône, with loads of alcohol and a gentle, juicy, spicy fruit perked up by a whiff of pepper, ideal for rosés and easy-going reds. Grenache achieves its greatest power and longevity at Châteauneuf-du-Pape.

GRENACHE BLANC (white) Widely planted in the southern Rhône, producing rich, appley wines with a strong whiff of aniseed. Good, but soft, so drink young.

MARSANNE (white) The dominant of the two grapes that go to make white Hermitage and Crozes-Hermitage, as well as white St-Joseph and St-Péray. Marsanne is weighty and can be flabby, but at its best it is rich and scented. Further south it makes burly, lanoliny wine, but is capable of rich, exotic peach and toffee flavours, too.

MOURVÈDRE (red) This vine relishes ample warmth and sunshine. It contributes backbone and tannin to blended wines, and on its own, as in Bandol, it develops wonderful smoky, leathery, meaty flavours as it ages.

MUSCAT (white) Used to great effect blended with Clairette to make the sparkling Clairette de Die, but more famous for Muscat de Beaumes-de-Venise.

ROUSSANNE (white) Altogether more delicate and fragrant than the Marsanne. Found chiefly in Hermitage and St-Péray in the North, though it also makes light, fragrant wines further south in Châteauneuf. Look out for *Beaucastel's* Roussanne *Vieilles Vignes* – pricy but superb.

SYRAH (red) The whole of the northern Rhône is dominated by Syrah – and it makes some of the blackest, most startling, pungent red wine in France. From Hermitage and Cornas, it rasps with tannin and tar and woodsmoke, backed by the deep, ungainly sweetness of black treacle. But give it five or ten years, and those raw fumes will have become sweet, pungent, full of raspberries, brambles and cassis.

UGNI BLANC (white) Boring workhorse grape planted all over the South to produce basic gulping stuff. The same as the Trebbiano of Italy, where it is hardly any more exciting.

VIOGNIER (white) The grape of Condrieu and Château-Grillet. It has one of the most memorable flavours of any white grape, blending the rich, musky scent of overripe apricots with that of spring flowers. The wine is made dry, but it is so rich you would hardly believe it. Sweet versions are making a comeback now. Viognier is becoming a bit of a cult, with plantings increasing in the southern Rhône, California and Australia.

WINE REGIONS

CHÂTEAU-GRILLET, AC (white; north) This single property is one of the smallest AC in France. Wildly expensive, it's 100 per cent Viognier and is often surpassed in freshness and quality by top Condrieus. But unlike Condrieu, it can age interestingly.

CHÂTEAUNEUF-DU-PAPE, AC (red, white; south) This can be delicious, deep, dusty red, almost sweet and fat, low in acidity, but kept appetizing by back-room tannin. *Can* be. It can also be fruit-pastilly and pointless, or dark, tough and stringy. Thirteen different red and white grapes are permitted, and the resulting flavour is usually slightly indistinct, varying from one property to another. Around one-third of the growers make good wine – and as much as two-thirds of the wine sold probably exceeds the permitted yields. So it makes sense always to go for a domaine wine and certainly not one bottled away from the region. The most reliable wine comes from *Château de Beaucastel*, the most celebrated (and expensive) from *Château Rayas*. Also recommended are *Clos du Mont Olivet, Château Fortia, Château St-André, La Nerthe, Chante-Cigale, Clos des Papes, Chante-Perdrix, le Vieux Donjon, Font de Michelle, Font du Loup, les Cailloux, la Gardine, la Janasse, Quiot, Domaine du Grand Tinel, Domaine de Mont Redon, Domaine du Vieux Télégraphe, Domaine Durieu, Bosquet des Papes, Lucien Gabriel Barrot, les Clefs d'Or, Chapoutier's la Bernadine* and *Henri Bonneau*.

Few whites are made, but they can be outstandingly perfumed with a delicious nip of acidity, leaving you wondering how on earth such aromatic wines could come from such a hot, arid region. Wonderful wines can be produced in the most unlikely places – and this is one of them. In its youth, the wine has a perfumed rush of springtime madness. Then it closes up for a few years, emerging at seven years as a rich, succulent, nutty mouthful. Best: *Château de Beaucastel* (its pure Roussanne *Vieilles Vignes* – and the Viognier white), *Clefs d'Or, Clos des Papes, Font de Michelle, Grand Tinel, Mont Redon, Nalys, Rayas, Vieux Télégraphe.*

CLAIRETTE DE DIE, AC (sparkling; south) Made half from Clairette, half from Muscat, this is delicious, light and off-dry. It used to be called Clairette de Die Tradition, and the much duller Champagne-method sparkler is now called Crémant de Die. The still wine is Coteaux Diois.

CONDRIEU, AC (white; north) Wonderful when made properly, with apricot scent that leaps out of the glass, and an exciting balance of succulent fruit and gentle acidity. Viognier is the only grape. Despite its high price, Condrieu is best young, but beware its high alcohol. Top names: *Château du Rozay, Chapoutier, Cuilleron, Delas, Dumazet, Guigal, Multier* (who, like some others, is using new oak), *Niero Pinchon, Jean Pinchon, Rostaing* and *Georges Vernay.*

CORNAS, AC (red; north) Black and tarry tooth-staining wine. It's usually rather hefty, jammy even, and lacks some of the fresh fruit that makes Hermitage such a remarkable wine, yet at ten years old it's impressive. Excellent blockbusters are made by *Auguste Clape, Robert Michel* and *Noël Verset.* It's also worth looking for *René Balthazar, Colombo (Domaine des Ruchets), Courbis, Delas, Jaboulet, Juge, Leménicier, Allemand, Jean Lionnet* (especially *Cuvée Rochepertuis), Alain Voge.*

COSTIÈRES DE NÎMES, AC (red, rosé; south) There are good rosés and meaty, smoky reds here, at prices that are still reasonable. Try *Ch. la Tuilerie, Dom. de l'Amarine, Ch. de Campuget, Mas de Bressades, Mas Carlot* (especially its top wines under the *Ch. Paul Blanc* label), *Ch. Mourgues du Grés.*

COTEAUX DU TRICASTIN, AC (red, white; south) Fast-improving, good-value, spicy, fruity reds, and fresh, fruity and quite full-flavoured whites, not as exciting as the reds. Best producers (reds): *Dom. de Grangeneuve, Tour d'Elyssas* (100 per cent Syrah), *Prods. Réunis Ardéchois* (co-op; also good white), *Dom. Saint-Luc, Dom. du Vieux Micocoulier.*

CÔTE-RÔTIE, AC (red; north) Together with Hermitage, the greatest wine of the northern Rhône. It can have exceptional finesse, thanks to the occasional addition of a dash of Viognier. Some exceptional single sites are named on the label, notably La Landonne. The greatest growers are *Guigal, Rostaing* and *Burgaud.* Look also for *Barge, Champet, Chapoutier, Clusel-Roch, Delas, Gaillard, Gerin, Jaboulet* and *Jasmin.*

CÔTES DU LUBÉRON, AC (red, white; south) Lubéron makes decent reds, usually rather light, but capable of stronger personality. The *Val Joanis* rosé is one of the best in the South. Try also *Château de Canorgue, Château de l'Isolette, Mas du Peyroulet, Val Joanis* (also to be seen under the names of *Domaines Chancel* or *Domaine de la Panisse), Vieille Ferme.* The whites are usually pleasant and light but little more, though much more fragrant, interesting styles come from *Château de l'Isolette, Mas du Peyroulet, Val Joanis* and *la Vieille Ferme.*

CÔTES DU RHÔNE, AC (red, white) Well-made basic Côtes du Rhône reds are delicious when young, wonderfully fresh and fruity, like a soft Beaujolais. Or they can be fierce, black, grapeskins-and-alcohol monsters. Many of the weightiest are made by Châteauneuf growers (*Cru de Coudoulet* from *Beaucastel*, *Château de Fonsalette* from *Rayas*) or northern Rhône producers like *Guigal* and *Clape*. *Château du Grand Moulas* is spicy and attractive, with plenty of body. Also good: *Château de Ruth*, *Château de Goudray*, *Clos du Père Clément*, *Dom. de Bel Air*, *Dom. de la Cantharide*, *Dom. de St-Estève*, *Dom. des Aussellons*, *Jean Lionnet* and *Chapoutier's* rosé. Whites are generally fresh and fruity.

CÔTES DU RHÔNE-VILLAGES, AC

(red, white; south) Good, full reds that can also age, combining earthy, dusty southern heat with spicy, raspberry fruit. They come from villages, 17 of which can add their names on the label, including Cairanne, Chusclan, Valréas, Beaumes-de-Venise and Rasteau. These wines often offer excellent value. Best: *Dom. Pelaquié* (Laudun); *Dom. de Grangeneuve*, *Dom. la Soumade* (Rasteau); *Jean-Pierre Cartier*, *Château de Trignon*, *Dom. de Boisson*, *Dom. St-Antoine*, *Dom. de Verquière*, *Jean-March Antran* (Sablet); *Dom. de l'Ameillaud*, *Dom. Brusset*, *Dom. l'Oratoire St-Martin*, *Dom. de la Présidente*, *Dom. Rabasse-Charavin*, *Marcel Richaud* (Cairanne); *Dom. Ste-Anne* (St-Gervais); *Dom. Courançonne*, *Dom. de Cabasse* (Séguret); *Roger Combe*, *Dom. des Grands Devers*, *le Val des Rois* (Valréas). The whites are increasingly fresh, fruity and gulpable, especially from the villages of Laudun and Chusclan. *Dom. Pelaquié* is tops, and *Dom. Ste-Anne* is good.

CÔTES DU VENTOUX, AC (red,

white, rosé; south) Good area producing lots of fresh, juicy wine; the red is the best. Can even be quite special. Best: *Domaine des Anges*, *Jaboulet*, *Pascal*, *la Vieille Ferme*, *Vieux Lazaret*.

CROZES-HERMITAGE, AC (red,

white; north) Red that varies from the light and juicy to well-structured smoky wine

recognizable as a lesser cousin of the great Hermitage. Sadly, prices of the best wines are rising fast. *Etienne Pochon* (*Château Curson*), *Chapoutier's les Meysonniers* and *Varonniers*, *Graillot's Guiraude*, *Jaboulet's Thalabert* are tops. Also good are *Albert Belle*, *Bernard Chave*, *Cave des Clairmonts*, *Domaine des Entrefaux*, *Cave de Tain*, *Fayolle*, *Laurent Combier*, *Stéphane Cornu*, *Pradelle* and *Vidal-Fleury*. The white is generally rather dull and strong, but there are good ones from *Château Curson*, *Entrefaux*, *Combier*, the *Tain co-op*, *Graillot*, *Fayolle*, *Jaboulet* and *Pradelle*.

GIGONDAS, AC (red; south) Big,

chunky, plummy wines that can be short on finesse. This is Grenache country, and proud of it. *Dom. de St-Gayan* is very good, as are the following: *Clos des Cazaux*, *Dom. de Cayron*, *Dom. les Gouberts*, *Dom. de Longue-Toque*, *Dom. l'Oustau Fauquet*, *Dom. les Pallières*, *Dom. Raspail-Ay*, *Dom. de Santa Duc*.

HERMITAGE, AC (red, white; north)

Grand, burly red; strong and fierily tough when young, it matures to a rich, brooding magnificence. There is always a stern, vaguely medicinal or smoky edge, and an unmatchable depth of raspberry and blackcurrant fruit. Although many people produce Hermitage of sorts, there have traditionally been only two stars, the marvellously good *Chave*, who produces small amounts of impeccable wine, and the ebullient, export-orientated *Paul Jaboulet Aîné*, who produces larger amounts of more variable wine. To them should be added *Chapoutier's le Pavillon*. Also good: *Delas Cuvée Marquise de la Tourette*, *Desmeure*, *Faurie*, *Guigal*, *Sorrel*, *Belle*, and *Jean-Louis Grippat*. The white is often heavy and dull, but it ages tremendously well to a soft, rich nuttiness. *Chave* makes magnificent white Hermitage even in modest vintages, and other good producers include *Chapoutier*, *Desmeure*, *Ferraton*, *Guigal*, *Grippat* and *Marc Sorrel*.

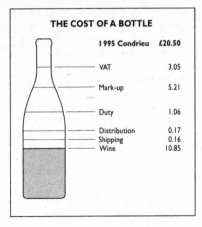

THE COST OF A BOTTLE

1995 Condrieu £20.50

VAT	3.05
Mark-up	5.21
Duty	1.06
Distribution	0.17
Shipping	0.16
Wine	10.85

LIRAC, AC (red, white, rosé; south) A good, often underrated area making light, attractive wines. Reds are packed with fruit, often tinged with a mineral edge. The rosés are remarkably fresh for so far south. Whites can be first-class when young, like a less exotic Châteauneuf: less exotic flavour; less exotic price. Best: *Ch. d'Aquéria, Dom. de Ch. St-Roch, Dom. des Causses et St-Eymes, Dom. les Garrigues, Dom. la Fermade, Maby, Dom. de la Tour.*

MUSCAT DE BEAUMES-DE-VENISE, AC (fortified white; south) The only Rhône village growing Muscat. This golden sweet wine – a *vin doux naturel* – is supremely delicious. Grapy, fresh, rich but not cloying. Best: *Dom. de Coyeux, Dom. Durban, Jaboulet, Beaumes-de-Venise co-op.*

RASTEAU, AC (fortified red, fortified white; south) Rasteau makes a few big, port-like fortified wines – *vins doux naturels* – both red and off-white. Young reds can have a delightful raspberry scent from the Grenache Noir. The whites are made from Grenache Blanc and can be frankly unpleasant. Production is pretty small. Try *Dom. de la Soumade, Rasteau co-op.*

ST-JOSEPH, AC (red; north) Almost smooth and sweet compared to their tougher neighbours, these reds can be fairly big, fine wines, stacked with blackcurrant in good years. *Chave, Coursodon, Cuilleron, Gripa, Grippat, Jaboulet, Courbis, Philippe Faury, Didier Morion* and *Trollat* are leading names. The co-op at *St-Désirat Champagne* makes lovely Beaujolais-type St-Joseph. The white is decent and nutty. *Grippat* is good, but *Florentin*, an old-style oxidative, headbanging white, is more controversial. White Crozes is usually better value.

ST-PÉRAY, AC (white; north) This tends to be rather stolid and short on freshness. The still whites are often dull, but quality is improving from the likes of *Chaboud, Grippat, Domaine de Fauterie,* and Cornas estates such as *Clape, Lionnet* and *Voge.*

TAVEL, AC (rosé; south) The AC only applies to one colour of wine – pink. The wines are quite expensive, certainly tasty, but too big and alcoholic to be very refreshing. Any of the Rhône grapes will do,

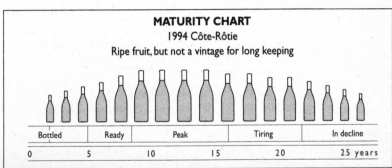

MATURITY CHART
1994 Côte-Rôtie
Ripe fruit, but not a vintage for long keeping

Bottled	Ready	Peak	Tiring	In decline

0	5	10	15	20	25 years

but generally it's Grenache-dominated, with the addition of a little Cinsaut. Best producers: *Château d'Aquéria, Château de Trinquevedel, Domaine de la Forcadière, Domaine de la Genestière.*

VACQUEYRAS, AC (red, white, rosé; south) Reds and rosés of character and structure. Some white wine is also produced, but it tends to be heavy. Cinsaut fanatic *Ch. de Montmirail* is good, as are *Clos des Cazau, Dom. de la Fourmone, Dom. la Garrigue, le Sang des Cailloux.*

VIN DE PAYS DES COLLINES RHODANIENNES (red; north) A usually impressive and expanding northern Rhône area, particularly for inexpensive, tasty Syrah-based reds, though the lighter, softer Gamays can also be good.

VIN DE PAYS DES COTEAUX DE L'ARDÈCHE (red, white; south) What vins de pays should be doing. A mixture of go-ahead co-ops and outside influences decided to plant grapes to make wine that would *sell*: delicious Nouveau-style Gamay, first-class Syrah, good Cabernet, plus Sauvignon, Pinot Noir – and Chardonnay, both for *Louis Latour's Chardonnay de l'Ardèche* and the local co-ops (which give higher quality for far lower prices).

RHÔNE VINTAGES

1996   This looks superb for the northern reds, which have bags of tannin, fruit and acidity and will last, and for the whites from the whole region, some of which are stunning. Quality is also less even in the South and the reds lack the intensity of those in the North.

1995   Top growers made very good wines, and there will be great wines in the North from those who, like Chapoutier and Chave, picked late.

1994   There were succulent reds and lively, flowery whites this year. A very good year but not a great one.

1993   Châteauneuf-du-Pape and Côtes du Rhône did best. In the North attractive whites but raw and rather dilute reds from Hermitage, Crozes and Cornas.

1992   A poor year; buy only from top growers and drink up quickly.

1991   Côte-Rôtie is generally better than in 1990. The South was only moderately good.

1990   The North was more successful than the South. Choose 1990 for the North (though Côte-Rôtie is dodgy); 1989 for the South.

1989   Some poor Hermitage and Cornas. Concentrated Châteauneuf-du-Pape.

1988   Best in Côte-Rôtie, Hermitage and Châteauneuf-du-Pape. Some is too tannic.

1987   The few good wines should have been drunk by now, though Côte-Rôtie and Hermitage provided some very good bottles, now drinking well.

1986   A rather joyless vintage for reds. Some very good Châteauneuf and Hermitage.

1985   Brilliant Côte-Rôtie, St-Joseph and Cornas. Châteauneuf is delicious and juicy.

1983   Outstanding dark, rich, complex Hermitage and very good Côte-Rôtie for keeping. Southern reds are good, though some are a bit tough.

RHÔNE PRICE GUIDES

RED

Under £4.00

Non-vintage
Côtes du Rhône Meffre £3.75 (VIC)
1996
Côtes du Rhone Domaine de la
  Mordorée ½ bottle £3.50 (LEA)
Côtes du Ventoux la Falaise £3.85 (GRE)
VdP de Vaucluse Le Petit Meyeaud £3.75
  (WS)
1995
Côtes du Rhône Domaine de la
  Renjardière £3.95 (EL)
Côtes du Ventoux la Falaise £3.92 (ROS)
Côtes du Ventoux les Cailloux £3.49 (OD)

£4.00 → £4.99

1996
VdP des Coteaux de l'Ardèche Gamay,
  Cave de St-Désirat £4.95 (YAP)
1995
Côtes du Rhône Domaine des Moulins
  £4.90 (NEZ) £4.99 (WR) £4.99 (THR)
Côtes du Rhône-Villages Château la
  Courançonne £4.99 (SAI)
Côtes du Ventoux Jaboulet £4.45 (NI)
  £4.99 (OD)
Côtes du Vivarais Domaine de Belvezet
  £4.50 (WS) £4.90 (TAN)
★ VdP des Coteaux de la Cèze Domaine
  Maby £4.95 (YAP)
★ VdP de Vaucluse Domaine de l'Ameillaud
  £4.55 (HAH)
1994
Coteaux du Tricastin Domaine de
  Grangeneuve £4.49 (ASD)
Côtes du Rhône Château St-Estève £4.50
  (SOM)
Côtes du Rhône Jaume £4.75 (WS)

£5.00 → £5.99

1996
Côtes du Rhône Château du Grand
  Moulas £5.60 (AD) £5.80 (TAN)
Côtes du Rhône Domaine de la
  Mordorée £5.95 (LEA)
Côtes du Ventoux le Mont La Vieille
  Ferme £5.00 (BIB)
1995
★ Coteaux du Tricastin Domaine de
  Grangeneuve £5.50 (YAP)
Côtes du Rhône Caves des Vignerons de
  Vacqueyras £5.50 (TAN)
Côtes du Rhône Château du Grand Moulas
  £5.45 (HAH) £5.79 (JON) £5.95 (POR)
Côtes du Rhône Château St-Estève £5.35
  (WS) £5.69 (BOT) £5.69 (WR)
Côtes du Rhône Domaine Cros de la
  Mure £5.95 (WS)
Côtes du Rhône Domaine St-Gayan,
  Roger Meffre £5.50 (YAP)
Côtes du Rhône Parallèle 45, Jaboulet
  £5.79 (NI) £5.95 (VIG) £5.99 (OD)
Côtes du Rhône-Villages Rasteau, Cave
  des Vignerons de Rasteau £5.49 (EL)
Côtes du Rhône-Villages Sablet, Château
  du Trignon £5.99 (MAJ)
1994
Côtes du Rhône-Villages Comté de
  Signargues £5.65 (SAI)
Lirac la Fermade, Domaine Maby £5.35 (WS)
1993
Coteaux du Tricastin Domaine de Vieux
  Micocoulier £5.32 (CHA)
Côtes du Rhône Jaume £5.39 (COU)
VdP de Vaucluse Château des Tours
  £5.95 (VIG)
1992
★ Côtes du Rhône Domaine de St-Georges
  £5.99 (PIP)

MERCHANTS SPECIALIZING IN THE RHÔNE
see Merchant Directory (page 413) for details

For the best ranges, try: Adnams (AD),
Bennetts (BEN), Bibendum (BIB), Anthony
Byrne (BY), Direct Wine (DI), Eldridge Pope
(EL), Ben Ellis (ELL), Farr Vintners (FA),
Gelston Castle, Justerini & Brooks, Lay &
Wheeler (LAY), Oddbins (OD), James
Nicholson (NI), Nobody Inn (NO), Raeburn
Fine Wines (RAE), Reid (REI), T&W Wines
(TW), Tanners (TAN), Ubiquitous Chip (UB),
Wine Society (WS), Yapp Bros (YAP)

£6.00 → £6.99

1996
Crozes-Hermitage Domaine des
Entrefaux £6.90 (PIP)
1995
Côtes du Rhône Belleruche, Chapoutier
£6.50 (DI) £6.50 (GRE)
★ Côtes du Rhône les Abeilles, Roux £6.55
(SUN)
Côtes du Rhône Domaine de la
Mordorée £6.66 (COU)
Côtes du Rhône-Villages Cairanne,
Domaine de l'Ameillaud £6.50 (AD)
Côtes du Rhône-Villages Château du
Grand Moulas £6.95 (AD)
Côtes du Rhône-Villages Jaboulet £6.69 (NI)
Crozes-Hermitage Cave de Vins Fins à
Tain-Hermitage £6.50 (GRE)
Crozes-Hermitage Cave des Clairmonts,
Borja £6.45 (WAI)
Vacqueyras Domaine le Sang des Cailloux
£6.90 (PIP)
1994
Côtes du Rhône Guigal £6.22 (WATT)
£6.25 (REI) £6.99 (EL) £6.99 (MAJ)
Crozes-Hermitage Cave de Vins Fins à
Tain-Hermitage £6.99 (AME)
Crozes-Hermitage Domaine des
Entrefaux £6.82 (BY)
Crozes-Hermitage les Jalets, Jaboulet
£6.75 (REI)
Lirac la Fermade, Domaine Maby £6.95
(YAP)
Lirac les Queyrades, Mejan £6.95 (AD)
1993
Côtes du Rhône Guigal £6.52 (BY) £6.99
(SOM) £6.99 (BO)
Côtes du Rhône-Villages Cairanne,
Domaine de l'Ameillaud £6.95 (ROB)
Côtes du Ventoux la Vieille Ferme £6.45
(ROB)
Crozes-Hermitage Cave de Vins Fins à
Tain-Hermitage £6.49 (POR) £6.85 (ROS)
Lirac Domaine de la Mordorée £6.75 (REI)
1990
Côtes du Rhône Cuvée Personnelle,
Pascal £6.50 (YAP)
Gigondas Domaine du Grand Montmirail
£6.85 (GAL)
1988
Côtes du Rhône Rascasses, Berard £6.31
(WAT)
Côtes du Rhône-Villages Cairanne,
Domaine de l'Ameillaud £6.50 (REI)

£7.00 → £7.99

1995
Châteauneuf-du-Pape les Galets Blancs
£7.35 (SAI)
Coteaux du Tricastin Domaine de Vieux
Micocoulier £7.38 (GN)
Côtes du Rhône Cépage Syrah, Jean
Lionnet £7.99 (OD)
Côtes du Rhône Château des Tours
£7.95 (LEA)
Côtes du Rhône-Villages Domaine Ste-
Anne £7.50 (LEA)
Côtes du Rhône-Villages Jaboulet £7.25
(STA)
Côtes du Rhône-Villages Rasteau,
Chapoutier £7.20 (TAN)
Crozes-Hermitage Pochon £7.95 (AD)
Lirac Domaine de la Mordorée £7.95 (LEA)
St-Joseph le Grand Pompée, Jaboulet
£7.99 (NI)
1994
Côtes du Rhône Coudoulet de Beaucastel
£7.78 (WATT) £7.99 (MAJ)
Côtes du Rhône Guigal £7.07 (FLE) £7.46
(PLA)
Côtes du Rhône-Villages Château du
Grand Moulas £7.19 (JON)
Côtes du Rhône-Villages Sablet, Château
du Trignon £7.51 (PLA)
Crozes-Hermitage Cave de Vins Fins à
Tain-Hermitage £7.51 (GN)
Crozes-Hermitage Cave des Clairmonts,
Borja £7.30 (HIC) £7.50 (YAP)
Crozes-Hermitage Cuvée Pierelle, Albert
Belle £7.99 (OD)
Crozes-Hermitage Domaine des
Entrefaux £7.05 (LON) £7.10 (TAN)
Crozes-Hermitage les Meysonniers,
Chapoutier £7.75 (REI)
Crozes-Hermitage Vidal Fleury £7.40 (SOM)
Gigondas Château du Trignon £7.99 (MAJ)
Vacqueyras Caves Bessac £7.20 (EL)
Vacqueyras Domaine le Clos des Cazaux
£7.90 (TAN)
1993
Côtes du Rhône Coudoulet de Beaucastel
£7.05 (WATT) £7.99 (OD)
Côtes du Rhône Guigal £7.50 (ROB)
Gigondas Domaine Raspail £7.55 (HA)
Lirac Domaine de Castel Oualou £7.95
(GRE)
Lirac Sabon £7.80 (SOM)
St-Joseph Clos de la Cuminaille, Gaillard
£7.95 (LEA)

1992
Côtes du Rhône Guigal £7.40 (UB) £7.99 (QUE)
Côtes du Rhône-Villages Rasteau, Domaine la Soumade £7.15 (WS)
1990
Gigondas Domaine du Grand Montmirail £7.49 (NEW)
Vacqueyras Domaine le Couroulu £7.99 (AME)
Vacqueyras Jaboulet £7.95 (WS)

£8.00 ➜ £8.99

1995
Côtes du Rhône-Villages Cuvée de l'Ecu, Château du Grand Moulas £8.95 (AD)
Côtes du Rhône-Villages Domaine Ste-Anne £8.50 (TAN)
Côtes du Rhône-Villages Rasteau, Domaine la Soumade £8.05 (PIP)
Crozes-Hermitage Graillot £8.25 (BY)
Vacqueyras Domaine le Clos des Cazaux £8.55 (AD)
1994
Châteauneuf-du-Pape Domaine du Père Caboche £8.49 (OD)
★ Châteauneuf-du-Pape le Chemin des Mulets £8.99 (TES)
Crozes-Hermitage Jaboulet £8.20 (HAH) £8.45 (WHI)
Crozes-Hermitage les Meysonniers, Chapoutier £8.90 (BER) £8.99 (OD)
★ Gigondas Cuvée de la Tour Sarrazine, Clos des Cazaux £8.70 (TAN)
★ Gigondas Domaine de Font-Sane £8.17 (BIB)
Lirac Domaine de la Mordorée £8.71 (COU)
St-Joseph Deschants, Chapoutier £8.70 (TAN)
St-Joseph Larmes du Père, Paret £8.99 (AME)
Vacqueyras Sélection Maître de Chais, Combe £8.60 (TAN)
1993
Gigondas Jaboulet £8.50 (NI)
Vacqueyras Cuvée des Templiers, Domaine Le Clos des Cazaux £8.75 (ROB)
Vacqueyras Domaine le Couroulu £8.80 (GN)

Stars (★) indicate wines selected by Oz Clarke in the Best Buys section which begins on page 12.

1990
Gigondas Domaine du Grand Montmirail £8.25 (YAP)
St-Joseph Cave de St-Désirat £8.99 (SO)
Vacqueyras Cuvée Spéciale, Pascal £8.50 (VIN)
1989
Gigondas Domaine de Gour de Chaulé £8.88 (HOG)

£10.00 ➜ £11.99

1995
Châteauneuf-du-Pape Chante-Cigale £10.75 (YAP)
Châteauneuf-du-Pape les Cèdres, Jaboulet £10.95 (NI)
Châteauneuf-du-Pape Vieux Mas des Papes, Brumiers £10.85 (AD)
Crozes-Hermitage Domaine de Thalabert, Jaboulet £10.00 (REI) £10.25 (NI) £10.49 (OD)
Crozes-Hermitage Graillot £10.50 (YAP)
Crozes-Hermitage les Meysonniers, Chapoutier £10.65 (AD)
St-Joseph Deschants, Chapoutier £10.95 (STA)
1994
Châteauneuf-du-Pape Chante-Cigale £10.95 (GRE) £11.49 (AME)

Châteauneuf-du-Pape Clos du Mont Olivet £11.99 (YOU)
Châteauneuf-du-Pape Domaine de Montpertuis £11.25 (EL)
Châteauneuf-du-Pape Domaine de Nalys £10.58 (COU)
Châteauneuf-du-Pape Domaine du Père Caboche £10.50 (YAP)
Châteauneuf-du-Pape Domaine la Roquette £10.90 (PIP)
Châteauneuf-du-Pape la Bernardine, Chapoutier £10.75 (REI) £11.95 (WAI)
Châteauneuf-du-Pape les Cailloux, Brunel £11.95 (POR) £11.99 (YOU)
Châteauneuf-du-Pape Lucien Barrot £11.70 (MV)

Châteauneuf-du-Pape Vieux Donjon
£11.25 (YAP)

Crozes-Hermitage Domaine de
Thalabert, Jaboulet £10.70 (TAN) £10.90
(NI) £11.30 (GAU)

Crozes-Hermitage la Guiraude, Graillot
£11.70 (LAY)

St-Joseph Delas £10.00 (WS)

St-Joseph Deschants, Chapoutier £10.90
(GAU) £11.29 (JON) £11.99 (NA)

St-Joseph Graillot £10.50 (LAY)

St-Joseph le Grand Pompée, Jaboulet
£10.50 (HAH)

1993

Châteauneuf-du-Pape Clos la Roquette,
Brunier Frères £10.60 (TAN)

Châteauneuf-du-Pape Domaine de
Beaurenard £11.65 (NEZ)

Châteauneuf-du-Pape Domaine Font de
Michelle £11.75 (WS)

Châteauneuf-du-Pape Domaine de Nalys
£10.43 (HOG) £11.50 (GRE)

Châteauneuf-du-Pape les Cailloux, Brunel
£11.99 (YOU)

Châteauneuf-du-Pape Vieux Donjon
£10.95 (YAP)

Gigondas Château du Trignon £10.33 (PLA)

Gigondas Domaine du Cayron £11.20 (AD)

Gigondas Domaine Raspail £10.65 (LAY)

1992

Châteauneuf-du-Pape Domaine Font de
Michelle £11.99 (BOT) £11.99 (AME)
£11.99 (WR) £11.99 (THR)

Crozes-Hermitage Graillot £10.97 (ELL)

Gigondas l'Oustau Fauquet, Combe et
Fille £10.60 (TAN)

St-Joseph Delas £10.99 (GN)

St-Joseph le Grand Pompée, Jaboulet
£10.44 (PLA)

Vacqueyras Château des Tours £10.25
(YAP) £10.50 (LEA)

1991

Crozes-Hermitage Domaine de
Thalabert, Jaboulet £10.50 (WS)

Gigondas l'Oustau Fauquet, Domaine la
Fourmone £10.75 (JON)

St-Joseph Clos de l'Arbalestrier, Florentin
£11.90 (GAU)

1990

Châteauneuf-du-Pape les Cèdres, Jaboulet
£11.99 (GRE)

Gigondas Guigal £10.99 (QUE)

1989

Châteauneuf-du-Pape Château de la Font
du Loup £11.00 (HOG)

1988

Gigondas Domaine les Pallières £10.50
(FLE)

1987

Cornas Jaboulet £10.20 (NI) £10.95 (WS)

St-Joseph Deschants, Chapoutier £10.50
(SOM)

1985

Crozes-Hermitage Jaboulet £11.50 (REI)

1983

Cornas Delas £11.50 (REI)

£12.00 ➜ £13.99

1995

Châteauneuf-du-Pape Clos des Papes,
Avril £13.02 (RAE) £13.51 (FA)

Châteauneuf-du-Pape Domaine de la
Mordorée £13.95 (LEA)

Châteauneuf-du-Pape Domaine du Vieux
Télégraphe £13.22 (ELL)

Châteauneuf-du-Pape Vieux Donjon
£12.75 (YAP)

St-Joseph Chave £13.50 (YAP)

St-Joseph Grippat £12.75 (YAP)

1994

Châteauneuf-du-Pape Château la Nerthe
£12.99 (NI)

Châteauneuf-du-Pape Delas £12.93 (PEN)

Châteauneuf-du-Pape Domaine de
Beaurenard £12.99 (NI)

Châteauneuf-du-Pape Domaine du Vieux
Télégraphe £12.45 (LAY) £12.95 (POR)

Châteauneuf-du-Pape la Bernardine,
Chapoutier £12.95 (DI) £13.90 (GAU)

Châteauneuf-du-Pape les Cèdres, Jaboulet
£12.95 (VIG)

Châteauneuf-du-Pape les Galéans, Brunier
£13.75 (BER)

Cornas Chapoutier £12.95 (WAI)

Cornas Cuvée des Coteaux, Robert
Michel £13.95 (HIC)

Cornas la Chaillot, Allemand £12.99 (RAE)

Cornas La Geynale, Robert Michel £13.90
(TAN)

St-Joseph Clos de la Cuminaille, Gaillard
£12.95 (ROB)

1993

Châteauneuf-du-Pape Château de
Beaucastel £13.51 (FA) £13.75 (NI)

Châteauneuf-du-Pape Château Fortia
£12.24 (AV)

Châteauneuf-du-Pape Domaine Grand
Veneur £12.71 (GN)

Châteauneuf-du-Pape Domaine du Vieux
Télégraphe £12.10 (TAN) £13.35 (DI)

Côte-Rôtie Gaillard £12.95 (LEA)
Gigondas Domaine les Pallières £12.50 (PIP) £12.99 (GN)
1992
Châteauneuf-du-Pape Château Fortia £12.50 (POR)
Châteauneuf-du-Pape Domaine du Vieux Télégraphe £12.25 (SOM) £13.59 (JON)
Cornas Chapoutier £12.66 (HOG)
Cornas la Chaillot, Allemand £13.50 (STA)
1991
Châteauneuf-du-Pape Château de Beaucastel £12.25 (REI) £13.95 (LAY)
Cornas Cuvée des Coteaux, Robert Michel £12.90 (TAN)
Côtes du Rhône Château de Fonsalette £13.50 (GAU)
St-Joseph Clos de l'Arbalestrier, Florentin £13.98 (RAE)
1990
Châteauneuf-du-Pape les Cèdres, Jaboulet £13.95 (STA)
1989
Cornas Jaboulet £13.95 (GRE)
1988
Hermitage Chapoutier £13.40 (BER)
1987
Cornas Delas £12.93 (PEN)
1984
Châteauneuf-du-Pape Château Fortia £13.50 (REI)
Cornas Michel £13.50 (GAU)

£14.00 → £15.99

1995
Châteauneuf-du-Pape Château de Beaucastel £15.45 (ELL)
Châteauneuf-du-Pape Clos des Papes, Avril £14.10 (ELL)
1994
Châteauneuf-du-Pape Clos des Papes, Avril £15.95 (VIG)
Cornas les Ruchets, Colombo £15.75 (BAN)
Cornas Noël Verset £14.70 (GAU)
Côte-Rôtie Cuvée du Plessy, Gilles Barge £14.85 (REI)
Côte-Rôtie René Rostaing £15.50 (REI)
Côtes du Rhône Château de Fonsalette £15.95 (DI)
1993
Châteauneuf-du-Pape Château de Beaucastel £14.00 (BUT) £14.85 (GAU) £14.99 (OD)
Châteauneuf-du-Pape Clos des Papes, Avril £14.50 (WS) £15.95 (RES)

Châteauneuf-du-Pape Domaine du Vieux Télégraphe £14.20 (PIP) £15.50 (STA) £15.95 (RES)
Châteauneuf-du-Pape la Bernardine, Chapoutier £14.75 (GRE)
Côtes du Rhône Château de Fonsalette £15.90 (GAU)
1992
Châteauneuf-du-Pape Château de Beaucastel £14.85 (GAU) £14.95 (NI) £14.99 (MAJ) £14.99 (BOT) £15.99 (RAE)
Châteauneuf-du-Pape la Bernardine, Chapoutier £15.80 (PLA)
Cornas Clape £15.95 (DI)
Côte-Rôtie Jamet £15.00 (BIB)
1991
Cornas Noël Verset £14.95 (RAE)
Côte-Rôtie Barge £15.99 (FUL)
Côte-Rôtie Gaillard £14.99 (FLE)
1990
Cornas Jaboulet £14.39 (PLA) £14.50 (WS)
Cornas Rochepertuis, Jean Lionnet £15.00 (BER)
Côtes du Rhône Château de Fonsalette £15.90 (HOG)
Crozes-Hermitage les Meysonniers, Chapoutier £14.50 (REI)
Gigondas Domaine les Pallières £14.50 (REI)
St-Joseph Clos de l'Arbalestrier, Florentin £14.50 (WS)
1989
Châteauneuf-du-Pape Château Fortia £14.95 (RES)
Cornas Rochepertuis, Jean Lionnet £15.30 (BER)
Côte-Rôtie Seigneur de Maugiron, Delas £15.60 (FOR)
Hermitage Chapoutier £14.25 (BER)
1988
Châteauneuf-du-Pape les Cèdres, Jaboulet £14.95 (STA)
Côte-Rôtie Chapoutier £14.90 (BER)
Hermitage Marquise de la Tourette, Delas £15.12 (FOR)
1986
Côte-Rôtie les Jumelles, Jaboulet £14.90 (HOG)
Hermitage Domaine des Remizières £15.47 (BUT)
1985
Châteauneuf-du-Pape Domaine de Mont-Redon £14.65 (REI)
Crozes-Hermitage Domaine de Thalabert, Jaboulet £15.00 (HOG) £15.96 (BUT)

£16.00 → £19.99

1995
Côte-Rôtie Burgaud £19.25 (YAP)
Hermitage la Sizeranne, Chapoutier £19.99 (OD)

1994
Châteauneuf-du-Pape Château de Beaucastel £16.50 (AD) £17.90 (TAN) £17.96 (COU) £18.99 (RAE) £19.39 (WATT) £19.39 (BUT) £19.39 (FA)
Cornas Chapoutier £16.89 (NA)
Cornas Clape £16.75 (YAP) £16.95 (VIG)
Côte-Rôtie Barge £17.30 (TAN)
Côte-Rôtie Chapoutier £18.60 (SOM)
Côte-Rôtie Côte Blonde, René Rostaing £19.50 (REI)
Côte-Rôtie Jasmin £19.75 (YAP)
Côtes du Rhône Château de Fonsalette £19.95 (VIG)
Hermitage la Sizeranne, Chapoutier £16.85 (REI) £19.00 (TAN)
St-Joseph Chave £16.50 (VIG)

1993
Châteauneuf-du-Pape Château de Beaucastel £17.50 (ROB)
Châteauneuf-du-Pape Clos des Papes, Avril £17.50 (ROB)
Châteauneuf-du-Pape Clos Pignan, Reynaud £17.90 (GAU)
Côte-Rôtie Champet £17.80 (PIP)
Côte-Rôtie Clusel-Roch £18.80 (COU)
Côte-Rôtie Guigal £17.99 (UN)
Côte-Rôtie Jamet £16.00 (BIB) £17.99 (MAJ)
Côte-Rôtie René Rostaing £17.59 (YOU) £18.95 (NI)

1992
Châteauneuf-du-Pape Château de Beaucastel £18.50 (MV) £18.80 (WATT)
Châteauneuf-du-Pape Château Fortia £16.75 (QUE)
Châteauneuf-du-Pape Clos des Papes, Avril £16.75 (LAY)
Châteauneuf-du-Pape Domaine Font de Michelle £18.85 (UB)
Châteauneuf-du-Pape Domaine du Vieux Télégraphe £16.95 (RES) £17.50 (ROB)
Cornas Clape £17.95 (VIG)
Cornas Noël Verset £16.85 (AD)
Côte-Rôtie Brune et Blonde, Guigal £17.83 (BY) £19.90 (SOM)
Côte-Rôtie Chapoutier £19.95 (VIG)
Côte-Rôtie Guigal £19.98 (QUE)
Côte-Rôtie René Rostaing £18.95 (LAY)
Hermitage Guigal £18.40 (BY)

1991
Châteauneuf-du-Pape Château Pignan £18.50 (VIG)
Côte-Rôtie Brune et Blonde, Guigal £18.90 (FA) £19.56 (LON)

Côte-Rôtie Brune et Blonde, Vidal-Fleury £18.95 (GRE)
Côte-Rôtie Gaillard £17.90 (BER)
Côte-Rôtie Seigneur de Maugiron, Delas £18.00 (WS)
Côtes du Rhône Château de Fonsalette £18.65 (UB)
Hermitage Domaine des Remizières £17.00 (BIB) £17.50 (RAE)
Hermitage Guigal £18.60 (SOM)
Hermitage la Sizeranne, Chapoutier £18.75 (SOM)

1990
Châteauneuf-du-Pape Domaine Font de Michelle £16.50 (REI)
Côte-Rôtie Chapoutier £18.00 (BER)
Côte-Rôtie Guigal £18.50 (GRE)
Crozes-Hermitage Graillot £16.94 (BUT)
Hermitage Sorrel £19.95 (RES)

1989
Côte-Rôtie les Jumelles, Jaboulet £19.95 (GRE)
Côte-Rôtie Seigneur de Maugiron, Delas £19.39 (PEN)
Hermitage la Sizeranne, Chapoutier £18.80 (GAU)

1988
Côte-Rôtie Barge £17.70 (GAU)
Côte-Rôtie la Viaillère, Dervieux-Thaize £19.20 (GAU)
Côte-Rôtie les Jumelles, Jaboulet £17.60 (HOG)
Hermitage Desmeure £18.90 (GAU)

1987
Côte-Rôtie Côte Brune, Gentaz-Dervieux £18.25 (JON)
Hermitage la Chapelle, Jaboulet £18.00 (STA)

1986
Châteauneuf-du-Pape Château Fortia £18.50 (REI)

Côte-Rôtie Côte Brune, Gentaz-
Dervieux £17.95 (RAE)
Hermitage Domaine des Remizières
£19.00 (VIG)
1985
Châteauneuf-du-Pape Cuvée Etienne
Gonnet, Domaine Font de Michelle
£17.85 (REI)
St-Joseph le Grand Pompée, Jaboulet
£17.50 (REI)
1984
Châteauneuf-du-Pape Château Rayas
£19.99 (RAE)
Côte-Rôtie la Chevalière d'Ampuis,
Jasmin £17.50 (JON)
1983
Cornas Clape £19.99 (SAT)
Côte-Rôtie les Jumelles, Jaboulet £16.50
(GAU)
Hermitage Jaboulet £19.50 (HOG)
1982
Cornas Clape £19.82 (SAT)
Côte-Rôtie Champet £18.42 (SAT)
1979
Châteauneuf-du-Pape les Cèdres, Jaboulet
£18.50 (BU)
1978
Gigondas Jaboulet £19.50 (REI)

£20.00 → £24.99

1995
Côte-Rôtie Jasmin £21.00 (YAP)
Crozes-Hermitage la Guiraude, Graillot
£20.54 (BY)
Hermitage Grippat £21.75 (YAP)
Hermitage la Sizeranne, Chapoutier
£24.60 (BEN)
1994
Côte-Rôtie Chapoutier £20.90 (GAU)
£22.50 (VIG)
Côte-Rôtie la Landonne, René Rostaing
£23.90 (NI)
Hermitage la Chapelle, Jaboulet £22.95
(REI) £24.90 (GAU) £24.99 (OD)
1993
Cornas les Ruchets, Colombo £22.50 (NI)
Côte-Rôtie Côte Blonde, René Rostaing
£24.95 (NI)
Hermitage la Sizeranne, Chapoutier
£20.75 (DI)
1992
Côte-Rôtie Gentaz-Dervieux £22.30 (GAU)
Côte-Rôtie Guigal £20.99 (AME) £21.30
(WHI) £21.45 (UB)
Hermitage Chave £23.50 (WS)

1991
Côte-Rôtie Brune et Blonde, Guigal
£23.50 (REI)
Côte-Rôtie Côte Brune, Gentaz-
Dervieux £21.95 (RAE)
Hermitage la Chapelle, Jaboulet £20.50 (REI)
Hermitage la Sizeranne, Chapoutier
£21.50 (GAU) £22.52 (ELL) £24.95 (NA)
1990
Châteauneuf-du-Pape Château de
Beaucastel £23.50 (FLE)
Côte-Rôtie Burgaud £22.50 (BER)
Côte-Rôtie Chapoutier £23.95 (DI)
Côte-Rôtie René Rostaing £20.86 (BUT)
Crozes-Hermitage Domaine de
Thalabert, Jaboulet £22.69 (NO)
Hermitage Albert Belle £21.50 (GAU)
1989
Côte-Rôtie Brune et Blonde, Champet
£21.99 (YOU)
Côte-Rôtie les Jumelles, Jaboulet £22.92
(PLA)
Crozes-Hermitage la Guiraude, Graillot
£22.91 (NO)
Hermitage Guigal £21.95 (DI)
Hermitage Marquise de la Tourette, Delas
£20.56 (PEN)
1988
Côte-Rôtie Burgaud £24.20 (GAU)
Côte-Rôtie Champet £24.50 (NO)
Hermitage la Chapelle, Jaboulet £20.30
(GAU)
1986
Côte-Rôtie Côte Brune, Gentaz-
Dervieux £23.79 (BUT)
Hermitage la Chapelle, Jaboulet £22.62
(HOG)
1985
Cornas de Barjac £22.00 (YOU)
Côtes du Rhône Château de Fonsalette
£24.28 (BUT)
Hermitage Cuvée des Miaux, Ferraton
£20.00 (YOU) £20.86 (BUT)
Hermitage Guigal £22.00 (JON)
Hermitage la Chapelle, Jaboulet £24.95 (DI)
Hermitage Sorrel £20.86 (BUT)

> *Please remember that*
> **Webster's** *is a price*
> *guide and not a price list. It*
> *is not meant to replace up-*
> *to-date*
> *merchants' lists.*

1983
Côte-Rôtie Brune et Blonde, Guigal
£21.84 (FA)
Côte-Rôtie Guigal £21.84 (BUT)
Hermitage Guigal £22.75 (JON)
1982
Côte-Rôtie Brune et Blonde, Guigal
£22.75 (JON)
1980
Hermitage la Chapelle, Jaboulet £23.95
(ROB)
1979
Châteauneuf-du-Pape Château Fortia
£22.50 (REI)
Hermitage Guigal £22.50 (REI)

£25.00 → £29.99

1995
Côte-Rôtie Chapoutier £26.90 (BEN)
Hermitage la Chapelle, Jaboulet £25.00
(REI) £26.75 (NI)
1994
Côte-Rôtie la Landonne, René Rostaing
£25.79 (YOU)
Hermitage Chave £28.50 (WAI) £28.50 (REI)
Hermitage la Chapelle, Jaboulet £25.80
(NI) £28.50 (GRE)
Hermitage le Gréal, Sorrel £25.90 (GAU)
1993
Côte-Rôtie Côte Blonde, René Rostaing
£25.29 (YOU) £26.95 (VIG) £26.95 (LAY)
Côte-Rôtie la Landonne, René Rostaing
£26.95 (VIG) £27.95 (LAY)
Hermitage Chave £26.75 (YAP)
1992
Côte-Rôtie Chapoutier £25.00 (RES)
Côte-Rôtie Gentaz-Dervieux £26.50 (ROB)
Hermitage Chave £29.50 (YAP) £29.95 (VIG)
Hermitage la Sizeranne, Chapoutier
£25.00 (GRE)
1991
Hermitage Chave £29.95 (DI)
Hermitage Guigal £27.96 (TW)
Hermitage la Chapelle, Jaboulet £27.20
(TAN) £27.90 (GAU)
1990
Châteauneuf-du-Pape Domaine du Vieux
Télégraphe £25.85 (WY) £28.69 (BUT)
Côte-Rôtie Brune et Blonde, Vidal-Fleury
£26.33 (NO)
Côte-Rôtie Chapoutier £28.95 (NA)
Côte-Rôtie la Chatillonne Côte Blonde,
Vidal-Fleury £26.75 (GRE)
Hermitage Marquise de la Tourette, Delas
£25.50 (GAU)

1989
Châteauneuf-du-Pape Château Rayas
£28.20 (BUT)
Cornas Clape £25.85 (UB)
Côte-Rôtie Jamet £26.73 (BUT)
1988
Châteauneuf-du-Pape Château de
Beaucastel £28.00 (TAN)
Côte-Rôtie Jamet £25.75 (BUT)
1985
Châteauneuf-du-Pape Château Fortia
£26.50 (REI)
Côte-Rôtie Jasmin £25.75 (BUT)
Côte-Rôtie les Jumelles, Jaboulet £29.38
(WY)
Hermitage la Chapelle, Jaboulet £28.75 (REI)
1983
Côte-Rôtie Brune et Blonde, Guigal
£29.38 (WY)
1982
Cornas Clape £27.50 (REI)
Côte-Rôtie Brune et Blonde, Guigal
£25.50 (REI)
1978
Hermitage Chapoutier £28.00 (REI)
1976
Châteauneuf-du-Pape Château Fortia
£26.50 (REI)
1975
Côte-Rôtie Brune et Blonde, Guigal
£26.50 (REI)

£30.00 → £49.99

1995
Hermitage Chave £32.50 (YAP)
Hermitage la Chapelle, Jaboulet £31.63 (FA)
1994
Châteauneuf-du-Pape Château Rayas
£36.95 (DI)
Hermitage Chapoutier £31.96 (AV)
1993
Châteauneuf-du-Pape Château Rayas
£32.30 (AD) £39.36 (TW) £39.90 (GAU)
1992
Côte-Rôtie la Landonne, Guigal £44.61 (BY)
Côte-Rôtie la Mouline, Guigal £44.61 (BY)
1990
Châteauneuf-du-Pape Château de
Beaucastel £31.63 (FA) £36.95 (BEN)
£40.44 (BUT)
1989
Châteauneuf-du-Pape Château de
Beaucastel £38.50 (REI) £42.59 (WATT)
£43.38 (FA)
Hermitage la Chapelle, Jaboulet £45.34 (FA)

1988
Châteauneuf-du-Pape Château de
   Beaucastel £40.00 (ROB)
Châteauneuf-du-Pape Château Pignan
   £39.85 (REI)
Côte-Rôtie les Jumelles, Jaboulet £30.00
   (VIG)
Hermitage Chave £30.00 (WS)
Hermitage la Chapelle, Jaboulet £45.37 (NO)
1986
Châteauneuf-du-Pape Château de
   Beaucastel £31.63 (FA) £36.95 (LAY)
Côte-Rôtie Jasmin £35.00 (AD)
1985
Châteauneuf-du-Pape Château de
   Beaucastel £36.52 (BUT) £39.50 (REI)
Cornas Clape £30.65 (BUT)
Cornas Jaboulet £30.00 (VIG)
Côte-Rôtie Brune et Blonde, Guigal
   £31.63 (BUT)
Hermitage Chave £35.00 (WS) £36.50
   (JON) £39.46 (FA) £40.44 (BUT)
Hermitage la Chapelle, Jaboulet £37.01
   (NO) £40.44 (BUT) £47.00 (WY)
Hermitage le Gréal, Sorrel £30.65 (BUT)
1983
Côte-Rôtie Champet £40.00 (VIG)
Côte-Rôtie les Jumelles, Jaboulet £35.25
   (WY)
Hermitage Grippat £32.90 (WY)
Hermitage la Chapelle, Jaboulet £43.99
   (NO) £49.25 (BUT)
1981
Châteauneuf-du-Pape Château de
   Beaucastel £47.50 (RES)
1978
Châteauneuf-du-Pape les Cèdres, Jaboulet
   £35.00 (WS)
Cornas Jaboulet £35.00 (WS)
1967
Châteauneuf-du-Pape la Grappe des
   Papes, Jaboulet £46.50 (REI)

£50.00 → £99.99

1994
Côte-Rôtie la Mordorée, Chapoutier
   £56.75 (BEN)
1992
Côte-Rôtie la Landonne, Guigal £66.88 (FA)
Côte-Rôtie la Mordorée, Chapoutier
   £51.95 (VIG)
Ermitage le Pavillon, Chapoutier £69.95
   (VIG) £79.50 (BEN)
1991
Côte-Rôtie la Landonne, Guigal £76.00 (EL)

1989
Châteauneuf-du-Pape Château de
   Beaucastel £50.23 (BUT) £59.50 (RES)
Châteauneuf-du-Pape Château Rayas
   £82.75 (UB)
1987
Côte-Rôtie la Mouline, Guigal £89.40 (FA)
   £90.73 (NO)
1986
Côte-Rôtie la Landonne, Guigal £99.19
   (BUT)
Côte-Rôtie la Mouline, Guigal £76.00 (EL)
1985
Châteauneuf-du-Pape Château de
   Beaucastel £72.30 (UB)
Châteauneuf-du-Pape Château Rayas
   £70.50 (FA)
Hermitage Chave £53.96 (NO)
1983
Hermitage la Chapelle, Jaboulet £59.95 (UB)
1981
Côte-Rôtie la Landonne, Guigal £69.82 (FA)
1978
Châteauneuf-du-Pape Château de
   Beaucastel £70.50 (FA)
Côte-Rôtie Champet £56.50 (REI)
Côte-Rôtie Jasmin £75.00 (REI)
Hermitage Guigal £75.00 (REI)
1976
Hermitage la Chapelle, Jaboulet £65.00
   (REI)
1972
Hermitage Chave £75.00 (VIG)
1967
Hermitage la Chapelle, Jaboulet £52.50
   (REI)
1962
Côte-Rôtie les Jumelles, Jaboulet £70.50
   (TW)
1961
Châteauneuf-du-Pape Domaine de Mont-
   Redon £65.50 (REI)

£100.00 → £199.99

1991
Côte-Rôtie la Landonne, Guigal £153.04
   (FA)
1990
Côte-Rôtie la Mouline, Guigal £162.84
   (FA) £175.00 (VIG)
1986
Côte-Rôtie la Landonne, Guigal £100.00
   (REI) £117.50 (TW) £120.00 (ROB)
Côte-Rôtie la Mouline, Guigal £100.00
   (REI) £117.50 (TW)

1983
Côte-Rôtie la Mouline, Guigal £172.40
(NO) £175.00 (REI)
1982
Côte-Rôtie la Mouline, Guigal £135.42
(FA) £143.25 (BUT)
1981
Côte-Rôtie la Landonne, Guigal £132.89
(NO)
1978
Châteauneuf-du-Pape Château de
Beaucastel £125.00 (RES)
Hermitage Chave £135.00 (ROB)
Hermitage la Chapelle, Jaboulet £167.73
(FA)
1971
Hermitage Chave £136.50 (REI)
1955
Côte-Rôtie les Jumelles, Jaboulet £188.00
(TW)

£200.00 → £299.99

1985
Côte-Rôtie la Landonne, Guigal £255.86
(BUT)
Côte-Rôtie la Mouline, Guigal £217.38
(FA) £225.00 (REI) £255.86 (BUT)
1983
Côte-Rôtie la Landonne, Guigal £211.79
(FA) £265.00 (RES)
Côte-Rôtie la Mouline, Guigal £211.79 (FA)
1976
Côte-Rôtie la Mouline, Guigal £246.75 (FA)

c. £776.00

1961
Hermitage la Chapelle, Jaboulet £775.50
(FA)

WHITE

Under £6.00

1996
VdP des Coteaux de l'Ardèche Viognier,
Duboeuf £5.90 (NEZ)
1995
Côtes du Rhône Jaume £4.95 (WS)
1994
VdP des Coteaux de l'Ardèche
Chardonnay, Latour £5.30 (HOG) £5.75
(POR) £5.79 (JON)
1992
Lirac la Fermade, Domaine Maby £5.70
(WS)

£6.00 → £7.99

1996
Côtes du Rhône Domaine St-Gayan,
Roger Meffre £6.25 (YAP)
Côtes du Rhône Seguret, Château
Goudrey £6.00 (BIB)
Côtes du Rhône-Villages Blanc de Blancs,
Château du Grand Moulas £6.95 (AD)
1995
Côtes du Rhône Château St Estève £6.95
(AD)
Côtes du Rhône Guigal £6.99 (UN)
Crozes-Hermitage Cave des Clairmonts,
Borja £7.75 (YAP)
Crozes-Hermitage Delas £6.65 (FOR)
Crozes-Hermitage Domaine des
Entrefaux £7.30 (PIP)
Lirac la Fermade, Domaine Maby £6.75
(YAP)
VdP des Coteaux de l'Ardèche
Chardonnay, Latour £6.25 (VIG)
1994
Côtes du Rhône Domaine Pélaquié £7.00
(BIB)
Côtes du Rhône Guigal £7.49 (JON)
Crozes-Hermitage Domaine des
Entrefaux £7.01 (BY) £7.10 (TAN)
VdP des Coteaux de l'Ardèche
Chardonnay, Latour £6.10 (FOR)

£8.00 → £9.99

1995
Côtes du Rhône Château des Tours
£8.00 (BIB)
Côtes du Rhône Coudoulet de Beaucastel
£9.40 (FA)
Crozes-Hermitage la Mule Blanche,
Jaboulet £8.99 (OD) £9.70 (GAU)
St-Joseph le Grand Pompée, Jaboulet
£8.95 (REI)
1994
Côtes du Rhône Coudoulet de Beaucastel
£9.11 (FA) £9.25 (REI)
Crozes-Hermitage la Mule Blanche,
Jaboulet £9.75 (NI) £9.90 (TAN)
St-Joseph Chapoutier £9.99 (DI)
St-Péray Thières £8.95 (YAP)

> *In each price band wines
> are listed in vintage order.
> Within each vintage they
> are listed in A–Z order.*

1993
Côtes du Rhône Château des Tours
£8.50 (VIG)
Côtes du Rhône Coudoulet de Beaucastel
£9.99 (OD)
Côtes du Rhône Viognier, Domaine Ste-
Anne £9.95 (LEA)
1992
St-Joseph Courbis £9.60 (ROS)

£10.00 ➜ £14.99

1996
Châteauneuf-du-Pape Château Fortia
£12.24 (AV)
Châteauneuf-du-Pape les Cèdres, Jaboulet
£12.95 (STA)
Côtes du Rhône Coudoulet de Beaucastel
£10.60 (TAN)
Crozes-Hermitage Graillot £10.25 (YAP)
1995
Châteauneuf-du-Pape Château Fortia
£12.82 (ROS)
Châteauneuf-du-Pape Domaine Font de
Michelle £12.60 (WS)
Châteauneuf-du-Pape Domaine Grand
Veneur £12.71 (GN)
Châteauneuf-du-Pape Domaine de Nalys
£11.36 (COU)
Châteauneuf-du-Pape Domaine du Père
Caboche £11.25 (YAP)
Châteauneuf-du-Pape les Cèdres, Jaboulet
£10.95 (REI)
Condrieu Coteaux du Chéry, Clusel-
Roch ½ bottle £11.25 (REI)
Côtes du Rhône Coudoulet de Beaucastel
£12.35 (BEN)
Côtes du Rhône Viognier, Dumazet
£13.50 (BIB)
St-Joseph Grippat £12.25 (YAP)
1994
Châteauneuf-du-Pape Clos la Roquette,
Brunier Frères £13.20 (LAY)
Châteauneuf-du-Pape Domaine du Vieux
Télégraphe £14.60 (AD)
Châteauneuf-du-Pape les Cèdres, Jaboulet
£12.45 (AD)
Condrieu Coteaux du Chéry, Clusel-
Roch ½ bottle £10.95 (LEA)
Côtes du Rhône Château St Estève
£11.35 (SOM)
Côtes du Rhône Coudoulet de Beaucastel
£10.75 (AD) £10.95 (VIG)
Crozes-Hermitage la Mule Blanche,
Jaboulet £10.75 (AD)
St-Joseph Grippat £11.95 (YAP)

1993
Châteauneuf-du-Pape Domaine de Nalys
£11.95 (GRE)
Côtes du Rhône Château de Fonsalette
£12.95 (VIG)
1992
Côtes du Rhône Viognier, Domaine Ste-
Anne £14.30 (TAN)
Hermitage la Tourette, Delas £14.78 (FOR)
1991
St-Joseph Clos de l'Arbalestrier, Florentin
£11.90 (GAU)
1989
Hermitage Chante-Alouette, Chapoutier
£11.85 (BER)
1986
St-Joseph Clos de l'Arbalestrier, Florentin
£11.45 (RAE) £13.30 (UB)

£15.00 ➜ £19.99

1996
Condrieu Dumazet £19.00 (BIB)
1995
Châteauneuf-du-Pape Château de
Beaucastel £16.94 (FA) £18.30 (TAN)
Châteauneuf-du-Pape Domaine du Vieux
Télégraphe £15.10 (TAN) £16.49 (JON)
Condrieu Coteaux de Chéry, Perret
£19.50 (WS)
Condrieu Guigal £19.99 (UN)
Condrieu les Cepes du Nebadon, Paret
£19.75 (AD)
1994
Châteauneuf-du-Pape Château de
Beaucastel £17.92 (FA)
Châteauneuf-du-Pape Domaine du Vieux
Télégraphe £16.20 (SOM)
Condrieu Chapoutier £18.80 (SOM)
Condrieu Coteaux du Chéry, Clusel-
Roch £19.95 (LEA)
Hermitage Chante-Alouette, Chapoutier
£17.80 (TAN)
Hermitage Chevalier de Stérimberg,
Jaboulet £16.50 (TAN) £16.75 (NI)
Hermitage Grippat £18.50 (YAP)
Hermitage la Tourette, Delas £17.50 (WS)
£19.39 (PEN)
1993
Châteauneuf-du-Pape Château de
Beaucastel £17.92 (FA) £18.95 (VIG)
Condrieu les Cepes du Nebadon, Paret
£19.50 (POR)
Condrieu Pinchon £18.95 (RAE)
Hermitage Chante-Alouette, Chapoutier
£19.95 (AD)

1992
Condrieu Coteaux de Chéry, Perret
£18.59 (NI)
Condrieu Delas £18.57 (PEN)
Condrieu Guigal £19.46 (BY)
Hermitage Chevalier de Stérimberg,
Jaboulet £16.44 (PLA)
Hermitage Guigal £18.40 (BY)
1990
Hermitage Desmeure £17.50 (GAU)
Hermitage Domaine des Remizières
£17.50 (RAE)
Hermitage la Tourette, Delas £19.39
(PEN)
1989
Châteauneuf-du-Pape Clos des Papes,
Avril £19.39 (BUT)
1986
Condrieu Château du Rozay £18.60 (FA)
Hermitage Domaine des Remizières
£15.95 (RAE) £17.45 (UB)

£20.00 → £29.99

Non-vintage
Hermitage Chante-Alouette, Chapoutier
£25.00 (VIG)
1995
Condrieu Barge £20.60 (TAN)
Condrieu Chapoutier £22.75 (DI) £24.99
(NA)
Condrieu Côte Fournet, Dumazet £28.50
(BIB)
Condrieu Coteau de Vernon, Vernay
£27.75 (YAP)
Condrieu Coteaux de Chéry, Perret
£21.20 (AD)
Condrieu la Bonnette, Rostaing £23.90
(NI)
Condrieu les Chaillets Vieilles Vignes,
Cuilleron £28.99 (YOU)
Condrieu Vernay £21.75 (YAP)
Hermitage Chave £29.75 (YAP)
1994
Condrieu Chapoutier £22.95 (VIG) £24.55
(BEN)
Condrieu Château du Rozay £22.75 (YAP)
Condrieu Guigal £21.85 (SOM)
Condrieu la Bonnette, Rostaing £21.99
(YOU) £26.22 (AD)
Hermitage Chante-Alouette, Chapoutier
£22.50 (BER)
Hermitage Chave £28.25 (YAP) £29.95
(VIG)
Hermitage les Rocoules, Sorrel £23.75
(GAU)

1993
Condrieu Chapoutier £26.95 (GRE)
Condrieu les Cepes du Nebadon, Paret
£21.88 (NO)
Hermitage Chante-Alouette, Chapoutier
£20.75 (UB) £21.65 (DI) £22.50 (GRE)
1992
Condrieu Chapoutier £22.95 (STA)
1991
Condrieu Coteaux de Chéry, Perret
£22.27 (NO)
Hermitage Chante-Alouette, Chapoutier
£20.35 (GAU)
Hermitage Chave £28.00 (WS)
Hermitage Guigal £23.38 (TW)
1990
Châteauneuf-du-Pape Roussanne Vieilles
Vignes, Château de Beaucastel £25.30
(AD)
Hermitage Chante-Alouette, Chapoutier
£21.90 (GAU)
1989
Châteauneuf-du-Pape Château Rayas
£27.90 (GAU)
Condrieu Guigal £27.61 (TW)
1988
Châteauneuf-du-Pape Clos des Papes,
Avril £29.95 (VIG)
Condrieu Guigal £28.20 (BUT)
1987
Châteauneuf-du-Pape Château de
Beaucastel £24.50 (REI)
1986
Hermitage Grippat £24.95 (BEN)
1985
Hermitage Chante-Alouette, Chapoutier
£20.50 (JON)
1981
Hermitage Guigal £26.50 (JON)

£30.00 → £39.99

1994
Château Grillet £30.75 (YAP)
Châteauneuf-du-Pape Château Rayas
£39.36 (TW)
Châteauneuf-du-Pape Roussanne Vieilles
Vignes, Château de Beaucastel £31.63 (FA)
1993
Châteauneuf-du-Pape Roussanne Vieilles
Vignes, Château de Beaucastel £30.50
(REI) £30.65 (FA)
Condrieu Vernay £30.58 (UB)
1992
Châteauneuf-du-Pape Château Rayas
£32.00 (WS)

1990
Côtes du Rhône Viognier, Dumazet
£30.65 (BUT)
1989
Hermitage Chave £34.95 (BEN)
1985
Hermitage Chante-Alouette, Chapoutier
£30.00 (VIG)
1983
Hermitage Chave £31.50 (JON)

c. £45.00

1978
Châteauneuf-du-Pape Château Rayas
£45.00 (REI)
1955
Hermitage la Tourette, Delas £45.00 (REI)

£50.00 → £59.99

1993
Ermitage de l'Orée Hermitage,
Chapoutier £55.00 (VIG)
1989
Château Grillet £59.95 (UB)
1982
Châteauneuf-du-Pape Château Rayas
£50.00 (VIG)

ROSÉ

Under £6.00

1996
Côtes du Rhône Domaine de la
Mordorée à Tavel £5.95 (LEA)

£6.00 → £7.99

1996
Tavel la Forcadière, Domaine Maby £7.50
(YAP)
1995
Tavel la Forcadière, Domaine Maby £6.95
(WS)
1994
Lirac Rosé la Fermade, Domaine Maby
£6.50 (YAP)
Tavel Château de Trinquevedel £6.14
(HOG) £6.45 (EL) £6.75 (GRE) £7.99 (GN)

£9.00 → £9.99

1996
Tavel Domaine de la Mordorée £9.50
(LEA)
1994
Tavel l'Espiègle, Jaboulet £9.95 (UB)

SPARKLING

c. £9.50

Non-vintage
Clairette de Die Brut Archard-Vincent
£9.25 (YAP)

FORTIFIED

Under £7.00

1996
Muscat de Beaumes-de-Venise Durban ½
bottle £6.75 (YAP)
1995
Muscat de Beaumes-de-Venise Domaine
de Coyeux £5.56 (AV)
Muscat de Beaumes-de-Venise Jaboulet ½
bottle £6.50 (VIG)
1994
Muscat de Beaumes-de-Venise Jaboulet ½
bottle £6.90 (WS)
1992
Muscat de Beaumes-de-Venise Domaine
de Coyeux ½ bottle £6.75 (AD)

£7.00 → £9.99

Non-vintage
Muscat de Beaumes-de-Venise Cave Co-
op. de Beaumes-de-Venise £8.99 (WHI)
Muscat de Beaumes de Venise Cave des
Vignerons à Vacqueyras £9.49 (POR)
1994
Muscat de Beaumes-de-Venise Domaine
de Coyeux £9.95 (GRE)
1993
Muscat de Beaumes-de-Venise Cave Co-
op. de Beaumes-de-Venise £7.99 (OD)
Muscat de Beaumes de Venise Cave des
Vignerons à Vacqueyras £8.95 (AD)

£10.00 → £13.99

1996
Muscat de Beaumes-de-Venise Domaine
de Durban £10.95 (YAP)
Muscat de Beaumes-de-Venise Jaboulet
£10.95 (WS)
1995
Muscat de Beaumes-de-Venise Domaine
de Durban £10.59 (EL) £13.20 (PIP)
Muscat de Beaumes-de-Venise Domaine
des Bernardins £13.90 (PIP)
Muscat de Beaumes-de-Venise Vidal-
Fleury £13.90 (SOM)

SOUTHERN FRANCE

Feeling broke? Feeling in need of excitement? Feeling in need of some Mourvèdre and Petit Manseng? Head south (or if you're an Australian winemaker, head north)

It's hard to sum up such a vast swathe of land in just a few words, but let me have a go. 'Innovation' – how's that? 'Originality' – there's another. 'Australian-influenced' – yes, certainly. And if I'm to be strictly fair, 'patchy' – because not everywhere in the South is motoring forward at the same pace. Some places are still tentatively in first gear. But everyone has started the engine.

Everybody knows by now that the South is France's most exciting area – exciting, that is, if you want fruit, and oak, and flavour, flavour, flavour. It's the one part of France that's in head-to-head competition with Australia. Australian winemaking techniques, designed to produce fresh, intense tastes in regions even hotter and even more uncompromising than the Midi, have been put to good work, often by peripatetic Australian winemakers keen to put their winter to good use.

But the south of France isn't just Barossa-on-Sea. It has its own secret weapons – grapes like Gros and Petit Manseng, Picpoul de Pinet, Tannat and Mauzac. These, and others, are found nowhere else in France, but in the South – particularly the South-West – they pop up in appellation after appellation. They're not always stunningly

good; in fact sometimes they are best combined with those old favourites, Cabernet or Chardonnay – but they always give a twist of originality to the wine. The really wacky wines are found in the far South-West; nearer Bordeaux you're more likely to find Bordelais styles.

Further east, Provence is probably being the most dogged about sticking to what it knows. It was top dog in the South in the days before flying winemakers had taken to the skies, and the serious producers there are still making good stuff. But prices aren't low. You've got to remember that a lot gets sold to tourists, who are apt to get so carried away with the sun setting over the hills that they don't notice the sun setting over their credit cards.

This leaves Languedoc-Roussillon, where good and improving appellations certainly exist – I'm thinking of Fitou, Minervois and Corbières, among others – but the main action is in vins de pays. This is where we get the best of all worlds: first-class winemaking from producers who deliberately shun the restrictions of an appellation, wonderful grape varieties like Syrah or Mourvèdre, and prices that don't look silly on the shelf.

WINE REGIONS

BANDOL, AC (Provence; red, white) Here Mourvèdre is king, but is assisted by Grenache, Cinsaut and Syrah to make herby, tobaccoey, long-lived wines of world class. The serious spicy rosés can also be excellent. Best estates: *Ch. Pradeaux, Ste-Anne, Dom. Bastide Blanche, Dom. du Cageloup, Dom. le Galantin, Dom. de Pibarnon, Dom. Ray-Jane, Dom. Tempier, Dom. Terrebrune, Dom. de la Tour du Bon*. The whites are made from the southern Rhône

grapes, together with an enlivening dash of Sauvignon, and can be delicious, with a lovely aniseed-and-apple bite to them. *Dom. de Pibarnon* and *Dom. Lafran Veyrolles* are among the most interesting.

BANYULS, AC (Languedoc-Roussillon; *vin doux naturel*, red) Grenache-based wine that can assume many guises: red or tawny, sweet or dryish, and can come, too, in an oxidized *rancio* style with burnt caramel flavours. *Dom. de la Rectorie, Mas Blanc* and *Mas Casa Blanca* are good. Wines aged for two and a half years in wood may be labelled *grand cru*.

LES BAUX-EN-PROVENCE, AC

(Provence; red, rosé) More intense and complex than their neighbours in Coteaux d'Aix-en-Provence, these wines include splendid rosés and several startlingly good reds, like the organic *Domaine de Trévallon*. Other organic wines are made at *Mas de la Dame* and *Mas de Gourgonnier*. *Mas Ste-Berthe* also produces a good red.

BÉARN, AC (South-West; red, rosé, white) The reds are mainly from the Tannat grape, with other local varieties and both Cabernets thrown in. In spite of this they are basically undistinguished but you could try the wines of the *Vignerons de Bellocq* co-op, or the co-op at *Crouseilles*. *Domaine Guilhemas* is also worth a punt.

BELLET, AC (Provence; red, white) An unusual nutty Rolle and Chardonnay white with a good local reputation. *Château de Crémat* and *Château de Bellet* are worth seeking out, though like everything else near Nice, they're expensive. There are also a few good, dark reds made at *Château de Bellet* and *Château de Crémat*.

BERGERAC, AC (South-West; red, rosé) Bergerac is a kind of Bordeaux understudy: the rosés are often extremely good, deep in colour, dry and full of fruit, but the reds are more exciting, with the fruit and bite of a good, simple Bordeaux without the rough edges. Like St-Émilion, they rely on the Merlot grape, with help from both Cabernets and Malbec, but the Bergerac reds are less substantial than St-Émilions. Bergerac Rouge is usually at its best at between one and four years old, depending on vintage and style. *Château la Jaubertie* is very good and has also produced a wood-aged *Reserve*. *Château le Barradis* and *Château Belingard* are also

good, and *Château Court-les-Mûts* makes a delicious rosé and a good red.

BERGERAC SEC, AC (South-West; white) Bordeaux lookalikes. *Château Belingard, Château Court-les-Mûts* and *Château de Panisseau* are good but the star is *Château la Jaubertie* where tremendous flavour and panache are extracted from a Sauvignon, Sémillon and Muscadelle blend. There's also a good dry varietal Muscadelle from *la Jaubertie*.

BUZET, AC (South-West; white) Claret lookalikes that can combine a rich blackcurrant sweetness with an arresting grassy greenness. They are for drinking at between one and five years old, depending on vintage and style. Look out for the wines of the co-op, which dominates the area: its *Château de Gueyze, Château Padère* and *Baron d'Ardeuil* are all pretty special.

CABARDÈS, VDQS (Languedoc-Roussillon; red) The aromatic originality and liveliness of these wines derives from the marriage of southern and south-western grape varieties, such as Merlot, Cabernet, Fer Servadou and Cot (Malbec). Best producers include *Château de la Bastide, Château de Rayssac, Domaine Jouclary, de Brau* and *Ventenac*.

CAHORS, AC (South-West; red) Of all the south-western country wines, Cahors is the most exciting. It's at least 70 per cent Auxerrois (Bordeaux's Malbec), the rest being made up of varying proportions of Merlot and Tannat.

With age, they become almost honeyed and raisiny, with plummy fruit that gets deeper, spicier and darker, often resembling tobacco and prunes. But another sort of Cahors has sprung up, too, lighter and easier, for drinking young. It can sometimes be very good. Good names: *Château des Bouysses* from the *Côtes d'Olt* co-op, *Château de Cayrou, Château de Chambert, Château de Haute-Serre, Clos de Gamot,*

Château St-Didier, Château de Treilles, Domaine du Cèdre, Clos la Coutale, Clos Triguedina, Domaine Eugénie, Domaine de Gaudou, Domaine de Paillas, Château de Poujol and *Domaine de Quattre*.

CASSIS, AC (Provence; red, white, rosé)
Some flavoursome reds and rosés can be unearthed here, notably *Dom. du Bagnol* and *Dom. de la Ferme Blanche*. The white is fine but expensive. Look out for *Domaine du Paternel* and *Clos Ste-Magdelaine*.

CLAIRETTE DU LANGUEDOC, AC
(Languedoc-Roussillon; white) The Clairette can be a difficult grape to vinify, but the quality of wines like *Dom. de la Condamine Bertrand*, the co-op at *Cabrières* and *Domaine St-André* show just what can be done.

COLLIOURE, AC (Languedoc-
Roussillon; red) Startling, intense reds dominated by Grenache, with increasing contributions from Mourvèdre. Best: *Dom. de la Rectorie, Dom. du Mas Blanc, Clos des Paulilles, Mas Casa Blanca*.

CORBIÈRES, AC (Languedoc-
Roussillon; red, white, rosé) Reds can be dramatic, ranging from juicy upfront wines produced using carbonic maceration to powerful, serious, traditionally made bottles like those of the marvellous *la Voulte-Gasparets*. Others: *Château Cabriac, Étang des Colombes, Château Hélène, Château les Ollieux, les Palais, Château Bories-Azea, Caraguilhes, Fontsainte, Villemajou, St-Auriol, Dom. du Révérend*. There is less white, but it's increasingly good.

COTEAUX D'AIX-EN-PROVENCE,
AC (Provence; red, white, rosé) An increasing use of Cabernet and Syrah and subtle use of new oak are combining to make interesting reds and rosés in a semi-Bordelais style – such as *Château Vignelaure*. Also good: *Château Crémade, Château de Calissanne, Domaine des Glauges* and *Château du Seuil*. There is little white, and frankly it's not that thrilling.

COTEAUX DU LANGUEDOC, AC
(Languedoc-Roussillon; red, white) This sprawling appellation incorporates 12 demarcated *terroirs* that may state their names on the labels. Among the better ones for reds are St-Saturnin, Pic St-Loup and La Clape. The classic southern grapes are used, and the growing presence of Syrah and Mourvèdre can be discerned in the complexity and breed of many wines. Best: *Château Moujan, Calage, Capion, Flaugergues, Pech-Céleyran, Pech-Redon, Lascaux, Domaine de la Coste, de la Roque, d'Aupilhac, Domaine de Payre-Rose, Domaine de Cazeneuve, Domaine de Brunet, Olivier Jullien, Domaine de la Roque, de Terre-Mégère* and *Domaine de l'Hortus*, especially the rosé, and the co-ops at *Cabrières, Montpeyrous, Neffiès, St-Saturnin* and *Gabian (la Carignano)*. White wine-making is being also taken more and more seriously. Best: *Chamayrac, Boscary, Claude Gaujal, Mas Jullien, Terre Mégère, Château de Granoupiac* and the co-ops at *Pine, Pomérols* and *St-Saturnin* (for its *le Lucian*).

COTEAUX VAROIS, AC (Provence;
red, rosé) Some very good, cheap reds and rosés, such as *Château St-Jean de Villecroze, Château St-Estève, Dom. de Triennes* and *Dom. du Loou*.

CÔTES DE BERGERAC, AC (South-
West; red, rosé) This is to Bergerac what Bordeaux Supérieur is to Bordeaux: from the same region, but with slightly higher minimum alcohol. It should be better, and often is. Many are still sold as basic Bergerac, although the excellent *Château Court-les-Mûts* now uses this AC.

CÔTES DE DURAS, AC (South-West;
red, white) Light, grassy claret lookalikes. *Château de Pilar* and *le Seigneuret* from the co-op are quite good and cheap. Also fairly good Sauvignon-based white that can be as

fresh as good Bordeaux Blanc, but just a little chubbier. *Château de Conti* is good, as is *le Seigneuret* from the co-op.

CÔTES DU FRONTONNAIS, AC
(South-West; red, rosé) At their best these are silky and plummy, sometimes with a touch of raspberry and liquorice, but always with a twist of fresh black pepper. The Négrette grape dominates, and is wonderfully tasty. Best producers are *Dom. de Baudare, Ch. Bellevue-la-Forêt, Ch. Flotis, Ch. la Palme* and *Ch. Montauriol,* owned by the ex-manager of Château Pichon-Lalande in Bordeaux.

CÔTES DE LA MALEPÈRE, VDQS
(Languedoc-Roussillon; red) The grape varieties are similar to those of Cabardès, with the addition of Cabernet Franc. Best: *Ch. de Festes, Cave du Razès, Dom. de Matibat.*

CÔTES DU MARMANDAIS, AC
(South-West; red) Simple, soft, fruity wines for drinking young, made from Cabernet Sauvignon, Cabernet Franc, Merlot, Fer and Abouriou. A few are designed for more serious aging, but it doesn't suit them.

CÔTES DE PROVENCE, AC
(Provence; red, white, rosé) Among the overpriced rosés made for the tourists there are many top-grade red and pink wines made by growers who take their calling seriously. They include *Commanderie de Peyrassol, Domaines de la Bernarde, St-Baillon, Rimauresque, Richeaume, Jas d'Esclans, Aumerade, Château de Selle, Mas de Cadenet, Presqu'île de St-Tropez* and *Domaine de Courtade.* For whites, *Dom. Arnaude, Clos Bernarde, Ch. Ferry-Lacombe, de Rasque, Dom. Richeaume, Castel Roubine, St-André de la Figuière* and *Réal Martin* are the leading lights.

COTES DE ST-MONT, VDQS
(South-West; red, white) These reds are increasingly made in a fresh, blackcurranty,

modern style. By far the best examples come from the *Plaimont* co-op.

FAUGÈRES, AC
(Languedoc-Roussillon; red) The grapes here are Grenache, Syrah, Mourvèdre and Carignan. The wines have real depth, class and character in which cassis, black cherries and liquorice predominate. In mature Faugères wines, complex game and leather aromas can often emerge. *Alquier, Louison, Lubac, Ollier-Taillefer, Vidal* and the co-op at *Laurens* must be in anyone's top ten.

FITOU, AC
(Languedoc-Roussillon; red) A highly variable, old-style red in which Carignan has traditionally been dominant, but Grenache and, increasingly, Syrah and Mourvèdre are being used to add interest. *Paul Colomer* and *Robert Daurat-Fort* are the leading lights, along with co-ops at *Villeneuve* and at *Tuchan,* where the *Caves de Mont Tauch* is producing some of the most serious Fitou of all.

GAILLAC, AC
(South-West; red, white) The white, based on the bracing Mauzac grape, can be *moelleux* (medium-sweet), *perlé* (very faintly bubbly) or dry; the dry is usually a little neutral, though a few have a quite big apple-and-liquorice fruit. The sparkling wines can be superb: peppery, honeyed, apricotty and appley all at the same time. From *Boissel-Rhodes, Canto Perlic* (a newcomer), *Cros* or *Robert Plageoles,* they are very good value. Other still wine producers to look out for are *Château Larroze, Domaine du Bosc Long* and *Domaine de Labarthe.* The co-op at *Labastide de Lévis* is improving. There are two styles of red, Duras plus Fer Servadou and Syrah, or Duras plus Merlot and Cabernet. *Domaine Jean Cros* is delicious. Others: *Lastours, Mas Pignou, Labarthe, Larroze.*

IROULÉGUY, AC
(South-West; red) Mostly quite rough, Tannat-based red, supplemented by both Cabernets. Try *Domaine Brana* and *Domaine Ilarria.*

JURANÇON, AC (South-West; white)
This can be sweet, medium or dry. The dry
wines are light and can be ravishingly
perfumed, while the sweet wines are
honeyed, raisiny and peachy, yet with a lick
of acidity. The pace-setter is *Henri
Ramonteu*; others are *Clos de la Vierge* (dry),
Cancaillaü (sweet), sweet *Cru Lamouroux*,
Clos Uroulat (sweet), *Dom. de Cauhapé*,
Dom. de Souch, *Dom. Bru-Baché* (dry), *Clos
Thou* (dry), *Dom. Larredya*, *Clos Lapeyre*,
Dom. Castera.

LIMOUX, AC (South-West; white)
Sparkling Blanquette de Limoux is mostly
from the Mauzac grape; Crémant de
Limoux has more Chardonnay, and is less
rustic. The still wines are based on barrel-
fermented Chardonnay, and tend to be
expensive. Best producers include: *Caves du
Sieur d'Arques*, *Antech*, *Delmas*, *Robert*,
Philippe Collin and *Sev Dervin*.

MADIRAN, AC (South-West; red)
Madiran is often likened to claret, but only
rarely approaches its finesse. Generally
about half Tannat, along with the Cabernets
and occasionally Fer, it can be astringent
and too tannic, though a new generation of
growers is mellowing its sturdy flavours.
Good ones include *Château d'Arricau-
Bordes*, *Château d'Aydie* (alias *Domaine
Laplace*), *Domaine Damiens*, *Château
Montus*, *Château Boucassé*, *Château Peyros*,
Domaine du Crampilh, *Domaine Meinjarre*,
Laffitte-Teston, *Domaine Berthoumieu* and
Domaine Moreau.

MAURY, AC (Languedoc-Roussillon; *vin
doux naturel*, red) Grenache without the
finesse of Banyuls, but more explosive in its
nutty, toffee, prunes-in-brandy intensity. It
can also be made in the oxidized *rancio*
style. Try *Mas Amiel* and the co-op at
Maury.

MINERVOIS, AC (Languedoc-
Roussillon; red, white, rosé) Interesting reds
with good peppery berry fruit. Best

producers include the co-op at *la Livinière*,
Château Fabas, *Château de Gourgazaud*,
Villerambert-Julien, *la Combe Blanche*,
Château du Donjon, *Domaine Maris*, *Ste-
Eulalie*, *la Tour Boisée*, *Château d'Oupia* and
the co-ops at *Peyriac* and *Azillanet*. White
Minervois is improving, and is increasingly
good and aromatic.

MONBAZILLAC, AC (South-West;
white) These sweet wines are never as rich
or weighty as a top Sauternes, but the
massive improvements in quality in
Sauternes have spurred the producers here
to sharpen up their act, too. The best are
very good indeed, and include *Château les
Hébras*, *Château du Treuil de Nailhac*,
Château Haut-Bernasse, *Château La
Fonrousse* and *Clos Fontindoule*. Grab any
1990s you can still find: coming from one of
the hottest, most botrytized vintages for
years, the best are terrific.

MONTRAVEL, AC (South-West; white)
Dry white from the Dordogne. Côtes de
Montravel is *moelleux* from the same area;
Haut-Montravel is a separate area and
sweeter. All are mostly sold as Bergerac or
Côtes de Bergerac.

MUSCAT (*vin doux naturel*, white) Not a
region but a grape. Wines range from the
syrupy *Tradition* made by the *Frontignan* co-
op to the elegant *Château de la Peyrade*
(Frontignan), *Domaine de la Capelle*
(Mireval), *Grés St-Paul* (Lunel), *Domaine de
Barroubie* and the co-op in *St-Jean-de-
Minervois*. All of these are made from the
Muscat à Petits Grains which gives more
finesse than the Muscat d'Alexandrie, used
in Muscat de Rivesaltes (*Cazes* and *Brial* are
the names to go for here).

PACHERENC DU VIC-BILH, AC
(South-West; white) One of France's most
esoteric whites, a blend of Gros and Petit
Manseng and Arrufiac – a grape peculiar to
the AC. At its best when dry and pear-skin-
perfumed – and sometimes when rich and

sweet. Best: *Château d'Aydie, Château Boucassé, Domaine Damiens* and *Domaine du Crampilh*.

PALETTE, AC (Provence; red, white, rosé) A tiny AC dominated by *Château Simone*. The rosé beats the others.

PÉCHARMANT, AC (South-West; red) The best red wine of Bergerac, this must be aged for a minimum of a year before sale to distinguish it from Bergerac, which can be sold after only six months. It is deliciously blackcurranty when young. *Château de Tiregand* is very good indeed, but *Domaine du Haut-Pécharmant* is even better, resembling a top-line Médoc.

ROUSSILLON, AC (Languedoc-Roussillon; red, white, rosé) While many good, fruity, dusty reds are made here, there isn't quite the same sense of pioneering adventurousness as there is in the Languedoc. The Côtes du Roussillon-Villages AC accounts for most of the best reds. *Vignerons Catalans' Mas Camo* and *Château Cap de Fouste* are excellent. Other serious winemakers here include the *Cazes* brothers, plus *Château Corneilla, Domaine Sarda-Malet* and *Domaine Gauby*.

ST-CHINIAN, AC (Languedoc-Roussillon; red, rosé) Improving and often very attactive wines. Among the top must be *Dom. des Jougla, Dom. Madalle, Ch. Cazal-Vieil, Ch. Coujan, la Dournie* and *Ch. Milhau-Lacugue* (especially for its brilliant rosé). The co-ops at *Roquebrun, Roueire* and *Berlou* are outstanding.

VIN DE CORSE, AC (Corsica; red, white, rosé) Still lagging far behind the mainland in quality. *Dom. de Torraccia* makes a tasty red redolent of spices and rosemary. Also good: *Clos Landry, Capitoro, d'Alzeto, Dom. Filippi* and *Dom. Peraldi*. Most wines of better than vin de table status take the all-island designation Vin de Pays de l'Île de Beauté.

VINS DE PAYS (red, white, rosé) This is where it's all happening. The most innovative winemakers love the vin de pays classification for the freedom it gives them. There's plenty of Cabernet Sauvignon being used here, but some of the most exciting flavours come from Syrah and the other good grapes of the South, like Grenache or Mourvèdre. There are some excellent varietals, particularly Syrah, Cabernet Sauvignon and Chardonnay. Australian influence in the winemaking is producing clear flavours and some creamy new oak. In the Pays d'Oc look for *Fortant de France, la Grange des Quatre Sous, Domaine de Condamine-l'Evêque, de l'Aigle, Quatre Sous, Peyrat, Cousserges, Raissac, Rives de l'Argent Double, Domaine de la Jonction, L'Enclos Domeque, Domaine de la Colombette, du Bosc, Domaine de l'Arjolle, Domaine de Limbardié, Chais Baumière* and *Domaine Virginie*.

In the Gard, seek out *Listel, Domaine de Gournier, Domaine de Monpertuis* and *Mas Montel*; and, in the Roussillon, *Chichet, Laporte* and *Vaquer*. In the Vaucluse, look for *Domaine de l'Ameillaud*.

In the Hérault, *Domaine de Poujol* and *Mas de Daumas Gassac*; the latter's reds are explosively concentrated. There's also a Viognier-based white. From the Comté Tolosan, *Ribeton* makes good white; from the Comtés Rhodaniens, *les Vignerons Ardéchois* have a tasty Viognier.

On the western side of France the Charente produces some good, grassy-fresh whites with fairly sharp acidity – which sometimes gets the better of the fruit. The region here is Vin de Pays Charentais. The equivalent from Armagnac country is Vin de Pays des Côtes de Gascogne. The Ugni Blanc is the major grape, and the Colombard adds a touch of class. Look for the co-op at *Plaimont*, though quality is variable. Also the *Grassa* family estates – notably *Domaines de Plantérieu* and *de Tariquet*. Also good are *Domaine St-Lannes, Domaine le Puts* and *San Guilhem*. See also page 277.

SOUTHERN FRANCE PRICE GUIDES

RED

Under £3.50

1995
VdP de l'Hérault Figaro £3.35 (SOM) £3.49 (BOT) £3.49 (THR) £3.49 (WR)
VdP d'Oc Cépage Merlot, Domaine des Fontaines £3.49 (WAI)
1993
Côtes de St-Mont, Producteurs Plaimont £3.15 (SOM)

£3.50 → £3.99

Non-vintage
Fitou Mme Claude Parmentier £3.99 (VIC)
1996
Côtes du Roussillon-Villages Château de Pena £3.95 (WS)
1995
Bergerac Château les Vigonies £3.95 (WS)
Coteaux du Languedoc Ermitage du Pic St Loup £3.99 (WAI)
Faugères Domaine Roque Gabarron £3.95 (WS)
Minervois Domaine du Moulin Rigaud £3.95 (WS)
VdP des Coteaux de Murviel, Domaine de Limbardie £3.50 (SOM)
VdP de l'Hérault Merlot, Domaine du Fraisse £3.95 (LEA)
VdP de l'Hérault Terrasses de Guilhem £3.95 (SOM)
1994
Côtes de St-Mont, Producteurs Plaimont £3.99 (JON)
Côtes du Frontonnais Château Baudare £3.99 (DI)
Fitou Caves du Mont Tauch £3.99 (MAR)

£4.00 → £4.99

Non-vintage
Côtes du Roussillon-Villages Vignerons Catalans £4.99 (MAR)
1996
VdP des Côtes de Thongue Cépage Syrah, la Condamine l'Évêque £4.50 (LEA)
VdP de l'Hérault Terrasses de Guilhem £4.22 (FLE)
1995
Cabardès Château de Pennautier £4.50 (GRE)
Corbières Château de Cabriac £4.75 (EL)
Corbières Château St-Auriol £4.99 (WAI)
Costières de Nîmes Château de Campuget £4.49 (POR)
Coteaux du Languedoc La Clape, Château de Pech-Celeyran £4.95 (AD)
Côtes de St-Mont, Producteurs Plaimont £4.45 (AD)
Marcillac Domaine du Cros, Teulier £4.95 (WS)
Minervois Domaine Piccinini £4.95 (WS)
VdP des Côtes de Thongue Domaine Comte de Margon £4.85 (TAN)
★ VdP du Gard Cépage Counoise, Domaine de Montpertuis £4.65 (EL)
VdP d'Oc Merlot, Domaine de Terre Megère £4.95 (LEA)
VdP d'Oc Merlot, Marquise de Bairac £4.69 (LAY)
VdP d'Oc Roussanne, Domaines Virginie £4.25 (REI)
★ VdP d'Oc Syrah, Domaine de la Jonction £4.47 (CB)
1994
Corbières Château de Montrabech £4.19 (JON)

MERCHANTS SPECIALIZING IN SOUTHERN FRANCE
see Merchant Directory (page 413) for details

Most good merchants have some. For particularly good lists try the following merchants: Adnams (AD), Averys of Bristol (AV), Bibendum (BIB), Anthony Byrne (BY) – always enterprising, Direct Wine (DI), Eldridge Pope (EL), Ben Ellis (ELL), Forth Wines (FOR), Fullers (FUL), Gauntleys (GAU), Gelston Castle, J E Hogg (HOG), Lay & Wheeler (LAY), Majestic (MAJ), Oddbins (OD), The Nobody Inn (NO), James Nicholson (NI), Thos. Peatling (PE), Terry Platt (PLA), Raeburn Fine Wines (RAE), Reid Wines (REI), Sainsbury (SAI), Somerfield/Gateway (SO), Tanners (TAN), Thresher (THR), Ubiquitous Chip (UB), The Wine Society (WS)

Corbières Chatellerie de Lastours £4.99
(POR)
Coteaux d'Aix-en-Provence Château de
Fonscolombe £4.79 (JON)

Coteaux du Languedoc La Clape, Château
de Pech-Celeyran £4.35 (WS) £4.95 (TAN)
Côtes de la Malepère Château Malvies
£4.59 (NA)
Côtes de St-Mont, les Hauts de Bergelle
£4.75 (TAN)
Côtes du Roussillon-Villages Château de
Pena £4.99 (DI)
Fitou Domaine Richard Astruc £4.90 (WS)
Fitou Les Contemporains £4.69 (POR)
Gaillac Domaine de Labarthe £4.25 (SOM)
Minervois Domaine de Ste-Eulalie £4.49
(THR) £4.49 (WR) £4.79 (JON) £4.95 (POR)
Minervois Domaine la Tour Boisée £4.25
(WAT)
St-Chinian Château Maurel Fonsalade
£4.75 (WS)
VdP des Coteaux de Murviel, Domaine de
Limbardie £4.90 (TAN)
VdP des Côtes de Thongue Cépage Syrah,
la Condamine l'Évêque £4.09 (JON)
VdP de l'Hérault, Domaine de Chapître
£4.00 (MV)
VdP des Maures, Domaine d'Astros £4.50
(BIB)
VdP d'Oc Cabernet Sauvignon, Chais
Baumière £4.75 (GRE) £4.99 (NA)
VdP d'Oc Merlot, Philippe de Baudin
£4.75 (GRE)
1993
Bergerac Domaine du Gouyat £4.89 (JON)
Cahors Château de Gaudou £4.99 (SOM)
Corbières Château de Cabriac £4.59 (JON)
Coteaux du Languedoc La Clape, Château
de Pech-Celeyran £4.69 (JON)
1991
Corbières Château les Ollieux £4.75 (REI)
1990
VdP du Comté Tolosan, Domaine de
Callary £4.70 (GAU)

£5.00 ➜ £5.99

1995
Bergerac Château Tour de Gendres £5.96
(GN)
Corbières Château Grand Moulin £5.95
(LEA)
Coteaux de Languedoc, Domaine de
Terre Megère £5.75 (LEA)
Coteaux du Languedoc Château
Flaugergues £5.55 (NA)
Coteaux du Languedoc Domaine de
l'Abbaye de Valmagne £5.15 (EL)
Côtes du Roussillon Cuvée des Rocailles,
Domaine Gauby £5.90 (GAU)
Pic St. Loup Château de Cazeneuve £5.45
(WS)
VdP des Coteaux Catalans Cuvée Pierre
Audonnet, Piquemal £5.50 (LEA)
VdP des Côtes de Thongue Cuvée de
l'Arjolle, Teisserenc £5.50 (TAN)
VdP de l'Hérault, Domaine du Poujol
£5.50 (BIB)
★ VdP d'Orange Domaine de la Janasse £5.99
(MAJ)
VdP de Vaucluse Domaine des Tours,
Reynaud £5.95 (LEA)
1994
Bergerac Château Tour de Gendres £5.75
(LEA)
Cahors Clos la Coutale £5.75 (WS)
Corbières Domaine Baillat £5.25 (WS)
Coteaux du Languedoc Château de
Lascaux £5.95 (NI)
Côtes du Frontonnais Château le Roc
£5.45 (COU) £5.50 (LEA)
Madiran Château Pichard £5.95 (WS)
Marcillac Domaine du Cros, Teulier £5.88
(AD)
St-Chinian Domaine de la Cessane £5.95
(SAI)
VdP des Côtes de Thongue Cuvée
Prestige, Domaine Boyer £5.45 (LEA)
VdP des Côtes de Thongue Mourvèdre,
Domaine de la Croix Belle £5.45 (LEA)
VdP d'Oc La Cuvée Mythique,
DuBernet/Vign. de Val d'Orbieu £5.99
(MAJ)
VdP d'Oc les Chemins de Bassac £5.59 (NI)
1993
Cahors Château St-Didier-Parnac, Rigal
£5.39 (OD)
Corbières Château de Lastours £5.79 (WR)
Coteaux d'Aix-en-Provence Domaine de
la Vallonge £5.95 (SOM)

Fitou Domaine Richard Astruc £5.55 (DI)
Madiran Domaine Capmartin £5.95 (LEA)
VdP d'Oc La Cuvée Mythique,
DuBernet/Vign. de Val d'Orbieu £5.99
(SAF)
1992
Côtes du Frontonnais Château Baudare
£5.99 (DI)
Madiran Collection Plaimont £5.89 (JON)
Minervois Château Villerambert Julien
Cuvée Opera £5.60 (TAN)
1991
Corbières Château de Cabriac £5.53 (NO)
1990
Côtes du Frontonnais Domaine de
Callory £5.99 (GAU)
Minervois Domaine de la Combe Blanche
£5.75 (GN)

£6.00 ➜ £7.99

1996
Côtes du Lubéron Château de Canorgue
£7.25 (YAP)
1995
Coteaux du Languedoc Château
Flaugergues £6.49 (MAJ)
Coteaux du Languedoc Château de
Lascaux £6.46 (DOM)
Coteaux du Languedoc Montpeyroux,
Domaine d'Aupilhac £7.50 (LEA)
Côtes de Provence Domaine Richeaume
Hoesch £7.75 (YAP)
Côtes du Frontonnais Cuvée Reservée,
Château le Roc £7.25 (LEA)
Côtes du Roussillon Domaine Gauby
£6.95 (WS)
VdP du Mont Baudile Carignan, Domaine
d'Aupilhac £7.95 (AD) £7.95 (LEA)
1994
Bandol Domaine de la Tour du Bon £7.75
(BIB)
Bergerac Cuvée la Gloire de Mon Père,
Château Tour de Gendres £7.95 (LEA)
Cahors Clos la Coutale £7.79 (COU)
Cahors Domaine Eugenie £6.25 (HIC)
Cahors Domaine de Paillas £7.75 (BIB)
Cahors Domaine de la Pineraie £6.75
(GRE)

*In each price band wines
are listed in vintage order.
Within each vintage they
are listed in A–Z order.*

Coteaux de Languedoc les Dolomies,
Domaine de Terre Megère £6.50 (VIG)
Coteaux du Languedoc Cuvée Prestige,
Domaine de la Coste £7.25 (LEA)
Coteaux du Languedoc Cuvée
Séléctionnée, Domaine de la Coste
£7.25 (LEA)
Côtes du Frontonnais Cuvée Reservée,
Château le Roc £7.50 (COU)
Faugères Château de la Liquière £6.10
(NEZ)
Faugères Gilbert Alquier £6.50 (LON)
£6.99 (BO) £7.35 (GAU)
Madiran Domaine Damiens £6.25 (BIB)
★ Madiran Domaine de Moureau £6.00
(TAN)
Madiran Vieilles Vignes, Domaine
Capmartin £7.95 (LEA)
1993
Cahors Château de Gaudou £6.89 (JON)
Corbières Cuvée Spéciale, Château
Grand Moulin £7.50 (LEA)
Côtes de Provence Château St Baillon
£6.50 (BIB)
Côtes du Marmandais Château de
Beaulieu £6.49 (NA)
Pécharmant Château de Tiregand £7.30
(TAN)
1992
Cahors Domaine de la Pineraie £6.10
(SOM) £6.31 (HOG)
Collioure Domaine de la Rectorie £7.85
(REI)
Faugères Gilbert Alquier £6.95 (JON)
VdP des Côtes de Thongue Cuvée de
l'Arjolle, Teisserenc £7.75 (WS)
VdP d'Oc Cuvée Pierre Elie, Les Chemins
de Bassac £6.50 (LEA)
1991
Côtes de Provence Château St Baillon
£6.51 (HOG)

Les Baux-en-Provence Mas de
Gourgonnier £7.90 (BEN)
Madiran Cave de Crouseilles £6.95 (SAI)

Madiran Chapelle l'Enclos, Domaine
Ducournau £7.40 (ws)
VdP d'Oc La Cuvée Mythique,
DuBernet/Vign. de Val d'Orbieu £6.59
(NI)
1990
Côtes de St-Mont, Château de Sabazan
£7.15 (ws)
1987
Madiran Château Pichard £6.95 (ws)

£8.00 → £9.99

1995
Coteaux du Languedoc les Nobles
Pierres, Château de Lascaux £8.95 (LEA)
1994
Cahors Domaine de la Pineraie £8.10
(GN)
Côtes de Bergerac Château le Tour des
Gendres £8.62 (GN)
Madiran Domaine Bouscassé, Alain
Brumont £8.95 (VIG)
Pic St Loup les Nobles Pierres, Château
de Lascaux £9.50 (LEA)
1993
Bandol Mas de la Rouvière, Bunan £8.95
(YAP)
Cahors Château Lagrezette £9.80 (NEZ)
★ Corbières Château Hélène £8.45 (WAT)
1992
Bandol Domaine Tempier £9.35 (REI)
£9.60 (SOM)
Madiran Cuvée du Couvent, Domaine
Capmartin £9.50 (LEA)
1991
VdP de l'Hérault, Mas de Daumas Gassac
£9.99 (NI)
1990
Cahors Château de Chambert £8.30 (DI)
Minervois Clos des Centeilles, P & D
Domergue £9.66 (NO)

£10.00 → £15.99

1994
Collioure Domaine du Mas Blanc £10.50
(GAU)
Madiran Château Montus £11.50 (VIG)
VdP de l'Hérault, Mas de Daumas Gassac
£13.28 (NO)
1993
Bandol Cuvée Tourtine £13.90 (COU)
£14.00 (ws) £15.95 (VIG)
Bandol Domaine Tempier £11.50 (ws)
VdP de l'Hérault, Mas de Daumas Gassac
£11.99 (BOT) £11.99 (WR) £11.99 (THR)

1992
Bandol Château de la Rouvière, Bunan
£11.25 (YAP)
Bandol Cuvée Migoua £10.75 (REI) £12.95
(VIG)
Bandol Cuvée Tourtine £10.75 (REI)
£14.59 (COU)
Bandol Domaine de Pibarnon £11.88 (FLE)
Bandol Domaine Tempier £11.99 (DI)
Coteaux d'Aix-en-Provence Domaine de
Trévallon £14.95 (DI)
Côtes de Provence Domaine de Trevallon
£15.40 (GAU)
VdP de l'Hérault, Mas de Daumas Gassac
£10.28 (FLE)
1991
Bandol Cuvée Tourtine £13.95 (VIG)
Bandol Mas de la Rouvière, Bunan £12.50
(ROB)
Coteaux du Languedoc Prieuré de St-Jean
de Bébian £12.50 (GAU)
1989
Madiran Château de Peyros £10.20 (GAU)
1985
Madiran Château Pichard £11.95 (ws)
1983
VdP de l'Hérault, Mas de Daumas Gassac
£13.22 (FA)

£16.00 → £19.99

1995
VdP de l'Hérault, Mas de Daumas Gassac
£16.00 (AD)
1993
VdP de l'Hérault, Mas de Daumas Gassac
£17.50 (ROB)
1992
Palette Château Simone £16.75 (YAP)

£20.00 → £25.99

1995
Les Baux-en-Provence Domaine de
Trévallon £21.50 (YAP)
1994
VdP de l'Hérault, Mas de Daumas Gassac
£25.00 (VIG)
1991
Les Baux-en-Provence Domaine de
Trévallon £25.70 (UB)
1983
VdP de l'Hérault, Mas de Daumas Gassac
£22.50 (NO)
1982
Coteaux d'Aix-en-Provence Château
Vignelaure £25.50 (REI)

£35.00 → £45.00

1983
VdP de l'Hérault, Mas de Daumas Gassac
£35.00 (VIG)
1979
VdP de l'Hérault, Mas de Daumas Gassac
£45.00 (VIG)

DRY WHITE

Under £4.00

1996
Le Petit Bosc Blanc de Blancs, Bésinet
£3.75 (WS)
VdP des Côtes de Gascogne Domaine de
Joy £3.95 (LEA)
VdP des Côtes de Gascogne Domaine
Bordes £3.75 (SAI)
VdP des Côtes de Gascogne Domaine de
Planterieu £3.65 (WAI)
VdP des Côtes de Gascogne le Prada
£3.75 (WS)
VdP des Côtes de Gascogne Producteurs
Plaimont £3.49 (MAR) £3.95 (PIP)
VdP de l'Hérault Grenache, Bésinet £3.75
(WS)
VdP d'Oc Sauvignon, Domaine des
Fontanelles £3.95 (WAI)
1995
Bergerac Sec Château la Besage £3.75 (WS)
Côtes de Duras, Moulin des Groyes £3.99
(SAI)
VdP des Côtes de Gascogne Domaine le
Puts £3.69 (MAJ)
VdP des Côtes de Gascogne Domaine de
Tariquet £3.99 (WR) £3.99 (THR)
VdP des Côtes de Gascogne Producteurs
Plaimont £3.79 (JON)

£4.00 → £4.99

Non-vintage
VdP d'Oc Chardonnay, James Herrick
£4.99 (WR) £4.99 (THR) £4.99 (BOT)
1996
Bergerac Château la Jaubertie £4.99 (CO)
Bergerac Château de Panisseau £4.25 (GAL)

*Stars (★) indicate wines
selected by Oz Clarke in the
Best Buys section which begins
on page 12.*

VdP des Côtes de Thongue Sauvignon de
l'Arjolle, Teisserenc £4.50 (WS)
VdP des Côtes de Gascogne Domaine de
Rieux £4.45 (AD) £4.49 (NA)
VdP d'Oc Chardonnay, Cave de la
Cessanne £4.45 (SAI)
VdP d'Oc Chardonnay, Domaine de
Gourgazaud £4.95 (WS)
VdP d'Oc Chardonnay, Fleur du Moulin
£4.29 (CO)
VdP d'Oc Chardonnay, Fortant de France
£4.49 (VIC)
VdP d'Oc Chardonnay, James Herrick
£4.99 (SAI)
VdP d'Oc Sauvignon Blanc, Philippe de
Baudin £4.45 (SAI) £4.99 (SAF)
1995
Bergerac Château la Jaubertie £4.99 (MAJ)
Côtes de St-Mont, Producteurs Plaimont
£4.45 (AD) £4.49 (LAY) £4.50 (TAN)
VdP des Côtes de Gascogne Domaine de
Rieux £4.29 (POR) £4.45 (REI) £4.55 (TAN)
VdP des Côtes de Gascogne Domaine San
de Guilhem £4.50 (MV)
VdP de l'Hérault Chardonnay, Domaine
du Fraisse £4.95 (LEA)
VdP de l'Hérault Marsanne, du Bosc £4.90
(WS)
VdP de l'Hérault Muscat Sec, Bésinet
£4.75 (WS)
VdP d'Oc Chardonnay, Les Domaines
Virginie £4.50 (REI)
VdP d'Oc Chardonnay, Philippe de Baudin
(alias Chais Baumière) £4.99 (CO)
VdP d'Oc Chardonnay, Ryman £4.99 (MAJ)
VdP d'Oc Laperouse £4.49 (CO) £4.69
(BOT) £4.69 (WR) £4.69 (THR)
1994
Coteaux d'Aix-en-Provence Château de
Fonscolombe £4.79 (JON)
Côtes de St-Mont, L'Abadie du Leez
£4.25 (WS)
Côtes de St-Mont, les Hauts de Bergelle
£4.75 (TAN)
VdP d'Oc Sauvignon Blanc, Philippe de
Baudin £4.75 (GRE)
VdP d'Oc Sauvignon, Domaine de la
Belonette £4.59 (JON)

£5.00 → £6.99

1996
Bergerac Domaine de Grandchamp £5.95
(SAI)
Bergerac Sauvignon Château Tour de
Gendres £5.75 (LEA) £5.96 (GN)

Costières de Nîmes Cuvée St Marc,
Château de Belle Coste £6.95 (LEA)
VdP des Côtes de Thongue Chardonnay,
Domaine de la Croix Belle £5.95 (LEA)
VdP des Côtes de Thongue Viognier, la
Condamine L'Évêque £6.95 (LEA)
VdP des Côtes de Gascogne Domaine des
Cassagnoles £5.29 (BOD) £5.29 (SUN)
VdP de l'Hérault Terret Blanc, Domaine
la Fadèze £5.24 (LAY)
VdP d'Oc Chardonnay, James Herrick
£5.20 (FLE)
VdP d'Oc Viognier, Domaine St Hilaire
£6.49 (PIP)

1995
Bergerac Sec Château de Tiregand £5.10
(TAN)
Corbières Domaine du Trillol £5.40 (WS)
Costières de Nîmes Cuvée St Marc,
Château de Belle Coste £6.55 (REI)
Coteaux de Languedoc Cuvée les Pierres
d'Argent, Château de Lascaux £6.95 (LEA)
Côtes du Roussillon Domaine Gauby
£5.90 (GAU)
VdP de l'Hérault Viognier, Domaine du
Bosc £6.75 (WS)

1994
Côtes du Lubéron la Vieille Ferme £6.45
(ROB)
Pacherenc du Vic-Bilh Domaine Boucassé
£6.75 (REI)
Pacherenc du Vic-Bilh Domaine Damiens
£6.25 (BIB)
VdP des Côtes de Gascogne Cuvée
Speciale, Domaine de Joy £6.95 (LEA)
VdP des Côtes de Gascogne Cuvée Bois,
Domaine de Tariquet £6.99 (NA)
VdP d'Oc Chardonnay, Four Terroirs
£5.95 (SAI)

1993
VdP d'Oc Viognier, Domaine St Hilaire
£6.96 (NO)

£7.00 → £9.99

Non-vintage
Costières de Nîmes Château Roubaud
£7.40 (GN)

1996
Coteaux de Languedoc Cuvée les Pierres
d'Argent, Château de Lascaux £8.95
(LEA)
Coteaux de Languedoc Domaine
d'Aupilhac £7.95 (LEA)
VdP d'Oc Viognier, Domaine de Terre
Megere £7.95 (LEA)

1995
Bandol Mas de la Rouvière, Bunan £8.75
(YAP)
Jurançon Sec Domaine Cauhapé £8.69
(NA) £8.75 (WS) £8.91 (ELL) £9.40 (TAN)
Limoux Chardonnay, Domaine de l'Aigle
Cuvée Classique £7.95 (LEA)
VdP des Côtes de Thongue Viognier, la
Condamine L'Évêque £8.44 (GN)
VdP d'Oc Cuvée la Galopine, Domaine de
Terre Megere £7.95 (LEA) £9.95 (VIG)
VdP d'Oc Viognier, Domaine de Terre
Megere £7.50 (VIG)

1994
Bergerac Château la Jaubertie £7.92 (NO)
Jurançon Sec Domaine Cauhapé £8.70 (MV)

1991
Jurançon Sec Domaine Cauhapé £8.06 (FLE)

£10.00 → £19.99

1996
VdP de l'Hérault, Mas de Daumas Gassac
£16.00 (AD) £17.50 (ROB)

1995
Bandol Château de la Rouvière, Bunan
£10.25 (YAP)
Cassis Clos Ste-Magdeleine, Sack £10.25
(YAP)

1994
Palette Château Simone £17.25 (YAP)

1993
Jurançon Sec Clos Guirouilh £10.40 (GN)
VdP de l'Hérault, Mas de Daumas Gassac
£16.99 (WR) £16.99 (BOT)

1992
VdP de l'Hérault, Mas de Daumas Gassac
£14.99 (NI) £17.50 (BEN)

1991
VdP de l'Hérault, Mas de Daumas Gassac
£16.90 (GAU)

c. £23.00

1994
VdP de l'Hérault, Mas de Daumas Gassac
£23.65 (UB)

SWEET WHITE

£7.00 → £12.00

1995
Monbazillac Château Theulet £8.79 (NA)
1994
Jurançon Moelleux, Domaine Cauhapé
£8.99 (NA) £10.25 (STA)
Jurançon Moelleux Vendange Tardive,
Domaine Cauhapé ½ bottle £7.50 (NA)
Monbazillac Château Theulet £8.95 (POR)
£9.90 (GN) £10.95 (ROB)
Monbazillac Château Tirecul la Graviere
£11.95 (LEA)
1993
Monbazillac Château Septy £7.69 (JON)
Pacherenc du Vic Bihl Cuvée St Albert,
Producteurs Plaimont £7.35 (SOM)
1990
Jurançon Clos Guirouilh £11.60 (GN)
1989
Jurançon Moelleux Vendange Tardive,
Domaine Cauhapé ½ bottle £7.87 (NO)

ROSÉ

Under £4.00

1996
Côtes de Provence Domaine Hilaire
Houchart £3.95 (WS)
1995
Côtes du Frontonnais Château le Roc
£3.95 (LEA)
VdP des Coteaux de Murviel, Domaine de
Limbardie £3.50 (SOM)

£4.00 → £5.99

1996
Bergerac Château la Jaubertie £4.99 (VIC)
Côteaux du Languedoc Château de
Lascaux £5.95 (LEA)
1995
Coteaux d'Aix-en-Provence Château de
Fonscolombe £4.79 (JON)
Côtes de Provence Carte Noire,
Vignerons de St-Tropez £5.85 (NEZ)
Côtes du Frontonnais Château le Roc
£4.95 (COU)
VdP d'Oc les Chemins de Bassac £4.95
(LEA)
1994
VdP des Coteaux de Murviel, Domaine de
Limbardie £4.69 (JON)

£8.00 → £15.99

1995
Bandol Mas de la Rouvière £8.75 (YAP)
1994
Palette Château Simone £15.75 (YAP)
1993
Bandol Mas de la Rouvière £9.25 (UB)

SPARKLING

Under £7.50

Non-vintage
Blanquette de Limoux Brut, Cave de
Blanquette de Limoux £6.59 (FUL)
1994
Crémant de Limoux Cuvée St Laurent,
Antech £7.50 (WS)

VINS DOUX NATURELS

Under £8.00

Non-vintage
Muscat de St-Jean-de-Minervois, Cave de
St-Jean-de-Minervois £6.50 (REI)
1994
Maury Vintage Mas Amiel ½ bottle £7.95
(LEA)

£8.00 → £9.99

Non-vintage
Muscat de Frontignan, Château de la
Peyrade £8.57 (ELL) £9.75 (WHI)
1995
Muscat de Rivesaltes Domaine Cazes
£9.95 (HIC)
1994
Muscat de Rivesaltes Domaine Piquemal
£9.95 (LEA) £9.96 (COU)

£10.00 → £15.99

Non-vintage
Maury 15 Ans d'Age, Mas Amiel £15.95
(LEA)
Muscat de Rivesaltes Domaine Cazes
£10.75 (GRE)
1993
Banyuls Domaine de la Rectorie £14.50
(VIG)
Muscat de Rivesaltes Domaine Cazes
£11.95 (ROB)
1986
Maury Mas Amiel £10.95 (VIG)

VINS DE PAYS

**These are my kind of wines: brilliant value, and with more than a touch
of Down Under in their pedigree**

You want to know the name of the latest wine brand? Simple: it's vin de pays.

Yes, I'm serious. We don't buy these wines because they come from the Languedoc or the Aude or anywhere else: we buy them for those three magical words on the label: vin de pays.

Quality is so good – and British wine merchants are so keen on selecting the best wines – that it's getting harder and harder to find the sort of fruitless, tannic reds and oxidized whites that used to be the norm. It would be a very lax wine merchant indeed who let anything like that in these days. (In France, of course, it's a different matter: if you want seriously bad French wines, you have to go to the country of origin.)

The reds are still the best. (I'm talking, of course, about the vins de pays of the South. Vins de pays certainly exist in other parts of France, but it's those of the South that have taken the world by storm.) They display all the spicy, rich fruit you could hope for, plus, at their best, an urbane polish of oak. The whites have improved – they taste more like wine and less like the contents of a sweet jar – but they're not yet showing much sign of developing any particular regional identity.

Australian winemaking, of course, is the key. The Midi isn't in fact totally overrun with Aussies, though a glance at the wine shelves might suggest that it is. But Aussie influence has been decisive in making wines with fruit, fruit, all the way.

Vins de pays come in three categories:

VINS DE PAYS RÉGIONAUX

There are four of these. Vin de Pays du Jardin de la France covers the whole Loire basin across almost to Chablis and down to the Charente. Vin de Pays du Comté Tolosan is for the South-West, starting just below Bordeaux, and covering Bergerac, Cahors, the Tarn and down to the Pyrénées, but not including the Aude and Pyrénées Orientales. Vin de Pays des Comtés Rhodaniens includes the northern Rhône and Savoie; Vin de Pays d'Oc covers Provence and the Midi all the way down to the Spanish border.

VINS DE PAYS DÉPARTEMENTAUX

These are also large groupings, and each one is defined by the boundaries of the *département*. So, for instance, any wine of vin de pays quality grown in the *département* of Vaucluse will qualify for the title 'Vin de Pays du Vaucluse'.

VINS DE PAYS DE ZONE

These are the tightest-controlled of the categories, and can apply to actual communes or carefully defined localities. The allowed yield is lower and there may be more control on grape varieties. So, for example, we could have a Vin de Pays de la Vallée du Paradis which is in the Aude, and could also be sold as Vin de Pays de l'Aude, or as Vin de Pays d'Oc.

MERCHANTS SPECIALIZING IN VINS DE PAYS
see Merchant Directory (page 413) for details

Most merchants have some vins de pays on their lists, but for particularly good ranges try the following: Adnams (AD), Avery's of Bristol (AV), Bibendum (BIB), Anthony Byrne (BY), Eldridge Pope (EL), Forth Wines (FOR), Lay & Wheeler (LAY), Majestic (MAJ), James Nicholson (NI), Oddbins (OD), Thos. Peatling (PE), Thresher (THR), The Ubiquitous Chip (UB), Wine Society (WS)

GERMANY

Fashion in Britain has left German wines behind. To my mind that means they're due for a revival – in fact I'm perfectly happy to lead my own personal, one-man revival of German wines

Do you like your wines upfront – or are you ready for a bit of subtlety?

The reason I ask is that if you want blockbuster flavours and enough new oak to fill a timber yard, then just don't bother about German wines: they're not for you. But if you want to look more closely, then you're in for a treat, because fine German wines (and I'm not talking about Liebfraumilch, Bereich Nierstein or any of those sugar-water abominations) are among the greatest bargains in the shops today.

Germany makes the most astounding fine wines. They balance fruit (peaches, apricots, that sort of thing) with high-tensile acidity, and it's not too difficult to find seven or eight-year old Riesling Kabinetts – absolutely classic wines, just the sort of thing I'm talking about – for £6 or £7. Now, that's a steal.

You'd like to try some, but are baffled by the labelling? Fair enough: read on. In the next few pages I'll be giving you a point-by-point guide to deciphering German wine.

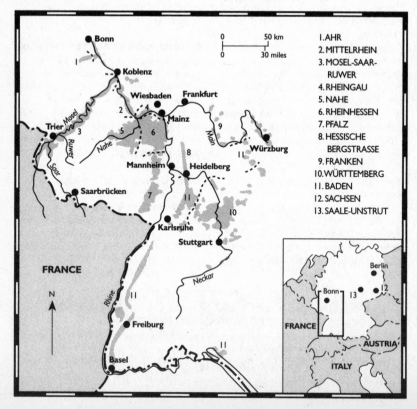

0 50 km	1. AHR
0 30 miles	2. MITTELRHEIN
	3. MOSEL-SAAR-RUWER
	4. RHEINGAU
	5. NAHE
	6. RHEINHESSEN
	7. PFALZ
	8. HESSISCHE BERGSTRASSE
	9. FRANKEN
	10. WÜRTTEMBERG
	11. BADEN
	12. SACHSEN
	13. SAALE-UNSTRUT

QUALITY CONTROL

You'll see one of these terms on every German wine label: they are simply a way of classifying wine according to the ripeness of the grapes when they are picked.

DEUTSCHER TAFELWEIN Basic German table wine of supposedly tolerable quality; low natural alcohol, sugared at fermentation to increase it, no specific vineyard origin stated. Usually little more than sugar-water. However, at the other end of the price spectrum are expensive 'designer table wines' from adventurous producers who may age them in oak.

LANDWEIN German version of vin de pays; table wine from one of 20 designated areas. It can be Trocken (dry) or Halbtrocken (half-dry). Rarely seen.

QbA (Qualitätswein bestimmter Anbaugebiete) Literally 'quality wine from designated regions' – Ahr, Hessische Bergstrasse, Mittelrhein, Nahe, Rheingau, Rheinhessen, Pfalz, Franken, Württemberg, Baden, Mosel-Saar-Ruwer, plus two regions in what was East Germany: Saale-Unstrut and Sachsen. Quality varies from poor to very good, depending on the producer. anything labelled Liebfraumilch, Niersteiner Gutes Domtal or Piesporter Michelsberg is unlikely to be worth a second glance. Go for top estates only.

QmP (Qualitätswein mit Prädikat) Literally, quality wine with special attributes. There are six categories, in order of increasing ripeness of the grapes: Kabinett, Spätlese, Auslese, Beerenauslese, Trockenbeerenauslese and Eiswein. Drier wines (usually Kabinett or Spätlese) may be either Trocken (dry) or Halbtrocken (half-dry). Not all styles are made every year.

KABINETT Made from ripe grapes. Usually lighter in alcohol than ordinary QbA, and often delicious.

SPÄTLESE From late-picked (therefore riper) grapes. Often moderately sweet, though there are now dry versions.

AUSLESE From selected bunches of very ripe grapes. Usually sweet and sometimes touched by 'noble rot', a fungus that concentrates the sugar and acidity in the grapes. In many southern regions, such as Baden, they are fermented dry, making rich and powerful wines.

BEERENAUSLESE (BA) Wines made from selected single grapes almost always affected by the noble rot fungus. Beerenauslese from new, non-Riesling grapes can be dull. But Riesling Beerenauslese, and many a Scheurebe or Silvaner, will be astonishing.

EISWEIN Just that – 'ice wine' – often picked before a winter dawn when the grapes are frozen. They are dashed to the winery by the frost-bitten pickers; once there, quick and careful pressing removes just the slimy-sweet concentrate; the water, in its icy state, stays separate. Eiswein always has a high acidity that needs to be tamed by bottle age, though you do lose the lovely frosty, green apple flavours of youth.

TROCKENBEERENAUSLESE (TBA) 'Shrivelled selected berries' – that's a pedestrian translation of one of the world's great tastes. Individually picked grapes, shrivelled by noble rot, produce small amounts of intensely sweet juice, making TBAs among the sweetest wines in the world. The risks and the costs are both enormous. The vines are making a glass of wine each instead of a bottle, and the weather can easily ruin it all anyway. That's why TBAs are expensive – usually starting at £20 a half-bottle ex-cellars. But, even then, a grower won't make money; it's his pride that makes him do it. And the wines can age for as long as most of us.

GRAPE VARIETIES

DORNFELDER (red) At its best this produces deep-coloured reds with great fruit concentration and firm structure. Made in two styles: reminiscent of Beaujolais and for early drinking (try *Lingenfelder's*) or aged in barriques for longer keeping. Best: *Knipser, Lergenmüller, Lingenfelder, Messmer, Siegrist, Heinrich Vollmer* (Pfalz).

MÜLLER-THURGAU (white) The most widely planted German grape, propagated in 1883 to get Riesling style plus big yields. Well, you can't do it. It produces soft, pot-pourri-scented wines of no distinction, but it produces plenty of them. Occasionally it's made dry and aged in oak; this style is particularly successful in Baden when yields are severely reduced. For the oaked style try *Dr Loosen, Gunderloch, Karl H Johner*.

RIESLANER (white) A sensational crossing of Riesling and Silvaner, but not widely planted. Ripe it tastes of apricots; unripe it tastes, less appealingly, of grass and gooseberries. Best as dessert wine from the Pfalz (especially *Müller-Catoir*) and Franken. Best producers: *Juliuspital, Rudolf Fürst, Robert Schmitt, Schmitt's Kinder* (Franken).

RIESLING (white) Most of Germany's best wines (except in Baden-Württemberg, where the soils are usually unsuitable) are made from this grape. When yields are controlled it produces wonderful flavours: from steely, slaty and dry as sun-bleached bones, through apples, peaches, apricots – more or less sweet according to the ripeness of the grapes and the intentions of the winemaker – and finally arriving at the great sweet wines. These can be blinding in their rich, honeyed concentration of peaches, pineapples, mangoes and even raisins, with acidity like a streak of fresh lime that makes them the most appetizing of sweet wines.

RULÄNDER (white) The French Pinot Gris. As Ruländer the style is strong, sweetish, broad-shouldered, with a whiff of spice and a splash of honey. When called Grauburgunder it is firm, dry, often aged in small oak barriques and can make exciting drinking. Best: *Schlossgut Diel* (Nahe); *Koehler-Ruprecht, Müller-Catoir, Münzberg* (Pfalz); *Bercher, Dr Heger, Karl H Johner, Salwey, Stigler* (Baden); *Johann Ruck* (Franken)

SCHEUREBE (white) A tricky grape. When it's unripe, it can pucker your mouth with its rawness. But properly ripe, there's honey, and a crackling, peppery fire which, in the Pfalz, Baden and Franken, produces dry wines as well as sweeter, sometimes outstanding Auslese and Beerenauslese. Best producers: *Darting, Lingenfelder,*

MATURITY CHART
1995 Rheingau Riesling Spätlese
Riesling Spätlese develops a more refined character after five years in bottle

Bottled	Ready	Peak	Tiring	In decline

0 1 2 3 4 5 6 7 8 9 10 11 12 13 14 15 16 17 18 19 20 years

Messmer, Müller-Catoir (Pfalz); Andreas Laible, Wolff-Metternich (Baden); Rudolf Fürst, Wirsching (Franken).

SILVANER (white) A workhorse grape, often dull, fat and vegetal, but can be impressive in Franken, where it develops honeyed weight with age. It suits the local porky cookery; good with asparagus, too.

SPÄTBURGUNDER (red) Though most German wines from the Spätburgunder (the Pinot Noir of Burgundy) remain pale and thin, there is a new, deeply coloured, rich and powerful style about. Top producers: Meyer-Nakel (Ahr); August Kelleler (Rheingau); Knipser, Koehler-Ruprecht (Pfalz); Bercher, Dr Heger, Bernhard Huber, Karl H Johner (Baden); Rudolf Fürst (Franken); Dautel (Württemberg).

WEISSBURGUNDER or **WEISSER BURGUNDER** (white) Can produce soft, creamy wines with a peach, melted butter, caramel and nuts flavour. Best: Dönnhoff (Nahe); Heyl zu Herrnsheim, Schales (Rhein-hessen); Bergdolt, Müller-Catoir, Rebholz, Wehrheim (Pfalz); Bercher, Dr Heger, Karl H Johner, Franz Keller, Salwey (Baden).

WINE REGIONS AND STYLES

AHR This small area contrives to be famous for red wines, though their flavour and colour are pretty light, and the Rieslings are in fact more interesting. Top producers: Deutzerhof, Meyer-Näkel.

BADEN Dry Ruländer and Weisser Burgunder can be really special here in the balmy South. The Pinot family generally – even Spätburgunder – is on top, although the Ortenau area has fine dry Riesling. The area is dominated by the vast Badische Winzerkeller co-operative. Top names: Bercher, Dr Heger, Bernhard Huber, Karl H Johner, Franz Keller, Andreas Laible, Schloss Neuweier, Salwey, Seeger, Wolff-Metternich.

BEREICH A collection of villages, usually trading on the name of the most famous of them. Bereich wine is usually dull, dull, dull.

DEUTSCHER SEKT Often a sure route to intestinal distress and sulphur-led hangover, although Deinhard makes a decent Riesling version called Lila; Dr Richter's and Georg Breuer's are outstanding, but expensive. Interesting but rare smaller brands are Graeger, Menger-Krug, Schloss Vaux. Avoid at all costs the stuff made from imported wines, labelled Sekt (not Deutscher Sekt), or worse, Schaumwein.

FRANKEN (Franconia) Dry wine country. The slightly earthy, slightly vegetal, big and beefy Franken wines in their flagon-shaped 'Bocksbeutel' bottles are usually based on Silvaner or Müller-Thurgau. Quality is mixed, with only a few wines worth the high prices. Top names: Rudolf Fürst, Juliusspital, Johann Ruck, Egon Schäffer, Schmitt's Kinder, Robert Schmitt, Wirsching.

GROSSLAGE An area smaller than a Bereich, but bigger than a single vineyard. The names sound like those of single vineyards (Piesporter Michelsberg is a Grosslage). Gross deceit is more like it.

HALBTROCKEN Half-dry. The wines need to have more body to balance the acidity, so the best Halbtrockens are from the Rheingau or Pfalz – not the Mosel.

HESSISCHE BERGSTRASSE A tiny side valley of the Rhine from which hardly anything is exported. Generally good Rieslings. Best: Staatsweingut Bergstrasse.

LIEBFRAUMILCH Liebfraumilch was a brilliant invention, an innocuous, grapy liquid that was the perfect beginner's wine. Now most is just cheap sugar-water. Blue Nun isn't bad, but then it's not so cheap.

MITTELRHEIN The Rhine at its most beautiful; tourists flock there and drink most of its wine, but *Toni Jost*'s racy Rieslings have got away. Also good: *Fritz Bastian, Dr Randolf Kauer, Helmut Madess.*

MOSEL-SAAR-RUWER When they are made from Riesling and come from one of the many steep, slaty, south-facing sites in the folds of the river, these northerly wines are unlike any others. Think of a thrilling spring flowers flavour, allied to an alcohol level so low that it leaves your head clear. The lightest yet most intense Rieslings in the world, with a minerally character from the slate soil. Best: *Joh. Jos. Christoffel, Fritz Haag, Reinhold Haart, von Hövel, Karthäuserhof, von Kesselstatt, Dr Loosen, Joh. Jos. Prüm, Max Ferd. Richter, Schloss Saarstein, Willi Schaefer, von Schubert, Selbach-Oster, Dr Wagner, Dr Weins-Prüm, Zilliken.*

NAHE Away from the central hub of quality, where the Rieslings have quite high acidity and a mineral edge, the wines are less reliable. The best now come from *Dönnhoff,* but *Crusius, Schlossgut Diel, Emrich-Schönleber, Kruger-Rumpf and Mathern* are also good. The *Staatliche Weinbaudomäne* is still struggling to regain top form.

PFALZ Used to be called the Rheinpfalz. The northern half clusters round extremely good villages like Forst, Wachenheim, Deidesheim and Ruppertsberg. There's lots of fiery Riesling, and Scheurebe is excellent. The South is Germany's most dynamic region, with fewer big names to fly its flag but an astonishing overall improvement in quality. Look for *Bergdolt, Josef Biffar, Dr Bürklin-Wolf, Fuhrmann-Eymael, Knipser, Koehler-Ruprecht, Messmer, Georg Mosbacher, Müller-Catoir, Rebholz, Karl Schaefer, Werheim, Werlle.*

RHEINGAU Some of Germany's most famous vineyards and renowned aristocratic wine estates are here, and its supremely elegant Rieslings once defined top-quality German wines. However, many of the big estates here have been resting on their laurels for years. The best sign recently has been the (still unofficial) classification of top vineyards. Look for: *Georg Breuer, Domdechant Werner, August Eser, Johannishof, August Kesseler, Frank Künstler, Josef Leitz, Schloss Reinharshausen, J Wegeler (Deinhard), Robert Weil.*

RHEINHESSEN The contrast between Rheinhessen's regular products and its top wines could not be more extreme. It is one of the main sources of Liebfraumilch, yet Nierstein's top Rieslings can match anything from the Rheingau. Top producers: *Gunderloch, Heyl zu Herrnsheim, Keller, St Antony, Schales, Georg Albrecht Schneider.*

SAALE-UNSTRUT The largest wine region in what used to be East Germany.

MATURITY CHART
1995 Mosel Riesling Kabinett
Another good year which will benefit from aging

Bottled	Ready	Peak	Tiring	In decline

| 0 | 1 | 2 | 3 | 4 | 5 | 6 | 7 | 8 | 9 | 10 | 11 | 12 | 13 | 14 | 15 years |

The climate is similar to Franken, the grapes mainly Müller-Thurgau and Silvaner. *Lutzkendorf* has good Riesling and Traminer.

SACHSEN Germany's smallest wine-growing region is rapidly overcoming the legacy of its GDR past. Müller-Thurgau dominates the vineyards, but the best dry wines come from Weissburgunder, Grauburgunder, Kerner, Traminer and Riesling. *Klaus Zimmerling* is the best producer, but *Schloss Proschwitz* and *Jan Ulrich* are also good.

SEKT bA (Sekt bestimmter Anbaugebiete). The best Deutscher Sekt comes from private estates. If the wine comes from one specific region it can be labelled accordingly – for instance, Rheinhessen Sekt – and is generally a step above Deutscher Sekt. Riesling Sekt bA is especially worth looking out for. Try *Schloss Wachenheim* or *Winzersekt*, or *Dr Richter*'s.

TROCKEN Dry: the driest German wines, austere and acidic in unripe vintages. The richer, more alcoholic wines of the Pfalz, Baden and Franken suit dryness best.

WÜRTTEMBERG Most wine from here is drunk on the spot. Its claim to fame – if fame is the right word – is for red. The best grape is Lemberger, dark, spicy and suited to oak aging. Best: *Graf Adelmann, Dautel, Graf von Neipperg, Haidle, Hohenlohe-Ohringen*.

PRODUCERS WHO'S WHO

GEORG BREUER ★★★★ (Rheingau) Convincing promoter of dry Rheingau Riesling. Rüdesheimer Berg Schlossberg and Rauenthaler Nonnenberg are best.

H DÖNNHOFF ★★★★★ (Nahe) Classic Rieslings of great aromatic subtlety and racy intensity. Magnificent Kabinett and Spätlese from the Niederhäuser Hermannshöhle vineyard, and sensational Auslese and Eiswein.

GUNDERLOCH ★★★★★ (Rheinhessen) Explosively fruity, rich, seductive Rieslings from the great Nackenheimer Rothenberg. Jean Baptiste Kabinett is good value; also Beerenauslese and Trockenbeerenauslese of other-worldly concentration and density.

FRITZ HAAG ★★★★ (Mosel-Saar-Ruwer) Wines of crystalline clarity and racy refinement from Brauneberger Juffer-Sonnenuhr.

VON HÖVEL ★★★★ (Mosel-Saar-Ruwer) Since 1992 these have taken a dramatic jump up in quality. Best are the succulent, beautifully balanced wines from Oberemmeler Hütte.

KARTHÄUSERHOF ★★★★★ (Mosel-Saar-Ruwer) Large Ruwer property making wines of concentration and character.

VON KESSELSTATT ★★★ (Mosel-Saar-Ruwer) Huge estate showing big improvements. Look for Rieslings from Graach, Piesport and Wiltingen.

KOEHLER-RUPRECHT ★★★★★ (Pfalz) Powerful dry Rieslings that could be mistaken for top Alsace, plus excellent oak-aged whites and Germany's best Pinot Noir reds, sold under the Philippi label.

FRANZ KÜNSTLER ★★★★★ (Rheingau) Powerful and long-lived Rieslings. Best are the majestic dry and dessert wines from the Hochheimer Hölle.

DR LOOSEN ★★★★★ (Mosel-Saar-Ruwer) Rieslings, Spätlesen and Auslesen from Urziger Würzgarten, Erdener Prälat and Treppchen are tops. For value, try wines without vineyard names.

EGON MÜLLER ★★★★★ (Mosel-Saar-Ruwer) The ultimate in Riesling Auslese, Beerenauslese, Trockenbeerenauslese and Eiswein. No honey tastes this good. Be prepared to pay world-class prices.

MÜLLER-CATOIR ★★★★★ (Pfalz) Highly expressive, rich, dry and naturally sweet wines. Superb Scheurebe and Rieslaner as well as Rieslings.

JOH. JOS. PRÜM ★★★★★ (Mosel-Saar-Ruwer) Wines that need time to show their best; after a few years of aging they are supremely elegant. Wehlener Sonnenuhrs can age for decades without losing vigour.

WILLI SCHAEFER ★★★★ (Mosel-Saar-Ruwer) Small production; wines of great depth and elegance from Graach.

VON SCHUBERT ★★★★★ (Mosel-Saar-Ruwer) Dr Carl von Schubert's Maximin Grünhaus Estate makes exquisitely delicate, fragrant Rieslings that gain enormously with long aging. There are excellent quality wines from QbA right up to TBA, with prices to match.

SELBACH-OSTER ★★★★ (Mosel-Saar-Ruwer) Superbly poised, concentrated Rieslings from Zeltingen.

WEINGUT ROBERT WEIL ★★★★ (Rheingau) Classic Rieslings which combine opulent fruit with clarity and crisp acidity. Best are the Kiedricher Gräfenbergs, all the others being sold without vineyard names.

ZILLIKEN ★★★★ (Mosel-Saar-Ruwer) Racy Saar Rieslings with minerally intensity. Fashionable Eiswein.

VINTAGES

1996   The best are concentrated, with good acidity. A year of extremes of quality: buy from good producers only.

1995   For Germany's top Riesling producers, at least, this looks to be the best vintage since 1990. Few BAs and TBAs, but lots of excellent Spätlese and Auslese.

1994   Strongest in the Mosel-Saar-Ruwer, but looking quite good generally. Outstanding at BA and TBA level.

1993   Rich, occasionally opulent wines that have developed quite quickly. Best in the Rheingau, Pfalz and Mosel. Very good for dry Riesling. Drink during the next few years.

1992   Very good. Like 1989 its problem may be acidity, making for opulent wines which may be short on bite.

1991   The best Rieslings from the Mosel-Saar-Ruwer and the Pfalz are like smaller versions of the 1990s. They will show much better with a year or two more aging.

1990   The best vintage for every region in Germany since at least 1971. Very concentrated, racy wines with great aging potential. Kabinetts are beginning to drink well, and the best Riesling Spätlese and Auslese will be magnificent from the end of the decade.

1989   A mixed vintage: some Kabinett and Spätlese wines are tiring. Best in the Mosel-Saar-Ruwer, Nahe and Pfalz. Some wonderful Auslese, BA and TBA, some not so good.

1988   Wonderful vintage in the Middle Mosel, giving rich wines with marvellous balance. Elsewhere very good. The best Riesling Spätlese and Auslese will still improve.

GERMANY PRICE GUIDES

Kab.	=	Kabinett
Spät.	=	Spätlese
Aus.	=	Auslese
BA	=	Beerenauslese
TBA	=	Trockenbeerenauslese

RHINE WHITE

Under £3.50

1996
Liebfraumilch St Ursula £2.59 (KWI)

£3.50 → £4.50

Non-vintage
Devil's Rock Riesling, St Ursula £3.69 (SO)
Rheingau Riesling, Schloss
  Reinhartshausen £3.65 (SO)
1996
Liebfraumilch Black Tower £3.99 (CO)
Liebfraumilch Blue Nun £3.99 (CO)
1995
Devil's Rock Riesling, St Ursula £3.69 (CO)
Rüdesheimer Rosengarten, Rudolf Müller
  £4.47 (GN)
Niersteiner Gutes Domtal, Rudolf Müller
  £3.70 (HAH) £3.71 (PEN)

£4.50 → £5.49

1995
Johannisberger Erntebringer Riesling Kab.,
  Müller £4.74 (FOR) £4.99 (UN)
Kreuznacher Kronenberg Kab.,
  Zentralkellerei £4.55 (AD)
Niersteiner Spiegelberg Riesling Spät.,
  Rudolf Müller £4.99 (UN)
Oppenheimer Krötenbrunnen, Rudolf
  Müller £4.97 (GN)
Ruppertsberger Hoheburg Riesling Kab.,
  Winzerverein £4.85 (WS)

1994
Niersteiner Auflangen Riesling Spät., R
  Müller £4.85 (AD) £4.95 (POR) £4.99
  (JON)
Niersteiner Spiegelberg Riesling Kab.,
  Rudolf Müller £4.55 (TAN)
1993
Deidesheimer Hofstück Kab., Rudolf
  Müller £4.59 (FOR)

£5.50 → £6.49

1995
Niederhäuser Pfingstweide Riesling, Paul
  Anheuser £5.75 (LON)
1994
Niersteiner Hölle Riesling Kab., Senfter
  £6.39 (HOG)
1993
Oppenheimer Schloss Müller-Thurgau
  Trocken, Guntrum £5.60 (WRI)
1988
Kiedricher Sandgrub Riesling Kab.,
  Schloss Groenesteyn £6.49 (VIC)

£6.50 → £7.49

1995
Hattenheimer Schützenhaus Riesling Kab.,
  Ress £7.04 (LON)
1992
Rheingau Riesling Kab., von Simmern
  £7.39 (JON)
1990
Ruppertsberger Gaisböhl Riesling Kab.,
  Bürklin-Wolf £7.10 (TAN)
Wachenheimer Luginsland Riesling Kab.,
  Bürklin-Wolf £7.49 (DI)
1989
Geisenheimer Mäuerchen Spät.,
  Schönborn £6.99 (WAI)
Schloss Vollrads Grün-Gold, Matuschka-
  Greiffenclau £6.99 (GRE)

MERCHANTS SPECIALIZING IN GERMANY
see Merchant Directory (page 413) for details

Adnams (AD), Averys of Bristol (AV), Bennetts (BEN), Bibendum (BIB), Butlers Wine Cellar (BU) – particularly old vintages, Direct Wine (DI), Eldridge Pope (EL), Gelston Castle, Douglas Henn-Macrae (HE), J E Hogg (HOG), Justerini & Brooks, Lay &

Wheeler (LAY), Longford Wines (LON), Oddbins (OD), Majestic (MAJ), James Nicholson (NI), The Nobody Inn (NO), Thos. Peatling (PE), Reid Wines (1992) Ltd (REI), Tanners (TAN), Ubiquitous Chip (UB), Waterloo Wine (WAT), Wine Society (WS)

£7.50 → £8.49

1996
Eltviller Sonnenberg Riesling Kab., von
Simmern £7.80 (PIP)
1995
Kreuznacher Kahlenberg Riesling Spät.,
Paul Anheuser £7.72 (LON)
Schlossböckelheimer Kupfergrube Riesling
Kab., Staatliche Weinbaudomäne £7.90
(TAN) £7.95 (AD)
1994
Schlossböckelheimer Kupfergrube
Riesling Kab., Staatliche
Weinbaudomäne £8.20 (LAY)
1992
Forster Ungeheuer Riesling Spät.,
Deinhard £8.21 (HOG)
1991
Hochheimer Königin Victoria Berg
Riesling Kab., Deinhard £7.70 (GN)
1990
Schloss Vollrads Blau-Silber, Matuschka-
Greiffenclau £8.28 (HOG)
1989
Johannisberger Mittelhölle Riesling Spät.,
Mumm £8.25 (WS)
Niersteiner Oelberg Riesling Aus.,
Guntrum £7.50 (WRI)
1988
Eltviller Sonnenberg Riesling Kab., von
Simmern £7.99 (JON)
Niersteiner Pettenthal Riesling Spät.,
Balbach £7.89 (VIC)
1987
Rüdesheimer Berg Roseneck Riesling
Kab., Deinhard £8.04 (PEN)

£8.50 → £9.99

1995
Hattenheimer Schützenhaus Riesling Kab.,
Ress £8.79 (COU)
Rüdesheimer Drachenstein Riesling Kab.,
Josef Leitz £9.65 (BER)
Schloss Johannisberg Riesling Kab.,
Metternich £8.75 (GRE)
Wachenheimer Rechbächel Riesling Kab.,
Bürklin-Wolf £9.95 (STA)

> In each price band wines
> are listed in vintage order.
> Within each vintage they
> are listed in A–Z order.

1994
Rüdesheimer Drachenstein Riesling Kab.,
Josef Leitz £8.95 (AD)
1992
Hattenheimer Nussbrunnen Riesling Kab.,
von Simmern £9.95 (AD)
Rüdesheimer Berg Roseneck Riesling
Spät., Josef Leitz £9.95 (AD)
1990
Schlossböckelheimer Kupfergrube
Riesling Spät., Staatliche
Weinbaudomäne £9.39 (JON)
1989
Geisenheimer Schlossgarten Riesling
Spät., Schönborn £8.99 (RAE)
Kiedricher Sandgrub Riesling Kab.,
Schloss Groenesteyn £8.50 (REI)
Schloss Vollrads Blau-Gold, Matuschka-
Greiffenclau £9.75 (EL)
Steinberger Riesling Kab., Staatsweingüter
Eltville £9.10 (HOG)
1988
Deidesheimer Hohenmorgen Riesling
Spät., Bassermann-Jordan £9.95 (RAE)
Forster Ungeheuer Riesling Spät.,
Deinhard £9.48 (PEN)
1986
Wachenheimer Goldbachel Riesling Spät.,
Bürklin-Wolf £9.99 (DI)
1985
Hochheimer Domdechaney Riesling Spät.,
Staatsweingüter Eltville £9.50 (REI)

£10.00 → £11.99

1995
Traiser Bastei Riesling Spät., Crusius
£11.20 (LAY)
1994
Forster Jesuitengarten Riesling Spät., von
Buhl £10.95 (AD)
Schloss Johannisberg Riesling Kab.,
Metternich £11.45 (BEN)
Wachenheimer Rechbächel Riesling Kab.,
Bürklin-Wolf £11.00 (BER)
1992
Riesling Spät. Trocken, Lingenfelder
£11.75 (AD)
Scheurebe Spät. Trocken, Lingenfelder
£10.75 (GRE)
1989
Niersteiner Oelberg Riesling Aus.,
Guntrum £11.50 (STA)
Schlossböckelheimer Kupfergrube
Riesling Spät., Staatliche
Weinbaudomäne £11.55 (HOG)

1988
Deidesheimer Hohenmorgen Riesling
Spät., Bassermann-Jordan £10.99 (JON)
1986
Niersteiner Oelberg Riesling Aus., Senfter
£10.88 (HOG)

£12.00 → £14.99

1996
Wachenheimer Gerümpel Riesling Spät.,
Bürklin-Wolf £12.60 (AD)

1995
Traiser Bastei Riesling Aus.,
Staatsweinbaudomänen £14.65 (AD)
1994
Erbacher Marcobrunnen Riesling Spät.,
von Simmern £14.10 (TAN)
1992
Erbacher Marcobrunnen Riesling Spät.,
von Simmern £14.95 (AD)
Rauenthaler Baiken Riesling Spät., von
Simmern £14.95 (AD)
1990
Forster Jesuitengarten Riesling Spät.,
Bassermann-Jordan £12.91 (GN)
Niersteiner Oelberg Riesling Aus., Senfter
£14.50 (ROB)
1989
Wachenheimer Gerümpel Riesling Spät.,
Bürklin-Wolf £12.65 (PIP) £14.95 (GRE)
Wachenheimer Mandelgarten Scheurebe
Aus., Bürklin-Wolf £13.99 (DI)
1985
Niederhäuser Hermannsberg Riesling
Spät., Staatliche Weinbaudomäne
£13.75 (WAT)
1983
Rauenthaler Baiken Riesling Spät.,
Staatsweingüter Eltville £12.50 (GRE)

£15.00 → £19.99

1994
Forster Jesuitengarten Riesling Spät., von
Buhl £15.95 (NI)

1991
Forster Kirchenstück Riesling Kab.,
Bassermann-Jordan £15.00 (BIB)
1989
Schlossböckelheimer Kupfergrube Riesling
Aus., Staatsdomäne £16.59 (HOG)
1983
Hochheimer Herrenberg Riesling Aus.,
Nagler £17.35 (UB)
Wachenheimer Mandelgarten Scheurebe
Aus., Bürklin-Wolf £17.95 (UB)

£20.00 → £29.99

1976
Niersteiner Hölle Gewürztraminer BA,
Senfter £25.00 (WS)
Oppenheimer Krötenbrunnen, Deinhard
£20.13 (PEN)

c. £42.50

1976
Binger Scharlachberg Riesling BA,
Staatliche Weinbaudomänen £42.50 (UB)

c. £85.00

1971
Geisenheimer Kläuserweg Riesling TBA,
Deinhard £85.00 (REI)

RHINE RED

c. £9.00

1993
Mittelheimer Goldberg Spätburgunder
Trocken, Nägler £8.95 (GRE)

MOSEL WHITE

Under £4.00

Non-vintage
Bereich Bernkastel, Rudolf Müller £3.79
(FUL)
1996
Piesporter Michelsberg Reh £3.99 (MAR)
Piesporter Michelsberg Schneider £3.87
(PLA)
1995
Bereich Bernkastel Riesling, Schneider
£3.51 (PLA) £3.79 (EL)
1994
Deinhard Green Label £3.96 (HOG)

£4.00 → £5.99

1996
Ockfener Bockstein Riesling, Dr Wagner
£5.45 (WAI)
1995
Ockfener Bockstein Riesling Kab., Rudolf
Müller £4.86 (FOR)
Piesporter Michelsberg Rudolf Müller
£5.04 (PEN)
Piesporter Michelsberg Schneider £4.20
(EL)
1994
Reiler vom Heissen Stein Kab., R Müller
£4.59 (JON)

£6.00 → £7.99

1994
Ockfener Scharzberg Riesling, F-W-
Gymnasium £6.70 (TAN)
Wiltinger Braunfels Riesling Kab.,
Kesselstatt £6.50 (WS)
1993
Erdener Treppchen Riesling Spät.,
Monchhof £6.99 (WAI)
1992
Wehlener Sonnenuhr Riesling Kab.,
Richter £7.90 (BER)
1991
Graacher Himmelreich Riesling Kab., F-
W-Gymnasium £6.79 (EL)

1989
Serriger Schloss Saarsteiner Riesling Kab.,
Schloss Saarstein £7.80 (LON)
Trittenheimer Apotheke Riesling Kab.,
Clusserath-Weiler £7.25 (GRE)
1988
Kanzemer Altenberg Riesling Kab.,
Bischöfliches Priesterseminar £7.99 (JON)

£8.00 → £9.99

1996
Wehlener Sonnenuhr Riesling Kab.,
Loosen £8.50 (REI)
1995
Erdener Treppchen Riesling Kab., Dr
Loosen £9.95 (VIG)
Graacher Himmelreich Riesling Kab., F-
W-Gymnasium £8.99 (JON)
Ockfener Bockstein Riesling Kab.,
Kesselstatt £8.50 (STA)
Scharzhofberger Riesling Kab., Kesselstatt
£8.89 (EL) £8.95 (STA) £9.59 (BY)
Trittenheimer Apotheke Riesling Spät., F-
W-Gymnasium £8.95 (POR)
Wehlener Sonnenuhr Riesling Kab., J.J.
Prüm £9.90 (PIP)
1994
Kaseler Nies'chen Riesling Kab.,
Bischöfliches Priesterseminar £8.95 (AD)
Oberemmeler Hutte Riesling Kab., von
Hövel £8.45 (WS)
Saarburger Rausch Riesling Kab., Zilliken
£8.95 (AD)
Scharzhofberger Riesling Kab., Kesselstatt
£8.65 (WS) £8.90 (PIP) £9.75 (GRE)
Wehlener Sonnenuhr Riesling Kab., Loosen
£9.25 (AD) £9.26 (NO) £9.95 (WRI)
1993
Scharzhofberger Riesling Kab., Kesselstatt
£8.65 (NI)
1992
Piesporter Goldtröpfchen Riesling Kab.,
Haart £9.99 (JON) £9.99 (ELL)
1991
Scharzhofberger Riesling Kab., Kesselstatt
£9.49 (DI)
Wehlener Sonnenuhr Riesling Kab.,
Weins Prüm £9.75 (GRE)

> *Stars (★) indicate wines
> selected by Oz Clarke in the
> Best Buys section which begins
> on page 12.*

1990
Wehlener Sonnenuhr Riesling Spät.,
  Deinhard £8.94 (HOG)
1989
Graacher Himmelreich Riesling Spät., Max
  Ferd Richter £8.79 (LON)
Ockfener Bockstein Riesling Spät.,
  Staatlichen Weinbaudomänen £9.10
  (HOG)

£10.00 → £11.99

1995
Graacher Himmelreich Riesling Kab.,
  Prüm £11.20 (LAY)
Graacher Himmelreich Riesling Spät., F-
  W-Gymnasium £11.79 (JON)
Josephshofer Riesling Spät., Kesselstatt
  £10.95 (STA)
Serriger Schloss Saarsteiner Riesling Spät.,
  Schloss Saarstein £11.45 (LON)
1994
Enkircher Batterieberg Riesling Spät.
  Halbtrocken, Carl Aug. Immich-
  Batterieberg £11.05 (AD)
Graacher Himmelreich Riesling Spät., F-
  W-Gymnasium £10.06 (AV)
Ockfener Bockstein Riesling Spät., Zilliken
  £11.80 (AD)
1992
Erdener Treppchen Riesling Kab., Dr
  Loosen £10.95 (AD)
1991
Oberemmeler Hutte Riesling Spät., von
  Hövel £10.87 (COU)
1990
Graacher Himmelreich Riesling Spät., F-
  W-Gymnasium £11.95 (ROB)
1989
Falkensteiner Hofberg Riesling Spät., F-
  W-Gymnasium £10.75 (GRE)
Ockfener Bockstein Riesling Spät.,
  Staatlichen Weinbaudomänen £10.45 (UB)
1988
Bernkasteler Badstube Riesling Spät.,
  Heidemanns-Bergweiler £10.50 (GRE)
Urziger Würzgarten Riesling Aus., Dr
  Loosen £11.69 (JON)
1986
Maximin-Grünhäuser Abtsberg Riesling
  Kab., Schubert £11.95 (GRE)

£12.00 → £14.99

1995
Maximin-Grünhäuser Abtsberg Riesling
  Spät., Schubert £14.95 (LAY)

Maximin-Grünhäuser Herrenberg Riesling
  Spät., Schubert £14.55 (AD)
Wehlener Sonnenuhr Riesling Spät., Dr
  Loosen £12.95 (VIG)
1994
Erdener Treppchen Riesling Spät., Dr
  Loosen £14.82 (NO)
Maximin-Grünhäuser Abtsberg Riesling
  Kab., Schubert £12.95 (LAY) £13.65 (AD)
Scharzhofberger Riesling Kab., Egon
  Müller £14.75 (BER)
1993
Scharzhofberger Riesling Aus., Kesselstatt
  £13.00 (WS)
Wehlener Sonnenuhr Riesling Kab.,
  Weins Prüm £13.25 (UB)
Wehlener Sonnenuhr Riesling Spät., Dr
  Loosen £12.65 (AD)
1992
Erdener Prälat Riesling Spät., Dr Loosen
  £14.95 (AD)

1990
Maximin-Grünhäuser Herrenberg Riesling
  Spät., Schubert £14.69 (JON)
Wehlener Sonnenuhr Riesling Spät.,
  Deinhard £14.70 (BEN)
Wehlener Sonnenuhr Riesling Spät., Dr
  Loosen £13.85 (NO)
1989
Erdener Treppchen Riesling Aus., Dr
  Loosen £12.59 (JON)
Maximin-Grünhäuser Herrenberg Riesling
  Kab., Schubert £13.50 (GRE)
Wehlener Sonnenuhr Riesling Spät.,
  Prüm-Erben £12.95 (DI)
1988
Scharzhofberger Riesling Aus., Kesselstatt
  £14.28 (BY)
1983
Bernkasteler Bratenhöfchen Riesling Aus.,
  Deinhard £12.83 (PEN)
Dhroner Hofberger Riesling Aus.,
  Bischöfliches Priesterseminar £12.25
  (GRE)

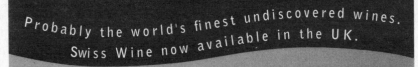

Probably the world's finest undiscovered wines. Swiss Wine now available in the UK.

Swiss Wines have been commented on favourably by connoisseurs for the last ten years and more. At the same time, however, they lamented their unavailability.

Now the good news is Swiss wine is firmly on the UK map.

Swiss wines offer a wide range of most palatable whites, reds and rosés, many of which stand comparison with the French, the German, the Australian, the Bulgarian - indeed a plethora of countries with which you are probably more familiar.

Whatever your interest in wine (as a wine lover, retailer, restaurateur or writer), now is the time to discover what's been missing for far too long.

A closer acquaintanceship with quality Swiss wine.

£15.00 → £19.99

1995
Erdener Treppchen Riesling Aus., Dr
    Loosen £19.45 (AD)
Saarburger Rausch Riesling Aus., Zilliken
    £19.95 (LAY)
Urziger Würzgarten Riesling Aus., Dr
    Loosen £18.68 (NO)
Wehlener Sonnenuhr Riesling Aus., J.J.
    Prüm £19.95 (LAY)
1994
Maximin-Grünhäuser Abtsberg Riesling
    Spät., Schubert £16.00 (WS)
Urziger Würzgarten Riesling Aus., Dr
    Loosen £16.50 (AD)
1993
Ayler Kupp Riesling Aus., Bischöfliches
    Priesterseminar £15.40 (TAN)
Wehlener Sonnenuhr Riesling Kab., J.J.
    Prüm £16.45 (ROB)
1992
Erdener Prälat Riesling Aus., Dr Loosen
    £19.60 (AD)
1991
Wehlener Sonnenuhr Riesling Aus. ½
    bottle, Dr Loosen £17.49 (ELL)
1990
Erdener Treppchen Riesling Aus., Robert
    Eymael £16.38 (GN)
Urziger Würzgarten Riesling Aus., Robert
    Eymael £16.55 (JON)
1989
Scharzhofberger Riesling Kab., Egon
    Müller £16.95 (ROB)
Wehlener Sonnenuhr Riesling Aus., S.A.
    Prüm-Erben £19.50 (DI)
1988
Urziger Würzgarten Riesling Aus.,
    Bischöfliches Priesterseminar £17.39
    (JON)

£20.00 → £29.99

1995
Zeltinger Sonnenuhr Riesling Aus.,
    Selbach-Oster £25.80 (LAY)
1992
Maximin-Grünhäuser Abtsberg Riesling
    Aus. Foudre 64, Schubert £26.75 (AD)
1991
Scharzhofberger Riesling Spät., Egon
    Müller £26.15 (UB)
1990
Bernkasteler Doctor Riesling Aus.,
    Deinhard £25.42 (GN) £27.95 (STA)

Erdener Prälat Riesling Aus., Dr Loosen
    £22.48 (NO)
Maximin-Grünhäuser Abtsberg Riesling
    Aus., Schubert £27.99 (JON)
1989
Josephshofer Riesling Aus., Kesselstatt
    £26.71 (BY)
1985
Bernkasteler Doctor Riesling Spät.,
    Deinhard £29.09 (PEN)

£30.00 → £49.99

1995
Brauneberger Juffer Sonnenuhr Riesling
    Aus. Goldkapsel, Haag £32.95 (VIG)
1993
Mulheimer Helenkloster Riesling Eiswein,
    Richter ½ bottle £40.03 (LON)

c. £53.00

1983
Bernkasteler Graben Riesling Eiswein,
    Deinhard ½ bottle £52.58 (AD)

c. £65.50

1975
Bernkasteler Bratenhöfchen Riesling BA
    Eiswein, Deinhard £65.50 (WRI)

c. £85.00

1959
Wehlener Sonnenuhr Aus., J.J. Prüm
    £85.00 (REI)

BADEN WHITE

Under £14.50

1994
Schloss Castell Silvaner Trocken, Fürstlich
    Castell'sches Domänenamt £8.00 (TAN)
1992
Escherndorfer Lump Riesling Kab.,
    Gebietswinzergenossenschaft £14.15 (UB)
1989
Iphofener Julius Echterberg Riesling Kab.,
    Juliusspital £9.88 (LON)

GERMAN SPARKLING

Under £8.00

Non-vintage
Henkell Trocken £6.59 (SAT) £6.99 (GRE)
Kupferberg Gold £7.69 (GN)

ITALY

In a country where high price tags are relished, and the names of famous regions offer little guarantee of quality, where do you look for value? In the next few pages, that's where

It's an odd place, Italy. In wine terms, anyway. The most famous names, like Soave or Valpolicella, have been devalued to such an extent that only by picking the top wines at top prices can one see why the wines became famous in the first place. To buy wine by appellation alone in Italy is to invite disappointment.

On the other hand, to buy wine by the name of the producer (the usual advice in such circumstances) is to throw away all guidelines. The premium vini da tavola which so many leading growers have opted to make come with no indications of comparative style or quality; all are wild cards. That's the way the producers like it. No wonder they aren't queuing up to insert their wines into the traditional DOC quality classification system, in spite of a new law that allows them to do so.

However, for anyone looking for good value in the middle price bracket (say under £7) the South is the place. Not all the South; there are plenty of producers cashing in on its new quality reputation by dunking large sackfuls of oak chips into otherwise ordinary wines, and charging extra. But dotted all over Campania, Apulia, Basilicata, Sicily, Sardinia, even Calabria, there are producers making wines of richness and structure, even finesse. Sometimes that even applies to the whites.

So in the end it comes back to the old advice: trust the producer. The truth is that there's no simple way to find good wines that you can afford, in Italy or anywhere else. But a small amount of homework before you go looking will pay dividends. Wine is made by individuals, and there is no country with more individuals than Italy.

GRAPE VARIETIES

AGLIANICO (red) A southern grape at its most impressive in Aglianico del Vulture (Basilicata) and Taurasi (Campania).

BARBERA (red) The most prolific grape of Piedmont and the North-West. The wines traditionally have high acidity and a sweet-sour, raisiny taste or even a brown-sugar sweetness. Some are lighter but intensely fruity. The grape does best in the Langhe hills around Alba in the hands of *Altare, Conterno-Fantino, Aldo Conterno, Gaja.*

BONARDA (red) Low acid, rich, plummy reds, often with a liquoricy, chocolaty streak and sometimes a slight spritz. It's found most often in Emilia-Romagna where it is blended with Barbera as Gutturnio; it is also found in the Oltrepò Pavese.

CABERNET FRANC (red) Fairly widely grown in the north-east of Italy, especially in Alto Adige, Trentino, Veneto and Friuli. It can make gorgeous grassy, yet juicy-fruited reds – wines that are easy to drink young but also capable of aging.

CABERNET SAUVIGNON (red) Cabernet has come of age in Italy – it is now part of the intelligent new DOC for Bolgheri Superiore – but so have the producers. It is not going to replace traditional varieties, and while it is still important in the North-East and Tuscany, it is no longer regarded as a panacea for all ills.

CHARDONNAY (white) The typical Italian style is unoaked: lean, floral and sharply balanced from the Alto Adige and

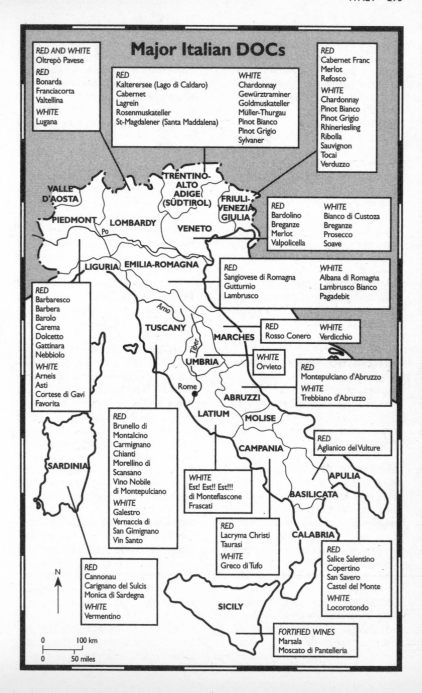

Major Italian DOCs

RED AND WHITE
Oltrepò Pavese

RED
Bonarda
Franciacorta
Valtellina

WHITE
Lugana

RED
Kalterersee (Lago di Caldaro)
Cabernet
Lagrein
Rosenmuskateller
St-Magdalener (Santa Maddalena)

WHITE
Chardonnay
Gewürztraminer
Goldmuskateller
Müller-Thurgau
Pinot Bianco
Pinot Grigio
Sylvaner

RED
Cabernet Franc
Merlot
Refosco

WHITE
Chardonnay
Pinot Bianco
Pinot Grigio
Rhineriesling
Ribolla
Sauvignon
Tocai
Verduzzo

RED
Bardolino
Breganze
Merlot
Valpolicella

WHITE
Bianco di Custoza
Breganze
Prosecco
Soave

RED
Sangiovese di Romagna
Gutturnio
Lambrusco

WHITE
Albana di Romagna
Lambrusco Bianco
Pagadebit

RED
Barbaresco
Barbera
Barolo
Carema
Dolcetto
Gattinara
Nebbiolo

WHITE
Arneis
Asti
Cortese di Gavi
Favorita

RED
Rosso Conero

WHITE
Verdicchio

WHITE
Orvieto

RED
Montepulciano d'Abruzzo

WHITE
Trebbiano d'Abruzzo

RED
Brunello di Montalcino
Carmignano
Chianti
Morellino di Scansano
Vino Nobile di Montepulciano

WHITE
Galestro
Vernaccia di San Gimignano
Vin Santo

RED
Aglianico del Vulture

WHITE
Est! Est!! Est!!! di Montefiascone
Frascati

RED
Lacryma Christi
Taurasi

WHITE
Greco di Tufo

RED
Salice Salentino
Copertino
San Savero
Castel del Monte

WHITE
Locorotondo

RED
Cannonau
Carignano del Sulcis
Monica di Sardegna

WHITE
Vermentino

FORTIFIED WINES
Marsala
Moscato di Pantelleria

VALLE D'AOSTA
PIEDMONT
LOMBARDY
TRENTINO-ALTO ADIGE (SÜDTIROL)
FRIULI-VENEZIA GIULIA
VENETO
LIGURIA
EMILIA-ROMAGNA
TUSCANY
MARCHES
UMBRIA
Rome
ABRUZZI
LATIUM
MOLISE
CAMPANIA
SARDINIA
BASILICATA
APULIA
CALABRIA
SICILY
Po
Arno
Tiber

N

0 ___ 100 km
0 ___ 50 miles

usually more neutral, Mâconnais-style from elsewhere. *Zeni* (Trentino) and *Gradnik* (Friuli) are prime examples. There is exciting, creamy, spicy, barrique-aged wine being made by the likes of *Gaja, Marchesi di Gresy* and *Pio Cesare* in Piedmont, *Zanella* in Lombardy, *Maculan* in the Veneto and both *Caparzo (Le Grance)* and *Avignonesi (Il Marzocco)* in Tuscany. Many wines, though, are inconsistent from year to year, and not all producers seem to have got their winemaking sorted out.

DOLCETTO (red) This is usually light and refreshing with a bitter-cherry twist, though from some producers in Alba, notably *Mascarello*, it is Dolcetto with attitude. Only age the very best.

GARGANEGA (white) The principal grape of Soave, soft yet green-apple fresh when well-made. Cheaper blends use too much characterless Trebbiano Toscano, which spoils things.

GEWÜRZTRAMINER (white) Most plantings are of the less flavoursome Traminer, rather than the spicier, more memorable Gewürztraminer of Alsace. When it is grown, Gewürztraminer can be lovely, needing some time in bottle to develop perfume.

GRECO/GRECHETTO (white) Greco makes crisp, pale and refreshing wines with lightly spicy overtones in the South. Grechetto is part of the same family and its delicious, nutty, aniseed character adds dramatically to Trebbiano-dominated blends in central Italy, as well as sometimes surfacing under its own colours in Umbria, where *Adanti* makes a splendid version.

LAGREIN (red) Local grape of the Alto Adige and Trentino, making delicious, dark reds, strongly plum-sweet when they're young, aging slowly to a smoky, creamy softness. It also makes good rosé called Lagrein Kretzer.

MALVASIA (white) This name and the related Malvoisie apply to a range of grape varieties, some not related. Malvasia is found mostly in Tuscany, Umbria and Latium, where it gives a full, creamy nuttiness to dry whites like Frascati. It also produces brilliant, rich dessert wines with the density of thick brown-sugar syrup and the sweetness of raisins, in Sardinia and the islands of Lipari north of Sicily.

MERLOT (red) Widely planted in the North-East. Often good in Friuli; provides lots of jug wine in the Veneto but when blended with Cabernet Sauvignon by *Loredan Gasparini* (Venegazzù) or *Fausto Maculan* (Trentino) achieves greater stature. Other Cabernet-Merlot blends are produced by *Mecvini* in the Marches and Trentino's *Bossi Fedrigotti* (Foianeghe). *Avignonesi* and *Castello di Ama* in Tuscany are promising, while *Ornellaia*'s *Masseto* (also Tuscany) is outstanding.

MONTEPULCIANO (red) A much underrated grape. Yes, it is tough, and yes it is tannic, but it also has lots of plummy, herby fruit behind that toughness. *Banfi* in Montalcino has high hopes for it. It grows mostly on the Adriatic Coast.

MOSCATO (white) The Alto Adige has various sorts of Muscat, including the delicious Rosenmuskateller and Goldmuskateller, making dry wines to equal the Muscats of Alsace and sweet wines of unrivalled fragrance. But it is at its best in Piedmont, where Asti is a delicious, grapy, sweetish fizz and Moscato Naturale is a heartily perfumed sweet wine. Moscato is best young, but *Ivaldi*'s Passito from Strevi can age beautifully. It also makes fine dessert wines on the island of Pantelleria, south of Sicily.

MÜLLER-THURGAU (white) On the high, steep Alpine vineyards of the Alto Adige this can produce glacier-fresh flavours; not bad in Trentino and Friuli too.

NEBBIOLO (red) The big, tough grape of the North-West, making – unblended – the famous Barolos and Barbarescos as well as Gattinara, Ghemme, Carema, Spanna and plain Nebbiolo. This is a surly, fierce grape, producing wines that can be dark, chewy, unyielding and harsh behind a shield of tannin and acidity for the first few years; but which then blossom out into a remarkable richness full of chocolate, raisins, prunes, and an austere perfume of tobacco, pine and herbs. The newer style still has a fairly hefty whack of tannin, but clever wine-making sheaths this in sleek and velvety fruit. These are ready much sooner. A few growers (*Altare, Clerico, Conterno-Fantino* and *Voerzio*) are producing some superb vini da tavola by aging their wine in barriques, or blending it with Barbera, or both, as in *Sebaste's Briccoviole*.

PINOT BIANCO (white) Produces some of its purest, honeyed flavours in the Alto Adige, and can do very well in Friuli where the best are buttery and full.

RHEINRIESLING/RIESLING RENANO (white) The true German Riesling is grown in the Alto Adige for sharp, green, refreshing, steely dry wines. It can be OK, and slightly fatter, in Friuli and Lombardy. Riesling Italico, nothing to do with real Riesling, is the lesser Olasz/Laski/Welsch Rizling, still good if it's fresh.

SANGIOVESE (red) This grape is the mainstay of Chianti and all the other major Tuscan DOCGs. The wines have in common an austere, tea-like edge balanced by rich fruit. But the grape is very sensitive to its environment, and changes character completely when planted in the cool hills of Chianti, the warm clay soil of the coastal strip or the arid slopes of Montalcino. This sensitivity also accounts for the fact that many vineyards in Chianti Classico, for instance, don't produce the quality they should. Hardly surprising: the soil is too rich, the slopes too gentle and the density of planting too high. The sensitive Sangiovese might respond better if it were moved up the hill a bit, where the soil is stonier. This is the lesson people are now learning, and early results augur well for the future.

SAUVIGNON BLANC (white) Spicy, grassy and refreshing from the Alto Adige and Friuli, though the style is usually more subtle than New World Sauvignon. Tuscan producers include *Volpaia, Castellare, Banfi* and *Avignonesi*.

SCHIAVA (red) Light reds with a unique taste that veers between smoked ham and strawberries. It's found in the Alto Adige, where the locals, who mostly speak German, call it Vernatsch.

SYLVANER (white) Grown very high in the northern valleys of the Alto Adige, at its best this can be dry, lemon-crisp and quite delicious.

TREBBIANO (white) The widely planted Trebbiano Toscano is a wretched thing, easy to grow, producing vast quantities of grapes with frightening efficiency. It is responsible for an awful lot of fruitless, oxidized, sulphured wine that makes you go 'blaagh'. Trebbiano di Soave, the Veneto clone, is much better. Lugana is a Trebbiano DOC of character (*Zenato's* is widely available and good). Abruzzi has a strain which *can* be tasty from producers like *Tenuta del Priore, Pepe* and *Valentini*.

VERNACCIA (white) There are several types of Vernaccia – including some red – but we mostly just see two. Vernaccia di Oristano in Sardinia is a sort of Italian sherry, best dry – when it has a marvellous mix of floral scents, nutty weight and taunting sourness – but also medium and sweet. Vernaccia di San Gimignano *can* be Tuscany's best traditional white – full, golden, peppery but with a softness of hazelnuts and angelica. *Fagiuoli* and *Teruzzi & Puthod* show what can be done.

WINE REGIONS

AGLIANICO DEL VULTURE, DOC

(Basilicata; red) Superb, thick-flavoured red from gaunt Monte Vulture, in the wilds of Italy's 'instep'. The colour isn't particularly deep, but the tremendous almond paste and chocolate fruit is matched by a tough, dusty feel and quite high acidity. What's more, it's *not* very expensive. *Paternoster* and *Fratelli d'Angelo* (especially barriqued *Canneto d'Angelo*) are two good producers.

ALBANA DI ROMAGNA, DOCG

(Emilia-Romagna; white) Uninspiring white DOCG. The wine is dry or sweet, still or slightly fizzy, or very fizzy. At least these days it's less likely to be oxidized and, at its best, the dry version can be delicately scented with an almondy finish. The only really decent producers are *Fattoria Paradiso* and *Zerbina*.

ALTO ADIGE various DOCs (red,

white, rosé) Wines from these dizzily steep slopes are much more Germanic than Italian, and the locals often know the region as the Südtirol. The reds are attractive light wines made from the Vernatsch/Schiava grape, especially Kalterersee and St Magdalener. Cabernet, Pinot Nero, Lagrein and the tea-rose-scented Rosenmuskateller all make reds – and rosés – with more stuffing and personality. But this is also one of Italy's top white regions, making light, dry and intensely fresh wines with spice and plenty of fruit. Best producers: *Lageder, Haas, Hofstätter, Schloss Schwanburg, Tiefenbrunner, Walch* and *Terlan, Schreckbichl,* and *St Michael-Eppan* co-ops.

ARNEIS (Piedmont; white) Potentially

stunning, apples-pears-and-liquorice-flavoured wines from an ancient white grape of the same name, with high prices to match. Best: *Arneis di Montebertotto* by *Castello di Neive, Bruno Giacosa, Deltetto, Malvirà, Negro, Vietti, Voerzio.*

ASTI, DOCG (Piedmont; white)

Elevation to DOCG status means that the 'Spumante' has been dropped from the name. At its best it's wonderfully frothy, fruit-bursting young wine.

CLASSIFICATIONS

Only about 13 per cent of the massive Italian wine harvest comes under the heading of DOC or DOCG, and the regulations are treated in a fairly cavalier manner by many growers. Some producers choose to operate outside the regulations and classify their – frequently exceptional – wine simply as vino da tavola, the lowest grade. A new law means that more of these will come under the DOC umbrella.

Vino da Tavola   This currently applies to absolutely basic stuff but also to maverick wines of the highest class such as Gaja's Piedmontese Chardonnay.

Indicazione Geografiche Tipici (or IGT for short)   This will apply to wines which are typical of their regions, but which do not qualify for DOC. It is equivalent to vin de pays.

Denominazione di Origine Controllata (DOC)   This applies to wines from specified grape varieties, grown in delimited zones and aged by prescribed methods. Most of Italy's traditionally well-known wines are DOC, but more are added every year.

Denominazione di Origine Controllata e Garantita (DOCG)   The top tier – a tighter form of DOC with more stringent restrictions on grape types, yields and a tasting panel. The new law should give recognition to particularly good vineyard sites in future.

BARBARESCO, DOCG (Piedmont; red) Toughness and tannin are the hallmarks of the Nebbiolo, Barbaresco's only grape, but there's also a delicious soft, strawberryish maturity, edged with smoke, herbs and pine. Expect more softness and finesse than in Barolo. Best: *Luigi Bianco, Castello di Neive, Cigliuti, Glicine, Giuseppe Cortese, Gaja, Bruno Giacosa, Marchesi di Gresy, Moresco, Pasquero, Pelissero, Pertinace, Pio Cesare, Produttori del Barbaresco, Roagna, Scarpa, La Spinona* and *Vietti*.

BARBERA, DOC (Piedmont and others; red) Barbera is Italy's second most widely planted red vine after Sangiovese, and makes a good, gutsy wine, usually with a resiny, herby bite, insistent acidity and fairly forthright, dry raisin sort of fruit. It is best in Piedmont, particularly as Barbera d'Alba or d'Asti, and in Lombardy under the Oltrepò Pavese DOC.

BARDOLINO, DOC (Veneto; red, rosé) Pale pinky reds with a frail, wispy cherry fruit and a slight bitter snap to the finish. There are also a few fuller, rounder wines like *Boscaini*'s *Le Canne* which can take some aging. Also *Arvedi d'Emilei, Guerrieri-Rizzardi, Lenotti, Masi* (*Fresco* and *La Vegrona*), *Portalupi* and *Le Vigne di San Pietro*.

BAROLO, DOCG (Piedmont; red)The remarkable flavours of the Nebbiolo – plums and cherries, tobacco and chocolate, liquorice and violets – whirl like a maelstrom in the best wines. The modernization of winemaking techniques in the last ten years has accentuated these flavours, and made wines that are drinkable in five years rather than 20.

Over the last 20 years, producers have been fighting for official classification of the top sites: many are already citing vineyards on the label. Single vineyard wines can be the absolute best (and absolute most expensive) but because anyone's free to put any old vineyard on, standards are not consistent. Best producers: *Altare, Azelia,*

Borgogno, Bovio, Brovia, Cavallotto, Ceretto, Clerico, Aldo and *Giacomo Conterno, Conterno-Fantino, Cordero di Montezemolo, Fontanafredda* (only its *cru* wines), *Bruno Giacosa, Marcarini, Bartolo* and *Giuseppe Mascarello, Pio Cesare, Pira, Prunotto, Ratti, Rocche dei Manzoni, Sandrone, Scarpa, Scavino, Sebaste, Vajra, Vietti* and *Voerzio*.

BIANCO DI CUSTOZA, DOC (Veneto; white) Thought of as a Soave lookalike, though generally better. It contains Tocai, Cortese and Garganega in addition to the less edifying Trebbiano, which helps. But the lack of pressure to make any old liquid as cheaply as possible must be as important. *Gorgo, Portalupi, Santa Sofia, Tedeschi, Le Tende, Le Vigne di San Pietro* and *Zenato* are good.

BOLGHERI, DOC (Tuscany; red, white, rosé) Not only does this DOC cover all colours, including red wines based on Cabernet, Merlot or Sangiovese in various combinations, it even has a special category for Sassicaia. This wine, previously vino da tavola, has intense Cabernet character but higher acidity and slightly leaner profile than most New World Cabernets. It needs about eight to ten years to begin to show at its best. 1985, '88 and '90 are excellent. Pre-1994 vintages are labelled as vino da tavola.

BREGANZE, DOC (Veneto; red) Little-known but excellent claret-like red from near Vicenza. *Maculan* ages it in new wood, which makes it more exciting.

BRUNELLO DI MONTALCINO, DOCG (Tuscany; red) A big, strong neighbour of Chianti. The reason why the wine can be disappointing is that it can lose its fruit during the three-and-a-half years' wood-aging required by law. But in the right hands the fruit can hold out, and then the wine can achieve an amazing combination of flavours: blackberries, raisins, pepper, acidity, tannin and a haunting sandalwood perfume, all bound together by an austere richness resembling liquorice and fierce black chocolate. The best wines come from *Altesino, Argiano, Campogiovanni, Caparzo, Casanova, Case Basse, Il Casello, Castelgiocondo, Col d'Orcia, Costanti, Pertimali, Il Poggione, Talenti* and *Val di Suga. Biondi Santi* is the most famous and the most expensive of all, but I've never had a bottle that justified the enormous cost.

CAREMA, DOC (Piedmont; red) The most refined of the Nebbiolo wines. *Luigi Ferrando* is the best producer; the wines need five to six years to be at their best.

CARMIGNANO, DOCG (Tuscany; red) A small enclave inside the Chianti zone where the soft, clear blackcurrant fruit of Cabernet Sauvignon makes a delicious blend with the somewhat stark flavours of the Sangiovese. There is also some good toasty, creamy rosé and some sweet *vin santo. Capezzana* is the original estate and the only one which is regularly seen here.

CHIANTI, DOCG (Tuscany; red) There are two basic styles of Chianti. The first is the sharp young red with a rather attractive taste: almost a tiny bit sour, but backed up by good, raisiny-sweet fruit, a rather stark, peppery bite and tobacco-like spice. The second type has usually been matured for several years. Expect a range of slightly raw strawberry, raspberry and blackcurrant flavours backed up by a herby, tobaccoey spice and a grapeskins roughness that makes the wine demanding but exciting. Top estates making wines to look for include *Badia a Coltibuono, Castellare, Castello di Ama, Castello dei Rampolla, Castello di San Polo in Rosso, Castello di Volpaia, Felsina Berardenga, Fontodi, Montesodi* and *Nipozzano* (Frescobaldi), *Isole e Olena, Pagliarese, Peppoli* (Antinori), *Riecine, San Felice, Selvapiana, Vecchie Terre di Montefili* and *Villa di Vetrice.*

The Chianti territory is divided into seven sub-zones: Classico, Colli Aretini, Colli Fiorentini, Colli Senesi, Colline Pisane,

Montalbano and Rufina. Classico and Rufina are almost always marked on the label, where appropriate, but most wines from the other zones are simply labelled 'Chianti'.

COLLI EUGANEI, DOC (Veneto; red, white) Generally simple wines, though *Vignalta* produces a Cabernet Riserva and Merlot-based *Gemola* that get high ratings.

COPERTINO, DOC (Apulia; red) The blend of Negroamaro and Malvasia Nera produces robust red wines that can be both elegant, and outstanding bargains. Best producer: the *Copertino* co-op.

DOLCETTO, some **DOC** (Piedmont; red) At its best, delicious. It's a full but soft, fresh, and dramatically fruity red, usually for gulping down fast and young, though some will age a few years. Wonderful ones come from *Altare, Castello di Neive, Clerico, Aldo Contemo, Giacomo Contemo, Marcarini, Mascarello, Oddero, Pasquero, Prunotto, Ratti, Sandrone, Scavino, Vajra, Vietti* and *Voerzio.*

ERBALUCE DI CALUSO, DOC (Piedmont; white) Half the price of Gavi, with a soft, creamy flavour, this is clean-living, plumped-out, affordable white. *Boratto, Ferrando* and *Marbelli* are good; *Boratto* also makes a rich but refreshing Caluso Passito.

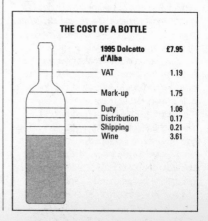

THE COST OF A BOTTLE

	1995 Dolcetto d'Alba	**£7.95**
	VAT	1.19
	Mark-up	1.75
	Duty	1.06
	Distribution	0.17
	Shipping	0.21
	Wine	3.61

FIANO DI AVELLINO, DOC

(Campania; white) Inexplicably famous wine from near Naples, though *Mastroberardino's* single-vineyard *Fiano di Avellino Vignadora* has a brilliant spring flowers scent and honey, peaches and pear skins taste.

FRANCIACORTA, DOCG (Lombardy;

red, white) Champagne method fizz made from Pinots Bianco and Nero and Chardonnay grapes. Best are *Ca' del Bosco* and *Bellavista*, though *Cavalleri, Monte Rosa, Ricci Curbastro* and *Uberti* are also recommended. The DOC of Terre di Franciacorta makes fine still white from Pinot and Chardonnay, and tasty red from Cabernet, Barbera, Nebbiolo and Merlot.

FRASCATI, DOC (Latium; white) Most

Frascati is bland and stale, though the best has a lovely, fresh, nutty feel with an unusual, attractive tang of slightly sour cream. Antonio Pulcini is way ahead with *Colli di Catone, Villa Catone* and *Villa Romana;* his *cru Colle Gaio* is special. Otherwise, *Fontana Candida's* limited releases are also worth a try.

FRIULI, some DOC (red, white) Six

different zones, of which Friuli Grave DOC is by far the most important quantitatively. The red wines are marked by vibrant fruit. In particular, 'international' grape varieties like Cabernet Franc and Merlot have an absolutely delicious, juicy stab of flavour; and Refosco has a memorable taste in the tar-and-plums mould – sharpened up with a fresh grassy acidity. Best: *Ca' Ronesca, Russiz Superiore, La Fattoria, Collavini, Pintar, Borgo Conventi*. There are also some very good fruity and fresh whites made from Pinot Bianco, Pinot Grigio, Chardonnay, Gewürztraminer, Müller-Thurgau, Riesling Renano, Ribolla and Sauvignon and the brilliantly nutty and aromatic white Tocai, all capturing the fresh fruit of the varietal for quick, happy-faced drinking. Best: *Abbazia di Rosazzo, Attems, Borgo Conventi, Collavini, Villa Russiz, Collavini, Dri, Eno Friulia, Volpe*

Pasini, Gravner, Jermann, Livio Felluga, Puiatti, Ronchi di Cialla, Schiopetto. The almost mythical Picolit sweet wine is beautifully made by *Al Rusignul*.

GALESTRO (Tuscany; white) A

collective brand name created to mop up the Trebbiano and Malvasia no longer used in red Chianti. Low alcohol, simple, lemony, greengage taste, high-tech style, best on its home territory.

GATTINARA, DOCG (Piedmont; red)

Nebbiolo-based red that can be good but often has an unappealingly volatile character. *Antoniolo, Brugo, Dessilani* and *Travaglini* are reliable.

GAVI, DOC (Piedmont; white) Cortese is

the grape here, Gavi the area. The wine is dry and sharp, like Sauvignon minus the tang, and fairly full, like Chardonnay without the class. Best are *Deltetto, Arione, Gavi Fior di Rovere* from *Chiarlo, Ca' Bianca*.

KALTERERSEE/LAGO DI
CALDARO, DOC (Alto Adige; red)

Good, light, soft red with an unbelievable flavour of home-made strawberry jam and woodsmoke, made from the Schiava (alias Vernatsch) grape in the Alto Adige (alias Südtirol). It is best as a young gulper. Best producers: *Gries* co-op, *Lageder, Muri-Gries, Hans Rottensteiner, St Michael-Eppan* co-op, *Tiefenbrunner* and *Walch*.

LACRYMA CHRISTI DEL
VESUVIO, DOC (Campania; red, white)

The most famous wine of Campania and Naples. It can be red, white, dry or sweet: *Mastroberardino's* is the best.

LAGREIN DUNKEL, some DOC (Alto

Adige; red) Dark, chewy red with a tarry roughness jostling with chocolate-smooth ripe fruit. The *Gries* co-op, *Lageder, Muri-Gries, Niedermayr* and *Tiefenbrunner* are all good names to seek out. *Tiefenbrunner* also makes very good pink Lagrein Kretzer.

LAMBRUSCO, some **DOC** (Emilia-Romagna; red, white) Good Lambrusco – lightly fizzy, low in alcohol, dry to vaguely sweet – should *always* have a sharp, almost rasping acid bite to it. Real Lambrusco with a DOC, from Sorbara, Santa Croce or Castelvetro (and it will say so on the label), is anything but feeble and is an exciting accompaniment to rough-and-ready Italian food. But most Lambrusco is not DOC and is softened for the British market for fear of offending us. *Cavicchioli* is one of the few 'proper' ones to brave British shelves.

LANGHE, DOC (Piedmont, red, white) This recent DOC covers wines previously sold as vino da tavola. Look for tasty young Langhe Nebbiolo from good Barolo and Barbaresco producers at attractive prices. The DOC also applies to reds Dolcetto and Freisa and white Arneis, Chardonnay and Favorita.

LUGANA, DOC (Lombardy; white) The Trebbiano di Lugana grape makes whites of solid structure and appealingly fruity flavours from *Ca' dei Frati, Premiovini, Provenza, Visconti* and *Zenato*.

MARSALA (Sicily; fortified) This has, at its best, a delicious, deep brown-sugar sweetness allied to a cutting, lip-tingling acidity that makes it surprisingly refreshing for a fortified dessert wine. The rare dry Marsala Vergine is also good. But a once-great name is now in decline. A few good producers keep the flag flying; *De Bartoli* outclasses all the rest, and even makes an intense, beautifully aged, but *unfortified* non-DOC range called *Vecchio Samperi*. His *Josephine Dore* is in the style of *fino* sherry.

MONTEFALCO, DOC and **SAGRANTINO DI MONTEFALCO, DOCG** (Umbria; red) Montefalco Rosso, a blend of Sangiovese, Merlot, Barbera and Sagrantino, is a tasty red that can show style. Sagrantino is a red of great size and strength, that comes in both a dry version

and a sweet Passito, made from semi-dried grapes. Both can age impressively from top producers *Adanti, Antonelli* and *Caprai*.

MONTEPULCIANO D'ABRUZZO, DOC (Abruzzi; red) Good ones are citrus-fresh and plummily rich, juicy yet tannic, ripe yet with a tantalizing sour bite. Best: *Pepe, Mezzanotte, Colle Secco, Illuminati* and *Valentini, Casal Thaulero* co-op.

MORELLINO DI SCANSANO, DOC (Tuscany, red) A similar grape-mix to that of Chianti here gives austere wines with earthy tannins, deep, ripe fruit, and tarry spice. *Le Sentinelle Riserva* from *Mantellassi* is good.

MOSCATO D'ASTI, DOCG (Piedmont; white) Sweet, slightly fizzy wine that captures all the crunchy green freshness of a fistful of ripe table grapes. Heavenly ones come from the following: *Ascheri, Dogliotti, Gatti, Bruno Giacosa, I Vignaioli di Santo Stefano, Michele Chiarlo, Rivetti* and *Vietti. Gallo d'Oro* is the most widely available.

MOSCATO PASSITO DI PANTELLERIA (Pantelleria; white) Big, heavy wine with a great wodge of rich Muscat fruit and a good slap of alcoholic strength.

OLTREPÒ PAVESE, some **DOC** (Lombardy; red, white, rosé) This covers just about anything, including dry whites, sweet whites and fizz. Almost the only wine we see is non-DOC fizz, usually Champagne-method, and based on Pinot Grigio/Nero/Bianco, and some red, which is good, substantial stuff.

ORVIETO, DOC (Umbria; white) Generally modern, pale and dry, sometimes peach-perfumed and honeyed. Best producers: *Scambia, Barberani, Palazzone, Decugnano dei Barbi, Bigi (Cru Torricella Secco* and medium-sweet *Cru Orzalume*

Amabile), Antinori (Cervaro della Sala vino da tavola). Sweet, unctuous, noble-rot affected wines (Antinori's *Muffato della Sala* and Barberani's *Calcaia*) are rarely seen but delicious.

PIEMONTE, DOC (Piedmont, red, white) This recently introduced regional appellation applies to quality wines not covered by the established DOCs of Piedmont. The reds include Barbera, Bonarda, Brachetto and Grignolino. Whites, which may be sparkling, come from Chardonnay, Cortese, Moscato, Pinot Bianco, Pinto Grigio and Pinot Nero.

POMINO, DOC (Tuscany; red, white) The DOC also includes some sweet *vin santo*. The red, based on Sangiovese with Canaiolo, Cabernet and Merlot, becomes rich, soft, velvety and spicy with age. The only producers are *Frescobaldi* and *Giuntini*.

PROSECCO, some **DOC** (Veneto; white) This can be either still or sparkling. It's a lovely fresh, bouncy, light white, often off-dry. Look for *Canevel, Le Case Bianche, Carpenè Malvolti, Collavini.*

ROSSO CONERO, DOC (Marches; red) Very good, sturdy red full of herb and fruit flavours, sometimes with some oak for richness. Producers to look for: *Bianchi, Garofoli, Marchetti, Mecvini* and *San Lorenzo (Umani Ronchi).*

ROSSO DI MONTALCINO, DOC (Tuscany; red) DOC for producers of Brunello who don't want to age wine for Brunello's statutory four years, or who, like the top châteaux of Bordeaux, want to make a 'second wine'. Softer, more approachable and cheaper than Brunello di Montalcino.

ROSSO DI MONTEPULCIANO, DOC (Tuscany; red) This is to Vino Nobile de Montepulciano what Rosso di Montalcino is to Brunello di Montalcino: for 'lesser' Montepulciano, aged for less time in the cellar. Much the same style as big brother, but lighter, more approachable and drinkable younger.

SALICE SALENTINO, DOC (Apulia; red) Impressive wines, deep in colour, ripe and chocolaty, acquiring hints of roast chestnuts and prunes with age. Producers to look for are *Candido, Taurino, Leone De Castris* and *Vallone.*

SOAVE, DOC (Veneto; white) Usually attractive, soft, fair-priced white; slightly nutty, even creamy. Drink it as young as possible, though; it doesn't improve. *Pasqua, Bertani* and *Zenato* make a lot of decent basic stuff.

On a higher level are *Anselmi* (try *Capitel Foscarino*) and *Pieropan*, especially single-vineyard wines *La Rocca* and *Calvarino*. Other good ones are *Boscaini, Zenato,*

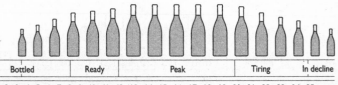

MATURITY CHART
1990 Barolo
A superb year in Piedmont, but patience is needed for the tannins to soften

Bottled	Ready	Peak	Tiring	In decline

0 1 2 3 4 5 6 7 8 9 10 11 12 13 14 15 16 17 18 19 20 21 22 23 24 25 years

Costalunga, Bolla's Castellaro, Santi's Monte Carbonare, Lenotti, Tedeschi's Monte Tenda and the local co-operative's Costalta. Anselmi also makes a Recioto di Soave dei Capitelli which is shockingly good in its pungent sweet-sour way, and Pieropan's unoaked Recioto di Soave is gorgeously redolent of apricots.

SPANNA (Piedmont; red) A Nebbiolo-based wine with a lovely raisin and chocolate flavour in the old style. Even cheap Spannas are a pretty good bet most of the time.

TAURASI, DOCG (Campania; red) Remarkable, plummy yet bitingly austere red, sometimes short on fruit or long on tannin. Mastroberardino is most important.

TOCAI, DOC (Friuli, Veneto; white) Full, aromatic, softly nutty, honeyed wines. Best producers include: Abbazia di Rosazzo, Borgo Conventi, Cà Bolani, Livio Felluga, Caccese, Collavini, Lazzarini, Maculan, Schiopetto, Villa Russiz, Volpe Pasini.

TORGIANO, DOC and **DOCG** (Umbria; red) A region whose fame has been entirely created by Lungarotti. The reds are strong, plummy, sometimes overbearing, usually carrying the trade name Rubesco. Single-vineyard Monticchio and San Giorgio Cabernet Sauvignon are exciting. Torgiano Rosso Riserva is DOCG. White wines here are also clean and good. Lungarotti also makes a good flor-affected sherry-type wine called Solleone.

TRENTINO, DOC (red, white) Some of Italy's best Pinot Bianco and Chardonnay comes from here, as well as some interesting whites from Riesling, Müller-Thurgau and excellent dry Muscat. But until they stop grossly overproducing we're never going to see the full potential. Trento Classico DOC applies to Champagne-method sparkling wines. Look especially for Conti Martini, Gaierhof, Istituto di San Michele, Mandelli, Pojer e Sandri, Spagnolli and Zeni. Fair vin santo (equivalent to Tuscan dessert wines) comes from Pisoni and Simoncelli. Reds are made either from local grape varieties such as Lagrein, Teroldego and Marzemino or from international grapes like Cabernet, Merlot and Pinot Noir. Best producers: Conti Martini, Foradori, Istituto di San Michele, Guerrieri-Gonzaga, Pojer e Sandri, de Tarczal and Zeni.

VALPOLICELLA, DOC (Veneto; red) Valpolicella should have delicious, light, cherry-fruit and a bitter almond twist to the finish – a bit fuller and deeper than Bardolino with a hint more sourness. Producers with good flavours: Allegrini, Boscaini, Guerrieri-Rizzardi, Quintarelli, Le Ragose, Santi, Tedeschi, Masi and Zenato.

There are a few single-vineyard wines, like Masi's Serègo Alighieri, which are way

---

MATURITY CHART
1990 Chianti Classico Riserva
A great Tuscan vintage with wines built to last a decade

Bottled		Ready		Peak		Tiring	In decline
0 1 2 3 4		5 6 7		8 9 10 11		12 13 14	15 years

ahead. They cost more, but Allegrini's *La Grola* or Tedeschi's *Ca' Nicalo* show what Valpolicella should be about. You might also look for wine made by the traditional *ripasso* method. In this system, new wine is pumped over the skins and lees of Recioto or Amarone, starting a small re-fermentation and adding an exciting sweet-sour dimension to the taste. *Masi, Quintarelli* and *Tedeschi* all do this really well.

But the wine which can be really great is the weird and wonderful Recioto Amarone della Valpolicella. It's made from half-shrivelled grapes and has a brilliant array of flavours – sweet grape skins, chocolate, plums and wood smoke – and a shocking, penetrating bruised sourness. The good stuff is usually about three times the price of simple Valpolicella, but it's still good value. If the label simply says 'Recioto della Valpolicella', the wine will be sweet and may still be excellent but will be, to my mind, a little less strangely special. Fine examples come from producers like *Allegrini, Bertani, Masi, Quintarelli, Le Ragose* and *Tedeschi*.

VALTELLINA, DOC (Lombardy; red) Slightly stringy Nebbiolo.

VERDICCHIO, DOC (Marches; white) Reliable rather than exciting – usually extremely dry, lean, clean, nutty with a streak of dry honey, sharpened by slightly green acidity. *Fazi-Battaglia's* single-vineyard vino da tavola *Le Moie* shows the potential. There is also some fizz. The two leading areas are Verdicchio dei Castelli di Jesi and Verdicchio di Matelica. The rarer Matelica wines often have more flavour. Good

producers: *Brunori, Bucci, Fabrini, Fazi-Battaglia, Garofoli, Mecvini, Monte Schiavo, Umani Ronchi, Zaccagnini*.

VERDUZZO, DOC (Friuli and Veneto) This is usually a soft, nutty, low acid yet refreshing light white. The DOC also includes a lovely, gentle fizz, and some of Italy's best sweet wines, in particular *Dri's Verduzzo di Ramandolo* and *Abbazia di Rosazzo's Amabile*.

VERNACCIA DI SAN GIMIGNANO, DOCG (Tuscany) Can be attractively nutty, but is too often a model of bland neutrality. Exceptions: *Frigeni, Fagiuoli, Falchini, San Quirico, Teruzzi & Puthod* and *La Torre*.

VINO NOBILE DI MONTEPULCIANO, DOCG (Tuscany) Like Chianti only more so. Usually, this means more pepper, acid and tannin at a higher price, but the best has a marvellously dry fragrance reminiscent almost of sandalwood, backed up by good Sangiovese spice, and a strong plumskins-and-cherries fruit. Best producers: *Avignonesi, Bindella, Boscarelli, Fattoria di Casale, La Casalte, Fassati, Fattoria del Cerro, Fognano, Poliziano* and *Trerose*.

VIN SANTO Can be one of the great sweet wines, but too often vaguely raisiny and very dull. It *should* have all kinds of splendid, rich fruit flavours – apricots, apples, the chewiness of toffee, smoke and liquorice. *Isole e Olena* seems the best, or try *La Calonica* or *Avignonesi* in Tuscany or *Adanti* in Umbria.

PRODUCERS WHO'S WHO

ABBAZIA DELL'ANNUNZIATA ★★★★ (Piedmont) One of the great producers of Barolo. All the wines made here are full of excitement and strongly perfumed, and they develop wonderfully in the bottle.

ALLEGRINI ★★★★★ (Veneto) Splendid single-vineyard Valpolicella, especially La Grola, Fieramonte and Palazzo della Torre. Amarone and Recioto is some of the best available. Also makes a good vino da tavola, La Poja.

ELIO ALTARE ★★★★ (Piedmont)
New wave producer – wines of firm
structure and tannin behind perfumed fruit.
Highly successful Barolo Vigna Arborina,
very good Barbera and Dolcetto and
barrique-aged Barbera Vigna Larigi.

ALTESINO ★★★★ (Tuscany) Excellent
Brunello and some good vini da tavola,
notably under the names of Alte d'Altesi
and Palazzo Altesi.

CASTELLO DI AMA ★★★★
(Tuscany) Excellent single-vineyard Chianti
Classico: San Lorenzo, La Casuccia,
Bellavista; also a Merlot, Vigna L'Apparita.

ANSELMI ★★★★★ (Veneto) Soave
with character. Cru Capitel Foscarino is as
good as it gets – as is his Recioto dei
Capitelli.

ANTINORI ★★★★ (Tuscany) One of
the great names of Chianti. Excellent
Chianti Classico from estates Pèppoli and
Badia a Passignano; also Tignanello, the
archetypal barrique-aged Sangiovese-
Cabernet blend. Solaia has more Cabernet.
Orvieto estate, Castello della Sala, makes
wonderful vino da tavola white Cervaro
della Sala. Brother Ludovico Antinori has his
own company making Ornellaia, a
Cabernet-based vino da tavola. High price,
high quality.

AVIGNONESI ★★★★ (Tuscany)
Serious Vino Nobile, and two excellent
Chardonnays: Terre di Cortona, without
oak, and Il Marzocco, oak-fermented and
aged wine of considerable depth. I Grifi is
barrel-aged Prugnolo and Cabernet Franc.

BADIA A COLTIBUONO ★★★
(Tuscany) Produces good Chianti and even
better 'Sangioveto', a vino da tavola made
from old vines.

BANFI ★★★ (Tuscany) US-owned
Montalcino winery making international

styles. Brunello Poggio all'Oro is best, and
Tavernelle Cabernet is good. Other wines
are sound.

FATTORIA DEI BARBI ★★★★
(Tuscany) Traditional methods produce
serious Brunello and Rosso di Montalcino,
as well as Brusco dei Barbi, and a single-
vineyard wine, Vigna Fiore.

BIONDI SANTI ★★★ (Tuscany) A
legendary family making a fabulously priced,
but not necessarily legendary wine;
however there are indications that quality is
improving again.

BOLLA ★★★ (Veneto) Large scale
producer of Soave and Valpolicella. Skip the
basic wines and go for Valpolicella Jago.

**BRAIDA-GIACOMO BOLOGNA
★★★** (Piedmont) Saw early the potential
of Barbera in barrique: cru Bricco dell'
Uccellone impresses with depth, balance
and richness. An equally good Bricco della
Bigotta. Unoaked, youthful Barbera, La
Monella. Good Moscato d'Asti and
Brachetto d'Acqui.

CA'DEL BOSCO ★★★ (Lombardy)
Good fizz from Franciacorta. Also vino da
tavola called Maurizio Zanella, blended
from both Cabernets and Merlot, which is
expensive but terrific.

CAPARZO ★★★★ (Tuscany) High
quality producer of Brunello di Montalcino
and Rosso di Montalcino; also an oak-
fermented Chardonnay called Le Grance,
and Ca' del Pazzo, a barrique-aged blend of
Cabernet Sauvignon and Sangiovese.

TENUTA DI CAPEZZANA ★★★★
(Tuscany) The leader in Carmignano, also
making very good Bordeaux blend, Ghiaie
della Furba.

CASTELLARE ★★★★ (Tuscany) Nice
Chianti, splendid vino da tavola I Sodi di San

Niccolò, with a little Malvasia Nera adding perfume to the Sangiovese.

CERETTO ★★★★ (Piedmont) Known for both Barolo and Barbaresco. Barolo Bricco Rocche Bricco Rocche (yes) and Barbaresco Bricco Asili are legendary with prices to match. Also Barolos Brunate, Prapo, Zonchera, and Faset in Barbaresco. Light Barbera and Dolcetto. Arneis is disappointing.

FATTORIA DEL CERRO ★★★ (Tuscany) Traditional producer of Vino Nobile, now working with barriques. Its best wine remains the DOCG Vino Nobile.

CLERICO ★★★★★ (Piedmont) Top-notch producer using barriques to fine effect in Nebbiolo-Barbera blend Arte. Barolo from two *crus* (Bricotto Bussia, Ciabot Mentin Ginestra) are among the best moderns.

ALDO CONTERNO ★★★★★ (Piedmont) Great Barolo, traditionally made, slow to mature but worth the wait. Bussia Soprana is very special, Cicala and Colonello remarkable. Gran Bussia is made in the best years only. Il Favot (barrique-aged Nebbiolo), powerful Barbera, Dolcetto and Freisa also good.

GIACOMO CONTERNO ★★★★★ (Piedmont) Aldo's brother, making excellent Monfortino Barolo, traditional in style.

CONTERNO FANTINO ★★★★ (Barolo, Monforte) Guido Fantino and Diego Conterno have earned a reputation for fine Barolo from the Ginestra hillside. Rich but forward, perfumed wines; should age well.

The Price Guides for this section begin on page 309.

PAOLO CORDERO DI MONTEZEMOLO ★★★ (Piedmont) Wines with the accent on fruit. Standard-bearer is *cru* Monfalletto from La Morra. *Cru* Enrico VI is from Castiglione Falletto, refined, elegant, scented. Also Barbera and Dolcetto.

CARLO DELTETTO ★★★ (Roero, Canale) Good understated, intriguing whites from Arneis and Favorita. Reliable Roero and Gavi.

FELSINA BERARDENGA ★★★ (Tuscany) Winery very much on the up. Vigneto Rancia is a single-vineyard Chianti, I Sistri a barrique-aged Chardonnay. Fontalloro is a Sangiovese, aged in barrique for 12 months.

FONTODI ★★★ (Tuscany) Sleek Sangiovese, in the form of single-estate Chianto Classico or vino da tavola red Flaccianello (plus white Meriggio, Pinot Bianco, Sauvignon and Traminer).

FRESCOBALDI ★★★ (Tuscany) The best Frescobaldi estate is Castello di Nipozzano, with a special selection Montesodi. Also excellent Pomino, including an oak-aged white, Il Benefizio. Excellent Brunello from the Castelgiocondo estate. Also good white wine under the Capitolato label. Mormoreto is a fine Cabernet red.

ANGELO GAJA ★★★★★ (Piedmont) Uses barriques for most wines, including all Barbarescos: Costa Russi, Sorì San Lorenzo, Sorì Tildìn. In the vanguard of Piedmontese Cabernet (Darmagi) and Chardonnay (Gaia and Rey) production. Also makes two Barberas (straight and *cru* Vignarey), two Dolcettos (straight and *cru* Vignabajla), Freisa and a top Barolo from the Marenca Rivette vineyard.

BRUNO GIACOSA ★★★★★ (Piedmont) Traditional wines of, at their best, mind-blowing quality, especially Barbaresco *cru* Santo Stefano and, best of all, Vigna Rionda Barolo. Rich, concentrated not overbearing, elegant. Also white Arneis and good fizz.

MARCHESI DI GRESY ★★★★★
(Piedmont) The leading site, Martinenga, produces Barbaresco, two *crus* – Camp Gros and Gaiun – and a non-wood-aged Nebbiolo called Martinenga; all elegant wines. Whites (Sauvignon and Chardonnay) are also notable.

ISOLE E OLENA ★★★★ (Tuscany)
Rapidly gaining a reputation for fine Chianti Classico. Also Cepparello, a rich pure Sangiovese wine, made from the oldest vines of the estate; outstanding sweet *vin santo* and a superb Syrah.

JERMANN (Friuli-Venezia Giulia) ★★★★
Characterful, subtle vini da tavola: oak-aged Vintage Tunina and daftly named Chardonnay, Where the Dreams have no End. Plain Pinot Grigio and Riesling are also very good.

LAGEDER ★★★ (Alto Adige)
Straightforward varietals are – well, straightforward. Single vineyard wines are far better: Sauvignon Lehenhof and Pinot Grigio Benefizium Porer.

LUNGAROTTI ★★★ (Umbria) The
main name in Torgiano. Also good Chardonnays, called Miralduolo and Vigna I Palazzi. San Giorgio is Cabernet plus Sangiovese.

GIUSEPPE MASCARELLO ★★★★★
(Piedmont) Makes superb *cru* Barolo Monprivato. Also Villero and other *crus*. Barbera d'Alba Ginestra is notable. Excellent inky Dolcetto is produced from a different vineyard each year.

MASI ★★★★ (Veneto) Very good Soave
and Valpolicella, especially Valpolicella

Campo Fiorin. Brilliant Amarone and Recioto. Toar is oaky new vino da tavola.

MASTROBERARDINO ★★★★
(Campania) Leading southern producer making noteworthy Taurasi, and a range of whites including Fiano di Avellino and Greco di Tufo.

MONTEVERTINE ★★★★ (Tuscany)
Outstanding Le Pergole Torte, a barrique-aged Sangiovese. It needs at least five years to open up. Il Sodaccio, from Sangiovese plus Canaiolo, can be drunk young.

CASTELLO DI NEIVE ★★★★
(Piedmont) Impeccable, finely crafted, austerely elegant Barbaresco from Santo Stefano. Barrique-aged Barbera from single *cru* Mattarello and firm, classic Dolcetto from three sites, the best of which is Basarin. Revelatory Arneis.

FRATELLI ODDERO ★★★
(Piedmont) Barolo, Barbera and Dolcetto from own vineyards in prime sites in the area and Barbaresco from bought-in grapes. Good roundness, balance, style and value.

PIEROPAN ★★★★★ (Veneto)
Stunning Soave, in particular La Rocca and Calvarino, both single vineyards. Recioto Le Colombare is divine.

PIO CESARE ★★★ (Piedmont) Full
spread of Barolo, Barbaresco, Nebbiolo d'Alba, Dolcetto, Barbera, Grignolino and Gavi. Wines are gaining elegance, losing a bit of punch but gaining harmony and balance. Experiments with barriques; also Nebbio (young-drinking Nebbiolo), Piodilei (barriqued Chardonnay).

QUINTARELLI ★★★★★ (Veneto)
Revelatory Valpolicella, especially Amarone and Recioto, though all are splendid.

REGALEALI ★★★★ (Sicily) Wonderful
vini da tavola from local grape varieties

ITALIAN VINTAGES

1996   Excellent.

1995   Excellent Barolo and Barbaresco, though Dolcetto was below par. Valpolicella was very good, and there'll be wonderful Amarone and Recioto. Also very good for Central Italian reds, though whites had a less good year all over the country.

1994   Central Italy came off best, with good quality across the board. North-eastern whites are also pretty good. In the North-West, Dolcetto, Moscato and Arneis are very good, but Barbera and Nebbiolo are less so.

1993   Best in the North-East, where the whites have more richness, perfume, length – well, more of everything – than the 1992s, while the reds are excellent. Central Italy looks fair, and the North-West patchy, though Dolcetto was generally successful.

1992   Light, early drinking wines were made across most of the country, though Carmignano is nearly as good as in 1990, and the Marches were also fortunate.

1991   A very fragmented year. Piedmont had a generally difficult time, as did Lombardy, but there was good Valtellina and some exceptional whites. Fair to good overall in the North-West. Tuscany is outstanding, and the Marches and Torgiano are very good. Veneto blessed its good fortune, Friuli made some excellent reds and elegant whites, but Trentino-Alto-Adige was less good.

1990   A fabulous vintage pretty well everywhere: wines of tremendous colour, richness and perfume, Barolo and Barbaresco for long aging and delicious Barbera. Wonderful Dolcetto again. Tuscan wines are built to last.

1989   Unlike the rest of Italy, Piedmont basked in glorious sunshine in 1989. Dolcetto looks even better than in the last five (excellent) vintages, and the Barbera is very good. Reds from elsewhere are less concentrated. Whites often had good perfume, but most should have been drunk by now.

1988   Dolcetto and Barbera have concentration and fruit. Nebbiolo is patchier. Tremendous quality in Central Italy and the North-East.

1987   Very good for Dolcetto and the whites, but patchy Barolo and Barbaresco. Central Italian reds are reasonable, in particular Carmignano; young Chiantis were good but aren't young any more.

1986   Barbaresco and Barolo are overshadowed by the great 1985s, but the quality is good. Chianti Riserva is very good, and Amarone Valpolicella is lovely and drinking beautifully now.

1985   Big rich wines in Central Italy. An exciting vintage in the North-West, when more growers decided to emphasize fruit and perfume.

1983   All but the best are fading, even in the North-West.

1982   Excellent, big ripe reds from Barolo which have the fruit to age. Everything else should have been drunk by now.

include red Rosso del Conte and white Nozze d'Oro. Excellent Chardonnay. The standard range is also very good.

RICASOLI ★★★ (Tuscany) As well as sound Chianti, Ricasoli makes a host of other Tuscan wines at Brolio. The Chianti is currently looking quite good.

GIUSEPPE RIVETTI ★★★ (Piedmont) Smallish quantities of magical Moscato d'Asti which sell out in a flash.

RUFFINO ★★★ (Tuscany) Large Chianti house. Riserva Ducale is its best-known wine. Good vini da tavola include lively Cabreo il Borgo (Cabernet) and succulent, oaky Chardonnay, Cabreo la Pietra. Romitorio di Santedame is Prugnolo (alias Sangiovese) and Colorino.

LUCIANO SANDRONE ★★★★ (Piedmont) A small producer making tiny quantities of perfumed new-style Barolo with lovely raspberry and black cherry flavours from the Cannubi-Boschis vineyard. Also excellent Dolcetto.

TENUTA SAN GUIDO ★★★★★ (Tuscany) Never heard the name? You may have heard of Sassicaia, Italy's leading Cabernet. It used to be vino da tavola; now it has the DOC of Bolgheri.

PAOLO SCAVINO ★★★★ (Piedmont) Hailed locally as one of the emerging masters of Barolo, Scavino makes superb wines which combine purity of fruit with depth and structure. Barolo Bric' del Fiasc' is his top wine; Cannubi and straight Barolo are not far behind. Delicious Dolcetto and Barbera.

TERUZZI & PUTHOD ★★★★ (Tuscany) Commonly acknowledged to be the best producer of Vernaccia di San Gimignano. Its most expensive wine is the oak-aged Terre di Tufo. Whites include Terre di Tufi and Carmen.

VIETTI ★★★★★ (Barolo, Castiglione Falletto) Classically perfect wines of their type, with a punch of acidity and tannin, plus elegance and class. Barolo (straight plus *crus* Rocche, Villero and Brunate) and Barbaresco (*normale* plus *crus* Masseria, Rabajà) are all intensely complex. Dolcetto and Barbera are very good, too. Also makes one of the top Moscato d'Astis and very good Arneis.

ROBERTO VOERZIO ★★★★ (Piedmont) Ultra-modern approach. Fine wines full of fruit and perfume, made with great skill, giving Roberto (not to be confused with brother Gianni) a reputation as a rising star. Produces Barolo, Dolcetto d'Alba, Barbera d'Alba, Freisa, and delicious barrique-aged Barbera-Nebbiolo blend Vignaserra, as well as fine Arneis.

CASTELLO DI VOLPAIA ★★★ (Tuscany) Leading Chianti estate with elegant wines. Balifico is a blend of Sangiovese and Cabernet, exotic and oaky-rich; Coltassala is lovely, austere Sangiovese that needs time.

WINE-FINDER: ITALY

In the Price Guides on the next 15 pages, we have divided Italy into the following geographical regions: North-West, North-East, Central and Southern. If you are unsure which part of the country the wine you're looking for comes from, this guide to some of the best-known names will help.

Asti – *North-West Sparkling*
Barbaresco – *North-West Red*
Barbera – *North-West Red*
Barolo – *North-West Red*
Brunello di Montalcino – *Central Red*
Chianti – *Central Red*
Dolcetto – *North-West Red*
Frascati – *Central White*
Vino Nobile di Montepulciano – *Central Red*
Montepulciano d'Abruzzo – *Southern Red*
Orvieto – *Central White*
Soave – *North-East White*
Valpolicella – *North-East Red*
Verdicchio – *Central White*

ITALY PRICE GUIDES

NORTH-WEST RED

Under £5.00

1996
Dolcetto d'Acqui Viticoltori dell'Acquese
£4.85 (GRE)
1995
Barbera d'Asti Superiore, Araldica £3.95
(WS)
1994
Barbera Bricco Zanone £4.99 (OD)
Dolcetto d'Asti Alasia £4.99 (THR) £4.99
(WR) £4.99 (BOT)
1993
Barbera d'Asti Ceppi Storici £4.99 (VA)

£5.00 → £5.99

1994
Dolcetto d'Asti Alasia £5.50 (GRE)
1993
Barbera d'Asti Ceppi Storici £5.15 (WS)

£6.00 → £6.99

1995
Barbera d'Asti Ceppi Storici £6.20 (PIP)
1994
Dolcetto d'Alba Ascheri £6.60 (EL)
Dolcetto Gemma £6.45 (BER)
1993
Barbera d'Alba Fontanafredda £6.09 (JON)
1990
Nebbiolo d'Alba Fontanafredda £6.95 (VIG)
1987
Gattinara Berteletti £6.05 (HOG)

£7.00 → £7.99

1995
Dolcetto d'Alba Prunotto £7.79 (JON)
Nebbiolo delle Langhe Cascina Morassino
£7.64 (PEN)
1993
Inferno Nino Negri £7.75 (GRE) £7.89 (VA)

1992
Barolo Giacosa Fratelli £7.99 (TES)
Barolo Terre del Barolo £7.89 (VIC)

£8.00 → £9.99

1996
Dolcetto d'Alba Sandrone £8.50 (TAN)
1995
Barbera d'Alba Enzo Bogliette £8.95 (LAY)
1994
★ Barbera d'Alba Sandrone £9.50 (TAN)
Barbera d'Alba Vigna Vigia, Bricco
Maiolica £8.50 (LEA)
Dolcetto d'Alba Aldo Conterno £9.95 (NI)
Dolcetto d'Alba Pian Romualdo,
Mascarello £8.25 (GRE)
Nebbiolo d'Alba il Cumot, Bricco
Maiolicaca £9.95 (LEA)
1993
Barbera d'Asti Guasti Clemente £8.60 (HOG)
Barolo Terre del Barolo £8.99 (SAF)
1992
Barolo Berteletti £9.75 (GRE)
Barolo Cordana, Castiglione Falletto
£9.45 (SOM)
Barolo Nicolello £9.75 (WAI)
1990
Gattinara Travaglini £8.17 (EL)

£10.00 → £12.49

1995
Dolcetto d'Alba Sandrone £11.99 (RAE)
1994
Barbera d'Alba Conca Tre Pile, Aldo
Conterno £10.75 (WS)
Barolo Ascheri £10.72 (FLE) £11.95 (STA)
1993
Barbera d'Alba Conca Tre Pile, Aldo
Conterno £12.25 (GRE)
Barolo Fontanafredda £11.49 (WR) £11.49
(BOT) £11.49 (THR)
Ruchè di Castagnole Monferrato, Casa
Brina £10.80 (NO)

MERCHANTS SPECIALIZING IN ITALY
see Merchant Directory (page 413) for details

These are the merchants to try: Adnams
(AD), Bennetts (BEN), Bibendum (BIB),
Butlers Wine Cellar (BU), Anthony Byrne
(BY), Direct Wine (DI), J E Hogg (HOG), Lay
& Wheeler (LAY), James Nicholson (NI),
Reid Wines (REI), Roberson (ROB), T&W
Wines (TW), The Ubiquitous Chip (UB),
Valvona & Crolla (VA)

1992
Barbaresco Fontanafredda £10.40 (HOG)
Barolo Ascheri £11.89 (VA)
Barolo Gemma £11.51 (GN)
1991
Barolo Ascheri £10.99 (AME)
Barolo Fontanafredda £10.65 (GRE) £10.98 (QUE)
Barolo Gemma £11.39 (SAT)
1990
Barolo Fontanafredda £11.40 (HOG)
1989
Bricco Manzoni, Rocche dei Manzoni £11.29 (YOU)
1982
Barolo Riserva Fontanafredda £11.80 (HOG)

£12.50 → £14.99

1994
Barbaresco Montestefano, Prunotto £13.20 (PIP)
Barbera d'Alba Aldo Conterno £14.49 (VA)
1993
Barbera d'Alba Aldo Conterno £12.85 (NI)
Monpra Conterno Fantino £14.45 (SOM)
1992
Barolo Brunate, Cogno-Marcarini £13.99 (RAE)
Barolo Oddero £13.95 (ROB)
1985
Bricco Manzoni, Rocche dei Manzoni £14.95 (BU)

£15.00 → £19.99

1994
Nebbiolo II Favot, Aldo Conterno £18.00 (PIP) £18.99 (GRE)
1993
Barolo Zonchera Ceretto £15.60 (PIP)
Sitorey, Gaja £17.24 (LAY)
1992
Barolo Pio Cesare £16.30 (HOG)
Barolo Zonchera Ceretto £15.50 (TAN) £15.99 (DI) £17.50 (ROB)
1991
Barolo Monprivato, Mascarello £19.50 (GRE)
1990
Barbaresco Santo Stefano, Castello di Neive £16.95 (VA)
Barolo Gemma £15.95 (BER)
Barolo Pio Cesare £15.50 (GRE)
Sfursat Nino Negri £17.95 (VIG)
1988
Barolo Monprivato, Mascarello £16.99 (AME)

1987
Nebbiolo II Favot, Aldo Conterno £15.75 (BU)
1982
Barolo Riserva Borgogno £18.50 (REI)
1978
Barolo Gattinera, Fontanafredda £15.30 (HOG)

£20.00 → £29.99

1993
Barbaresco Montestefano, Prunotto £20.95 (LAY)
Barolo Bricco Rocche Brunate, Ceretto £22.30 (PIP)
Barolo Bussia, Prunotto £25.95 (LAY)
1991
Barolo Bussia Soprana, Aldo Conterno £20.50 (REI) £20.95 (NI)
Barolo Mascarello £27.50 (RES)
1990
Barbaresco Montestefano, Prunotto £25.00 (RES)
Barbera Vignarey, Gaja £25.26 (FA)
1988
Maurizio Zanella, Ca' del Bosco £25.35 (VA)
1987
Darmagi Gaja £29.50 (REI)
1978
Barolo Franco Fiorina £24.50 (REI)
Barolo Marchesi di Barolo £24.50 (REI)

1971
Barolo Borgogno £29.50 (GRE)
1967
Barolo Borgogno £27.50 (BU)

£30.00 → £39.99

1982
Barbaresco Martinenga, Tenute Cisa Asinari dei Marchesi di Gresy £30.00 (VIG)
1978
Barolo Borgogno £34.95 (VA)

£40.00 → £60.00

1993
Barbaresco Gaja £44.95 (LAY)

1991
Barbaresco Gaja £41.65 (TW)
Darmagi Gaja £41.95 (LAY)
1985
Darmagi Gaja £49.00 (VA) £60.00 (REI)
1967
Barolo Mascarello £59.95 (RES)
1964
Barolo Bussia, Prunotto £55.00 (REI)
1955
Barolo Pio Cesare £40.00 (REI)
1954
Barolo Riserva Borgogno £40.00 (BU)

£70.00 → £105.00

1990
Barbaresco Gaja £105.00 (RES)
1989
Barbaresco Costa Russi, Gaja £76.67 (FA)
Darmagi Gaja £80.00 (VA)
1986
Barbaresco Gaja £70.00 (VA)
Barbaresco Sori San Lorenzo, Gaja £71.38
(NO) £79.90 (TW)
1982
Barbaresco Gaja £72.00 (UB)
1979
Barbaresco Sorì Tildìn, Gaja £90.00 (REI)
1978
Barbaresco Costa Russi, Gaja £95.50 (BEN)

NORTH-WEST WHITE

Under £6.00

Non-vintage
Moscato d'Asti, Araldica £3.95 (WS) £4.34
(ROS)
1996
Cortese del Piemonte, Araldica £4.49 (VA)
Gavi Arione Vini £5.60 (AV)
1995
Chardonnay del Piemonte, Alasia £4.75 (WS)
Cortese del Piemonte, Araldica £4.95 (SAI)
Moscato d'Asti, Araldica £3.75 (SOM)
£4.50 (GRE) £4.69 (JON)

£6.00 → £7.99

1995
Moscato d'Asti Sourgal, Elio Perrone
£6.85 (REI)
1994
Arneis del Roero, Malvirà £7.75 (BIB)
Favorita Malvira £7.75 (AD)
Gavi La Raia £6.50 (BIB)

£8.00 → £11.99

1996
Arneis del Piemonte Renesio, Damonte
£9.95 (AD)
1995
Arneis Blange Ceretto £11.99 (DI)

£13.00 → £22.99

1995
Gavi dei Gavi, la Scolca £22.95 (ROB)
1994
Alteni di Brassica, Gaja £22.50 (LAY)
Chardonnay Rossj Bass, Gaja £17.50 (REI)
1990
Erbaluce di Caluso Passito Boratto £16.95
(VA)

c. £46.50

1994
Chardonnay Gaia & Rey, Gaja £46.50 (REI)

NORTH-WEST SPARKLING

Under £6.00

Non-vintage
Asti Baldovino £5.75 (PLA)
Asti Calissano £5.25 (JON) £5.99 (POR)
Asti Cinzano £4.55 (HOG)
Asti Gancia £5.99 (QUE)
Asti Martini £5.99 (VIC) £5.99 (SO) £5.99
(SAF) £5.99 (UN) £5.99 (CO) £5.99 (WAI)
£5.99 (BOT) £5.99 (TES)
Gancia Spumante £4.99 (VA)

£6.00 → £6.99

Non-vintage
Asti Arione £6.40 (AV)
Asti Martini £6.75 (GRE) £6.85 (FUL)
Asti Sandro £6.45 (WAT)
Gancia Pinot di Pinot £6.99 (VA)

£7.00 → £8.99

Non-vintage
Asti Fontanafredda £7.20 (UB) £8.59 (VA)

NORTH-EAST RED

Under £4.50

1995
Merlot del Veneto, Canaletto £3.84 (ROS)
Valpolicella Rocca Merlata £3.59 (JON)
£3.79 (POR) £3.90 (HAH)

£4.50 → £4.99

1995
Valpolicella Campagnola £4.89 (NA)
Valpolicella Classico Allegrini £4.95 (WS)
1993
Valpolicella Classico Masi £4.99 (OD)

£5.00 → £5.99

1996
Bardolino Classico Ca' Bordenis £5.95 (STA)
Marzemino del Trentino Letrari £5.80 (WS)
Valpolicella Classico Superiore Tedeschi £5.15 (AV)
1995
Bardolino Classico Superiore Masi £5.60 (PIP)
Bardolino Classico Superiore Rizzardi £5.50 (GRE)
Cabernet Sauvignon Atesino, Geoff Merrill £5.69 (SAI)
Valpolicella Classico Allegrini £5.60 (SOM)
Valpolicella Classico Superiore Masi £5.40 (PIP)
Valpolicella Classico Superiore Rizzardi £5.50 (GRE)
1994
Maso Lodron Letrari £5.95 (WS)
Valpolicella Classico Superiore Masi £5.99 (DI)
Valpolicella Classico Superiore Rizzardi £5.20 (HOG)
Valpolicella Classico Superiore Valverde, Tedeschi £5.60 (AD)
1993
Valpolicella Classico Castello d'Illasi, Santi £5.50 (TAN)
Valpolicella Classico Superiore Valverde, Tedeschi £5.49 (EL)
1992
Bardolino Classico Superiore Rizzardi £5.20 (HOG)
Valpolicella Classico Superiore Masi £5.69 (JON)
Valpolicella Classico Superiore Zenato £5.69 (THR) £5.69 (BOT) £5.69 (WR)

£6.00 → £7.99

1996
Valpolicella Classico Allegrini £6.50 (GRE)
1995
Bardolino Classico Ca' Bordenis £6.30 (TAN)

Cabernet Franc Grave del Friuli, Le Monde £6.00 (BIB)
1994
Cabernet Sauvignon Cantina Sociale Della Valdadige Veronese £7.50 (LEA)
1993
Campo Fiorin Masi £7.49 (OD) £7.50 (GRE) £7.99 (VA)

£8.00 → £9.99

1995
Molinara Quintarelli £8.20 (AD)
1994
Marzemino di Isera de Tarczal £8.50 (ROB)
Molinara Quintarelli £8.50 (BIB)
1993
Palazzo della Torre, Allegrini £8.99 (VA) £9.99 (OD)
Valpolicella Classico la Grola, Allegrini £8.99 (VA)
Valpolicella Classico Superiore La Grola, Allegrini £8.50 (WS)
Valpolicella Classico Superiore Zenato £9.95 (BER)
1992
Valpolicella Classico la Grola, Allegrini £9.45 (SOM) £9.49 (HOG)
1991
Amarone della Valpolicella Tedeschi £9.75 (SOM)
1990
Amarone della Valpolicella Tedeschi £9.99 (FUL)

£10.00 → £12.99

1994
Amarone della Valpolicella Masi £11.99 (OD)
Amarone della Valpolicella Montresor £10.66 (HOG)
Venegazzù della Casa Loredan-Gasparini £11.65 (REI)
1993
Amarone della Valpolicella Tedeschi £10.99 (MAJ)
Venegazzù della Casa Loredan-Gasparini £11.39 (VA)
1992
Amarone della Valpolicella Classico, Campagnola £11.99 (WR) £11.99 (THR) £11.99 (BOT)
1991
Amarone della Valpolicella Negrar £10.85 (EL)
Amarone della Valpolicella Santi £11.95 (GRE)

1988
Venegazzù della Casa Loredan-Gasparini
£10.85 (GRE)

£13.00 → £14.99

1993
Amarone della Valpolicella Masi £13.80
(PIP) £13.95 (DI)
1992
Venegazzù della Casa Black Label,
Loredan-Gasparini £14.95 (VA)
1990
Amarone della Valpolicella Allegrini
£13.75 (SOM) £13.95 (WS) £14.89 (VA)
1988
Amarone della Valpolicella Allegrini
£13.89 (ROS)
Amarone della Valpolicella Bolla £13.89
(VA)

£15.00 → £19.99

1993
Amarone della Valpolicella Allegrini
£17.95 (STA)
Amarone della Valpolicella Classico,
Tommaso Bussola £16.50 (LAY)
Amarone della Valpolicella Montresor
£19.49 (VA)
Amarone della Valpolicella Vaio Armaron,
Alighieri £15.30 (PIP)
Recioto della Valpolicella Classico
Allegrini £17.50 (AD)
Valpolicella Classico Superiore La Grola,
Allegrini £15.40 (PIP)
1991
Amarone della Valpolicella Santi £15.99
(QUE)
1989
Valpolicella Classico Superiore Quintarelli
£15.50 (BIB)
1988
Granato Foradori £16.98 (NO)
Recioto della Valpolicella Classico Capitel
Monte Fontana, Tedeschi £15.99 (DI)

£20.00 → £29.99

1994
Venegazzù della Casa Black Label,
Loredan-Gasparini £20.95 (STA)
1991
La Poja, Allegrini £24.49 (VA)
1990
Amarone della Valpolicella Le Ragose
£23.05 (UB) £23.95 (GRE)
La Poja, Allegrini £24.25 (STA)

1986
Amarone della Valpolicella Le Ragose
£23.50 (ROB)
La Poja, Allegrini £25.50 (BEN)
1983
Recioto della Valpolicella Classico Serègo
Alighieri, Masi £29.75 (AD)

£30.00 → £35.00

1986
Amarone della Valpolicella Quintarelli
£30.50 (VA)
1979
Recioto della Valpolicella Riserva
Quintarelli £35.00 (RAE)

NORTH-EAST WHITE

Under £4.00

1996
Bianco di Custoza Geoff Merrill £3.49 (SAI)
Pinot Grigio Ca' Donini £3.99 (VIC)
1995
Soave Rocca Merlata £3.59 (JON) £3.79
(POR)
1994
Soave Via Nova £3.40 (SOM)

£4.00 → £4.99

1996
Bianco di Custoza Teresa Rizzi £4.49 (VA)
Lugana di San Benedetto, Zenato £4.95
(SAI)
Soave Boscaini £4.99 (CO)
Soave Campagnola £4.89 (NA)
1995
Chardonnay Ca' Donini £4.77 (ROS)
Chardonnay del Veneto, Canaletto £4.02
(ROS)
Lugana Riserva Villa Flora, Zenato £4.95
(WAI)
Pinot Bianco della Bergamasca £4.50 (BIB)
Pinot Grigio Cantina Sociale Della
Valdadige Veronese £4.95 (LEA)
Pinot Grigio Ca'vit £4.00 (FLE) £4.79 (NEW)
Soave Classico Vigneto Colombara,
Zenato £4.95 (WAI)

> *In each price band wines*
> *are listed in vintage order.*
> *Within each vintage they*
> *are listed in A–Z order.*

1994
Pinot Grigio Ca'vit £4.79 (POR)

£5.00 → £5.99

1996
Pinot Grigio La Casona £5.50 (GN)
Pinot Grigio Mezzacorona £5.99 (DI)
Soave Classico Monte Tenda, Tedeschi
£5.15 (AV)
Soave Classico Superiore Masi £5.40 (PIP)
1995
Chardonnay Atesino Geoff Merrill £5.49
(SAI)
Chardonnay Trentino, Mezza Corona
£5.75 (WHI)
Pinot Grigio del Veneto Campagnola
£5.79 (NA)
Pinot Grigio Due Torri £5.59 (JON)
Pinot Grigio Trentino, Mezza Corona
£5.99 (WHI)
Soave Classico Monte Tenda, Tedeschi
£5.60 (AD)
Soave Classico Superiore Masi £5.69 (JON)
£5.99 (DI)
Soave Lenotti £5.49 (DI)

£6.00 → £7.99

1996
Pinot Grigio Grave del Friuli, Le Monde
£6.00 (BIB)
Soave Classico Superiore Anselmi £6.99
(VA)
Soave Classico Superiore Pieropan £6.99
(VA) £7.95 (STA)
1995
Lugana Cà dei Frati, Dal Cero £7.25 (WS)
£7.99 (VA)
Pinot Grigio Vigneti di Castagnari,
Valdadige Veronese £6.95 (LEA)
Soave Classico Col Baraca, Masi £7.30 (PIP)
Soave Classico di Monteforte Santi £6.20
(TAN)
Soave Classico Pieropan £7.53 (ROS)
£7.95 (GRE)
Soave Classico Superiore Pieropan £7.90
(TAN)
Soave Classico Zenato £6.39 (NA)
1994
Lugana Cà dei Frati £6.70 (SOM)
Soave Classico Pieropan £7.49 (NI)
£7.95 (BEN)
Soave Classico Superiore Pieropan £6.40
(SOM)
1993
Chardonnay Lageder £7.95 (NI)

£8.00 → £9.99

1995
Breganze di Breganze, Maculan £8.95 (LEA)
Chardonnay EnoFriulia £8.30 (PIP)
Lugana Cà dei Frati, Dal Cero £8.00 (TAN)
£8.30 (BEN)
Pinot Bianco Collio, Puiatti £9.99 (ELL)
Pinot Bianco Jermann £8.95 (NI)
Pinot Grigio Collio, Puiatti £9.20 (SOM)
Soave Classico Capitel Foscarino, Anselmi
£9.99 (VA)
Soave Classico Superiore Anselmi £9.30
(UB)
Soave Classico Vigneto la Rocca, Pieropan
£9.99 (GRE)
1994
Recioto di Soave dei Capitelli, Anselmi ½
bottle £9.50 (REI)
Soave Classico Monte Carbonare, Suavia
£8.00 (BIB)

£10.00 → £11.99

1995
Chardonnay Jermann £11.65 (REI)
Soave Classico Vigneto Calvarino,
Pieropan £10.59 (JON)
1994
Recioto di Soave dei Capitelli, Anselmi ½
bottle £11.95 (ROB)
1993
Recioto di Soave le Colombare, Pieropan
£10.50 (WS)

£12.00 → £13.99

1996
Pinot Grigio Jermann £13.80 (STA) £13.95
(BEN)
1995
Pinot Grigio Jermann £12.15 (UB)
1993
Pinot Bianco Jermann £13.75 (ROB)
Torcolato Vino Liquoroso Maculan
£12.95 (LEA)

£15.00 → £25.99

1995
Tunina Jermann £22.60 (STA)
Vintage Tunina, Jermann £22.95 (VA)
1994
Recioto di Soave dei Capitelli, Anselmi
£16.10 (SOM)
1991
Torcolato Vino Liquoroso Maculan
£25.30 (AD)

NORTH-EAST SPARKLING

Under £4.50

Non-vintage
Alionza Frizzante di Castelfranco £4.25
(SUN) £4.25 (BOD)

£7.50 → £8.50

Non-vintage
Prosecco di Conegliano Carpenè Malvolti
£7.95 (LEA) £8.49 (VA)

£16.00 → £19.00

Non-vintage
Berlucchi Brut £16.49 (VA)
Ferrari Brut £18.99 (VA)

CENTRAL RED

Under £4.50

1996
Sangiovese di Toscana Cecchi £3.79 (SAI)
1995
Chianti Rufina Villa di Vetrice £4.39 (WR)
£4.39 (THR)
Sangiovese di Toscana Cecchi £3.89 (VIC)
1994

Chianti Rufina Villa di Vetrice £4.49 (POR)
£4.49 (JON)
1993
Chianti Rufina Villa di Vetrice £4.39 (BOT)

£4.50 → £4.99

1996
Bolgheri Poggio Fiorito, le Macchiole
£4.95 (LEA)
1995
Chianti Rufina Grati £4.50 (WS)
Chianti Vernaiolo £4.59 (NI)
Rosso Conero San Lorenzo, Umani
Ronchi £4.59 (CO)
Santa Cristina, Antinori £4.89 (GRE)

1994
Chianti Rufina Villa di Vetrice £4.55 (HAH)
£4.60 (AD) £4.65 (TAN) £4.99 (GRE)
Rosso Conero San Lorenzo, Umani
Ronchi £4.99 (NI)
1992
Chianti Rufina Villa di Vetrice £4.50 (SOM)
1990
Chianti Rufina Riserva Villa di Vetrice
£4.95 (WS)

£5.00 → £5.99

1995
Chianti Classico Aziano, Ruffino £5.86
(HOG)
Chianti Classico Rocca delle Macie £5.49
(MAJ)
Chianti Classico Ruffino £5.99 (VA)
Chianti Classico Otto Santi £5.49 (CO)
Chianti Colli Senesi Campriano £5.95 (LEA)
Chianti Rufina Villa di Vetrice £5.30 (PIP)
1994
Chianti Classico Rocca delle Macie £5.40
(GRE) £5.69 (NI)
Chianti Rufina Riserva Tenuta di Remole,
Frescobaldi £5.95 (VA)
Montefalco Rosso d'Arquata Adanti £5.49
(OD)
Parrina Rosso La Parrina £5.99 (VA)
Rosso di Montalcino Villa Banfi £5.99 (MAJ)
Santa Cristina, Antinori £5.39 (BOT) £5.39
(WR)
1993
Chianti Classico Castello di Fonterutoli
£5.95 (WAI)
Chianti Rufina Riserva Villa di Vetrice
£5.19 (BOT) £5.19 (WR) £5.19 (THR)
Rosso Conero San Lorenzo, Umani
Ronchi £5.99 (THR) £5.99 (BOT) £5.99
(WR)
Santa Cristina, Antinori £5.89 (VIC)

1992
Parrina Rosso La Parrina £5.15 (SOM)
1990
Vino Nobile di Montepulciano Cerro
£5.99 (HOG)

£6.00 → £6.99

1996
Rosso di Montepulciano Dei £6.95 (LEA)
1995
Carmignano Barco Reale, Capezzana
£6.50 (WS) £6.74 (FLE)
Rosso de Montepulciano Poliziano £6.95
(LEA)
Rosso di Montepulciano Dei £6.95 (LEA)
Val di Cornia Gualdo del Ré £6.95 (LEA)
1994
Chianti Classico Castello di Fonterutoli
£6.75 (VIC)
Chianti Classico Castello Vicchiomaggio
£6.99 (QUE)
Chianti Classico la Lellera, Matta £6.99
(WHI)
Chianti Classico Villa Cafaggio £6.84 (ROS)
Rosso Conero San Lorenzo, Umani
Ronchi £6.39 (VA) £6.75 (GRE)
1993
Chianti Castello di Volpaia £6.99 (OD)
Chianti Classico Riserva Castello di
Volpaia £6.95 (POR) £6.99 (JON)
Chianti Classico Riserva Villa Antinori
£6.95 (GRE) £6.99 (FUL)
Chianti Rufina Castello di Nipozzano
£6.79 (MAJ)
Chianti Rufina Selvapiana £6.62 (FLE)
Parrina Rosso La Parrina £6.30 (BEN)
1992
Chianti Classico Riserva Castello di
Nipozzano, Frescobaldi £6.75 (HOG)
1991
Chianti Classico Riserva Castelgreve
£6.45 (SAI)
Chianti Classico Villa Antinori £6.35 (HOG)
Grifi Avignonesi £6.85 (REI)
1990
Chianti Rufina Riserva Villa di Vetrice
£6.10 (PIP) £6.39 (JON) £6.65 (AD) £6.90
(BEN)

---

*Stars (★) indicate wines
selected by Oz Clarke in the
Best Buys section which begins
on page 12.*

£7.00 → £7.99

1995
Carmignano Barco Reale, Capezzana
£7.25 (GRE) £7.95 (AD)
Rosso di Montalcino Argiano £7.95 (WS)
Rosso di Montalcino Col d'Orcia £7.49 (VA)
Rosso di Montalcino Villa Banfi £7.40 (PEN)
Bolgheri Vigneto le Contessine, le
Macchiole £7.95 (LEA)
1994
Chianti Classico Castello di Volpaia £7.95
(AD)
Chianti Classico Fontodi £7.95 (WS)

Chianti Classico la Lellera, Matta £7.59
(EL)
Chianti Classico Riserva Antinori £7.69
(NEW) £7.99 (QUE)
Chianti Classico Riserva Villa Antinori
£7.99 (VA)
Chianti Rufina Selvapiana £7.95 (ROB)
Rosso di Montalcino Altesino £7.49 (POR)
Rosso di Montalcino Argiano £7.55 (SOM)
Rubesco Rosso di Torgiano Lungarotti
£7.90 (TAN)
Bolgheri Vigneto le Contessine, le
Macchiole £7.50 (LEA)
1993
Chianti Classico Isole e Olena £7.95 (SOM)
Chianti Classico Riserva Antinori £7.69
(WR) £7.69 (BOT) £7.69 (THR)
Chianti Classico San Felice £7.85 (GRE)
Ser Gioveto, Rocca delle Macie £7.95 (NI)
1992
Ornellaia Le Volte, Tenuta dell'Ornellaia
£7.99 (AME)
1991
Rubesco Rosso di Torgiano Lungarotti
£7.95 (ROB)
1985
Chianti Rufina Riserva Villa di Vetrice
£7.07 (ROS)

£8.00 → £8.99

1995
Chianti Classico San Felice £8.30 (HOG)
Morellino di Scansano le Pupille £8.95 (LEA)
Ornellaia Le Volte, Tenuta dell'Ornellaia
£8.50 (PIP)
Rosso di Montalcino il Poggione £8.95 (AD)
1994
Chianti Classico Felsina Berardenga £8.80
(PIP)
Chianti Classico Riserva Villa Antinori
£8.20 (LAY)
Chianti Colli Senesi Villa Sant' Anna £8.15
(REI) £8.95 (LEA)
Ornellaia Le Volte, Tenuta dell'Ornellaia
£8.75 (BU) £8.75 (CO) £8.80 (STA)
Rosso di Montalcino Talenti £8.50 (BIB)
1993
Chianti Classico Castello di Fonterutoli
£8.39 (NA)
Chianti Classico Riserva Ducale, Ruffino
£8.00 (FOR) £8.06 (HOG)
Chianti Rufina Selvapiana £8.59 (DI)
Parrina Reserva, La Parrina £8.70 (BEN))
Pomino Rosso Frescobaldi £8.99 (OD)
Rosso di Montalcino Lambardi £8.95 (LEA)
Rubesco Rosso di Torgiano Lungarotti
£8.20 (HAH)
Vino Nobile di Montepulciano Avignonesi
£8.75 (WAI)
Vino Nobile di Montepulciano Bindella
£8.75 (BIB)
1992
Chianti Classico Isole e Olena £8.99 (GRE)
1991
Chianti Classico Felsina Berardenga £8.39
(AME)
Chianti Classico Riserva Castello di
Volpaia £8.49 (JON)
Grifi Avignonesi £8.20 (LAY)
Parrina Reserva, La Parrina £8.29 (JON)
1990
Ser Gioveto Toscana £8.60 (GRE)
1986
Carmignano Riserva, Villa Capezzana
£8.51 (FLE)
Vinattieri Rosso Secondo £8.95 (LEA)

£9.00 → £9.99

1994
Chianti Classico Isole e Olena £9.65 (STA)
£9.99 (VA)
Chianti Classico Pèppoli, Antinori £9.45
(GRE) £9.95 (VA)

Chianti Classico Querciabella £9.32 (PEN)
£9.50 (LEA)
Vino Nobile di Montepulciano Dei £9.95
(LEA)
1993
Chianti Classico Felsina Berardenga £9.50
(COU) £9.60 (BEN)
Rosso Conero Cumaro, Umani Ronchi
£9.80 (SOM)
Rosso Conero Fattoria le Terrazze £9.98
(BER)
Vino Nobile di Montepulciano Poliziano
£9.95 (AME)
1992
Chianti Classico Felsina Berardenga £9.89
(DI)
Rosso di Montalcino Argiano £9.39 (NI)
1991
Chianti Classico Felsina Berardenga £9.59
(VA)
Chianti Classico Riserva Castello di
Volpaia £9.20 (AD)
1989
Chianti Classico Riserva Montevertine
£9.50 (REI)
1988
Chianti Classico Riserva di Fizzano, Rocca
delle Macie £9.50 (GRE)
1986
Chianti Classico Riserva Monsanto £9.95
(RAE)
1983
Elegia Poliziano £9.95 (LEA)
Sangioveto Badia a Coltibuono £9.77 (FLE)

£10.00 → £11.99

1995
Rosso Conero Cumaro, Umani Ronchi
£10.85 (REI)
Rosso de Montepulciano Poliziano £10.95
(LEA)
1994
Chianti Classico Riserva Pèppoli, Antinori
£10.20 (TAN)
Chianti Classico Riserva San Polo in
Rosso £11.95 (BER)
Chianti Classico Vecchie Terre di
Montefili £11.85 (WS)
Vino Nobile di Montepulciano Bigi £10.50
(GRE)
1993
Chianti Classico Riserva Marchese
Antinori £10.95 (GRE)
Chianti Classico Vecchie Terre di
Montefili £10.99 (RAE)

Chianti Rufina Riserva Selvapiana £10.20 (BEN)

Vino Nobile di Montepulciano Villa Sant' Anna £10.95 (LEA)

1992

Chianti Classico Fontodi £10.29 (DI)

Felciaia Villa la Selva £10.95 (LEA)

Vino Nobile di Montepulciano le Casalte £11.49 (JON) £11.50 (TAN) £11.95 (UB)

1991

Vino Nobile di Montepulciano Riserva, Dei £10.95 (LEA)

1990

Vino Nobile di Montepulciano Avignonesi £10.89 (VA)

Vino Nobile di Montepulciano Baiocchi £10.49 (VA)

Vino Nobile di Montepulciano le Casalte £10.49 (AME)

£12.00 → £14.99

1994

Chianti Classico Riserva Marchese Antinori £13.95 (LAY)

Il Latini, Il Vivaio £13.50 (WS)

1993

Balifico Castello di Volpaia £14.99 (OD)

Chianti Classico Riserva Felsina Berardenga £13.35 (STA)

Chianti Classico Riserva Querciabella £13.63 (PEN) £13.95 (LEA)

Chianti Classico Riserva Villa Cafaggio £13.95 (BER)

Grosso Senese, Il Palazzino £14.50 (BIB)

Vigna il Vallone Villa Sant' Anna £14.50 (LEA)

Vino Nobile di Montepulciano Riserva, Dei £13.95 (LEA)

Vino Nobile di Montepulciano Vigneto Caggiole, Poliziano £14.95 (LEA)

1992

Brunello di Montalcino Val di Suga £14.99 (DI)

Vigna il Vallone Villa Sant' Anna £13.95 (LEA)

1991

Brunello di Montalcino Argiano £14.20 (SOM)

Brunello di Montalcino Castelgiocondo £12.20 (HOG)

Coltassala Castello di Volpaia £13.95 (AD)

1990

Rosso Conero Cumaro, Umani Ronchi £12.50 (GRE)

Tavernelle Villa Banfi £13.84 (PEN)

1988

Chianti Classico Riserva Castell'in Villa £13.50 (UB)

1986

Bongoverno Farneta £14.21 (NO)

Il Sodaccio, Montevertine £14.50 (ROB)

1985

Sangioveto Badia a Coltibuono £14.28 (NO)

Vinattieri Rosso £12.95 (LEA)

1981

Chianti Classico Riserva Montagliari £13.50 (WS)

£15.00 → £19.99

1994

Elegia Poliziano £17.95 (LEA)

Bolgheri Paleo, le Macchiole £18.95 (LEA)

1993

Chianti Classico Riserva Badia a Coltibuono £15.36 (AV)

Chianti Classico Riserva Montevertine £17.50 (REI)

Bolgheri Paleo, le Macchiole £17.50 (LEA)

Le Stanze Cabernet Sauvignon, Poliziano £17.95 (LEA)

Vino Nobile di Montepulciano Vigna Asinone, Poliziano £15.95 (LEA)

1992

Brunello di Montalcino Argiano £16.90 (PIP)

Brunello di Montalcino Barbi £19.00 (PIP)

Brunello di Montalcino Villa Banfi £19.60 (GN)

Ghiaie della Furba, Capezzana £18.20 (TAN)

1991

Brunello di Montalcino Barbi £17.25 (NI)

Brunello di Montalcino Casanova di Neri £15.99 (VIC)

Brunello di Montalcino Fattoria dei Barbi £17.00 (JON) £17.95 (VA) £18.75 (VIG)

Brunello di Montalcino Talenti £17.00 (BIB)

Cepparello, Isole e Olena £16.75 (REI) £18.99 (NI)

Tignanello Antinori £19.99 (FUL)

1990

Brunello di Montalcino Villa Banfi £17.61 (NO)

Carmignano Riserva, Villa Capezzana £15.90 (TAN) £15.95 (GRE)

Cepparello, Isole e Olena £19.50 (BEN)

Chianti Classico Riserva Fontodi £18.11 (WATT)

Chianti Classico Riserva Vigneto Rancia, Felsina Berardenga £17.43 (WATT)

Fontalloro, Felsina Berardenga £16.45
(SOM)
Il Latini, Il Vivaio £19.95 (LAY)
1989
Brunello di Montalcino Barbi £16.85 (QUE)
1986
Fontalloro, Felsina Berardenga £17.85 (BER)
1982
Sangioveto Badia a Coltibuono £19.50 (REI)
1974
Chianti Classico Riserva Monsanto £18.95
(RAE)

£20.00 → £24.99

1994
Cepparello, Isole e Olena £22.95 (VA)
1993
Quercia Grande, Capaccia £21.50 (VA)
Saffredi le Pupille £23.95 (LEA)
Tignanello Antinori £23.95 (LAY) £24.25
(HAH) £24.95 (LEA) £24.99 (BOT) £24.99
(WR)
1992
Brunello di Montalcino Fattoria dei Barbi
£20.95 (STA)
Ornellaia Tenuta dell'Ornellaia £24.50
(PIP)
Quercia Grande, Capaccia £22.98 (GN)
Tignanello Antinori £23.00 (TAN)
1991
Camartina Querciabella £22.50 (LEA)
Ornellaia Tenuta dell'Ornellaia £23.90
(TAN)
Tignanello Antinori £21.95 (GRE) £23.95
(DI)
1990
Brunello di Montalcino Argiano £20.75
(GRE)
Brunello di Montalcino Riserva, Col
d'Orcia £20.99 (YOU)
Brunello di Montalcino Villa Banfi £23.50
(PEN)
Sangioveto Badia a Coltibuono £23.99
(YOU)
1989
Cepparello, Isole e Olena £21.99 (YOU)
1987
Camartina Querciabella £22.95 (VIG)
1983
Brunello di Montalcino Villa Banfi £22.50
(REI)

£25.00 → £29.99

1994
Tignanello Antinori £25.95 (VA) £28.39 (GN)

1993
Le Pergole Torte, Montevertine £27.25
(REI)
1992
Ornellaia Tenuta dell'Ornellaia £26.50
(BU) £26.95 (VA) £27.95 (LEA)
1991
Ornellaia Tenuta dell'Ornellaia £26.50
(STA)
1990
Tignanello Antinori £25.00 (HOG)
1988
Tignanello Antinori £25.79 (NO)
1975
Brunello di Montalcino Poggio alle Mura
£27.03 (PEN)
1965
Chianti Classico Santa Cristina, Antinori
£28.50 (REI)

£30.00 → £39.99

1993
Sassicaia Incisa della Rocchetta £32.85
(REI) £36.52 (FA)
Tignanello Antinori £30.00 (RES)
1992
Sassicaia Incisa della Rocchetta £32.61 (FA)
1991
Brunello di Montalcino Argiano £30.00
(VA)
Sassicaia Incisa della Rocchetta £33.42
(TAN) £34.99 (BO)
1990
Camartina Querciabella £35.00 (LEA)
1986
Sammarco Castello dei Rampolla £32.50
(VIG)
1977
Brunello di Montalcino Barbi £35.00 (BU)
1975
Brunello di Montalcino Poggio alle Mura
£37.50 (BU)
1967
Chianti Classico Villa Antinori £30.00 (REI)
1966
Chianti Classico Brolio £35.00 (REI)

> *Please remember that*
> ***Webster's** is a price*
> *guide and not a price list. It*
> *is not meant to replace up-*
> *to-date*
> *merchants' lists.*

1964
Brunello di Montalcino Barbi £35.00 (REI)
Chianti Classico Riserva Brolio £32.50
   (REI)
Chianti Classico Santa Cristina, Antinori
   £35.00 (REI)
Chianti Classico Villa Antinori £35.00 (REI)
1962
Chianti Classico Badia a Coltibuono
   £35.00 (REI)
Chianti Classico Riserva Badia a
   Coltibuono £32.50 (REI)

£40.00 → £49.99

1993
Masseto Tenuta dell'Ornellaia £42.50 (REI)
Sassicaia Incisa della Rocchetta £41.00
   (LEA) £42.50 (RES)
1992
Masseto Tenuta dell'Ornellaia £41.50 (REI)
   £48.50 (BEN)
Sassicaia Incisa della Rocchetta £40.95 (DI)
   £42.59 (WR) £42.59 (THR) £42.59 (BOT)
1991
Sassicaia Incisa della Rocchetta £47.00
   (VA)
1987
Tignanello Antinori £45.00 (REI)
1985
Le Pergole Torte, Montevertine £45.00
   (REI)
1971
Brunello di Montalcino Barbi £42.50 (BU)
1968
Brunello di Montalcino Barbi £47.50 (BU)

£50.00 → £79.99

1991
Solaia Antinori £51.95 (DI)
1989
Ornellaia Tenuta dell'Ornellaia £50.00 (REI)
Sassicaia Incisa della Rocchetta £55.00 (VA)
1988
Ornellaia Tenuta dell'Ornellaia £55.13 (FA)
Solaia Antinori £61.12 (NO)
Tignanello Antinori £55.13 (BUT)
1987
Sassicaia Incisa della Rocchetta £53.17 (BUT)
1986
Sassicaia Incisa della Rocchetta £79.61 (BUT)
1982
Tignanello Antinori £64.63 (FA)
1977
Brunello di Montalcino Biondi-Santi
   £74.00 (VA)

£85.00 → £99.99

1990
Ornellaia Tenuta dell'Ornellaia £95.00
   (REI)
1989
Sassicaia Incisa della Rocchetta £85.00
   (REI)
1988
Solaia Antinori £85.00 (REI) £99.19 (BUT)

£100.00 → £149.99

1990
Sassicaia Incisa della Rocchetta £128.56
   (BUT)
1982
Sassicaia Incisa della Rocchetta £112.90
   (FA) £128.56 (BUT)
Solaia Antinori £112.90 (FA)
1980
Sassicaia Incisa della Rocchetta £146.88 (FA)
1975
Brunello di Montalcino Biondi-Santi
   £135.00 (VA)

CENTRAL WHITE

Under £4.00

1996
Frascati Superiore Satinata, Colle di
   Catone £3.99 (ASD)
1995
Est! Est!! Est!!! di Montefiascone, Bigi
   £3.79 (POR)
Grechetto dell'Umbria, Il Vignolo £3.99
   (OD)
Orvieto Classico Secco Cardeto £3.99
   (VIC)
Orvieto Secco Conte Vaselli £3.99 (TES)

£4.00 → £4.49

1995
Colli Amerini, Cotarella £4.39 (OD)
Frascati Superiore Satinata, Colle di
   Catone £4.25 (OD)
Orvieto Classico Secco Antinori £4.42
   (HOG)
Verdicchio dei Castelli di Jesi Classico,
   Umani Ronchi £4.20 (NI)
1994
Frascati Superiore Villa Rufinella £4.08
   (FLE)
Verdicchio dei Castelli di Jesi Classico,
   Umani Ronchi £4.08 (FLE)

£4.50 → £4.99

1996

Bianco Vergine Valdichiana, Avignonesi £4.99 (SUN) £4.99 (BOD)

Frascati Fontana Candida £4.99 (VA)

Verdicchio dei Castelli di Jesi Classico, Umani Ronchi £4.99 (VA)

1995

Frascati Superiore Fontana Candida £4.99 (MAJ) £4.99 (VA)

Frascati Superiore Monteporzio £4.65 (HOG)

Frascati Superiore Villa Catone £4.75 (GRE)

Orvieto Classico Abboccato Antinori £4.56 (HOG) £4.95 (GRE)

Orvieto Classico Secco Antinori £4.99 (VIC)

Orvieto Classico Secco Campogrande, Antinori £4.75 (GRE)

Verdicchio dei Castelli di Jesi Classico, Schiavo £4.75 (GRE)

Vernaccia di San Gimignano Signano £4.95 (WS)

1994

Frascati Superiore Fontana Candida £4.99 (NI)

Orvieto Classico Secco Antinori £4.99 (JON)

Orvieto Secco Antinori £4.99 (NEW)

£5.00 → £5.99

1996

Frascati Superiore Fontana Candida £5.95 (STA)

Frascati Superiore Satinata, Colle di Catone £5.29 (BOT) £5.29 (THR)

Orvieto Classico Abboccato Antinori £5.70 (TAN)

Orvieto Classico Amabile Bigi £5.49 (VA)

Orvieto Classico Secco Bigi £5.60 (STA)

Orvieto Secco Antinori £5.40 (PIP)

Orvieto Secco Bigi £5.49 (VA)

1995

Bianco di Avignonesi, Avignonesi £5.65 (REI) £5.95 (LEA)

Orvieto Classico Campogrande, Antinori £5.75 (GN)

Orvieto Classico Secco Antinori £5.29 (THR) £5.29 (WR) £5.30 (TAN)

Orvieto Classico Secco Bigi £5.17 (ROS)

Orvieto Classico Vigneto Torricella, Bigi £5.50 (SOM)

Orvieto Secco Antinori £5.29 (BOT)

Verdicchio dei Castelli di Jesi, Brunori £5.50 (BIB)

1994

Orvieto Classico Abboccato Antinori £5.49 (WR) £5.49 (BOT) £5.49 (THR)

1993

Frascati Superiore Monteporzio £5.40 (FOR)

£6.00 → £6.99

1996

Orvieto Classico Vigneto Torricella, Bigi £6.75 (GRE) £6.85 (STA) £6.89 (VA)

Verdicchio dei Castelli di Jesi Classico, Casal di Serra £6.39 (VA) £6.85 (STA)

Vernaccia di San Gimignano Riserva, Pietrafitta £6.50 (GRE)

Vernaccia di San Gimignano Teruzzi e Puthod £6.35 (REI)

1995

Bianco Villa Antinori £6.20 (TAN) £6.35 (HAH)

Frascati Superiore Villa Simone £6.25 (BIB)

Grechetto Barrique Villa Gioiosa £6.99 (OD)

Orvieto Classico Vigneto Torricella, Bigi £6.95 (AD)

Verdicchio dei Castelli di Jesi Classico, Casal di Serra £6.35 (REI) £6.75 (GRE) £6.90 (NI)

Vernaccia di San Gimignano Falchini £6.99 (RAE)

1994

Verdicchio dei Castelli di Jesi Classico, Casal di Serra £6.25 (FUL)

Verdicchio dei Castelli di Jesi Classico, Fazi-Battaglia £6.90 (TAN)

Vernaccia di San Gimignano Teruzzi e Puthod £6.35 (SOM)

£7.00 → £9.99

Non-vintage

Vin Santo Antinori £7.11 (HOG) £7.85 (GRE) £8.25 (JON) £8.49 (VA) £8.95 (DI)

1996

Castello della Sala, Antinori £8.20 (PIP)

Vernaccia di San Gimignano Montenidoli £7.50 (BIB)

1995

Bianco di Avignonesi, Avignonesi £7.69 (NA)

Stars (★) indicate wines selected by Oz Clarke in the Best Buys section which begins on page 12.

1994
Grechetto del Collio Martani, Adanti
£7.20 (LAY)
Verdicchio di Matelica, Fattoria
Monacesca £8.20 (LAY)
Vernaccia di San Gimignano Teruzzi e
Puthod £7.69 (JON) £8.35 (ROB)
1992
Il Vignola, Avignonesi £9.95 (REI)

£10.00 → £12.99

1994
Chardonnay I Sistri, Felsina Berardenga
£12.75 (STA)
Il Marzocco, Avignonesi £11.50 (REI)
1993
Pomino il Benefizio, Frescobaldi £11.99
(VA) £12.80 (PIP)
1992
Il Marzocco, Avignonesi £10.95 (LEA)

£13.00 → £19.99

Non-vintage
Vin Santo Isole e Olena £15.85 (SOM)
1995
Frascati Superiore Vigna Adriana, Castel
de Paolis £16.50 (LAY)
Vernaccia di San Gimignano Terre di Tufi,
Teruzzi e Puthod £13.95 (BEN)
Vernaccia di San Gimignano Teruzzi e
Puthod £13.99 (VA)
1993
Cervaro della Sala, Antinori £19.95 (VA)
Chardonnay I Sistri, Felsina Berardenga
£13.60 (BEN)
1991
Pomino il Benefizio, Frescobaldi £14.50
(REI)
1979
Vin Santo Villa di Vetrice £17.11 (ROS)

c. £21.00

1994
Querciabella Bâtard £20.95 (LEA)

CENTRAL SPARKLING

Under £6.00

Non-vintage
Lambrusco Amabile Luigi Gavioli £3.58
(HOG)
Lambrusco di Sorbara Cavicchioli £4.50
(ELL)
★ Villa Pigna Riserva Extra Brut £5.99 (TES)

SOUTHERN RED

Under £4.00

1996
Montepulciano d'Abruzzo Tollo £2.79 (ASD)
Zagara Nero d'Avola, Kym Milne £3.99
(SAF)
1995
Montepulciano d'Abruzzo Umani Ronchi
£3.99 (WAI)
1994
Settesoli Rosso £3.99 (HOG)

£4.00 → £5.99

1995
Cirò Classico Librandi £5.50 (GRE)
Montepulciano d'Abruzzo, Roxan £4.99
(LAY)
Uva di Troia Cantele £5.99 (MAJ)
1994
Corvo Rosso Duca di Salaparuta £5.78
(HOG)

Montepulciano d'Abruzzo Cornacchia
£4.29 (MAJ)
Salice Salentino Vallone £5.29 (AME) £5.78
(GN)
1993
Cent'Are Rosso Duca di Castelmonte
£4.95 (WS)
Copertino Riserva, Cantina Copertino
£5.15 (SOM)
Rosso Brindisi Santa Barbara £5.39 (SAT)
Salice Salentino Riserva Candido £5.29
(MAJ) £5.65 (REI) £5.90 (PIP) £5.99 (GRE)
1992
Aglianico del Taburno, Cantina del
Taburno £5.85 (WS)
Carignano del Sulcis, Santadi £5.79 (JON)
Montepulciano d'Abruzzo Umani Ronchi
£4.20 (NI)

Salice Salentino Riserva Candido £4.95
(WS) £5.45 (SOM) £5.70 (ROS) £5.99 (NI)
1991
Corvo Rosso Duca di Salaparuta £5.90
(FOR) £5.99 (GRE)
1990
Salice Salentino Candido £5.99 (THR)
£5.99 (BOT)
Salice Salentino Riserva Candido £5.99 (WR)
1988
Rosso del Salento Notarpanaro Taurino
£4.90 (SOM) £4.99 (MAJ)

£6.00 → £8.99

1994
Carignano del Sulcis, Santadi £6.25 (STA)
Rosso del Salento Cappello di Prete £6.35
(REI)
Rosso Regaleali £6.35 (GRE) £6,45 (PIP)
£6.99 (DI)
1993
Aglianico del Vulture, Fratelli d'Angelo
£7.99 (VA) £7.99 (TAN) £8.50 (BU) £8.50
(ROB)
Aglianico del Vulture, Paternoster £8.95
(BU)
Rosso del Salento Cappello di Prete £6.95
(VIG) £6.99 (JON)
1991
Pier delle Vigne Rosso delle Murge,
Botromagno £6.30 (REI)

£9.00 → £9.99

1995
Carignano del Sulcis, Santadi £9.40 (PIP)
1994
Aglianico del Vulture, Paternoster £9.50
(GRE)
1992
Montepulciano d'Abruzzo Cornacchia
£9.50 (REI)

c. £28.50

1964
Corvo Rosso Duca di Salaparuta £28.50
(REI)

SOUTHERN WHITE

Under £4.00

1995
Settesoli Bianco £3.99 (HOG)
Vermentino di Sardegna C.S. di Dolianova
£3.99 (OD)

£4.00 → £5.99

1996
Settesoli Bianco £4.29 (VA)
1995
Alcamo Duca di Castelmonte £4.70 (WS)
Gravina Bianco, Botromagno £4.75 (AD)
Greco di Puglia Cantele/Kym Milne £4.99
(OD)
Regaleali Bianco £5.79 (HOG)
1994
Corvo Bianco Duca di Salaparuta £5.78
(HOG) £5.99 (GRE)
Gravina Bianco, Botromagno £5.95 (ROB)

£6.00 → £7.99

1996
Corvo Bianco Duca di Salaparuta £7.19
(VA)
Regaleali Bianco £6.45 (PIP)
Regaleali Conte Tasca d'Almerita £6.89
(VA)
1995
Greco di Tufo Feudi di San Gregorio
£7.95 (POR)
Regaleali Conte Tasca d'Almerita £6.99
(DI)
1994
Corvo Colomba Platino Bianco £6.75 (REI)
Terre di Ginestra vdt £6.20 (AD)
1993
Regaleali Bianco £6.35 (DI)

c. £11.00

1996
Lacryma Christi del Vesuvio,
Mastroberardino £10.99 (VA)

SOUTHERN FORTIFIED

£11.00 → £14.99

Non-vintage
Il Marsala Superiore, de Bartoli £11.95 (BU)
Vecchio Samperi 30-year-old, de Bartoli
£14.95 (BU)

Please remember that
Webster's *is a price
guide and not a price list. It
is not meant to replace up-
to-date
merchants' lists.*

NEW ZEALAND

Think of New Zealand, think of individuality. The small country with the cool climate is making a point of excelling in wines that most find somewhat tricky

An Aussie winemaker said to me recently that Australia is behind California on the learning curve, and New Zealand is behind Australia. Fair? Yes, probably. New Zealand's fine wine revolution is far more recent, for one thing; her rapid success with Sauvignon Blanc, outclassing French versions from the Loire in only a few vintages, has tended to disguise the fact that success with red wines has been patchier.

But for heaven's sake, let's give her a chance. What New Zealand seems to be wonderfully good at is the cool-climate wines that much of the New World finds so difficult. Nobody else makes Sauvignons of the crisp gooseberry pungency that New Zealanders seem to find positively easy; and only California is making more good examples of Pinot Noir.

That's a fantastic record. Add to it Chardonnays of elegance and intensity and botrytized sweet wines of tremendous richness and acidity – and sparklers as good as any in the New World and better than many – and you can point to a country with justified confidence in its ability to take on the world.

What about the other reds, the ones not involving Pinot Noir? Well, until the good vintage of 1996 – and 1997 also looks promising – these had had a rough ride, enduring several lean, green years. My advice is to skip them and go straight for the 1996s – that is, if you want ripe fruit. New Zealand is not a hot country, and grapes like Cabernet need appropriate sites and good summers to do well there. And finding the right sites is one of the things that a learning curve is all about.

GRAPES & FLAVOURS

CABERNET SAUVIGNON (red) Only really succeeds in the hotter North Island, where Waiheke, Matakana and Hawkes Bay can make good Cabernet in most years. NZ's best Cabernet has deliciously ripe berry flavours, often with a touch of mint, but most needs a dollop of Merlot to soften its greenness. *Te Mata Coleraine* is the leading wine to search out for stylishness, *Stonyridge Larose* wins for concentration while *Vidal* and *Villa Maria Reserve* deserve an award for consistency. Other top wines include *Waimarama, Matua Ararimu, Esk Valley, Heron's Flight, Te Motu, Fenton Estate* and *Delegat's.*

CHARDONNAY (white) Styles range from the soft peaches-and-cream of Gisborne to the grapefruit of Hawkes Bay and the light, zesty wines of Marlborough. Auckland, Nelson, Wairarapa and Canterbury have less defined styles. Best: *Babich* (Irongate), *Cloudy Bay, Collards* (Rothesay, Hawkes Bay), *Corbans* (Marlborough Private Bin, Gisborne Cottage Block), *Church Road, Coopers Creek, Delegats, Hunter's, Kumeu River, Matua Valley* (Ararimu), *Montana* (Ormond Estates), *Morton Estate* (Black Label), *Neudorf, Nobilo* (Dixon, Marlborough), *Te Mata, Vidal, Villa Maria.*

CHENIN BLANC (white) Not widely exported here, and generally sound but not thrilling. Best producers: *Millton Vineyards'* Chenin is a serious heavyweight, whereas *Collards* and *Esk Valley* are lighter, more supple wines.

GEWÜRZTRAMINER (white) Gewürz is well suited to NZ's cool climate, and tends to be well-structured with some elegance. *Rippon* has spicy, focussed fruit. *Villa Maria* and *Montana Patupahi Estate* are good from Gisborne, as is *Vidal* from Hawkes Bay.

MERLOT (red) Mostly blended with Cabernet although there is an emerging band of top varietals from *Delegats'* (delicately plummy/peppery), *Corbans'* (rich and gamy) and the concentrated *Vidal*.

MÜLLER-THURGAU (white) The mainstay of bag-in-the-box production. Good ones in bottle include the White Cloud blend from *Nobilo,* and delicately fruity wines from *Babich* and *Montana*. Also good are *Collards* and *Matua Valley*.

PINOT NOIR (red) With California, NZ is the best New World source of this, though few have the complexity of good Burgundy. *Martinborough Vineyard* is closest to the Burgundy benchmark. *Ata Rangi* and *Dry River*, also from the Wairarapa, make more obviously New World styles with strong plum and cherry fruit. Also: *Waipara Springs, Corbans, Giesen Estate, Rippon, Neudorf, Mark Rattray, Palliser* and *St Helena*.

RIESLING (white) Generally well made and attractive, but priced at between £7.50 and £9 New Zealand Rieslings are seldom particularly good value. The best dry Riesling is made by *Dry River, Neudorf, Redwood Valley, Hunter's, Seifried, Palliser, Stoneleigh, Giesen* and *Corbans* (Amberley). For off-dry wines try *Corbans Stoneleigh, Montana, Coopers Creek, Collards* and *Millton*. The best sweet botrytized ones are made by *Villa Maria, Corbans, Coopers Creek* and *Palliser*.

SAUVIGNON BLANC (white) This is what made NZ famous, and it's still the country's best wine. It can be divided into the pungently aromatic, herbaceous and zesty South Island (mainly Marlborough) styles, and the fleshier, riper and softer wines with stone-fruit flavours made on the North Island. Best of the South include: *Cloudy Bay, Hunter's, Jackson Estate, Montana, Selaks, Stoneleigh, Vavasour* and *Wairau River*. Best North Island: *Matua Valley, Morton Estate, Palliser* and *Vidals*.

SEMILLON (white) This is riper, and less aggressively grassy than it used to be. *Villa Maria* and *Collards* are the best. *Selaks'* Sauvignon-Semillon is clearly the best of the Semillon blends.

WINE REGIONS

AUCKLAND (North Island) A catch-all area that includes such sub-regions as Kumeu/Huapai, Waiheke Island (hailed by some as NZ's top red region thanks to robust Bordeaux blends from *Stonyridge, Te Motu* and *Goldwater*), Henderson and Northland/Matakana. *Coopers Creek, Kumeu River, Matua Valley, Nobilo, Selaks, Babich, Corbans, Delegats, Villa Maria* – a whole range of stars are here, often bringing in grapes from outside.

CANTERBURY (South Island) This is dominated by the excellent *Giesen*, with a particular reputation for sweet botrytized

Riesling. In addition the sub-region of Waipara can boast Pinot Noir specialist *Mark Rattray Vineyards*, plus *Waipara Springs* and *Pegasus Bay*.

CENTRAL OTAGO (South Island) A fast-growing region in which Pinot Noir is rapidly becoming the most planted vine. *Rippon, Gibbston* and *Chard Farm* are the leading producers.

GISBORNE (North Island) Local growers and winemakers have dubbed this region the Chardonnay capital of NZ to mark the high number of award-winning wines they have produced in recent years. Gisborne is also a spiritual home of Gewürztraminer, and (less promisingly) a centre of bulk production of Müller-Thurgau. there are approximately as many wine styles here as there are wineries. Reds are less exciting than whites, although expanding vineyards of Pinot Noir are now being grown for good Champagne-method sparklers.

HAWKES BAY (North Island) Potentially NZ's greatest wine region. Chardonnay, Cabernet Sauvignon, Cabernet Franc and Merlot are the leading grape varieties, though there's also good Sauvignon Blanc, generally softer and riper than that of Marlborough. It has been established for over 100 years and yet we are only now beginning to see what it can do. *Te Mata* is the region's leading resident winemaker with *Brookfields, Church Road, Esk Valley, Ngatarawa, Vidal, CJ Pask* and *Waimarama* close behind. Top producers of Hawkes Bay wines based outside the region include *Babich, Cooks, Matua Valley, Mills Reef, Morton Estate* and *Villa Maria.*

MARLBOROUGH (South Island) NZ's biggest region by far specializes in Sauvignon Blanc and makes the archetypal NZ style, all gooseberries and cut grass. Riesling does well here, making wines from dry to sweet; Chardonnay is more difficult, but complex and distinctive when successful. Reds have fared less well although Pinot Noir is in great demand when it can be spared from the buoyant Champagne-method fizz industry. There's good botrytized wine here as well. Best: *Cellier Le Brun (for fizz), Cloudy Bay, Corbans, Grove Mill, Hunter's, Jackson Estate, Nautilus, Selaks* and *Vavasour.*

NELSON (South Island) *Neudorf,* making subtle, nutty Chardonnay, and *Seifried,* with complex Riesling, are the leading lights here.

WAIRARAPA (North Island) This includes the sub-region of Martinborough, which is the source of some of NZ's most exciting Pinot Noirs. *Martinborough Vineyard, Ata Rangi* and *Dry River* are the Pinot stars; *Palliser Estate* makes concentrated Chardonnay and Sauvignon Blanc, and there's promising Riesling and Pinot Gris, too.

PRODUCERS WHO'S WHO

ALLAN SCOTT ★★★(★) Producer of lively Marlborough Sauvignon Blanc, pungent medium-dry Riesling and nicely elegant Chardonnay.

ATA RANGI★★★★ There's good subtle Pinot Noir here, plus an intense Cabernet-Merlot-Shiraz blend called Célèbre, and nice Chardonnay.

BABICH ★★★(★) Fresh Fumé Vert (Chardonnay, Semillon, Sauvignon), zesty Marlborough Sauvignon, elegant Irongate Chardonnay and Cabernet-Merlot. The Syrah so far is less noteworthy.

CELLIER LE BRUN ★★★★(★) Excellent, Champenois-run specialist sparkling wine producer.

CLOUDY BAY ★★★★★ Excellent, complex Sauvignon, fattened with a little Semillon. There's top Champagne-method sparkling wine under the Pelorus brand, with the ability to age well, and Chardonnay is also good.

COLLARDS ★★★★ A top Chardonnay maker. There's buttery Chenin Blanc and luscious botrytized Riesling when the vintage allows.

COOPERS CREEK ★★★★ The best of the Hawkes Bay Rieslings, made in both medium dry and sweet styles. Also produces a top range of Chardonnays from Hawkes Bay and Gisborne, attractive Sauvignon Blanc from Marlborough, and good Bordeaux-style reds.

CORBANS ★★★(★) Stoneleigh Sauvignon Blanc, Chardonnay and Riesling range from reliable to very good. Cooks Winemaker's Reserve Cabernet and Chardonnay are concentrated.

DELEGATS ★★★★ Look out for the Marlborough range: it's called Oyster Bay. Fine Chardonnay and Cabernet with a good botrytized Riesling. Proprietor's Reserve wines are limited-release.

DE REDCLIFFE ★★★ State-of-the-art winery producing good, consistent Chardonnay and Riesling with occasionally very good oak-aged Sauvignon Blanc. Look out for the Bordeaux-blend reds.

DRY RIVER ★★★★★ Micro winery making mega quality. The Pinot Noir, Gewürztraminer and Pinot Gris are among the best in the country; Chardonnay and botrytized styles are also up with the leaders.

ESK VALLEY ESTATE ★★★ The red wines here are based on blends of Bordeaux varieties, but the blend changes according to the year, which gives flexibility in a marginal climate. Decent Chardonnay.

GIBBSTON VALLEY ★★★ Small Otago winery making good Pinot Noir and Chardonnay. Sauvignon Blanc is somewhat more variable.

GIESEN ★★★(★) Elegant lime-fruited dry and luscious sweet Riesling are the wines to look for here. There's also big, buttery Chardonnay.

GOLDWATER ★★★★ Big Waiheke reds and the island's only Chardonnay, plus good Marlborough Chardonnay. Sauvignon Blanc is called Dog Point.

GROVE MILL ★★★(★) Weighty Riesling and rich Chardonnay from Marlborough. Top reds in good years.

HUNTER'S ★★★★(★) Jane Hunter makes top-of-the-line Sauvignon Blanc and elegant Chardonnay. There's also sparkling wine with potential.

JACKSON ESTATE ★★★★ Classic Marlborough Sauvignon Blanc, complex Chardonnay and rather good vintage sparkling wine.

KUMEU RIVER ★★★★(★) Top Chardonnay – but it's not exactly mainstream. Good North Island Sauvignon Blanc and a Merlot-Cabernet blend.

MARTINBOROUGH VINEYARDS ★★★★ NZ's best-known Pinot Noir, big and complex Chardonnay, lovely Riesling.

MATUA VALLEY ★★★★ Look for top Ararimu Chardonnay and Cabernet. There's also luscious Sauvignon and Gewürztraminer, and good Shingle Peak range from Marlborough.

MILLS REEF★★★ Big, ripe Hawkes Bay Chardonnay, stylish limy Riesling and rich, ripe, mouthfilling fizz.

MISSION ★★★(★) A quality drive here has produced impressive Chardonnays, delicate Riesling and an occasional sweet botrytis style when the year allows.

MONTANA ★★★(★) Huge company aiming at large quantities of good value wines. Grassy Sauvignon. Top Champagne-method fizz (Deutz); good Chardonnay and botrytized Riesling.

MORTON ESTATE ★★★★ Chardonnay, especially Black Label, is reliable and attractive. There's also fresh Sauvignon and Gewürztraminer, and impressive fizz. Reds are pretty good.

The Price Guides for this section begin on page 329.

NAUTILUS ★★★★ Tight, quality-focussed range includes top Marlborough Chardonnay, Sauvignon Blanc and firm, bottle-fermented fizz.

NEUDORF ★★★★ Remarkably subtle Burgundian-style Chardonnay; nice Sauvignon Blanc, too, and Pinot Noir.

NGATARAWA ★★★ Attractive Chardonnay, Cabernet-Merlot and botrytized Riesling. The Glazebrook label is top of the range.

NOBILO ★★★(★) Good Dixon vineyard Chardonnay. Stylish Sauvignon. Popular White Cloud is a reliable Müller-Thurgau and Sauvignon blend.

PALLISER ★★★★ Source of some nice Sauvignon, Pinot Noir and concentrated Chardonnay.

C J PASK ★★★(★) Flavoursome reds from Cabernet, Merlot, Pinot Noir, and Chardonnay from excellent vineyard sites.

PEGASUS BAY ★★★(★) Great Riesling, unconventional full-bodied Sauvignon Blanc-Semillon and big, chewy Pinot Noir.

MARK RATTRAY VINEYARDS ★★★★ Very good Waipara-based Pinot Noir producer. Excellent Chardonnay, as well.

RIPPON VINEYARD ★★★ Organic vineyard with a promising Pinot Noir. there's also some Syrah. Whites include decent Chardonnay and Sauvignon Blanc.

ST CLAIR ★★★(★) Classic Marlborough Sauvignon Blanc, well made, elegant Chardonnay and pungent medium dry Riesling.

ST HELENA ★★★(★) Good Chardonnay, Pinot Gris and Pinot Blanc.

ST NESBIT ★★★ A red specialist with a Cabernet-Merlot blend. It's pretty consistently good.

SEIFRIED ESTATE ★★★ A winery making very good Riesling, more complex than most. Sauvignon Blanc, too, is distinguished and well-made.

SELAKS ★★★★ Great Sauvignon and Sauvignon-Semillon. Founder's Selection is the top label.

STONYRIDGE ★★★★★ NZ's top red producer. Intense, ripe Cabernet blend (Larose) with less intense version as the second label.

TE MATA ★★★★★ Coleraine and Awatea are sought-after Cabernet-Merlot blends. There's also Burgundian-style Chardonnay under the Elston label, and one of NZ's first Syrahs.

THE MILLTON VINEYARD ★★★★ This is NZ's first organic winemaker. There's lush, smoky, medium-dry Riesling, big, rich Chenin Blanc and balanced Chardonnay.

VAVASOUR ★★★★ Top Chardonnay and reds and very good Sauvignons. The Vavasour label is used for the top wines; those under the Dashwood label have less aging ability.

VIDAL ESTATE ★★★ The Gewürztraminer here is very good, long and structured. Chardonnay is also worth seeking.

VILLA MARIA ★★★★ Villa Maria owns Vidal and Esk Valley, though they are independently run. From this label there's top Sauvignon Blanc and botrytized Riesling.

WAIPARA SPRINGS WINES ★★★ Good Chardonnay from a youngish label. Sauvignon Blanc looks promising.

NEW ZEALAND PRICE GUIDES

RED

Under £5.50

1994
Cabernet Sauvignon Cooks £4.99 (UN)
Cabernet Sauvignon Cooks Hawke's Bay
   £4.99 (JON)

£5.50 → £6.99

1995
Cabernet Sauvignon Montana
   Marlborough £5.63 (FLE) £5.99 (THR)
   £5.99 (WR) £5.99 (WR) £5.99 (CO)
Cabernet Sauvignon/Merlot Montana
   McDonald Church Road £5.90 (GRE)
   £5.99 (OD)
1994
Cabernet Sauvignon Cooks Hawke's Bay
   £6.15 (AS)
Cabernet Sauvignon Montana
   Marlborough £5.99 (QUE)
Cabernet Sauvignon Stoneleigh
   Marlborough £6.99 (VIC) £6.99 (MAJ)
Cabernet Sauvignon/Merlot Montana
   McDonald Church Road £6.80 (HOG)
1992
Cabernet Sauvignon Stoneleigh
   Marlborough £6.99 (TES)

£7.00 → £8.99

1995
Cabernet Sauvignon Montana Church
   Road £8.20 (PIP)
Pinot Noir Matua Valley £7.45 (SAI)
1994
Cabernet Sauvignon Montana Church
   Road £7.99 (VIC) £7.99 (THR) £7.99 (WR)
Cabernet Sauvignon Nobilo £8.50 (AV)
Cabernet Sauvignon Redwood Valley
   Estate £8.00 (FIZ) £8.81 (DOM) £8.95 (STA)

Cabernet Sauvignon Stoneleigh
   Marlborough £8.35 (AS)
1993
Cabernet Sauvignon Montana Church
   Road £8.80 (GN)
1992
Cabernet Sauvignon Montana Church
   Road £7.99 (CO)
Cabernet Sauvignon Stoneleigh
   Marlborough £7.35 (UB)

£9.00 → £10.99

1996
Pinot Noir Te Kairanga £10.00 (BIB)
1995
Cabernet Sauvignon C J Pask £9.20 (TAN)
   £9.80 (HAH)
Cabernet/Merlot C J Pask Hawke's Bay
   £9.95 (POR)
Pinot Noir Hunter's £10.90 (TAN)
Pinot Noir Martinborough £10.99 (OD)
Pinot Noir Palliser Estate £10.02 (BY)
Pinot Noir Mark Rattray Vineyard £9.99
   (WAT) £10.99 (DI)
Pinot Noir Waipara Springs £10.99 (DI)
1994
Cabernet/Merlot C J Pask Hawke's Bay
   £9.65 (AD)
Pinot Noir Hunter's £9.36 (HOG)
Pinot Noir Martinborough £10.85 (NO)
   £10.95 (NI)
Pinot Noir Palliser Estate £10.02 (BY)
   £10.99 (THR) £10.99 (BOT) £10.99 (WR)
1993
Pinot Noir Hunter's £9.95 (DI)
Pinot Noir Martinborough £9.30 (SOM)
1992
Cabernet/Merlot C J Pask Hawke's Bay
   £10.39 (JON)
1990
Cabernet Sauvignon Nobilo £9.41 (ROS)

MERCHANTS SPECIALIZING IN NEW ZEALAND
see Merchant Directory (page 413) for details

Nobody has very long lists of these (except Fine Wines of New Zealand), but most good merchants have at least a small selection. For a slightly wider choice, try: Adnams (AD), Averys of Bristol (AV), Anthony Byrne (BY), Fine Wines of New Zealand (FIZ), J E Hogg (HOG), Lay & Wheeler (LAY), Tanners (TAN), Thresher (THR), The Ubiquitous Chip (UB), Wine Society (WS)

£11.00 → £14.99

1996

Cabernet Sauvignon/Merlot Montana
  McDonald Church Road £11.60 (PIP)
Pinot Noir Fromm Winery La Strada
  £11.95 (LAY)
Pinot Noir Te Kairanga Reserve £11.50
  (BIB)

1995

Pinot Noir Martinborough £12.95 (AD)
  £12.99 (THR) £12.99 (BOT) £12.99 (WR)
Pinot Noir St Helena £11.30 (PIP)
Pinot Noir Waipara Springs £11.68 (GN)

1994

Cabernet Sauvignon/Merlot Morton
  Estate Black Label £12.95 (NEZ)
Pinot Noir Martinborough £11.99 (JON)
  £11.99 (BEN) £12.50 (ROB)

1993

Pinot Noir Neudorf Moutere £12.40 (SOM)

1991

Cabernet/Merlot Ngatarawa Glazebrook
  £12.30 (AD)

£15.00 → £19.99

1994

Cabernet Sauvignon/Merlot Te Mata
  Coleraine £19.95 (NA)
Pinot Noir Rippon Vineyard £15.00 (FIZ)
  £19.95 (NA)

1991

Cabernet Sauvignon Te Mata Coleraine
  £17.99 (AME)

£23.00 → £26.50

1995

Cabernet Stonyridge Larose £26.10 (TAN)

1994

The Terraces Esk Valley £23.01 (ELL)

WHITE

Under £4.50

1997

Sauvignon Blanc Lawson's Dry Hills ½
  bottle £4.00 (BIB)

> *Stars (★) indicate wines
> selected by Oz Clarke in the
> Best Buys section which begins
> on page 12.*

1996

White Cloud Nobilo £4.33 (HOG) £4.39
  (CO) £4.49 (VIC) £4.49 (SAI)

1995

Timara Dry White £4.49 (THR) £4.49
  (BOT) £4.49 (VIC) £4.49 (WR) £4.49 (SAF)
White Cloud Nobilo £4.45 (GRE)

£4.50 → £4.99

Non-vintage

White Cloud Nobilo £4.99 (UN)

1996

Chardonnay Cooks Gisborne £4.99 (THR)
  £4.99 (WR) £4.99 (BOT)
Chardonnay Cooks Hawke's Bay £4.99
  (WAI)
Chardonnay Montana Marlborough £4.98
  (HOG) £4.99 (FUL) £4.99 (WHI)
Sauvignon Blanc Montana Marlborough
  £4.98 (HOG) £4.99 (WHI)
Timara Dry White £4.99 (GN)
White Cloud Nobilo £4.99 (AV)

1995

Chardonnay Cooks Gisborne £4.99 (VIC)
  £4.99 (JON)
Chardonnay Cooks Hawke's Bay £4.99
  (TES)
Chardonnay Montana Marlborough £4.99
  (OD)
Riesling Stoneleigh £4.99 (MAJ) £4.99 (THR)
  £4.99 (WR) £4.99 (BOT)
Sauvignon Blanc Cooks £4.99 (NEW) £4.99
  (JON)
Sauvignon Blanc Montana Marlborough
  £4.99 (FUL) £4.99 (OD)
White Cloud Nobilo £4.96 (AV)

1994

Chardonnay Montana Marlborough £4.99
  (SAT)
Sauvignon Blanc Montana Marlborough
  £4.99 (SAT)

£5.00 → £5.99

1997

Chardonnay Lawson's Dry Hills ½ bottle
  £5.00 (BIB)
Gewürztraminer Villa Maria Private Bin
  £5.29 (OD)

1996

Chardonnay Montana Marlborough £5.33
  (FLE) £5.49 (CO) £5.49 (VIC) £5.49 (SAF)
  £5.49 (SAI) £5.49 (BO) £5.49 (THR)
Chardonnay Selaks £5.99 (UN)
Sauvignon Blanc Aotea £5.95 (FIZ)
Sauvignon Blanc Cooks £5.20 (GRE)

Sauvignon Blanc Montana Marlborough
£5.33 (FLE) £5.45 (GRE) £5.49 (CO) £5.49
(BO) £5.49 (BOT) £5.49 (MAJ) £5.49 (SAF)
£5.49 (VIC) £5.49 (THR) £5.49 (SAI)
Sauvignon Blanc Stoneleigh Marlborough
£5.95 (SAI) £5.99 (THR) £5.99 (WR)
Semillon/Chardonnay Babich Gisborne
£5.95 (STA)
1995
Chardonnay Cooks Hawke's Bay £5.20
(GRE)
Chardonnay Corbans £5.95 (AD) £5.99 (EL)
Chardonnay Delegat's £5.93 (HOG)
Sauvignon Blanc Babich Hawke's Bay
£5.87 (HOG)
Sauvignon Blanc Esk Valley £5.85 (SOM)
Sauvignon Blanc Kemblefield Estate £5.95
(LEA)
Sauvignon Blanc Stoneleigh Marlborough
£5.95 (NEW) £5.99 (VIC) £5.99 (AME)
Sauvignon Blanc Villa Maria Private Bin
£5.99 (OD)
Semillon/Chardonnay Millton £5.99 (SAF)
1994
Chenin Blanc Esk Valley Wood-aged
£5.65 (SOM)

£6.00 → £6.99

1996
Chardonnay Aotea £6.80 (STA) £6.95 (FIZ)
Chardonnay Villa Maria Private Bin £6.25
(WS) £6.49 (BO)
Sauvignon Blanc Aotea £6.15 (STA) £6.45
(EL) £6.95 (ROB) £6.95 (LEA)
Sauvignon Blanc Esk Valley £6.99 (AUR)
Sauvignon Blanc Grove Mill Marlborough
£6.95 (SAI) £6.99 (OD)
Sauvignon Blanc Kemblefield Estate £6.60
(STA)
Sauvignon Blanc Nobilo Marlborough
£6.62 (HOG)
Sauvignon Blanc C J Pask Hawke's Bay
£6.90 (HAH)
Sauvignon Blanc Stoneleigh Marlborough
£6.99 (NO)
Sauvignon Blanc Vidal £6.95 (FIZ)
★ Sauvignon Blanc Villa Maria Private Bin
£6.25 (WS) £6.46 (ELL) £6.49 (BOT) £6.49
(WAI) £6.49 (WR) £6.49 (THR) £6.49 (UN)
£6.49 (SAI) £6.49 (BO)
Semillon/Chardonnay Millton £6.65 (AUR)
1995
Chardonnay Matua Valley £6.95 (SAI)
Chardonnay Stoneleigh £6.99 (BOT) £6.99
(THR) £6.99 (TES) £6.99 (WR)

Chardonnay Villa Maria Private Bin £6.49
(VIC) £6.49 (UN) £6.49 (BOT) £6.49 (THR)
Chenin Blanc Esk Valley Wood-aged
£6.33 (PLA)
Sauvignon Blanc Aotea £6.50 (MV)
Sauvignon Blanc Matua Valley £6.39 (NI)
£6.66 (ROS)
Sauvignon Blanc Selaks £6.99 (NA)
Sauvignon Blanc Villa Maria Private Bin
£6.49 (VIC) £6.49 (SAF) £6.49 (TES)
Sauvignon Blanc Wairau River £6.85 (SOM)

£7.00 → £7.99

1997
Gewürztraminer Lawson's Dry Hills
£7.50 (BIB)
Sauvignon Blanc Lawson's Dry Hills £7.50
(BIB)
1996
Chardonnay Coopers Creek £7.15 (SO)
Chardonnay Giesen £7.99 (NI)
Chardonnay Villa Maria Cellar Selection
£7.99 (OD)
Chardonnay Villa Maria Private Bin £7.25
(HIC)
Riesling Coopers Creek Hawkes Bay
£7.99 (UN)
Riesling Giesen £7.25 (NI)
Sauvignon Blanc Coopers Creek
Marlborough £7.49 (SO) £7.99 (UN)
Sauvignon Blanc Dashwood £7.49 (FUL)
Sauvignon Blanc Forrest Estate £7.95 (AD)
£7.99 (BEN)
Sauvignon Blanc Jackson Estate
Marlborough £7.99 (TES)
Sauvignon Blanc Lawson's Dry Hills £7.99
(WAI)
Sauvignon Blanc Matua Valley £7.50 (PLA)
£7.76 (PEN)
Sauvignon Blanc Morton Estate £7.60 (PIP)
Sauvignon Blanc Nautilus Hawke's Bay
£7.81 (HOG)
Sauvignon Blanc Nobilo £7.55 (AV)
★ Sauvignon Blanc Palliser Estate £7.65 (BY)
Sauvignon Blanc Seifried Redwood Valley
£7.95 (WS)
Sauvignon Blanc Te Kairanga £7.50 (BIB)
Sauvignon Blanc Villa Maria Cellar
Selection £7.99 (OD)
★ Sauvignon Blanc Wairau River £7.99 (REI)
1995
Chardonnay Delegat's Oyster Bay £7.95
(SAI) £7.99 (MAJ)
Chardonnay Montana McDonald Church
Road £7.95 (SAI) £7.99 (FUL)

Chardonnay Selaks £7.99 (NA)
Sauvignon Blanc Collards Marlborough
£7.93 (DOM)
Sauvignon Blanc Esk Valley £7.44 (COU)
Sauvignon Blanc Martinborough £7.99 (NI)
Sauvignon Blanc Matua Valley £7.82 (COU)
Sauvignon Blanc Nautilus Hawke's Bay
£7.75 (NI)
Sauvignon Blanc Palliser Estate £7.95 (BY)
Sauvignon Blanc C J Pask Hawke's Bay
£7.49 (JON)
Sauvignon Blanc Seifried Redwood Valley
£7.65 (REI)
Sauvignon Blanc Stoneleigh Marlborough
£7.00 (TAN) £7.20 (AS) £7.35 (UB)

1994
Chardonnay Montana McDonald Church
Road £7.50 (WHI) £7.99 (VIC)
Chardonnay Wairau River £7.95 (REI)
Riesling Jackson Estate Dry Marlborough
£7.70 (TAN)

1993
Chardonnay Stoneleigh £7.49 (AUR)
Riesling Martinborough £7.81 (NO)

£8.00 → £8.99

1996
Chardonnay Lawson's Dry Hills £8.75 (BIB)
Chardonnay Te Kairanga £8.75 (BIB)
Pinot Blanc St Helena £8.90 (PIP)
Sauvignon Blanc Allan Scott £8.99 (LAY)
Sauvignon Blanc Dashwood £8.30 (NI)
Sauvignon Blanc Jackson Estate
Marlborough £8.00 (TAN) £8.32 (NO)
£8.49 (POR) £8.76 (ELL) £8.90 (PIP) £8.92
(PLA) £8.99 (AME)
Sauvignon Blanc Martinborough £8.50 (BIB)
Sauvignon Blanc Palliser Estate £8.46 (FLE)
Sauvignon Blanc Seifried Redwood Valley
£8.11 (DOM) £8.25 (FIZ) £8.85 (STA)

1995
Chardonnay Coopers Creek £8.99 (TES)
Chardonnay Giesen £8.99 (EL)
Chardonnay Hawke's Bay £8.29 (EL)
Chardonnay Morton Estate £8.32 (ELL)
£8.60 (PIP)
Chardonnay Palliser Estate £8.85 (BY)
Chardonnay C J Pask £8.95 (AD)
Chardonnay Vidal Hawke's Bay £8.00 (FIZ)
Pinot Blanc St Helena £8.68 (PLA)
Riesling Allan Scott £8.98 (GN)
Sauvignon Blanc Collards Rothesay £8.52
(DOM)
Sauvignon Blanc Dashwood £8.49 (OD)
£8.99 (AME)

Sauvignon Blanc Forrest Estate £8.40 (BER)
Sauvignon Blanc Jackson Estate
Marlborough £8.90 (AS) £8.99 (GRE)
£8.99 (JON)
Sauvignon Blanc Ngatarawa £8.15 (AD)
£8.95 (VIG)

1994
Chardonnay Jackson Estate Marlborough
£8.75 (AS)
Chardonnay Montana Renwick Estate
£8.99 (HOG)
Chardonnay Redwood Valley £8.75 (REI)
£8.81 (DOM)
Chardonnay Wairau River £8.20 (SOM)
Chenin Blanc Esk Valley Wood-aged
£8.50 (BER)
Sauvignon Blanc Montana Brancott Estate
£8.99 (HOG)
Sauvignon Blanc Te Mata Castle Hill £8.49
(AME)

£9.00 → £10.99

1996
Chardonnay Jackson Estate Marlborough
£9.60 (PIP) £10.60 (GN)
Chardonnay Martinborough Vineyards
£10.99 (AME)
Sauvignon Blanc Cloudy Bay £9.50 (NI)
£9.99 (VIC) £10.50 (WRI)
Sauvignon Blanc Hunter's £9.20 (HOG)
£9.49 (FUL) £9.75 (LAY) £9.99 (GRE)
£10.30 (PIP) £10.92 (PLA)
Sauvignon Blanc Hunter's Wood-Aged
£10.99 (GRE)
Sauvignon Blanc Jacckson Estate
Marlborough £9.25 (HIC) £9.25 (WRI)
Sauvignon Blanc Palliser Estate £9.95 (WS)

1995
Chardonnay Cloudy Bay £10.15 (NI)
Chardonnay Dashwood £9.95 (HAH)
Chardonnay Jackson Estate Marlborough
£9.40 (TAN) £9.69 (PLA) £9.75 (WRI)
Chardonnay Oyster Bay £9.50 (BER)
Chardonnay C J Pask £9.15 (HAH)
Chardonnay Selaks Founders Reserve
£10.49 (NA)
Gewürztraminer Hunter's £9.50 (GRE)
Sauvignon Blanc Hunter's £9.99 (OD)
Sauvignon Blanc Seifried Redwood Valley
£9.25 (WRI) £9.75 (NA)
Sauvignon Blanc Te Mata Castle Hill £9.25
(VIG)

1994
Chardonnay Collards Rothesay £10.52
(DOM)

Chardonnay Martinborough Vineyards
£9.25 (SOM) £10.95 (NI) £10.99 (OD)
Chardonnay Montana Ormond Estate
Gisborne £10.99 (BOT) £10.99 (THR)
Chardonnay Morton Estate £9.95 (ROB)
Chardonnay C J Pask £9.69 (JON)
Chardonnay Redwood Valley £9.00 (FIZ)
£9.95 (STA)
Sauvignon Blanc/Semillon Selaks £9.79 (NA)

£11.00 → £12.99

1996
Chardonnay Te Kairanga Reserve £11.50
(BIB)
Sauvignon Blanc Cloudy Bay £11.26 (WATT)
Sauvignon Blanc Dry River £11.99 (RAE)
Sauvignon Blanc Hunter's £12.95 (BER)
Sauvignon Blanc Hunter's Wood-Aged
£11.90 (TAN)
1995
Chardonnay Cloudy Bay £11.60 (TAN)
£11.99 (RAE) £12.00 (MV) £12.05 (HAH)
Chardonnay Elston £12.71 (PEN)
Chardonnay Hunter's £11.20 (PIP)
Chardonnay Martinborough Vineyards
£11.95 (AD) £11.99 (WR) £11.99 (BEN)
Chardonnay Ngatarawa Glazebrook
£11.50 (WS)
1994
Chardonnay Babich Irongate £12.60 (TAN)
Chardonnay Cloudy Bay £11.95 (WRI)
Chardonnay Hunter's £11.45 (GRE) £11.99
(THR) £11.99 (BOT) £11.99 (WR)
Chardonnay Kumeu River £12.24 (FA)
Sauvignon Blanc Palliser Estate £12.04 (BUT)
1993
Chardonnay Kumeu River £12.24 (FA)
Sauvignon Blanc Hunter's Wood-Aged
£11.90 (NO)
1992
Chardonnay Te Mata Elston £12.49 (AME)

£13.00 → £15.99

1995
Chardonnay Kumeu River £14.95 (BEN)
Chardonnay Te Mata Elston £13.69 (WR)
£13.69 (THR) £13.69 (BOT) £13.75 (WS)
Sauvignon Blanc Cloudy Bay £15.96 (BUT)

*In each price band wines
are listed in vintage order.
Within each vintage they
are listed in A–Z order.*

1994
Chardonnay Fromm Winery La Strada
Reserve £15.94 (LAY)
Chardonnay Neudorf Moutere £15.99
(SOM)
Sauvignon Blanc Vavasour Oak-Aged
Reserve £13.25 (BER)
1990
Chardonnay Palliser Estate £13.02 (BUT)

SPARKLING

Under £7.50

Non-vintage
Lindauer Brut £6.99 (FUL) £7.25 (GRE)
£7.49 (VIC) £7.49 (WAI) £7.49 (POR)
£7.49 (BO) £7.49 (SAI) £7.49 (TES) £7.49
(SAF) £7.49 (OD) £7.49 (CO) £7.49 (THR)
£7.49 (JON) £7.49 (WR) £7.49 (BOT)
Lindauer Rosé £7.25 (GRE) £7.49 (BOT)
£7.49 (THR) £7.49 (VIC) £7.49 (WR)

£7.50 → £9.99

Non-vintage
Deutz Marlborough Cuvee £9.99 (TES)
£9.99 (BOT) £9.99 (WR) £9.99 (VIC)
£9.99 (OD) £9.99 (THR)
Lindauer Special Reserve £8.99 (BOT)
£8.99 (WR) £8.99 (THR) £8.99 (OD)

£11.00 → £12.99

Non-vintage
Daniel Le Brun Brut £12.90 (NO)
1992
Pelorus £12.75 (BEN) £12.99 (OD)
1991
Deutz Blanc de Blanc £11.99 (OD)

£13.00 → £16.50

Non-vintage
Daniel Le Brun Brut £14.49 (JON) £16.50
(ROB)
1992
Pelorus £13.02 (NO)
1990
Pelorus £15.96 (BUT)

FORTIFIED

c. £5.50

1994
Muscat Matua Valley Late Picked ½ bottle
£5.35 (ROS)

PORTUGAL

Don't think of Portugal as a bargain basement any more. There are increasing numbers of good, tasty wines from here – if you're prepared to pay just a little more

The picture in Portugal is changing. A year or two ago I'd have said – yes, there's lots of good cheap grog here, head for the South and you'll be happy. Now I'll say: trade up.

That's as it should be. So much EU money has poured into Portuguese wineries and been transformed into stainless steel tanks and new presses and all the other paraphernalia that turns everyday plonk into something rather better, that if quality wasn't on the way up I'd want to know why. The only disappointment is that the really cheap, tasty wines of a few years ago are tasting dilute and stretched – and aren't even so cheap any more.

But by paying a bit more there's fantastic value to be had. Some of it is due to Australian winemaking – but, interestingly,

the Down-Under influence here is quite different from that in the South of France. There it's flying winemakers who have made the difference, and the grapes are the international ones: Cabernet, Syrah, Chardonnay, Sauvignon. In Portugal the Aussie winemakers tend to be resident, and they've fallen in love with Portuguese grapes. That means local flavours, revved up with some really good winemaking.

According to one Aussie, the Portuguese have gone wild for varietal wines. I'm not sure that I like the sound of that. It's not that Portugal doesn't have good grapes; rather that a blend can be more than the sum of its parts. A good blend, that is. The truth is that Portugal is still discovering the potential of its own wines – with a little help from its friends.

WINE REGIONS

ALENTEJO, DOC (red, white) We're seeing some polarization of quality here, with cheap and cheerful brands like *Borba* and *Redondo* neither as cheap nor as cheerful as they were, but on the other hand some seriously good quality from the more ambitious companies. The trick is to look at the name of the producer, and not buy on price. The names to go for are *José Maria da Fonseca, JP Vinhos, Esporão, Fonseca, J S Rosado Fernandes, Paço dos Infantes, Cartuxa, Reguengos de Monsaraz, Pera Manca* and *Quinta do Carmo*.

ALGARVE (red, white) Mostly undistinguished, alcoholic reds. There are four DOCs here, *Lagos, Portimão, Lagoa* and *Tavira*, and none of them deserves its status. Among producers, the *Lagoa* co-op is probably the best bet.

BAIRRADA, DOC (red, white) The reds produced here frequently overshadow the more famous Dão wines. They're apt to be tannic, but the Baga grape gives sturdy, peppery, plum-and-blackcurrant fruit. The best Bairrada wines age remarkably well. The best producers are: *São João, Aliança, Sogrape* (look for its *Nobilis*), *Luis Pato, Casa de Saima, Gonçalves Faria, Sidonia de Souza*, co-ops at *Vilharino do Bairro, Cantanhede* and *Mealhada*. There are also some increasingly good dry whites. *Sogrape* and *Caves Aliança* are the best sources for these.

BEIRAS (red, white) This was traditionally a sparkling wine area, but a few interesting reds are starting to appear now. The producer to look for is *Quinta da Foz de Arouce*.

BUCELAS, DOC (white) Popular in Wellington's day, this dry white was almost extinct, with *Caves Velhas* left as the sole producer. *Prova Regia* is a new arrival, but lacks concentration.

CARCAVELOS, RD (fortified) Just when Carcavelos looked as if it was about to disappear for ever, along comes a new vineyard. *Quinta dos Pesos* is making a good, nutty, fortified version rather like an aged Tawny port.

COLARES, DOC (red) Based on the scented Ramisco grape, the young wine has fabulous cherry perfume but is *numbingly* tannic. As it ages it gets an exciting rich pepper-and-bruised-plums flavour; current vintages of *Chitas,* and the vinhos de mesa of *Beira Mar Garrafeira* and *Casal da Azenha* are 1984, 1987 and 1988 respectively.

DÃO, DOC (red, white) Portugal's most famous, if not always her most appetizing reds. They are reputed to become velvet-smooth with age. My experience is that they rarely achieve this and are best with less aging in wood and more in bottle, developing a strong, dry, herby taste, almost with a pine resin bite, in the process. But prices are not that low. Best buys are from *Sogrape, Caves São João, Caves Aliança, José Maria da Fonseca, Quinta das Maias, Quinta da Alameda* and *Quinta dos Roques.*

White Dão was traditionally (and mostly still is) yellow, tired and heavy. But a few companies are now making a lighter, fresher, fruitier style. White *Grão Vasco* from *Sogrape* is good and lemony.

DOURO, DOC (red, white) The Douro Valley is famous for the production of port. But only a proportion of the crop – usually about 40 per cent – is made into port, the rest being sold as table wine. Some of Portugal's best reds now come from here. The flavour can be delicious – soft and glyceriny, with a rich raspberry-and-peach fruit, and a perfume somewhere between

liquorice, smoky bacon and cigar tobacco. *Sogrape* produces a number, from the rare and expensive *Barca Velha,* through *Reserva Espécial,* to the young and fruity *Esteva.* Other port shippers are beginning to follow suit, like *Redoma* from *Niepoort,* and *Quinta de la Rosa.* Look out also for *Quinta da Cismeira, Calços do Tanho, Seara d'Ordem* among the producers of easy-drinking wines, and *Quinta do Côtto Grande Escolha, Quinta do Crasto, Quinta do Vale da Raposa* and *Quinta da Gaivosa* among the heavyweight styles.

Nearly all the best table wines are red, though among the whites *Sogrape's Planalto* and *Douro Reserva, Esteva* from *Ferreira* and *Quinta do Valprado* Chardonnay are well worth trying.

MADEIRA, RD (fortified) Each Madeira style is supposedly based on the grape from which it takes its name: there are four of them, and they are Malmsey (Malvasia), Bual, Verdelho and Sercial. In practice cheaper Madeiras, those of up to 5 years old, are almost all made from the inferior Tinta Negra Mole. At least these are now calling themselves, more honestly, 'Pale Dry', 'Dark Rich', and so on. So anything calling itself Sercial, Verdelho or whatever should be made 85 per cent from that grape.

The Malmsey grape makes the sweetest Madeira, reeking sometimes of Muscovado sugar, dark, rich and brown, but with a smoky bite and surprisingly high acidity that makes it positively refreshing after a long meal. The Bual grape is also rich and strong, less concentrated, sometimes with a faintly rubbery whiff and higher acidity. Verdelho makes pungent, smoky, medium-sweet wine with more obvious, gentle fruit, and the Sercial makes dramatic dry wine, savoury, spirity, tangy, with a steely, piercing acidity. To taste what Madeira is all about you need a 10-year-old, and, frankly, really good Madeira should be two or three times that age.

Blandy, Cossart Gordon, Rutherford & Miles and *Leacock* are all good producers, and all under the same ownership anyway. *Henriques & Henriques* is the most widely available of the Portuguese-owned Madeira houses.

OESTE (red, white) Quality is patchy in this large region; but where it's good prices are still low, so the wines are worth seeking out. The region sub-divides into seven principal IPRs: Arruda, Alenquer, Óbidos, Torres Vedras, Alcobaça, Estremadura and Encostas d'Aire. Arruda makes strong, gutsy reds, while Alenquer makes softer, glyceriny wine. Look out for *Quinta da Boa Vista's Espiga, Quinta das Setencostas* and *Palha Canas*. The *Obidos* reds are drier, more acidic, but good in a cedary way. *Torres Vedras'* reds are lighter than Arruda. *Quinta de Abrigada* and *Casa de Pancas, Beira Mar* and *Casal de Azenha* are all worth looking for. Whites can be nicely aromatic, but need drinking young.

PORT (DOURO, DOC) (fortified) Port falls into two broad categories: that aged in bottle (vintage and single quinta vintage) and that aged in wood, which is bottled when ready to drink. Ruby, tawny, late-bottled vintage, crusted, vintage character and branded ports are all ready to drink immediately. Confusingly, however, the best late-bottled vintage and crusted ports can age in bottle as well, and throw a deposit – so you have to decant them, just like vintage.

That's the basic outline. The simplest and cheapest port available in Britain is labelled 'Ruby' and 'Tawny'. Ruby is a tangy, tough, but warmingly sweet wine to knock back uncritically. It should have a spirity rasp along with the sweetness. Cheap Tawny at around the same price as Ruby is simply a mixture of light Ruby and White ports, and is almost never as good as the Ruby would have been, left to itself.

PORTUGUESE CLASSIFICATIONS

Portugal's wines are divided into four tiers of quality. At the top there are **Denominaçoes de Origem Controlada** or DOCs. **Indicaçãos de Proveniência Regulamentada** or IPRs, are similar to the French VDQS. VQPRD (**Vinho de Qualidade Produzido em Região Determinada/Demarcada**) is similar, and can also apply to the DOC regions. **Vinhos Regionais** are regional wines, and **Vinhos de Mesa** are table wines.

Calling these inferior concoctions 'Tawnies' is very misleading because there's a genuine 'Tawny', too. Proper Tawnies are kept in wooden barrels for at least five, but preferably ten or more years, to let the colour leach out and a gentle fragrance and delicate flavour of nuts, brown sugar and raisins develop. Most of these more expensive Tawnies carry an age on the label, which must be a multiple of ten: 10, 20, 30 or even 40 years old, but the figure indicates a style rather than a true date: a 10-year-old Tawny might contain some 6-year-old and some 14-year-old wine. Lack of age on a Tawny label – however often it says 'Fine', 'Old', and so on – is a bad sign and usually implies a cheap Ruby-based blend, though there are some good brands like *Harvey's Director's Bin Very Superior Old Tawny* or *Delaforce's His Eminence's Choice*. Most Tawnies reach their peak at somewhere between ten and 15 years, and few ports improve after 20 years in barrel, so don't pay inflated prices for 30- and 40-year-old wine. Try *Cockburn, Ferreira, Fonseca, Dow's, Taylor's, Graham, Quinta da Ervamoira. Colheitas* – single-vintage Tawnies – are increasingly available, usually from Portuguese houses, and can be really delicious. Look for *Cálem* and *Niepoort.*

Vintage ports are the opposite of Tawnies, since the object here is to make a big, concentrated rather than a delicate mouthful. Vintage years are 'declared' by port shippers when the quality seems particularly good – usually about three times a decade. The wines will age for a decade or two in bottle to develop an exciting, complex tangle of flavours; blackcurrant, plums, minty liquorice, pepper and herbs, cough mixture and a lot more besides.

If you want a peek at what a declared Vintage port can be like, buy single-quinta vintage wine. These are usually from the best vineyards in the slightly less brilliant years when a declaration is not made; they mature faster and can be extremely good. Look particularly for Taylor's *Quinta da Vargellas,* Dow's *Quinta do Bomfim,* Warre's *Quinta da Cavadinha,* Fonseca's *Quinta do Panascal,* Niepoort's *Quinta do Passadouro,* Cockburn's *Quinta da Eira Velha,* and *Quinta do Vesuvio* and *Quinta de la Rosa.*

Crusted port is a non-vintage blend that manages to combine a peppery attack with the exotic perfumed sweetness of Vintage. *Churchill's* and *Dow's* are good.

Two other types of port like to think of themselves as vintage-style, though Vintage Character and Late Bottled Vintage are usually short on personality. The best are from *Fonseca, Niepoort, Smith Woodhouse, Ramos Pinto* and *Warre.*

There are two styles of White port, dry and sweet. In general, the flavour is a bit thick and alcoholic, the sweet ones even tasting slightly of rough grape skins. But there are a few good dry ones, though I've never felt any great urge to drink them anywhere except in the blinding mid-summer heat of the Douro Valley when they're refreshing with a few ice-cubes and a big splash of lemonade or tonic.

RIBATEJO (red, white) An exciting area, the source of both inexpensive brands and some of Portugal's best *garrafeira* wines – in particular *Romeira* of *Caves Velhas,* and the *garrafeiras* of *Carvalho Ribeiro* and *Ferreira.* Decent brands include red and white *Lezíria, Segada, Falcoaria* and *Torre Velha.* Classier wines come from *Quinta das Varandas, Quinta da Lagoalva, Bright Bros* at *Quinta da Granja,* the *Margaride* estate (*Dom Hermano, Margarides, Casal do Monteiro* and *Convento da Serra*).

SETÚBAL, DOC (fortified) This is good, but it's always a little spirity and never quite as perfume-sweet as one would like, perhaps because they don't use the best sort of Muscat. It comes in a 6-year-old and a 25-year-old version, and the wines do gain in concentration with age – the 25-year-old does have a lot more character and less overbearing spiritiness. You can still occasionally find older wines like *José Maria* *da Fonseca,* or its intense, pre-phylloxera *Toma Viagem,* with a powerful treacle toffee character balanced by a sharp acidic tang.

TERRAS DO SADO (red, white) This is where international grape varieties have made most inroads.The oak-aged *Cova da Ursa* Chardonnay is the sort of thing. Others are blends of international and local varieties. J P Vinhos does a nifty dry Muscat; also look for *Pasmados* and *Quinta da Camarate.* Reds are from Cabernet, Merlot and local grapes like Periquita.

TRÁS-OS-MONTES (red, white) Export production is only just beginning here. Look out for *Casal de Valle Pradinhos.*

VINHO VERDE, DOC (red, white) Roughly half of all Vinho Verde produced is

red, wonderfully sharp, harsh even, but hardly ever seen outside the country. Adnams have the excellent red from the *Ponte da Lima* co-op, for anybody feeling brave.

But the wine we see is white, and *Verde* means green-youthful, un-aged, not the colour of a croquet lawn. Ideally, the whites are bone dry, positively tart, often aromatic, and brilliantly suited to heavy, oily northern Portuguese food. But we almost always get the wines slightly sweetened and softened, which is a pity.

Authentic versions come from *Palácio da Brejoeira, Solar das Bouças, Quinta de Tamariz, Quinta da Franqueira, Quinta da Azevedo, Casa de Sezim, Grinalda* and *Terras de Corga. Gazela* is off-dry, as is *Aveleda.* All Vinho Verde should be drunk as young as possible.

PRODUCERS WHO'S WHO

CAVES ALIANÇA ★★★★ (Bairrada) Up-to-date and quality oriented. Making good stuff in the Alentejo (red Monte da Terrugem) as well as in Bairrada.

QUINTA DA AVELEDA ★★★ (Vinho Verde) Largest producer of Vinho Verde, with commercially sweetened Casal Garcia and Aveleda as well as excellent dry Grinalda.

CÁLEM ★★★★ (Port) Important Portuguese shipper producing excellent 10-, 20-, 30- and 40-year-old Tawnies, good Colheitas, and good Vintage from the reliable Quinta da Foz at Pinhão.

CHURCHILL GRAHAM ★★★(★) (Port) Young company making intense and concentrated Vintage, LBV and single-quinta Agua Alta.

COCKBURN ★★★★ (Port) Shippers of the best-selling 'Fine Old Ruby' and 'Special Reserve'. Recent Vintage ports have been stunning; witness the 1994.

CROFT ★★(★) (Port) Quinta da Roeda near Pinhão forms the backbone of Croft's Vintage wines, but many wines are over-delicate. 1994 is Croft's best Vintage for ages.

DELAFORCE ★★(★) (Port) The Tawny, His Eminence's Choice, is its best-known wine. Good 1994 Vintage.

DOW ★★★★★ (Port) Quinta do Bomfim at Pinhão produces the backbone of Dow's firm-flavoured, long-living Vintage and is also a single-quinta wine. Dow's style is relatively dry; its 1994 Vintage is a triumph.

HERDADE DE ESPORÃO ★★★★ (Alentejo) Australian winemaking plus local and international grapes. Esporão Reserva and Aragonês are very good reds.

> *The Price Guides for this section begin on page 342.*

MATURITY CHART
Vintage Ports

1983   A vintage for mid-term drinking

| Bottled | Ready | Peak | Tiring | In decline |

0   5   10   15   20   25   30 years

1985   An excellent vintage for laying down

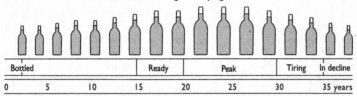

| Bottled | Ready | Peak | Tiring | In decline |

0   5   10   15   20   25   30   35 years

1991   1991 ports are likely to be ready before the 1985s

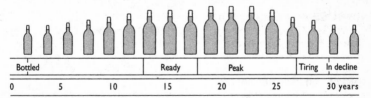

| Bottled | Ready | Peak | Tiring | In decline |

0   5   10   15   20   25   30 years

1994   Possibly even better than 1991

| Bottled | Ready | Peak | Tiring | In decline |

0   5   10   15   20   25   30 years

FERREIRA ★★★★ (Port) Elegant, early-maturing Vintages and two superb Tawnies: 10-year-old Quinta do Porto and 20-year-old Duque de Bragança.

FONSECA GUIMARAENS ★★★★★ (Port) Family-run shippers belonging to Taylor, Fladgate and Yeatman. Fonseca's wines are sweeter and less austere than Taylor's. The Vintage ports are often outstanding, as is the 1994, and the quality of its commercial releases is reassuring.

JOSÉ MARIA DA FONSECA SCCRS ★★★★ (Countrywide) Delicious range of table wines, particularly Quinta de Camarate red and white and expensive red, Primum. Not connected to Fonseca port.

GRAHAM ★★★★★ (Port) Usually rich and sweet. Apart from Vintage there is Malvedos, produced in off-vintage years, and fine Tawnies. Very good 1994 Vintage. Six Grapes is attractive Vintage Character.

HENRIQUES & HENRIQUES ★★★★ (Madeira) Good quality across the board.

JP VINHOS ★★★★ (Setubal) Brilliant winemaking. Look for João Pires Branco, red Tinto de Anfora, red Quinta da Bacalhôa, Cova da Ursa Chardonnay.

MADEIRA WINE COMPANY ★★★★ (Madeira) Blandys, Cossart Gordon, Rutherford & Miles and Leacock are grouped together under this ownership. Rutherford & Miles and Cossart Gordon wines are slightly drier; otherwise there's not much between them.

NIEPOORT ★★★★★ (Port) Look for aged Tawnies, traditional LBVs, Colheitas and long-lasting Vintage (especially 1994), plus single-quinta Quinta do Passadouro.

QUINTA DO NOVAL ★★★ (Port) Noval's Nacional wines, made from ungrafted vines, are legendary and fetch a stratospheric price at auction. Other Noval wines don't attempt such heights, but are usually good, if light. Noval LB isn't that special; the Tawnies and Colheitas are much better. 1994 Vintage looks promising.

OFFLEY FORRESTER ★★★(★) (Port) Famous for 'Boa Vista' Vintage and LBV ports. Vintage is mostly based on its own Quinta da Boa Vista and can be insubstantial. Excellent Baron de Forrester Tawnies.

RAMOS PINTO ★★★ (Port) There are delicious Tawnies from two single-quintas – Ervamoira and Bom Retiro – both of which are elegant, nutty and delicate.

SANDEMAN ★★★ (Port) Currently being shaken up, and heading towards quality rather than quantity. Single-quinta is Quinta do Vau.

SMITH WOODHOUSE ★★★★ (Port) Some delicious Vintage and LBVs. Concentrated Vintage wines which tend to mature early, though 1994 is gutsy. Full-flavoured Crusted.

SOGRAPE ★★★★ (North) Producer of Mateus Rosé, plus excellent Grão Vasco Dão and many others with emphasis on fruit. Very go-ahead.

TAYLOR, FLADGATE AND YEATMAN ★★★★(★) (Port) Taylor's has a very high quality range, but some recent commercial releases have seen standards slip a bit, and its Vintage port is no longer ahead of the field. 1994 is excellent, however. Quinta de Vargellas is still one of the best single-quinta wines on the market.

WARRE ★★★★★ (Port) Serious wines: good LBVs and Vintage (especially in 1994) and fine 'Nimrod' Tawny. Quinta da Cavadinha is a single-quinta wine.

PORT VINTAGES

Not every year produces a crop of fine enough quality for vintage-dated wine to be made, and a few houses may not make Vintage port even in a generally good year. Announcing the intention to bottle Vintage port is known as 'declaring'. It all depends on the quality the individual house has produced, although it is extremely rare for a house to declare two consecutive years.

1996 So far this looks good – it's too early to say if it will be declared.

1995 A vintage with a lot of colour and tannin, but slightly unbalanced. Above average, but missed being top grade. Unlikely to be widely declared.

1994 Excellent year, declared by almost all houses. They're ripe, fleshy and intense, with lovely fruit. They're also much more expensive than the last generally declared year, 1991.

1992 Declared by four shippers: *Fonseca, Taylor, Niepoort* and *Burmester*. Rich, fruity wines, lusher than the 1991s. Cynics note that 1992 was Taylor's tercentenary.

1991 Generally declared, but quantities were small. The wines need at least ten years.

1987 *Ferreira, Martinez, Niepoort* and *Offley* declared this small but good vintage. Most shippers opted instead for single-quinta wines for medium-term drinking.

1985 Declared by every important shipper. The quality is exceptionally good, with a juicy ripeness of fruit. *Croft, Offley* and *Cockburn* are very good, and *Fonseca* is rich and lush. My favourites are *Graham, Warre, Dow, Gould Campbell* and *Churchill*. All need five years.

1983 Marvellous wine, strong and aggressive, but with a deep, brooding sweetness which is all ripe, clean fruit. Not one of the most fragrant vintages, but it will be a sturdy classic.

1982 Not as good as it was at first thought. *Croft* and *Delaforce* are already drying out, and most need to be drunk already.

1980 A good vintage, though excessively expensive when first offered. Although they were consequently unpopular, the wines are developing a delicious, drier than usual style. They're becoming ready to drink now, but there's no hurry.

1977 Brilliant wine, now beginning to mature. The flavour is a marvellous mixture of great fruit sweetness and intense spice and herb fragrance. Not quite ready yet.

1975 These in general don't have the stuffing that a true vintage style demands, but many are excellent for drinking now. *Noval, Taylor, Dow, Warre* and *Graham* need no apologies. Most of the others do.

1970 Exceptional, balanced port, now good to drink, sweet and ripe with a fascinating citrus freshness – and it'll last. All the top houses are special, led by *Fonseca, Taylor, Warre, Graham* and *Dow*, but lesser houses like *Cálem* and *Santos Junior* are also excellent.

1966 This has gained body and oomph and can be drunk with pleasure. Doesn't *quite* have the super-ripe balance of the '70 or the startling, memorable character of the '63, but a very good year. *Fonseca* is the star at the moment.

1963 The classic year. It's big, deep, and spicy, with remarkable concentration of flavours. One or two have lost colour, but *Fonseca, Taylor, Graham, Dow* or *Cockburn* are excellent.

PORTUGAL PRICE GUIDES

RED

Under £3.50

Non-vintage
Ramada Tinto £3.19 (THR) £3.19 (WR)

£3.50 → £3.99

Non-vintage
Periquita J.M. da Fonseca £3.99 (TES)
1996
Beiras Piornos £3.95 (AD)
1992
Dão Grão Vasco £3.99 (GRE)
1991
Dão Grão Vasco £3.99 (VIC)
1990
Bairrada Reserva Dom Ferraz £3.79 (BOT)
£3.79 (THR) £3.79 (WR)

£4.00 → £4.99

1995
Dão Reserva, Caves Aliança £4.75 (STA)
Tinta da Anfora João Pires £4.49 (FUL)
1994
Alentejo Borba Adega Co-operativa £4.29 (UN)
Bairrada Reserva Caves Aliança £4.75 (STA)
Dão Reserva, Caves Aliança £4.96 (GN)
Douro Quinta de la Rosa £4.85 (SOM)
Periquita J.M. da Fonseca £4.29 (MAJ)
1993
Periquita J.M. da Fonseca £4.99 (GRE)
1992
Alentejo Montado, Fonseca £4.45 (WS)
Bairrada Reserva Caves Aliança £4.49 (DI)
Dão Reserva, Caves Aliança £4.47 (PEN)
Dão Terras Altas J.M. da Fonseca £4.88 (PIP)
Douro Vila Regia £4.50 (GRE)

1991
Dão Garrafeira Grão Vasco £4.95 (GRE)
Dão Terras Altas J.M. da Fonseca £4.29 (MAJ)
1987
Dão Terras Altas J.M. da Fonseca £4.42 (SAT)

£5.00 → £5.99

1995
Douro Duas Quintas Tinto £5.75 (GRE)
Douro Quinta de la Rosa £5.95 (GRE)
★ Douro Quinta do Crasto £5.75 (OD)
★ Quinta de Panças Cabernet Sauvignon £5.09 (SO)
1994
Douro Duas Quintas Tinto £5.25 (WS)
Douro Quinta de la Rosa £5.25 (REI) £5.50 (LEA) £5.99 (BEN)
Quinta de Panças Cabernet Sauvignon £5.49 (CO)
1993
Douro Duas Quintas Tinto £5.49 (MAJ)
Quinta da Bacalhôa £5.99 (SAI)
1992
Bairrada Reserva Dom Ferraz £5.19 (JON)
Dão Duque de Viseu £5.49 (CO) £5.85 (GRE)
Douro Duas Quintas Tinto £5.72 (NO)
Garrafeira Particular Caves Aliança £5.99 (DI)
Pasmados J.M. da Fonseca £5.65 (PIP)
Tinta da Anfora J P Vinhos £5.49 (SAF)
1991
Douro Esteva £5.95 (VIG)
Quinta da Camarate, J.M. da Fonseca £5.58 (PIP)
Tinta da Anfora J.M. da Fonseca £5.49 (MAJ)
1990
Douro Vila Regia £5.29 (SAT)

MERCHANTS SPECIALIZING IN PORTUGAL
see Merchant Directory (page 413) for details

Nearly all merchants sell some port, but only a few have interesting Portuguese table wines. Adnams (AD), Bibendum (BIB) – especially port, on fine wine list, Direct Wine (DI) – for port and Madeira, Eldridge Pope (EL) – ditto, Farr Vintners (FA) – for Vintage port, J E Hogg (HOG) – especially port, Justerini & Brooks, Lay & Wheeler (LAY), Thos. Peatling, Raeburn Fine Wines (RAE) – old colheitas from *Niepoort*, Reid Wines (1992) Ltd (REI) – particularly for port, T&W Wines (TW) – including ports back to 1937, Tanners (TAN) – particularly port, Thresher (THR), Wine Society (WS), Peter Wylie Fine Wines (WY) – old ports and Madeiras

£6.00 → £6.99

1995
Douro Quinta de la Rosa £6.36 (ELL)
1993
Alentejo Vinha do Monte Sogrape £6.59
   (NA)
Douro Quinta de la Rosa £6.35 (UB)
1992
Dão Duque de Viseu £6.25 (WS) £6.79 (NA)
1991
Bairrada João Pato, Luis Pato £6.49 (BOT)
1990
Quinta da Camarate, J.M. da Fonseca
   £6.25 (GRE)

£7.00 → £9.99

1994
Alentejo Cartuxa £9.25 (WRI)
Dão Quinta das Maias £7.50 (COU) £8.75
   (HIC)
Dão Quinta dos Roques Reserva £8.74 (GN)
Douro Quinta do Crasto Reserve £7.49
   (OD)
1992
Bairrada Terra Franca £9.49 (NA)
1989
Garrafeira Particular da Silva £9.51 (VIN)

£13.00 → £16.50

1994
Quinta do Côtto Grande Escolha,
   Champalimaud £13.60 (AD)
1975
Dão Porta dos Cavaleiros £16.50 (REI)

£24.00 → £27.50

1985
Barca Velha, Ferreira £24.95 (GRE) £27.49
   (NO) £27.50 (REI)

WHITE

Under £3.50

Non-vintage
João Pires Branco £2.99 (FUL)
1994
Vinho Verde Chello Dry £3.49 (VIC)

£3.50 → £3.99

Non-vintage
Vinho Verde Aveleda £3.79 (GRE)
Vinho Verde Cambriz £3.95 (WS)
Vinho Verde Gazela, Sogrape £3.99 (GRE)

£4.00 → £4.99

Non-vintage
Vinho Verde Casal Garcia £4.21 (HOG)
Vinho Verde Casal Mendes Caves Aliança
   £4.31 (ROS) £4.35 (DI)
Vinho Verde Gazela, Sogrape £4.04 (FLE)
   £4.19 (OD) £4.30 (TAN) £4.30 (PIP)
1996
Minho Quinta de Azevedo Vinho Verde,
   Sogrape £4.75 (WS)
1995
Bairrada Caves Aliança £4.49 (DI)
Dão Grão Vasco £4.79 (NA)
Dão Terras Altas J.M. da Fonseca £4.55 (PIP)
João Pires Muscat Branco £4.49 (MAJ)
Vinho Verde Casal Garcia £4.95 (STA)

c. £5.80

1995
Vinho Verde Aveleda £5.79 (NA)

£6.00 → £7.99

1995
Bairrada Quinta de Pedralvites £6.49 (NA)
Vinho Verde Casal Mendes Caves Aliança
   £6.60 (GN)
1993
Bucelas Quinta de Romeira £6.29 (VIN)

ROSÉ

Under £4.00

Non-vintage
Mateus Rosé £3.99 (TES) £3.99 (VIC) £3.99
   (SO) £3.99 (SAI) £3.99 (SAF) £3.99 (UN)
   £3.99 (CO) £3.99 (THR) £3.99 (WR)
1994
Nobilis Bairrada, Sogrape £3.99 (GRE)

c. £5.00

1996
Nobilis Bairrada, Sogrape £4.79 (NA)

FORTIFIED

Under £22.00

Non-vintage
Moscatel de Setúbal 20-year-old J.M. da
   Fonseca £15.20 (PIP) £21.08 (NO)
1960
Moscatel de Setúbal J.M. da Fonseca
   £20.00 (VIG)

PORT

Under £6.50

Non-vintage

Churchill's Dry White ½ bottle £5.63 (QUE)
Churchill's Finest Vintage Character ½ bottle £4.99 (GN)
Cockburn's Fine Tawny £6.11 (HA) £6.49 (HOG)
Cockburn's Special Reserve ½ bottle £4.69 (SAF)
Quinta do Noval Old Coronation Ruby £6.11 (HOG)
Smith Woodhouse Fine Tawny £6.49 (UN)
Smith Woodhouse Ruby £6.49 (UN)
Van Zellers Ruby £6.35 (WHI)

£6.50 → £6.99

Non-vintage

Cockburn's Fine Ruby £6.99 (UN) £6.99 (WHI)
Graham Ruby £6.50 (NI)
Quinta do Noval Extra Dry White £6.99 (VIC)
Quinta do Noval Old Coronation Ruby £6.50 (GRE) £6.99 (AUR)
Sandeman Fine Old White £6.99 (BOT) £6.99 (THR) £6.99 (WR)
Sandeman Tawny £6.99 (OD)
Warre's Tawny £6.99 (VIC)

£7.00 → £8.99

Non-vintage

Churchill's Dry White £8.99 (AME)
Churchill's Finest Vintage Character £8.90 (PIP)
Cockburn's Fine Ruby £7.29 (WR) £7.29 (SAF) £7.29 (VIC) £7.29 (THR) £7.29 (BOT)
Cockburn's Special Reserve £7.15 (HA) £7.49 (FUL) £7.74 (HOG) £7.99 (UN) £8.29 (SAF) £8.29 (WHI) £8.29 (WAI) £8.29 (BOT) £8.29 (THR) £8.29 (VIC)
Dow's Fine Ruby £8.50 (ROB)
Dow's Fine Tawny £7.59 (PEN) £8.50 (ROB)
Dow's No. 1 White £7.40 (PEN)
Dow's Vintage Character £8.79 (HOG)
Fonseca Bin 27 £7.84 (HOG) £7.99 (VIC) £8.35 (GRE) £8.89 (ROS) £8.95 (STA) £8.99 (NEW) £8.99 (FUL) £8.99 (DI)
Graham Ruby £8.75 (GRE)
Niepoort Dry White £7.40 (GN) £7.50 (BIB)
Niepoort Ruby £7.60 (GN)
Quinta de la Rosa £7.95 (SOM)

Quinta do Noval Late Bottled £7.60 (HOG) £7.89 (WHI) £8.00 (FLE) £8.25 (AUR) £8.25 (GRE) £8.49 (FUL) £8.99 (UN)
Quinta do Noval White £7.55 (QUE)
Ramos-Pinto Ruby £8.40 (BEN)
Ramos-Pinto Tawny £8.85 (QUE)
Sandeman Fine Old White £7.75 (BO)
Sandeman Founder's Reserve £8.89 (FUL)
Taylor First Estate Quinta de Lugar das Lages £8.49 (NEW)
Taylor Special Ruby £7.58 (FOR)
Taylor Special Tawny £8.35 (BEN)
Warre's Warrior £7.29 (WR) £7.29 (THR) £7.29 (WHI) £7.29 (BOT) £7.99 (AME) £7.99 (UN) £7.99 (MAJ) £7.99 (VIC) £7.99 (TES) £7.99 (SAF) £8.48 (ROS) £8.50 (DI)

1991

Dow's Late Bottled £8.99 (WAI) £8.99 (THR) £8.99 (WR)

1985

Dow's Crusted Port £8.50 (REI)

1970

Sandeman £7.89 (WHI)

£9.00 → £10.99

Non-vintage

Churchill's Dry White £9.40 (TAN)
Dow's Vintage Character £10.08 (PEN) £10.50 (WRI)
Fonseca Bin 27 £9.05 (FOR) £9.25 (WRI) £9.41 (VIN) £9.50 (BEN) £9.75 (QUE)
Graham 10-year-old Tawny £10.95 (NI)
Niepoort Senior Fine Old Tawny £10.00 (BIB) £10.85 (GN)
Quinta de la Rosa £9.95 (ROS)
Quinta do Noval Late Bottled £9.30 (WRI) £9.30 (TAN)
Ramos Pinto Quinta da Urtiga Vintage Character £9.70 (STA)
Taylor Chip Dry White Port £9.21 (HOG) £9.74 (PLA) £9.99 (GRE) £10.66 (ROS) £10.75 (STA)

1992

Cockburn's Anno Late Bottled £9.99 (UN) £9.99 (SAF)
Cockburn's Late Bottled £9.42 (HA)
Niepoort Late Bottled £9.95 (RAE)
Taylor Late Bottled £10.39 (AUR)

1991

Croft Late Bottled £10.49 (BOT) £10.49 (THR) £10.49 (WR)
Fonseca Late Bottled £10.75 (DI)

Graham Late Bottled £9.67 (WAT) £9.99 (WR) £9.99 (WAI) £9.99 (BOT) £9.99 (THR) £10.25 (WHI) £10.50 (REI)
Sandeman Late Bottled £9.59 (OD) £9.99 (NEW)
Taylor Late Bottled £9.99 (WR) £9.99 (BOT) £9.99 (THR)
1990
Churchill's Late Bottled £9.20 (GN) £9.50 (AS)
Churchill's Traditional Late Bottled £10.78 (GN) £10.95 (LEA)
Dow's Late Bottled £9.11 (LON) £9.25 (OD) £9.49 (AME)
Graham Late Bottled £10.49 (TES) £10.50 (HOG)
Niepoort Late Bottled £10.00 (BIB)
Quinta do Noval Late Bottled £9.75 (HAH) £10.00 (GAL)
Taylor Late Bottled £9.16 (WAT) £9.57 (HOG) £9.99 (WAI) £9.99 (GRE) £9.99 (UN) £9.99 (MAJ) £10.99 (QUE)
1989
Cockburn's Late Bottled £9.99 (VIC)
Dow's Late Bottled £9.99 (VIC)
Graham Late Bottled £9.99 (UN) £9.99 (VIC) £10.19 (PEN)
Ramos-Pinto Late Bottled £9.80 (HAH) £9.99 (GRE)
Taylor Late Bottled £9.99 (VIC)
1988
Dow's Crusted Port £10.49 (SAT)
Graham Late Bottled £9.99 (SAF) £10.59 (SAT)
Taylor Late Bottled £9.99 (SAF) £10.99 (FUL)
1987
Niepoort Late Bottled £9.95 (RAE)
1985
Royal Oporto £10.99 (FUL)
1980
Warre's ½ bottle £10.58 (WY)

£11.00 ➡ £12.99

Non-vintage
Churchill's Crusted Port £11.99 (JON) £12.60 (WRI)
Dow's Crusted Port £11.99 (TES)
Fonseca 10-year-old Tawny £12.91 (HOG)
Quinta do Noval 10-year-old Tawny £12.95 (WAI)
Tanners Crusted £11.90 (TAN)
Taylor Chip Dry White Port £11.40 (BEN) £12.10 (FOR)
Wellington Wood Port £11.75 (BER)

1991
Dow's Crusted Port £11.77 (ROS)
Graham Late Bottled £11.20 (HAH) £11.99 (QUE)
1990
Niepoort Late Bottled £11.35 (GN)
1988
Churchill's Crusted Port £11.27 (PLA)
Taylor Late Bottled £11.07 (ROS)
1987
Cálem Colheita £11.28 (HOG)
Churchill's Crusted Port £11.49 (WAI) £11.75 (SOM)
Niepoort ½ bottle £12.84 (GN)
1983
Quarles Harris £11.25 (REI)
Royal Oporto £11.75 (WY)

£13.00 ➡ £14.99

Non-vintage
Cálem 10-year-old Tawny £14.99 (UN)
Churchill's 10-year-old Tawny £13.95 (LEA)
Dow's 10-year-old Tawny £14.49 (THR) £14.49 (WR) £14.49 (BOT)
Fonseca 10-year-old Tawny £13.99 (FUL)
Graham 10-year-old Tawny £14.99 (OD)
Martinez 10-year-old Tawny £13.99 (AME) £14.06 (ROS) £14.70 (PIP)
Quinta da Ervamoira 10-year-old Tawny £14.75 (GRE) £14.79 (JON)
Quinta do Noval 10-year-old Tawny £13.49 (UN) £13.50 (QUE)
Taylor 10-year-old Tawny £13.75 (WHI) £13.95 (GRE) £14.69 (PLA) £14.75 (ROS) £14.80 (FOR) £14.86 (VIN)
1996
Fonseca 10-year-old Tawny £13.02 (WATT)
Taylor 10-year-old Tawny £13.90 (WATT)
1994
Quinta de la Rosa £14.59 (NI)
Warre's ½ bottle £14.83 (FA)
1992
Niepoort ½ bottle £13.50 (ROB)
1988
Churchill's Crusted Port £13.50 (LEA)
Quinta de la Rosa £13.95 (VIG)

> *Please remember that*
> **Webster's** *is a price guide and not a price list. It is not meant to replace up-to-date merchants' lists.*

1987
Cálem Quinta da Foz £14.99 (UN)
1985
Barros £14.75 (BU)
Offley Boa Vista £14.50 (BU)
Warre £14.69 (WY)
1984
Graham Malvedos £14.99 (OD)
Warre's Late Bottled £14.39 (WHI)
Warre's Quinta da Cavadinha £14.99 (OD)
1983
Croft Quinta da Roeda £14.95 (POR)
Gould Campbell £14.30 (WATT)
Offley Boa Vista £13.75 (BU)
Smith Woodhouse £14.50 (PIP)
1982
Churchill £13.50 (REI)
Feuerheerd £13.50 (BU)
Fonseca Guimaraens £14.99 (GRE)
Royal Oporto £13.49 (TES)
Sandeman £13.25 (WAT)
Warre's Late Bottled £14.33 (NO) £14.85
 (HAH)
Warre's Traditional Late Bottled £13.99
 (SAF) £14.45 (WAI)
1980
Croft Quinta da Roeda £14.04 (PLA)
Warre's ½ bottle £13.50 (ROB)
1975
Ferreira £14.50 (BU)
Gould Campbell £14.50 (REI) £14.90 (BER)
Sandeman £14.75 (BER)

£15.00 → £16.99

Non-vintage
Cockburn's 20-year-old Tawny £16.20 (HA)
Fonseca 10-year-old Tawny £15.50 (VIG)
 £15.95 (BEN)
Graham 10-year-old Tawny £15.75 (GRE)
Taylor 10-year-old Tawny £15.00 (TAN)
 £15.49 (MAJ) £15.49 (BO) £15.49 (THR)
 £15.49 (BOT) £15.49 (WR) £16.25 (STA)
1991
Cockburn £15.99 (HOG) £16.79 (JON)
Graham £15.85 (NI)
Niepoort £16.95 (RAE)
1987
Quinta da Eira Velha £15.32 (NO) £16.99
 (AME)
1985
Delaforce £16.95 (POR)
Fonseca £16.50 (NO)
Niepoort Colheita £16.99 (RAE)
Quinta do Noval £15.96 (BUT) £16.56 (TAN)
Smith Woodhouse £15.95 (DI)

1984
Fonseca Guimaraens £16.95 (DI)
Fonseca Guimaraens Quinta do Panascal
 £15.20 (LAY) £16.00 (THR) £16.00 (BOT)
 £16.00 (WR) £16.99 (NA)
Smith Woodhouse Late Bottled £15.25
 (HIC)
Taylor Quinta de Vargellas £15.75 (GRE)
 £15.95 (HAH) £16.95 (LAY)
Warre's Late Bottled £15.40 (TAN) £15.95
 (PIP)
Warre's Quinta da Cavadinha £16.50 (DI)
1983
Churchill's Quinta do Agua Alta £16.32
 (PLA)
Dow £16.50 (REI)
Quarles Harris £15.49 (YOU) £16.50 (BU)
1982
Churchill £15.50 (COU) £15.95 (BER)
Fonseca Guimaraens £15.61 (HOG) £16.60
 (ELL)
Quinta do Noval £15.50 (REI) £15.65
 (HOG)

Sandeman £16.00 (WR) £16.00 (BOT)
 £16.00 (THR) £16.50 (HOG)
Taylor Quinta de Vargellas £16.96 (HOG)
Warre's Traditional Late Bottled £16.49
 (AME)
1981
Warre's Late Bottled £16.33 (PEN)
1980
Gould Campbell £15.29 (TAN)
Sandeman £16.50 (BU)
Warre £16.50 (REI)
1977
Royal Oporto £15.95 (BU)

£17.00 → £18.99

Non-vintage
Quinta do Bom Retiro 20-year-old Tawny
 £17.65 (NEZ)
1994
Martinez £17.99 (OD)
Quinta de la Rosa £17.63 (MV)

1991
Cálem £18.60 (TAN)
Cockburn £18.52 (HA)
Dow £18.00 (HOG) £18.99 (FUL)
Warre £18.99 (BO)
1986
Churchill's Crusted Port £17.43 (BUT)
Warre's Quinta da Cavadinha £18.55 (WHI)
1985
Croft £17.14 (WATT) £18.00 (BOT)
Martinez £18.28 (NO)
Quarles Harris £17.50 (PIP)
Quinta do Noval £17.95 (POR)
Sandeman £17.43 (WATT) £18.95 (WAT)
Taylor ½ bottle £17.85 (HAL)
1984
Dow Quinta do Bomfim £17.95 (SAT)
Taylor Quinta de Vargellas £17.20 (TAN)
  £17.90 (GAU) £17.95 (VIG) £17.99 (UN)
1983
Dow £17.45 (NO) £17.95 (TAN)
Fonseca £18.50 (REI)
Gould Campbell £17.87 (NO)
Royal Oporto £17.85 (UN)
Smith Woodhouse £17.97 (PEN) £17.99
  (BOT) £17.99 (WR) £17.99 (THR)
Taylor £18.99 (FUL)
1982
Fonseca Guimaraens £17.75 (LAY) £17.95
  (VIG) £18.21 (PEN) £18.95 (WRI) £18.99
  (BOT) £18.99 (THR) £18.99 (WR))
Taylor Quinta de Vargellas £18.49 (TES)
1980
Gould Campbell £18.75 (BER)
Offley Boa Vista £17.50 (WHI)
Smith Woodhouse £18.80 (PEN) £18.99
  (THR) £18.99 (WR) £18.99 (BOT)
1978
Fonseca Guimaraens £17.05 (ROS) £17.65
  (HAH)
Graham Malvedos £18.00 (BU)
1977
Quarles Harris £18.99 (BO)
1975
Cockburn £17.50 (BER)
Delaforce £18.99 (THR) £18.99 (BOT)
1970
Royal Oporto £17.75 (WHI)

> In each price band wines
> are listed in vintage order.
> Within each vintage they
> are listed in A–Z order.

£19.00 ➔ £20.99

Non-vintage
Cálem 20-year-old Tawny £19.99 (VIC)
  £19.99 (UN)
Graham 20-year-old Tawny £20.50 (NI)
1994
Gould Campbell £20.52 (NI)
Niepoort £19.88 (FA)
1991
Warre £19.99 (FUL) £20.07 (WATT)
1990
Churchill's Traditional Late Bottled
  £19.50 (PIP)
1991
Churchill's Quinta do Agua Alta £19.00 (AS)
1985
Cockburn £20.82 (HA) £20.89 (JON)
Croft £19.90 (GAU)
Delaforce £20.95 (NA)
Dow £19.88 (FA) £20.37 (BUT)
Fonseca £19.99 (FUL)
Warre £19.50 (HOG) £20.56 (WATT)
1984
Dow Quinta do Bomfim £19.99 (THR)
  £19.99 (WR) £19.99 (BOT) £20.43 (VIN)
Graham Malvedos £19.53 (NO) £19.99
  (THR) £19.99 (BOT) £19.99 (WR)
Warre's Quinta da Cavadinha £19.70
  (TAN) £19.99 (WR) £19.99 (BOT) £19.99
  (THR) £20.75 (LAY) £20.80 (PEN) £20.90
  (PIP) £20.95 (AME)
1983
Cockburn £19.00 (HOG) £20.79 (HA)
Dow £19.39 (WATT) £20.50 (ROB)
Fonseca £19.99 (FUL) £20.75 (JON)
Graham £19.99 (FUL) £20.75 (JON)
Warre £19.39 (BUT) £19.49 (LAY)
1982
Croft £19.95 (VIG)
Smith Woodhouse £20.00 (SAT)
1980
Fonseca £19.39 (WATT)
Graham £19.99 (NEW)
Sandeman £19.99 (NEW)
Taylor £19.99 (NEW)
1977
Delaforce £19.95 (POR)
Offley Boa Vista £20.00 (BU)
Quarles Harris £19.50 (BER)
1975
Croft £19.50 (POR) £19.95 (BER)
Dow £19.95 (BER) £19.99 (FUL)
1967
Croft £19.50 (REI)

£21.00 → £22.99

Non-vintage
Dow's 20-year-old Tawny £21.95 (WAI)
Sandeman 20-year-old Tawny £22.00 (OD)
Sandeman Imperial 20-year-old Tawny
£22.50 (LEA)
1994
Cockburn £21.84 (FA)
Gould Campbell £22.81 (BUT)
Quarles Harris £22.81 (BUT)
Warre £22.90 (NI)
1991
Quinta do Vesuvio £22.49 (BO)
Taylor Quinta de Vargellas £22.03 (ELL)
Warre £21.50 (STA)
1985
Cockburn £21.74 (PLA)
Dow £22.79 (YOU)
Quinta do Noval £22.00 (PIP)
Sandeman £21.95 (ROB)
Warre £22.75 (NA) £22.91 (PLA)
1983
Churchill's Quinta do Agua Alta £21.95 (AD)
Dow £22.00 (POR) £22.00 (HOG)
Fonseca £21.00 (GAL) £21.75 (GRE)
Graham £21.15 (PEN) £22.95 (HAH)
Niepoort Colheita £21.95 (GN)
Taylor £21.85 (GRE)
Warre £21.99 (WR) £21.99 (THR) £21.99
(BOT) £21.99 (YOU) £22.00 (HOG)
1982
Niepoort Colheita £22.00 (BIB)
Sandeman £22.99 (UN)
1980
Niepoort 20-year-old Tawny £21.50 (RAE)
Dow £21.00 (BER)
Fonseca £21.15 (WY) £22.00 (BOT) £22.00
(THR) £22.00 (WR) £22.50 (FOR)
Graham £22.19 (JON)
Taylor £21.15 (WY) £22.59 (HOG) £22.88
(QUE)
Warre £21.00 (BER)
1977
Croft £22.99 (BOT) £22.99 (WR)
Quarles Harris £22.00 (THR) £22.00 (WR)
£22.00 (BOT)
Smith Woodhouse £22.33 (PEN)
1970
Cockburn £22.00 (YOU)
1967
Cockburn £21.50 (REI)
Taylor Quinta de Vargellas £22.50 (REI)
1960
Rebello Valente £21.00 (REI)

£23.00 → £24.99

Non-vintage
Ferreira Duque de Braganca 20-year-old
Tawny £24.97 (NO)
1994
Graham £23.42 (NI)
Taylor ½ bottle £24.63 (FA)
1992
Quinta do Vesuvio £24.10 (AD)
1991
Dow £24.50 (LAY)
Fonseca Guimaraens £23.50 (ROB)
Graham £23.01 (WATT)
Warre £23.50 (LAY)
1985
Cockburn £23.99 (VIC)
Dow £23.00 (WR) £23.00 (THR) £23.00
(BOT) £23.99 (VIC) £24.25 (HAH)
1983
Dow £23.50 (AV)
Fonseca £23.01 (WATT) £24.95 (DI)
Graham £23.50 (ROB)
Taylor £23.85 (JON)
Warre £23.50 (ROB)
1982
Quinta do Noval £24.95 (VIG)
1980
Fonseca £23.00 (BER) £24.75 (GRE)
Graham £23.00 (BER) £24.50 (ROB)
Taylor £23.50 (FOR) £24.99 (JON)
1977
Delaforce £24.50 (WHI)
Gould Campbell £23.00 (BER) £23.99
(WATT)
Offley Boa Vista £23.49 (VIC)
1976
Fonseca Guimaraens £23.50 (PEN)
1970
Cockburn £24.68 (FA)
Quinta do Noval £24.50 (REI)
1960
Croft £24.50 (REI)

£25.00 → £29.99

Non-vintage
Dow's 20-year-old Tawny £27.50 (QUE)
Fonseca 20-year-old £27.03 (PLA)
Graham 20-year-old Tawny £26.75 (GRE)
Quinta do Bom Retiro 20-year-old Tawny
£25.50 (GRE)
Taylor 20-year-old Tawny £27.50 (GRE)
£28.90 (UN) £28.95 (LAY) £29.00 (FOR)
£29.35 (VIN)
Taylor Crusted £27.50 (VIG)

1994
Croft £29.18 (BUT)
Dow £29.18 (BUT) £29.67 (FA)
Graham £29.95 (GRE)
Quinta do Vesuvio £29.95 (GRE)
Warre £27.71 (FA) £27.71 (BUT)
1991
Fonseca Guimaraens £25.99 (YOU)
Taylor Quinta de Vargellas £25.00 (VIG)
   £25.99 (YOU)
1985
Barros £26.96 (AV)
Croft £29.50 (UN)
Dow £29.50 (RES) £29.50 (GAU)
Fonseca £27.10 (HOG) £27.49 (JON)
   £27.50 (GAL) £29.75 (GRE) £29.95 (DI)
Graham £26.99 (VIC) £27.49 (JON) £29.50
   (UN) £29.50 (GRE)
Quinta do Noval £25.00 (WRI)
Sandeman £29.50 (UN)
Smith Woodhouse £28.00 (UN)
Taylor £29.38 (PLA) £29.39 (JON) £29.75
   (GRE) £29.99 (VIC)
1983
Dow £27.50 (UN)
Fonseca £25.00 (HOG)
Graham £28.75 (LAY)

Niepoort £25.00 (RAE)
Niepoort Colheita £25.50 (VIG)
Taylor £25.00 (HOG) £25.95 (ROB) £27.50
   (VIG) £27.90 (FOR) £28.50 (BEN) £29.50
   (UN)
Warre £27.50 (UN) £29.50 (GAU)
1980
Fonseca £27.95 (BEN)
Graham £29.50 (LAY) £29.75 (GRE)
Taylor £25.50 (RES) £25.85 (EL) £26.24
   (ROS) £27.75 (GRE) £29.95 (ROB)
1977
Croft £25.50 (REI) £28.78 (AV) £29.75 (BER)
Dow £29.99 (FUL)
Gould Campbell £26.95 (BU)
Sandeman £27.50 (BER) £28.89 (WATT)

1975
Fonseca £29.95 (ROB)
Quinta da Eira Velha £25.00 (VIG)
Taylor £28.00 (BER)
1970
Cálem £26.00 (HOG)
Cockburn £29.38 (WY)
Croft £29.50 (WHI)
Delaforce £25.00 (BER)
1966
Sandeman £28.20 (WY)
1960
Sandeman £29.50 (BU)

£30.00 ➔ £39.99

Non-vintage
Fonseca 20-year-old £34.95 (BEN)
Taylor 20-year-old Tawny £30.60 (TAN)
   £32.49 (THR) £32.49 (WR) £32.49 (BOT)
1994
Fonseca £37.50 (WRI)
Graham £33.59 (FA) £34.07 (BUT)
Quinta do Vesuvio £33.59 (BUT) £33.59 (FA)
1985
Cockburn £30.00 (UN)
Fonseca £30.00 (VIG) £30.65 (FA) £31.82
   (WATT) £32.50 (REI) £35.00 (ROB)
Graham £30.35 (WATT) £30.65 (FA)
Niepoort £35.00 (RAE)
Taylor £31.50 (UN) £31.63 (FA) £31.82
   (WATT) £32.30 (TAN) £32.50 (WRI)
   £38.50 (STA)
1983
Fonseca £32.90 (GAU)
Taylor £32.20 (TAN) £34.00 (STA)
1980
Dow £31.14 (VIN)
Taylor £35.00 (LAY)
Warre £39.00 (SAT)
1977
Croft £33.00 (NA) £39.95 (DI)
Dow £31.50 (LAY) £33.05 (PEN) £35.00
   (VIG) £36.65 (VIC) £39.00 (RES)
Graham £39.50 (RES) £39.50 (WRI)
Niepoort £39.00 (RAE)
Offley Boa Vista £32.37 (VIN)
Warre £30.55 (JON) £33.02 (HA) £35.25
   (TW) £36.03 (WATT) £39.50 (WRI)
1975
Graham £30.00 (VIG)
Taylor £31.50 (TAN)
1970
Cockburn £32.59 (JON) £34.51 (HA)
Croft £38.90 (BEN)
Dow £34.07 (BUT)

Offley Boa Vista £30.00 (VIG)
Quinta do Noval £30.00 (YOU) £34.66
  (PLA) £38.00 (BER)
Sandeman £33.50 (ROB)
Warre £30.00 (FLE) £35.00 (BU) £35.25
  (WATT) £36.52 (BUT)
1966
Dow £37.60 (WY)
Gould Campbell £36.00 (BER)
Offley Boa Vista £34.00 (BER)
Quinta do Noval £35.02 (PEN) £37.50 (BU)
  £37.95 (BEN)
Rebello Valente £31.63 (BUT)
1963
Ferreira £39.50 (BU)
Feuerheerd £37.50 (BU)
Martinez £36.75 (WHI) £39.50 (BU)
Offley Boa Vista £30.00 (MV) £32.50 (REI)
  £37.50 (BU)
1960
Cockburn £35.00 (BU)
Croft £38.97 (WATT)
Delaforce £35.00 (BU)
Dow £35.00 (BU) £35.25 (WY) £38.48
  (BUT)
Fonseca £33.50 (REI)
Graham £31.50 (REI)
Quinta do Noval £32.50 (BU)
Sandeman £31.73 (WY) £38.97 (WATT)
1958
Mackenzie £35.00 (BU)

£40.00 → £49.99

1994
Niepoort £45.00 (VIG)
Taylor £46.32 (FA) £46.80 (BUT) £48.27
  (WY)
1992
Fonseca £45.00 (WRI) £46.32 (FA)
1977
Dow £45.00 (OD) £45.00 (BER)
Fonseca £47.00 (JON)
Graham £41.79 (JON)
Taylor £45.69 (JON) £48.95 (BEN)
Warre £42.50 (ROB) £45.00 (OD) £45.00
  (GRE)
1970
Cockburn £48.50 (GRE) £42.50 (ROB)
Dow £41.13 (WY) £42.00 (BER)
Warre £44.00 (BER) £44.50 (LAY) £44.65
  (EL) £46.50 (STA) £48.50 (ROB)
1966
Croft £43.78 (WY)
Graham £45.00 (BU)
Quinta do Noval £49.49 (JON)

1963
Cockburn £42.50 (REI)
Croft £44.50 (MV)
Martinez £45.00 (RES)
Niepoort Colheita £46.95 (RAE)
Quinta do Noval £42.50 (REI)
Rebello Valente £42.50 (BU)
Sandeman £45.00 (BU)
1958
Quinta do Noval £45.00 (REI)

£50.00 → £74.99

Non-vintage
Quinta do Noval 40-year-old Tawny
  £66.00 (QUE)
Taylor 40-year-old Tawny £62.66 (FOR)
  £64.50 (GRE) £69.90 (UN) £70.50 (PEN)
1992
Fonseca £50.23 (BUT) £54.83 (TAN)
1977
Dow £50.00 (ROB)
Taylor £50.41 (NO) £57.50 (AD) £58.55
  (WATT) £59.00 (GAU)
1970
Fonseca £56.40 (WY) £59.50 (REI) £71.28
  (WATT)
Graham £63.45 (WATT) £65.00 (RES)
Taylor £55.23 (WY) £62.25 (ROB) £62.50
  (REI) £65.11 (WATT)
Warre £50.00 (RES)
1966
Fonseca £67.75 (BEN)
Graham £53.95 (BEN) £64.50 (REI) £66.50
  (ROB)
Taylor £50.00 (BU) £67.95 (BEN) £69.50
  (ROB) £71.77 (BUT)
1963
Cockburn £50.23 (WY) £55.95 (DI)
Croft £50.23 (WY) £51.90 (WATT) £54.90
  (GAU) £55.00 (VIG) £65.00 (RES)
Delaforce £55.00 (VIG)
Dow £68.50 (REI) £68.54 (FA)
Feuerheerd £50.00 (VIG)
Martinez £55.00 (REI)
Quinta do Noval £69.50 (RES) £70.00 (ROB)
Warre £70.50 (WY) £73.50 (ROB)

> *Please remember that*
> **Webster's** *is a price*
> *guide and not a price list. It*
> *is not meant to replace up-*
> *to-date*
> *merchants' lists.*

1960
Fonseca £55.00 (RES)
Quinta do Noval £50.00 (VIG)
Sandeman £50.00 (VIG)
Taylor £51.70 (WY) £65.00 (RES)
1955
Quinta do Noval £74.50 (POR)
Rebello Valente £57.28 (FOR)
Sandeman £65.00 (REI)
1952
Quinta do Noval Tawny £58.50 (REI)
1950
Cockburn £50.00 (BU) £58.75 (WY)
Sandeman £59.50 (BEN)

£75.00 → £99.99

1992
Taylor £91.85 (BUT)
1977
Fonseca £90.00 (RES)
Taylor £75.00 (ROB)
1970
Fonseca £75.00 (ROB) £78.00 (BER)
Graham £78.50 (GAU)
Taylor £75.00 (LAY) £80.00 (RES)
1966
Warre £75.00 (RES)
1963
Cockburn £75.00 (ROB)
Dow £85.00 (RES)
Graham £75.00 (BU) £98.00 (REI)
Warre £97.50 (RES)
1955
Ferreira £87.00 (RES)
Martinez £75.00 (BU)
1952
Niepoort Garrafeira £89.50 (RAE)

£100.00 → £149.99

1980
Quinta do Noval Nacional £139.83
　(TW)
1977
Fonseca £102.81 (WATT)
1963
Fonseca £110.00 (REI)
Graham £104.77 (FA) £105.75 (WY)
　£112.00 (BEN)
Taylor £110.00 (REI) £127.00 (ROB)
　£135.00 (RES)
1955
Cockburn £105.75 (WY) £148.00 (REI)
Croft £111.63 (WY) £140.00 (REI)
Quinta do Noval £125.00 (RES)
Taylor £148.00 (REI)

1947
Quinta do Noval £145.00 (LEA)
1945
Ferreira £135.00 (BU)
1924
Rebello Valente £111.63 (WY)

£150.00 → £199.99

1963
Fonseca £155.00 (ROB) £175.00 (RES)
1955
Graham £150.00 (ROB)
Taylor £158.63 (FA)
1945
Dow £150.00 (REI)
1935
Sandeman £175.00 (REI)
1927
Graham £175.00 (REI)
Rebello Valente £155.00 (REI)
1920
Croft £182.13 (WY)
Dow £176.25 (WY)
Warre £193.88 (WY)

£200.00 → £299.99

1970
Quinta do Noval Nacional £225.00 (ROB)
　£234.93 (NO)
1966
Quinta do Noval Nacional £271.64 (NO)
1955
Fonseca £295.00 (RES)
Taylor £239.00 (RES)
1948
Taylor £245.00 (BEN)
1945
Quinta do Noval £225.00 (REI) £287.88 (WY)
1935
Cockburn £264.38 (WY)
Sandeman £293.75 (WY)
1927
Croft £225.00 (ROB)

£319.00 → £350.00

1945
Fonseca £350.00 (REI)
Graham £325.00 (REI)

£416.00 → £599.99

1963
Quinta do Noval Nacional £513.90 (NO)
　£599.25 (TW)
1945
Taylor £416.15 (WY)

MADEIRA

Under £8.50

Non-vintage
Duke of Cumberland Blandy £8.45 (WAT)

£8.50 → £9.99

Non-vintage
Bual Old Trinity House Rutherford &
  Miles £9.50 (ROB)
Duke of Cambridge Blandy £9.99 (VIN)
  £9.99 (QUE)
Duke of Clarence Blandy £8.50 (NI) £8.75
  (HAH) £8.99 (SAF) £8.99 (BOT) £8.99
  (FUL) £8.99 (WR) £8.99 (THR) £9.95 (GRE)
  £9.99 (VIN)
Duke of Cumberland Blandy £8.50 (NI)
  £8.99 (BOT) £8.99 (WR) £8.99 (FUL)
  £8.99 (THR) £9.95 (GRE) £9.99 (VIN)
Duke of Sussex Blandy £8.50 (NI) £8.99
  (FUL) £8.99 (WR) £8.99 (BOT) £8.99 (THR)
  £9.10 (HAH) £9.95 (GRE) £9.99 (QUE)
  £9.99 (VIN)
Full Rich Henriques & Henriques £8.71
  (ELL) £8.95 (STA) £9.35 (ROS) £9.95 (LEA)
Medium Dry Henriques & Henriques
  £8.95 (STA) £8.99 (PEN) £9.35 (ROS)
Medium Rich Cossart Gordon £8.99 (PEN)
Medium Rich Henriques & Henriques
  £8.71 (ELL) £9.35 (ROS) £9.95 (LEA)
Sercial Henriques & Henriques £8.99 (PEN)
Sercial Old Custom House Rutherford &
  Miles £9.50 (ROB)

£10.00 → £14.99

Non-vintage
10-year-old Malmsey Blandy £14.17 (WAT)
  £14.50 (NI) £14.52 (NO) £14.79 (JON)
  £14.95 (WAI)
10-year-old Verdelho Henriques &
  Henriques £14.56 (HOG)
5-year-old Bual Blandy £10.36 (HOG)
  £11.90 (HAH) £12.50 (GRE)
5-year-old Bual Cossart Gordon £12.95
  (VIG) £12.96 (COU) £13.30 (GN) £13.50
  (DI) £14.20 (HIC)
5-year-old Malmsey Blandy £12.50 (GRE)
5-year-old Malmsey Cossart Gordon
  £13.30 (GN) £14.75 (AD)
5-year-old Sercial Blandy £12.50 (GRE)
5-year-old Sercial Cossart Gordon £12.95
  (VIG) £13.30 (GN) £13.50 (DI) £14.20
  (HAH)

5-year-old Verdelho Blandy £10.36 (HOG)
  £12.50 (GRE)
Medium Dry Henriques & Henriques
  £10.99 (AME) £11.95 (LEA)
Medium Rich Henriques & Henriques
  £11.95 (LEA)

£15.00 → £19.99

Non-vintage
10-year-old Malmsey Blandy £15.20 (HOG)
  £16.20 (HAH) £17.25 (GRE) £17.63 (QUE)
10-year-old Malmsey Henriques &
  Henriques £15.33 (NO) £15.99 (AME)
  £16.40 (ELL) £16.75 (HIC) £17.95 (LEA)
  £19.00 (AS)
10-year-old Sercial Henriques &
  Henriques £16.40 (ELL) £17.95 (LEA)
10-year-old Verdelho Cossart Gordon
  £17.55 (GN) £17.95 (DI) £18.80 (AD)
10-year-old Verdelho Henriques &
  Henriques £17.95 (LEA)
Sercial Henriques & Henriques £15.33 (NO)

£45.00 → £85.00

1950
Sercial Rutherford & Miles £45.00 (GRE)
1940
Sercial Vintage Cossart Gordon £85.00 (REI)
1933
Malmsey Justino Henriques £62.50 (REI)

£100.00 → £175.00

1880
Verdelho Solera 1880 Blandy £120.00
  (VIG)
1863
Malmsey Solera 1863 Leacock £111.63 (FA)
1954
Bual Blandy £100.00 (VIG)
1940
Sercial Rutherford & Miles £120.00 (VIG)
1934
Bual Vintage Cossart Gordon £125.00 (REI)
1920
Bual Vintage Leacocks £145.00 (REI)
1907
Bual Blandy £125.00 (REI)

c. £205.00

1934
Verdelho Vintage Rutherford & Miles
  £205.00 (REI)

SOUTH AFRICA

South African wine is still more dross than gold – but the gold is worth snapping up. Here's how

Okay, so you think you would like to experiment with South African wine. What's the one thing you look for? Simple. You look for the name of the producer first. And then take a glance at the grape variety.

The reason is that quality in South Africa is patchy. Improving, yes, and improving fast; but still patchy. There's still an awful lot of poor wine around – far more than there is good wine. But the good news is that even the top wines (which are very good indeed) are extremely affordable.

And yes, we do see them over here. Think in terms of paying between £5 and £10 and you can expect wines of character and style. Not much regional style as yet, though that will come as more and more good producers head for cooler climates. And while the wines are usually fashioned in a New World mould – upfront fruit plus new oak – they are neither Australian lookalikes nor Californian copycats. With every year that passes, they are becoming truer to themselves.

GRAPE VARIETIES

CABERNET SAUVIGNON, CABERNET FRANC AND BORDEAUX BLENDS (red) Good ones have clean, minty aromas and fresh fruit. Old-style ones persist with a tough greenness or a dusty dryness. The Bordeaux blends (either or both of the Cabernets plus Merlot) tend to be more successful than either Cabernet straight. Best Cabernets include: *Avontuur Reserve, Backsberg, Bellingham, Blaauwklippen Reserve, Neil Ellis, Excelsior, Glen Carlou, Hartenberg, Haute Provence, Landskroon Cabernet Franc, Le Bonheur, Liefland, Nederburg, Plaisir de Merle, Springfield, Stellenryck, Swartland Co-operative, Thelema, De Trafford, Vergelegen*. Best blends: *Avontuur Baccarat, Buitenverwachting Grand Vin, Clos Malverne Devonet, Fairview Charles Gerard Red Reserve, Glen Carlou Les Trois, Grangehurst, Groot Constantia Gouverneur's Reserve, Klein Constantia Marlbrook, La Motte Millennium, Lievland DVB, Meerlust, Nederburg Auction, Rustenberg Gold, Villiera Cru Monro, Welgemeend, Zonnebloem Laureat*.

CHARDONNAY (white) The best wines have lingering lemon-lime freshness with subtle oak. Inevitably, there's some over-oaking disguising some underpowered winemaking, too, so choose carefully and go for: *Alphen, Backsberg, Graham Beck Lonehill, Bellingham Reserve, Blaauwklippen, Bouchard Finlayson, Buitenverwachting, De Leuwen Jagt, De Wetshof Bateleur, Dieu Donne, Neil Ellis, Hamilton Russell, Haute Provence, Jordan, Klein Constantia, Glen Carlou Reserve, Groot Constantia, Louisvale, Van Loveren, Nederburg Auction, Schoon Gevel, Slaley Sentinel, Simonsig, Springfield, Stellenryck, Thelema, Vergelegen Les Enfants, Weltevrede, Zandvliet, Zevenrivieren, Zevenwacht, Zonnebloem*.

CHENIN BLANC (white) This usually dominates the blend in off-dry commercial whites. However, a new drive to revive its fortunes is under way. Dry versions are best young, when their crisp, honeyed guava

WINE OF ORIGIN

Every bottle of wine sold in South Africa must bear the Wine of Origin seal. This certifies the wine's area of origin, grape variety (or varieties) and vintage.

flavours are freshest. Best: *Boland, Boschendal, Glen Carlou, Leopard's Rock, Van Zylshof, Villiera, Wildekrans.*

CINSAUT (red) Crossed with Pinot Noir, it produced the Pinotage. By itself it mostly gives light, undistinguished reds, although *Rosenview* is attractive.

COLOMBARD (white) Crisp, commercial whites with flowery freshness.

MERLOT (red) By itself Merlot makes rich, ripe, easy reds – even better aged in new oak. Good are *Avontuur Reserve, Bellingham, Benguela Current, Boschendal, De Trafford, Drostdy-Hof, Fairview Reserve, Glen Carlou, Hoopenburg, Jacana, Meerlust, Steenberg, Uiterwyk, Villiera, Warwick, Wildekrans, Zonnebloem.*

MUSCAT (white) Sweet Muscadels are usually the best bet, and include: *De Leuwen Jagt, Klein Constantia Vin de Constance, KWV, Nederburg Eminence, Van Loveren Blanc de Noir, Van Loveren, Vredendal.*

PINOTAGE (red) This crossing of Pinot Noir with Cinsaut can be used to make either light and easy rosé or red, or reds that are a great deal more substantial. The abrasive, estery styles of old are being taken over by cleaner, more intense fruit. Good ones: *Beyerskloof, Beyers Truter, Avontuur, Clos Malverne, Jacana, KWV Cathedral Cellars, Simonsig, Swartland co-op, Wildekrans.*

PINOT NOIR (red) The coolest parts of the country are producing supple and understated Pinot Noirs of world class. Best are: *Bouchard Finlayson, Glen Carlou, Hamilton Russell, Haute Cabrière.*

RIESLING (white) Sweet ones are excellent; the dry and off-dry ones can be too. Best dry: *Buitenverwachting, Neethlingshof.* Best off-dry: *De Leuwen Jagt, Hartenburg, Klein Constantia, Liefland, Sinnya.* Best sweet botrytized Rieslings: *Danie De Wet Edeloes, KWV Noble Late Harvest, Nederburg Noble Late Harvest and Neetlingshof Noble Late Harvest.*

SAUVIGNON BLANC (white) Too many are pale, dilute and lack the grape's typical pungency. Try examples from *Bellingham, Neil Ellis, Klein Constantia, Steenberg, Villiera.*

SHIRAZ (red) Shiraz can make savoury, raspberry-fruited wines, although perhaps lacking the fleshy sweetness of the best of the Rhône and Australia. Best: *Bertrams, Fairview, Groot Constantia, Hartenberg, La Motte, Lievland, Sentinel, Zonnebloem.*

SPARKLING WINES 'Methode Cap Classique' (MCC) is the name for Champagne-method fizz. Best brands so far are *Graham Beck, Blaauwklippen Barouche, Boschendal, Charles de Fere Tradition, Pierre Jourdan* (from *Clos Cabrière*), *J C Le Roux Chardonnay* and *Pongracz.*

WINES & WINE REGIONS

CONSTANTIA South Africa's oldest existing wine region is one of its most dynamic. *Steenberg's* Sauvignon Blanc, *Buitenverwachting* and *Klein Constantia* are the names to watch.

DURBANVILLE Cape Town is threatening the vineyards of Durbanville. A pity, since it's cool. Sauvignon Blanc is particularly good.

FRANSCHHOEK White grapes rule, yet the new reds are promising. Look for *Cabrière* fizz and Pinot Noir, *Bellingham's* fantastic new Cabernet Franc, *Dieu Donne* and *Haute Provence* Cabernet Sauvignon.

OLIFANTS RIVER Irrigated bulk wine area, making some good everyday stuff as well. Hugh Ryman's Impala wines from the *Citrasdal co-op* taste great in SA, less good after UK bottling. *Klawer* and *Spruitdrift* co-ops both make good Merlot.

PAARL The *KWV* is based in the town of Paarl, as is *Nederburg*. There is also *Backsberg, Villiera, Glen Carlou, Fairview, De Leuwen Jagt* and *Landskroon*, with good wines from almost every variety. *Villiera* even has a good Sauvignon, and *Glen Carlou* one of South Africa's best Pinot Noirs.

ROBERTSON A region rapidly gaining a reputation for Chardonnay. *Danie de Wet, Springfield Estate, Van Loveren, Sandvliet, Weltevred* and *Astonvale, Van Zylshof, Sinnya* and *Leopard's Rock* are names to look for.

STELLENBOSCH The heart of the wine industry. *Stellenbosch Farmers' Winery's, Bergkelder* and *Gilbeys* are all here. Both reds and whites are successful. Look for: *Avontuur, Bertrams, Blaauwklippen, Clos Malverne, Neil Ellis, Hartenberg, Kanonkop, Lievland, Meerlust, Mulderbosch, Neetlingshof, Rust-en-Vrede, Simonsig, Stellenzicht, Thelema, Vriesenhof, Zevenwacht.*

SWARTLAND Hot and dry; Chenin Blanc, Sauvignon Blanc, Colombard and Pinotage do best. The *Swartland* and *Riebeek* co-ops and *Allesverloren* estate are the best producers.

WALKER BAY Some of the best Pinot Noir comes from here and there's good Chardonnay, too. Top names: *Hamilton-Russell, Bouchard Finlayson, Wildekrans, Southern Right.*

PRODUCERS WHO'S WHO

BACKSBERG ★★★★ Luscious Chardonnay and superb reds, including top Malbec and Pinotage.

BELLINGHAM ★★★★★ Super flinty Sauvignon and an elegant, peachy Chardonnay. The new Cabernet Franc is stunning.

BOSCHENDAL ★★★★(★) Stronger on reds than whites. Look for intense, peppery Shiraz, juicy, chocolaty Merlot, and superb Lanoy red blend.

BOUCHARD FINLAYSON ★★★★★ Burgundian-style Chardonnays and some of South Africa's best Pinot Noir.

CABRIÈRE ESTATE ★★★★ Assertively dry and steely Pierre Jourdan Brut, elegant Blanc de Blanc, and perfumed, raspberry-packed Pinot Noir.

CATHEDRAL CELLAR ★★★ KWV's top range. Good New World-style Cabernet Sauvignon, vibrant Pinotage and grassy Sauvignon Blanc.

CLOS MALVERNE ★★★(★) Makes a lovely Pinotage and a very good value blend by the name of Devonet from Cabernet and Merlot.

DE WETSHOF ★★★(★) Top Chardonnays with great elegance and poise, and spicy Rhine Riesling.

NEIL ELLIS WINES ★★★(★) Top negociant producing excellent Sauvignon from Elgin and Darling. Tropical tasting Chardonnay, intense Cabernet.

FAIRVIEW ★★★★(★) Great Cabernet, Shiraz, Merlot, and new Zinfandel-Cinsaut blend. The Sauvignon-Semillon blend is the top white.

GLEN CARLOU ★★★★ Tropically rich, leesy Chardonnay and impressive red Bordeaux blends.

HAMILTON RUSSELL ★★★★★ Elegant Chardonnay and supple, ripe, even silky Pinot Noir that brilliantly straddle Old and New Worlds.

HAUTE PROVENCE ★★★(★)
Newish Franschhoek winery with excellent reds and whites, including a Burgundian-style Chardonnay and a cedary Cabernet.

JORDAN VINEYARD ★★★
International styles made with great aplomb. Look for the Chardonnays.

KANONKOP ★★★★★ Pinotage king of the Cape. There's also rich, mouthfilling Cabernet and complex Paul Sauer Bordeaux blend.

KLEIN CONSTANTIA ★★★★
Stunning Sauvignon Blanc, toasty Chardonnay and classic claret-style Marlbrook red.

LA MOTTE ★★★★ Excellent reds, in particular big spicy Shiraz and ripe oak-splashed Cabernet.

LOUISVALE ★★★ Buttery, biscuity Chardonnay and a good Cabernet-Merlot.

MEERLUST ★★★★ Look for stunning Chardonnay, complex Rubicon Cabernet blend and a new range of grappa.

PLAISIR DE MERLE ★★★(★) Rapidly improving Chardonnay and Cabernet.

RUSTENBERG ★★★ Cabernet blends that cellar well. Whites haven't been up to the same standard, but could be improving.

SIMONSIG ★★★★ Concentrated, unwooded Pinotage and brilliant Shiraz.

SPRINGFIELD ESTATE ★★★ An estate that has only just started to bottle its wines. Cabernets are very good and age well; Sauvignon is good and lean, Chardonnay complex.

STEENBERG ★★★(★) Constantia's rising star. Crisp, nettly Sauvignon Blanc and powerful, inky Merlot.

THELEMA ★★★★ First-rate Sauvignon Blanc and Chardonnay, gutsy Cabernet Reserve and fruit-driven Cabernet-Merlot.

VERGELEGEN ★★★(★) Massive investment is producing good results: supple Cabernet and rich Chardonnay. Look out for the Merlot.

VILLIERA ★★★★ Consistently excellent Merlot and a new Chenin that nudges ahead of the tangy Sauvignon.

VRIESENHOF ★★★(★) Very intense Chardonnay; super Kallista Bordeaux blend.

WARWICK ★★★★(★) Red specialist making fabulous bush-trained Pinotage, dense, mouthfilling Cabernet Franc and a complex Bordeaux blend called Trilogy.

WELGEMEEND ESTATE ★★★★
Tremendous reds from Bordeaux grape varieties, including Malbec and Petit Verdot.

SOUTH AFRICA PRICE GUIDES

RED

Under £4.00

1996
Cinsault/Pinotage Kumala £3.79 (VIC)
£3.99 (SAF)
1994
Pinotage Culemborg Paarl £3.49 (WAI)

£4.00 → £4.99

Non-vintage
Pinotage KWV £4.75 (BO)
1996
Adelberg Simonsig Estate £4.50 (WS)
Caresse Marine Wildekrans £4.30 (SOM)
Devonet Clos Malverne £4.99 (OD)
1995
Adelberg Simonsig Estate £4.81 (ROS)
Pinotage Nederburg £4.95 (NEW)
Roodeberg KWV £4.99 (VIC)
Shiraz Fairview £4.99 (ASD)
1994
Adelberg Simonsig Estate £4.83 (PEN)
Cabernet Sauvignon KWV £4.52 (HOG)
Roodeberg KWV £4.36 (HOG)
1993
Cabernet Sauvignon KWV £4.49 (WR)
Pinotage KWV £4.59 (THR) £4.59 (BOT)
£4.59 (WR) £4.70 (HOG) £4.99 (UN)
Roodeberg KWV £4.39 (FUL) £4.49 (WR)
£4.49 (BOT) £4.49 (THR) £4.49 (WAI)
£4.85 (GRE) £4.95 (CAP) £4.99 (UN)
Shiraz KWV £4.75 (FUL)
1992
Cabernet Sauvignon KWV £4.59 (FUL)
£4.75 (GRE) £4.99 (UN)
Shiraz KWV £4.85 (GRE) £4.89 (UN)

£5.00 → £5.99

1996
Pinotage Beyerskloof £5.49 (VIC) £5.49 (OD)
Shiraz Sentinel £5.99 (OD)

1995
Cabernet Sauvignon Fairview £5.99 (VIC)
Devonet Clos Malverne £5.95 (POR)
Pinotage Beyerskloof £5.30 (SOM) £5.49
(WR) £5.49 (BOT)
Pinotage Clos Malverne £5.99 (POR)
Pinotage Delheim £5.99 (WR) ·
Pinotage Nederburg £5.35 (CAP)
Pinotage Vriesenhof Paradyskloof £5.50
(TAN)
Shiraz Fairview £5.99 (TES) £5.99 (FUL)
1994
Cabernet Sauvignon Nederburg Paarl
£5.25 (NEW)
Pinotage Backsberg £5.43 (HOG) £5.93
(CAP)
Pinotage Nederburg £5.20 (UB) £5.80
(WRI)
Shiraz KWV £5.24 (CAP)
1993
Cabernet Sauvignon Nederburg Paarl
£5.70 (TAN)
Dry Red Rustenberg £5.60 (TAN) £5.75
(BU)
Roodeberg KWV £5.86 (BY)
Shiraz Klein Constantia £5.45 (GRE) £5.95
(BU) £5.99 (DI)
1992
Baronne Nederburg £5.35 (CAP)
Cabernet Sauvignon KWV £5.15 (CAP)
Cabernet Sauvignon Nederburg Paarl
£5.07 (HOG) £5.74 (CAP)
Edelrood Nederburg £5.07 (HOG) £5.64
(CAP)
Pinotage KWV £5.24 (CAP)
1991
Cabernet Sauvignon Neil Ellis £5.65 (UB)
1990
Cabernet Sauvignon Nederburg Paarl
£5.40 (UB)
Merlot De Leuwen Jagt £5.86 (PEN)
1988
Shiraz Klein Constantia £5.58 (PEN)

MERCHANTS SPECIALIZING IN SOUTH AFRICA
see Merchant Directory (page 413) for details

Averys of Bristol (AV), Bibendum (BIB),
Cape Province Wines (CAP) – who do
nothing else, Direct Wine (DI), J E Hogg
(HOG), Lay & Wheeler (LAY), Oddbins (OD),

Thos. Peatling, Terry Platt (PLA),
Roberson (ROB), Sainsbury (SAI), Tanners
(TAN), Thresher (THR), The Ubiquitous
Chip (UB)

£6.00 ➜ £7.99

1996
Cabernet Sauvignon Thelema £7.97 (FLE)
Cabernet Sauvignon/Merlot Louisvale
    £7.49 (OD)
Kallista Vriesenhof £7.50 (HIC)
Pinotage Clos Malverne £6.49 (OD) £6.49
    (WAI) £7.17 (GN) £7.20 (AD)
Pinotage Fairview £6.80 (AD)
Pinotage Groot Constantia £7.69 (EL)
Pinotage Simonsig £7.99 (EL)
Pinotage Wildekrans £7.49 (OD)
1995
Pinotage Vriesenhof Paradyskloof £6.46
    (COU)
Pinotage Wildekrans £6.10 (SOM) £7.83
    (COU) £7.95 (LEA)
Shiraz Fairview Reserve £7.98 (BER)
1994
Cabernet Sauvignon Backsberg £6.99
    (WHI) £6.99 (CAP)
Devonet Clos Malverne £6.15 (GN)
Klein Babylonstoren Backsberg £7.98
    (PLA) £7.99 (WHI)
Merlot/Cabernet Brampton £6.99 (LAY)
Pinotage Backsberg £6.19 (WHI)
Pinotage Groot Constantia £7.14 (CAP)
Pinotage Kanonkop £7.99 (TES)
Pinotage Meerendal £7.50 (GRE) £7.56
    (CAP)
Pinotage Zonnebloem £6.60 (WRI)
    £6.95 (STA) £7.28 (PLA)
Shiraz Backsberg £7.60 (PIP)
Shiraz Fairview £7.50 (AS)
Shiraz Stellenzicht £6.99 (CAP) £7.99 (EL)
1993
Cabernet Sauvignon Backsberg £7.04
    (PLA) £7.25 (EL)
Cabernet Sauvignon Bellingham £7.67
    (CAP)
Cabernet Sauvignon Klein Constantia
    £7.46 (AV) £7.90 (TAN) £7.95 (POR)
Cabernet Sauvignon Zonnebloem £6.75
    (GRE)
Laborie KWV £6.05 (PLA)
Pinotage Zonnebloem £6.12 (ROS) £6.50
    (GRE) £6.77 (CAP) £6.99 (NA)

---

*Webster's is an annual
publication. We welcome
your suggestions for next
year's edition.*

Shiraz Backsberg £6.99 (WHI)
Shiraz Groot Constantia £6.69 (HOG)
    £7.14 (CAP)
Shiraz Simonsig £7.32 (CAP)
Tinta Barocca Allesverloren £7.50 (GRE)
    £7.90 (CAP)
1992
Cabernet Sauvignon Groot Constantia
    £7.34 (HOG)
Cabernet Sauvignon Nederburg Paarl
    £6.15 (STA) £6.40 (WRI)
Cabernet Sauvignon Uiterwyk £7.88 (NO)
Kallista Vriesenhof £7.95 (LEA)
Laureat Zonnebloem £7.50 (WRI)
Shiraz Klein Constantia £6.19 (UN)
Shiraz Zonnebloem £6.77 (CAP)
    £6.99 (NA)
1991
Cabernet Sauvignon Nederburg Paarl
    £6.66 (QUE)
Cabernet Sauvignon Zonnebloem £6.34
    (ROS) £6.99 (NA) £7.02 (CAP)
Edelrood Nederburg £6.66 (QUE)
Kallista Vriesenhof £7.40 (TAN)
Marlbrook Klein Constantia £6.51 (HOG)
    £6.95 (GRE) £7.50 (WRI)
Pinotage Meerendal £6.49 (MAJ)
Shiraz Backsberg £7.65 (BY)
Shiraz KWV £6.17 (BY)
Shiraz Zonnebloem £6.12 (ROS) £6.50
    (GRE)
Tinta Barocca Allesverloren £6.88 (HOG)
    £7.99 (EL)
1990
Cabernet Sauvignon Klein Constantia
    £7.49 (JON) £7.99 (DI)
Cabernet Sauvignon Vriesenhof £7.85
    (UB)
1989
Cabernet Sauvignon Klein Constantia
    £7.47 (CAP)
Shiraz Zandvliet £7.75 (WRI)

£8.00 ➜ £9.99

1996
Pinot Noir Bouchard Finlayson Overberg
    £9.95 (BIB)
Pinotage Grangehurst £9.95 (BIB)
Shiraz Fairview £9.48 (GN)
1995
Cabernet Sauvignon De Trafford £8.75
    (BIB)
Merlot De Trafford £8.75 (BIB)
Pinotage Kanonkop £9.40 (SOM)
Pinotage Wildekrans £8.95 (BER)

1994

Cabernet Sauvignon De Trafford £9.45 (WS)

Cabernet Sauvignon Neil Ellis £8.95 (WS)

Cabernet Sauvignon Warwick Farm £8.99 (VIC)

Cabernet Sauvignon/Merlot Louisvale £9.25 (ROB)

Merlot De Trafford £8.99 (VIC)

Merlot Grangehurst £9.50 (BIB)

Pinot Noir Hamilton Russell £8.99 (JON) £9.95 (LAY)

Pinotage Uiterwyk £9.80 (UB) £9.95 (LAY)

Shiraz Rust-en-Vrede £8.11 (FLE)

1993

Cabernet Sauvignon Neil Ellis £9.95 (ROB) £9.99 (MAJ)

Cabernet Sauvignon Jordan Vineyards £9.30 (STA)

Cabernet Sauvignon Klein Constantia £8.70 (AD)

Cabernet Sauvignon Thelema £9.49 (ENO)

Laureat Zonnebloem £8.36 (CAP) £8.50 (GRE)

1992

Cabernet Sauvignon Groot Constantia £8.10 (CAP)

Cabernet Sauvignon Stellenryck £8.75 (CAP)

Cabernet Sauvignon Thelema £8.25 (SOM)

Cabernet Sauvignon Uiterwyk £8.30 (SOM)

Cabernet Sauvignon Warwick Farm £8.50 (WS)

Rubicon Meerlust £9.93 (NO)

1991

Cabernet Sauvignon Meerlust £9.95 (BU)

Carlonet Uitkyk £9.74 (CAP)

Gold Rustenberg £9.50 (GRE)

Merlot Meerlust £9.95 (TAN)

Shiraz Allesverloren £8.44 (CAP) £8.50 (STA)

Tinta Barocca Allesverloren £8.30 (WRI) £8.70 (AD)

1990

Cabernet Sauvignon Klein Constantia £8.15 (HAH)

1989

Cabernet Sauvignon Stellenryck £8.95 (POR) £9.99 (NI)

Cabernet Sauvignon Stellenryck Collection £9.15 (WRI)

Carlonet Uitkyk £8.46 (HOG)

Shiraz Zandvliet £9.80 (CAP)

1982

Shiraz Zonnebloem £9.45 (ROS)

£10.00 → £12.99

1995

Pinot Noir Hamilton Russell £11.90 (AV) £12.20 (TAN) £12.30 (PIP) £12.50 (POR) £12.95 (WRI)

Pinotage Beyerskloof £10.83 (NO)

Pinotage Grangehurst £10.50 (WS)

Pinotage Kanonkop £11.30 (PIP) £12.00 (WS)

1994

Cabernet Sauvignon Beyerskloof £10.99 (OD)

Cabernet/Merlot Grangehurst Reserve £10.95 (BIB)

Gouverneurs Reserve Groot Constantia £10.49 (EL)

Pinot Noir Hamilton Russell £11.50 (HOG)

Pinotage Grangehurst £12.16 (NO)

Pinotage Kanonkop £10.46 (NO)

Pinotage Uiterwyk £11.28 (NO) £11.95 (ROB)

1993

Cabernet Sauvignon Grangehurst £10.00 (BIB)

Cabernet Sauvignon Thelema £10.50 (NI) £10.75 (BU) £10.95 (BEN) £11.50 (WS)

Estate Wine Rust-en-Vrede £11.99 (LAY)
Merlot Uiterwyk £12.35 (SOM)
Red Wellington Claridge £10.51 (GN)
1992
Cabernet Sauvignon Rust-en-Vrede
£10.93 (CAP) £12.14 (NO)
Cabernet Sauvignon Thelema £10.87 (CAP)
Rubicon Meerlust £10.11 (HOG) £11.50
(POR) £12.85 (QUE) £12.95 (VIG)
1991
Cabernet Sauvignon Meerlust £10.75 (WRJ)
Merlot Meerlust £10.75 (BU) £10.80 (BEN)
£11.50 (POR)
Rubicon Meerlust £10.60 (HAH) £10.80
(BEN) £10.95 (WRI) £11.20 (CAP)
1989
Cabernet Sauvignon Warwick Farm
£11.95 (VIG)
Carlonet Uitkyk £10.25 (BEN)
Rubicon Meerlust £10.50 (NI)

£13.00 → £13.99

1994
Shiraz Rust-en-Vrede £13.32 (NO)
1991
Estate Wine Rust-en-Vrede £13.99 (JON)

£15.00 → £25.00

1993
Estate Wine Uiterwyk £17.95 (LAY)
1992
Cabernet Sauvignon Beyerskloof £16.50
(BER)
Paul Sauer Kanonkop £15.37 (NO)
1975
Cabernet Sauvignon Nederburg Paarl
£25.00 (VIG)

WHITE

Under £3.50

1996
Blanc de Noir Red Muscadel Van Loveren
£3.49 (TES)
Colombard Namaqua £3.20 (SOM)

£3.50 → £3.99

1996
Chenin Blanc KWV £3.66 (HOG) £3.79
(MAR) £3.99 (VIC) £3.99 (WR)
★ Chenin Blanc Rylands Grove £3.99 (TES)
Roodeberg KWV £3.99 (VIC)
1995
Chenin Blanc KWV £3.99 (UN) £3.99 (FUL)

£4.00 → £5.99

1997
Chardonnay Springfield Estate £5.50 (BIB)
Sauvignon Blanc Simonsig £5.58 (DOM)
1996
Caresse Marine Wildekrans £4.30 (SOM)
Chardonnay De Wetshof Grey Label
£5.45 (SAI)
Chardonnay Dieu Donné Vineyards
Unoaked £5.23 (HOG) £5.99 (EL)
Chardonnay Louisvale Chavant Unoaked
£5.49 (OD)
Chardonnay Nederburg £5.25 (NEW)
£5.69 (VIC) £5.74 (CAP)
Chardonnay Sentinel £5.99 (OD)
Chenin Blanc De Wet Cellars Cape Bay
£4.20 (AD)
★ Chenin Blanc Jacana Bush Vine £4.99 (FUL)
Crouchen/Chardonnay Fairview £5.50 (AD)
Sauvignon Blanc Haute Provence £5.49 (OD)
Sauvignon Blanc KWV £4.49 (THR) £4.49
(BOT) £4.49 (VIC) £4.49 (WR)
Sauvignon Blanc Neil Ellis £5.99 (SAI)
Sauvignon Blanc Villiera Blue Ridge £5.99
(SAF)
★ Sauvignon Blanc West Peak £4.49 (POR)
Sauvignon Blanc Wildekrans £4.75 (SOM)
1995
Chardonnay Dieu Donné Vineyards
Unoaked £5.65 (GRE)
Chardonnay Louisvale Chavant Oaked
£5.99 (OD)
Chardonnay Louisvale Chavant Unoaked
£5.50 (SOM)
Chardonnay Nederburg £5.15 (HOG)
Roodeberg KWV £4.95 (CAP)
Sauvignon Blanc KWV £4.11 (HOG) £4.39
(FUL) £4.50 (GRE) £4.66 (CAP) £4.69 (UN)
Sauvignon Blanc Simonsig £5.32 (ROS)
Sauvignon Blanc Wildekrans £5.97 (COU)
Stein Nederburg £4.56 (HOG) £5.25 (CAP)
1994
Chardonnay Rustenberg £5.96 (PEN)
Chenin Blanc KWV £4.59 (NO)
Sauvignon Blanc Simonsig £5.78 (PEN)
1993
Chardonnay De Leuwen Jagt £5.60 (PEN)
Chardonnay Klein Constantia £5.99 (WAI)
Roodeberg KWV £5.09 (BY)
Sauvignon Blanc KWV £5.57 (BY)
Stein Nederburg £5.99 (QUE)
1986
Steen Special Late Harvest KWV £4.29
(PEN)

£6.00 → £7.99

1997
Chardonnay Zonnebloem £7.75 (GRE)
Sauvignon Blanc Bouchard Finlayson Oak
  Valley £7.95 (BIB)
Sauvignon Blanc De Wetshof £6.30 (PIP)
1996
Chardonnay Boschendal £6.45 (SAI) £7.16
  (CAP)
Chardonnay Brampton £6.99 (LAY)
Chardonnay Dieu Donné Vineyards
  Unoaked £7.17 (GN)
Chardonnay Groot Constantia £7.14
  (CAP)
Chardonnay Uiterwyk £6.99 (LAY) £7.28
  (NO)
Chardonnay Vergelegen £6.45 (SAI)
Chardonnay Zonnebloem £7.72 (CAP)
  £7.99 (NA)
Riesling Groot Constantia Weisser £6.18
  (CAP)
Sauvignon Blanc Backsberg £6.10 (WRI)
Sauvignon Blanc Brampton £6.50 (WS)
  £6.74 (LAY)
Sauvignon Blanc Jordan Vineyards £7.58
  (ELL) £7.60 (STA)
Sauvignon Blanc Klein Constantia £6.25
  (GRE) £6.47 (CAP) £6.69 (NO) £6.95 (VIG)
  £7.75 (DI) £7.75 (HAH)
Sauvignon Blanc L'Ormarins £6.34 (CAP)
Sauvignon Blanc Le Bonheur £6.34 (CAP)
Sauvignon Blanc Steenberg £7.65 (REI)
Sauvignon Blanc Thelema £6.99 (SOM)
  £7.95 (SAI)
Sauvignon Blanc Uiterwyk £6.33 (NO)
Sauvignon/Chardonnay Uiterwyk
  Rosenburg £6.20 (WRI)
Semillon Haute Provence £6.49 (OD)
1995
Chardonnay Backsberg £7.33 (NO)
Chardonnay Boschendal £6.49 (UN)
Chardonnay Claridge £7.20 (FLE)
Chardonnay Hamilton Russell £7.65 (UB)
  £7.73 (HOG)
Chardonnay Klein Constantia £6.70 (CAP)
  £6.99 (UN)
Chardonnay Louisvale £7.99 (OD)
Chardonnay Louisvale Chavant Unoaked
  £7.95 (ROB)
Chardonnay Nederburg £6.66 (QUE)
Chardonnay Neil Ellis £7.99 (MAJ) £7.99
  (FUL)
Chardonnay Thelema £7.90 (SOM)
Chardonnay Vergelegen £6.49 (SAF)

Chardonnay Vriesenhof £6.50 (TAN)
Chardonnay Zonnebloem £6.97 (ROS)
Laborie KWV £6.18 (CAP)
Riesling Neethlingshof Weisser £6.48
  (CAP)
Sauvignon Blanc Klein Constantia £6.90
  (TAN)
Sauvignon Blanc L'Ormarins £6.50 (WRI)
Sauvignon Blanc Le Bonheur £6.49 (DI)
Sauvignon Blanc Neil Ellis £6.99 (FUL)
  £7.95 (ROB)
Sauvignon Blanc Thelema £6.99 (WR)
1994
Chardonnay Backsberg £6.98 (BY) £7.45
  (WRI)
Chardonnay Thelema £7.69 (WR)
Sauvignon Blanc Klein Constantia £6.39
  (JON)

£8.00 → £9.99

1997
Chardonnay Bouchard Finlayson
  Kaaimansgat £9.50 (BIB)
1996
Chardonnay Hamilton Russell £8.50 (FLE)
  £9.50 (GRE) £9.57 (AV) £9.90 (TAN)
  £9.95 (POR)
Chardonnay Jordan £8.20 (PIP) £8.65 (STA)
Chardonnay Zonnebloem £8.85 (STA)
Sauvignon Blanc Buitenverwachting £8.60
  (LAY)
Sauvignon Blanc Klein Constantia £8.50
  (LAY)
Sauvignon Blanc Mulderbosch £8.81 (FA)
  £9.20 (LAY)
Sauvignon Blanc Thelema £8.55 (NI) £8.75
  (WAI) £8.99 (BEN) £9.17 (NO) £9.50 (VIG)
1995
Chardonnay Bouchard Finlayson Oak
  Valley £8.95 (WS)
Chardonnay Bouchard Finlayson Walker
  Bay £8.99 (FUL)
Chardonnay Fairview £8.50 (BU)
Chardonnay Hamilton Russell £8.20 (ROS)
  £8.99 (JON)
Chardonnay Jordan £8.95 (WS)
Chardonnay Mulderbosch £9.11 (FA)
Chardonnay Neil Ellis £8.80 (COU)

*Stars (★) indicate wines
selected by Oz Clarke in the
Best Buys section which begins
on page 12.*

Chardonnay Simonsig £8.49 (EL)
Chardonnay Thelema £8.50 (REI) £8.57
(HOG) £8.95 (SAI) £9.85 (NI) £9.95 (BEN)
Chardonnay Vergelegen Reserve £8.95
(SAI)
Sauvignon Blanc Buitenverwachting £8.99
(EL)
Sauvignon Blanc Mulderbosch £9.40 (NO)
Sauvignon Blanc Neil Ellis £8.10 (UB)
Sauvignon Blanc Thelema £8.35 (REI)
Semillon Fairview £8.27 (GN)
1994
Chardonnay Claridge £9.50 (GN)
Chardonnay Klein Constantia £8.49 (JON)
Chardonnay Louisvale £8.95 (LEA) £9.30
(HAH)

£10.00 → £13.99

1996
Chardonnay Hamilton Russell £10.95
(LEA) £10.99 (EL) £12.95 (BER)
Sauvignon Blanc Klein Constantia £10.45
(BER)
Sauvignon Blanc Mulderbosch £10.95
(ROB)
Sauvignon Blanc Thelema £10.50 (ROB)
1995
Chardonnay Buitenverwachting £10.99
(EL)
Chardonnay Hamilton Russell £10.50
(WRI)
Chardonnay Thelema £10.40 (TAN)
£12.40 (BER)
Sauvignon Blanc Mulderbosch £13.95 (UB)
Sauvignon Blanc Mulderbosch Barrel-
fermented £10.47 (NO)
1994
Chardonnay Mulderbosch £10.70 (NO)
1989
Vin de Constance Klein Constancia ½ litre
£12.95 (ROB)
1988
Vin de Constance Klein Constancia ½ litre
£11.35 (JON) £11.95 (GAU)

ROSÉ

Under £5.50

1995
Cabernet Sauvignon Blanc de Noir KWV
£4.56 (CAP)
Cabernet Sauvignon Blanc de Noir
Nederburg £5.35 (CAP)
Rosé Nederburg £5.25 (CAP)

SPARKLING

Under £6.00

Non-vintage
KWV Mousseux Blanc Cuvée Brut £5.76
(CAP)
Nederburg Premiere Cuvée Brut £5.99
(HOG)

£6.00 → £8.99

Non-vintage
Graham Beck Brut £6.99 (SAF)
Laborie Blanc de Noir £6.26 (CAP)
Nederburg Premiere Cuvée Brut £6.68
(CAP)
Pongrácz Cap Classique £8.76 (HOG)

£9.00 → £10.99

Non-vintage
Pongrácz Brut, Bottle-fermented £10.10
(CAP)
Pongrácz Cap Classique £9.50 (GRE) £9.92
(ROS) £10.29 (JON) £10.55 (QUE))

FORTIFIED

Under £4.50

Non-vintage
Mymering Pale Extra Dry £4.16 (HOG)
Onzerust Medium £4.16 (HOG)
Renasans Dry Amontillado £4.16 (HOG)

£4.50 → £4.99

Non-vintage
Cavendish Fine Old Ruby £4.61 (HOG)
Mymering Pale Extra Dry £4.69 (CAP)
Onzerust Medium £4.69 (CAP)
Renasans Pale Dry £4.69 (CAP)

£5.00 → £6.99

Non-vintage
Cavendish Fine Old Ruby £5.44 (CAP)
Onzerust Medium £5.50 (DI)
Renasans Pale Dry £5.50 (DI)
1979
Cavendish Vintage £5.95 (HOG) £6.60
(CAP)

£7.00 → £8.99

1979
Cavendish Vintage £7.95 (DI)
1963
Cavendish Vintage £8.84 (PEN)

SPAIN

**The most excitement is coming from regions that have neither
fame nor high prices to boast of; but they do have
some terrific tastes**

Spain doesn't have many famous wines. You don't believe me? Name me three. There's Rioja, and Sherry, and – and....

Fame isn't everything, especially in the Spain of today. Toro isn't famous, but it's making terrific wines. I know it's got a silly name, but I can't help that. The wines are – well, okay, they're beefy. And then there's Somontano: great value, great flavours. Priorato's another good region; Navarra, too. These are the sort of places I'm looking at for Spanish wines at the moment.

Penedés? I'm not sure. These days it's not looking quite so sprightly, quite so innovative. That burst of energy that sent Miguel Torres and Jean León to the top of

the Spanish tree never quite seemed to filter down to the majority of producers. At the moment Penedés looks just a tiny bit routine.

Rioja? Ribero del Duero? There are good wines in both. There's not much news to report in Rioja – I get the feeling that they stick to what they know – but Ribero del Duero could at last be starting to make the sort of wines that justify its prices. I'm not against wine being expensive – you only have to read this book to see that – but I can't get too enthusiastic about wines that charge the prices but don't deliver the flavours. Overall, Spain is doing quite a lot at the moment to keep me happy.

GRAPE VARIETIES

AIRÉN (white) Believe it or not, this is the most planted grape variety on earth. It's the vast acreage of Spain's central plateau that is responsible: mile after mile of Airén. Yet the world isn't drowning in the stuff: why not? Simply because the parched conditions mean that yields are tiny. Traditionally, the wine has been tired, alcoholic, yellow plonk aimed at the bars of Madrid. But new, cool wine-making methods can transform it into some of the most refreshing basic white yet produced in Spain, with a delicious light apple, lemon and liquorice flavour.

ALBARIÑO (white) Lovely, peachy, fresh wines with elegant acid balance from Rías Baixas. It's also grown over the border in Portugal for Vinho Verde, but it's called Alvarinho there. The wine has had the disadvantage of being very expensive, but prices are getting more reasonable. Try *Condes de Albarei*.

BOBAL (red) Quite good deep-coloured, fruity red and stylish rosados in Utiel-Requena and Valencia. It has reasonable acidity and relatively low alcohol, which keep the wines comparatively fresh and appetizing.

CABERNET SAUVIGNON (red) Not a native Spanish variety, but making inroads in Penedés and Navarra, where it is generally rich and heavy with oak.

CARIÑENA (red) A source of dark and prodigiously tannic wine. It plays only a small part in the DO wine which carries its name, and most Cariñena (it's the same as the Carignan of southern France) is grown in Catalonia, usually as a beefy blender. It is also a minority grape in Rioja under the name Mazuelo. With its high tannin and acidity, and its aroma of ripe plums and cherries, it complements Tempranillo and adds to its aging potential. Try the varietal Mazuelo from *Campo Viejo*.

CHARDONNAY (white) Quite popular in Catalonia, where it is made in a big, oaky, international style.

GARNACHA (red) This, known as Grenache in France, grows everywhere in Spain except Andalusia, and makes big, broad, alcoholic, sometimes peppery or spicy wines. The wines are dark, and don't last well, but they can be delicious young. The greatest examples are to be found in Priorato.

GARNACHA BLANCA (white) This makes wines that are high in alcohol, low in acidity and with a tendency to oxidize, so they are usually blended in with wines of higher acidity, like Viura.

GRACIANO (red) On the verge of extinction, the excellent Graciano grape has been rescued by the DOC upgrade in Rioja, where conscientious winemakers are seeking it out once again for the extra quality it gives to the wine.

MALVASÍA (white) This interesting, aromatic, flavourful grape tends, in Spain, to produce wines of low acidity that turn yellow and oxidize rapidly. When well made, it's full-bodied, fairly strongly scented, spicy or musky, often with a hint of apricots, and sometimes slightly nutty as well. Ten years ago, good white Rioja *reservas* really *did* taste like white Burgundy – because of the high proportion of Malvasía used in the blend. Still flying the flag for this late-lamented style are the excellent *Marqués de Murrieta* and *CVNE*, with its *Monopole* and its *Reserva*. But Malvasia is also still widely grown in the Canary Islands where it makes light, fresh whites, sometimes mixed with Viura/Macabeo.

MENCÍA (red) Mainly used in light, fruity young wines in Ribeiro and Bierzo.

MERSEGUERA (white) Valencia's mainstay white grape, also grown in Alicante and Tarragona, produces light, delicately aromatic and characterful wines.

MONASTRELL (red) Used to add body and guts to many Catalonian Tempranillo blends. It's grown right down the eastern seaboard in Alicante, Jumilla, Almansa, Yecla and Valencia – usually dry and stolid but sometimes made sweet. Jumilla's *Altos de Pio* is traditional, Yecla's *Pozuelo* more elegant.

MOSCATEL (white) Almost all Spanish Moscatel is the second-line Muscat of Alexandria rather than the top-quality Muscat à Petits Grains. But it makes a lot of good wine – rich and brown in Málaga, or fresh and grapy in Valencia. *Torres* makes a good, off-dry, aromatic version mixed with Gewürztraminer in Penedés, as does *de Muller* in Tarragona. Muscat de Chipiona from *Burdon* is rich and peachy. Also used to sweeten cream sherries.

PALOMINO (white) This is the dominant grape of the sherry region, making up all of the dry sherries, and an increasing proportion of the others. Although it produces great fortified wine it is not in itself a great grape. It plays a minor role in Montilla-Moriles. As a table wine grape, it produces dull, fat stuff, even with modern wine-making techniques, but in the sherry bodegas it reacts brilliantly to the *flor* yeast which imparts to *fino* that characteristic bone-dry, stark-sour nose.

PARELLADA (white) Touted as the provider of all the perfume and finesse in Catalonia's whites and in Cava fizz, but Parellada doesn't honestly have much to say for itself, except from the best producers: *Torres Viña Sol* is refreshing and lemony; also good are *Ferret i Mateu* and *Miret*.

PEDRO XIMÉNEZ (white) This used to be the chief component of sweet sherries, and is sometimes made into dessert wine,

deeply coloured and thick. It covers most of the nearby Montilla-Moriles vineyards, as well as providing richness in Málaga; otherwise used extensively for rather dull dry whites.

TEMPRANILLO (red) The fine red grape of Rioja and Navarra crops up all over Spain as far south as the province of Cádiz, but with a different name in almost every region. It's Cencibel on the plains of La Mancha and Valdepeñas, Tinto Fino in Ribera del Duero; elsewhere it may be Tinto de Madrid, Tinto de Toro, Tinto del País.... The wines have a spicy, herby, tobacco-like character, with plenty of sweet strawberry or sour cherry fruit, firm acidity and some tannin. Tempranillo makes vibrantly fruity wines for gulping down young, as well as more robust wines for aging – and it mixes brilliantly with oak. It's often blended, especially with Garnacha.

VERDEJO (white) One of Spain's more interesting white grapes. In Rueda it makes soft, creamy and slightly nutty white, sometimes a touch honeyed, with good, green acidity.

VIURA (white) The main white grape of Rioja, made nowadays apple-fresh and clean and, at best, rather neutral; at worst it is sharp and grapefruity. It achieves similarly mixed results, under the name Macabeo, in Catalonia. Made in this light, modern style, it's a wine for gulping down young, in its first year. But if you take the trouble to blend it with Malvasía, top it up with a slug of acidity and leave it to age for a while in oak barrels, Viura can make wonderful, rich, almost Burgundy-like white Rioja. What white Rioja used to be like, in fact.

XAREL-LO (white) One of the three main white grapes of Catalonia, this is heavier, more alcoholic and even less aromatic than the barely aromatic Parellada and Macabeo, with which it is generally blended.

WINE REGIONS

ALELLA, DO (white) Catalan region whose best-known wine is the off-dry, very fruity *Marqués de Alella*. Also look for the light, pineapple-fresh Chardonnay and appley *Marqués de Alella Seco*, as well as the sparkling, greengagy *Parxet*, which beats most famous Cavas hands down.

ALICANTE, DO (red) Heavy, earthy reds made in south-east Spain from Monastrell and mostly useful for blending.

ALMANSA, DO (red) Strong spicy reds from Monastrell and Garnacha, and even better reds from Tempranillo. *Bodegas Piqueras* makes very good wines under the *Castillo de Almansa* and *Marius* labels.

AMPURDÁN-COSTA BRAVA, DO (red, white, rosado) This part of Catalonia is a major supplier to the Costa Brava. Seventy per cent is rosado, but there is also some so-called 'Vi Novell', supposedly modelled on Beaujolais Nouveau.

BIERZO, DO (red) Emergent zone for the promising Mencía grape. Older wines are blends from before it became a DO.

BINISSALEM, DO (red, white, rosado) Young and *crianza* reds and light young whites and rosados from Mallorca. The main producer is *Bodegas Franja Roja*.

BULLAS, DO (red) In the province of Murcia, great big heady Monastrell reds, mostly from co-operatives.

CALATAYUD, DO (red) Mainly Garnacha reds, plus some Tempranillo, usually for drinking young.

CAMPO DE BORJA, DO (red) Hefty alcoholic reds made from Cariñena and Garnacha, now making way for lighter reds and good rosados. *Bodegas Bordejé* and the *Borja* and *Santo Cristo* co-ops look promising.

CANARY ISLANDS There are eight DOs in the islands: Abona, El Hierro, Lanzarote, La Palma, Tacoronte-Acentejo, Valle de Güimar, Valle de la Orotava and Ycoden-Daute-Isora. Most of the wines are white (Tacoronte-Acentejo is the only serious producer of red) and mainly pleasant enough for the beach. There is still

---

CLASSIFICATIONS

Denominación de Origen Calificada (DOC) is a new super-category (equivalent to the Italian DOCG) for wines which have a long tradition of high quality and are prepared to submit themselves to more rigorous quality scrutiny. So far there's only one DOC, and that's Rioja.

Denominación de Origen (DO) is roughly equivalent to the French AC: the basic quality wine designation. There are 51 of them.

Country wines fall into two groups: there are **Vinos Comarcales**: perhaps 'county wines' is the nearest translation into English. These have some local significance but few pretensions to promotion. The second and more important group comprises 22 **Vinos de la Tierra**, which translates as 'country wines', like French vins de pays. These are smaller areas, more tightly controlled and, in many cases, with ambitions to apply for DO status at some time in the future.

 Vino de Mesa, basic table wine, doesn't usually carry any kind of regional name, nor a vintage date. A few maverick winemakers such as the Marqués de Griñón in Toledo and the Yllera family in Rueda use a legal nicety to put a general regional name on the label.

some sweet, fortified Malvasia, but it's not seen outside the islands.

CARIÑENA, DO (red) The best here are the pleasant, full, soft reds, mostly made from the fat, jammy Garnacha. Whites and rosados can be pleasant, but are mostly dull. The reds of the *Bodegas San Valero* co-op are sold here as *Don Mendo* and *Monte Ducay*.

CAVA, DO (white, rosado) The Spanish name for Champagne-method fizz, nearly all of which is from Catalonia. When Cava was promoted to DO status, several regions lost the right to use the name, and their wines (some, admittedly excellent) must now be called *Método Tradicional*. However, the two biggest outsiders, *Bodegas Inviosa* in Extremadura and *Torre Oria* in Valencia have permission to continue using the name.

Cava gets criticized in Britain for its earthy, old-fashioned style. Some companies are starting to turn out fresher, less earthy Cavas by better wine-making and less excessive aging, and by including some Chardonnay. Most appetizing are *Cavas Hill Reserva Oro Brut Natur, Codorníu Première Cuvée Brut, Juvé y Camps, Mont Marçal Cava Nature* (and *Chardonnay*), *Parxet, Raïmat, Segura Viudas* and *Rovellats, Freixenet* and its subsidiary company *Condé de Caralt*. From being rather fresher a couple of years ago, Cava at the moment seems to be returning to its earthy roots.

CEBREROS, Vino de la Tierra (red) In Castilla-León, a source of good, honest local wines, mostly red and cheap.

CIGALES, DO (red, rosado) Near Ribera del Duero, famed for rosados but with some serious reds as well, made from Tempranillo/Garnacha mixes.

CHACOLÍ, DO (red, white) There are two of these, in neighbouring Basque provinces: Chacolí de Getaria (the local spelling is Getariako Txakolina) and Chacolí de Bizcaia (Bizkaiko Txakolina). The wines are sharp, fresh and uncomplicated with the local seafood. They're seldom seen outside the area, however.

CONCA DE BARBERÁ, DO (red, white) The fresh, fruity Santara brand comes from here, via flying winemaker Hugh Ryman. *Concavins* also makes a decent Merlot.

CONDADO DE HUELVA, DO (white, fortified) Wines not unlike Montilla are made and mostly drunk locally.

COSTERS DEL SEGRE, DO (red, white) Formerly a virtual one-producer DO, in the form of *Raïmat. Raïmat Abadía*, based on Cabernet Sauvignon, Tempranillo and Garnacha and aged in oak, is normally good, as is the Pinot Noir. The Cabernet Sauvignon is also very good – ripe but light,

MATURITY CHART
1994 Ribera del Duero
A very good vintage that should keep well

Bottled				Ready		Peak			Tiring		In decline	
0	1	2	3	4	5	6	7	8	9	10	11	12	13 years

blackcurranty-oaky wine. The Tempranillo isn't so very different; Merlot is plummy and rich. Whites include the light, lemony, gently oaked Chardonnay, as well as a good sparkler, Chardonnay Blanc de Blancs. *Castell del Remei*, producing Cabernet, Merlot, Chardonnay, Macabeo and Tempranillo, is now also in Britain.

JUMILLA, DO (red) Super-ripe reds, usually sold in bulk for beefing up blends elsewhere. However, French investment is now creating a new fresh-flavoured red style. The *Condestable* brands, *Castillo de Jumilla* and *Con Sello*, are quite good and gentle as is the ripe, plummy *Taja* from French merchants *Mahler-Besse*.

MÁLAGA, DO (fortified) We don't see much Málaga here – in fact no-one sees much anywhere because Malaga's wine industry is beset by encroaching tourism. Málaga is usually full, brown and sweet in a raisiny, but not a gooey way and is slightly smoky too. There is some dry Málaga, but you'll have to take a long weekend on the Costa del Sol to see much. *Scholtz Hermanos* has closed, leaving only one producer, *Bodega López Hermanos*, of any size. It has substantial soleras of old wines. Enjoy it.

LA MANCHA, DO (red, white) Spain's enormous central plateau – making 40 per cent of all its wine – is bringing in cool fermentation and drawing out unexpectedly fresh flavours. Some are bland, but young and bright-eyed. Only ten per cent is red, most of which is pale semi-red plonk for the bars of Madrid. The reds *can* be enjoyable, yet so far only *Vinicola de Castilla, Cueva del Granero* and *Bodegas Rodriguez & Berger* are proving this with any regularity. *Arboles de Castillejo* from *Bodegas Torres Filoso* is a Tempranillo worth a try. But you have to catch them *very* young. Others: *Casa la Teja, Castillo de Alhambra, Lazarillo, Señorío de Guadianeja, Viña Santa Elena, Yuntero, Zagarrón*.

MANCHUELA, Vino de la Tierra (red) Mainly traditional-style robust reds made from the Bobal grape. Look out for ripe, plummy wines from *Viñaclar* and *Montefiel*.

MÉNTRIDA, DO (red) Strong, sturdy reds produced bang in the middle of Spain and seldom travelling much further.

MONTILLA-MORILES, DO (fortified) Montilla wines are usually thought of as lower-priced – and lower-strength – sherry lookalikes but there is a great deal of quite good wine here. In general the dry wines, from Pedro Ximénez grapes, do not have the bite of really good sherry, but some of the mediums and sweets can be all right.

NAVARRA, DO (red, white, rosado) The neighbouring region to Rioja grows the same grapes, but with more Garnacha.

The best red is the single-estate *Magaña*, which has Cabernet and Merlot. Other potentially good names are *Chivite* and *Bodegas Príncipe de Viana,* which also uses the label *Agramont. Monte Ory* and *Bodegas Ochoa* are now much fresher. *Vinicola Navarra* makes old-fashioned, oaky reds – look for *Castillo de Tiebas* – and the modernized *Bodegas Irache* is producing both fruity and oak-aged styles. The whites used to be mostly very ordinary, cool-fermented, neutral Viura which died in the bottle waiting for someone to buy it. However, young and fresh white Navarra is pleasant and slurpable: look for *Agramont* from *Bodegas Príncipe de Viana*, which is fermented in new Alliers oak.

PENEDÉS, DO (red, white, rosado) Catalonia's leading wine region, though no longer as exciting as it used to be. High spots include *Jean León*'s Cabernet Sauvignon – a weighty, impressively long-lasting red, though lighter than it used to be. *Torres* wines run from the rich, rather sweetly oaky basic reds, right up to the exciting Cabernet Sauvignon-based *Mas La*

Plana and the 100% Pinot Noir *Mas Borras*. Torres also extracts a lean, lemony, sharply refreshing flavour from his Parellada. *Jean León* makes a delicious oaky, pineappley Chardonnay. Also look out for are *Cavas Hill, Ferret i Mateu, Masia Bach, Mont Marçal, Vallformosa, René Barbier, Jaume Serra*.

PRIORATO, DO (red) You need 13.5 degrees of alcohol here to get your DO. The reds from Garnacha and Cariñena are renowned – rich and full-bodied in style, and *Masia Barril, Scala Dei* and *de Muller* are worth trying. Also look for *Masia Duch, Clos Dofi, Clos Martinet, Clos l'Obac, Clos Mogador* and, if you've won the lottery, *Clos l'Ermita*.

RÍAS BAIXAS, DO (red, white) Fresh and fragrant Albariño is the star grape here: *Martín Codax* is good, as are *Condado de Tea, O Rosal, Bodegas Morgadío, Santiago Ruiz, Granja Fillaboa* and *Lagar de Cervera*.

RIBEIRA SACRA, DO (white) Newish Galician DO making excellent and good value whites from Godello, Albariño, Treixadura and others.

RIBEIRO, DO (red, white) There is fresh white wine made from Treixadura and Torrontés here: try *Casal da Barca* from *Bodega Alanis*.

RIBERA DEL DUERO, DO (red) The big name in this big-name region is *Vega Sicilia*. Its wines are arguably the best in Spain, and unquestionably the most expensive. However, new names and faces are coming to the fore. *Pesquera* from Alejandro Fernández fetches high prices (usually too high). Others include *Félix Callejo, Señorío de Nava, Viña Pedrosa, Balbás, Vega Izan, Ribeño, La Cepa Alta* and (potentially excellent) *Pago de Carraovejas*. There were very good vintages in both 1994 and 1995.

RIOJA, DOC (red, white) Classic reds that taste of oak and vanilla toffee, plus rather light, sometimes peppery fruit with a strawberry jam sweetness.

Practically all the Rioja on sale here comes from firms who blend and age wines from different grapes and parts of the region to a house style. Some use more of

RIOJA CLASSIFICATIONS

Rioja is divided into three geographical sub-regions: Rioja Alta, Rioja Alavesa and Rioja Baja: most wines will be a blend from all three. The wine's age, indicated on the label, falls into one of four categories.

Sin crianza   Without aging, or with less than a year in wood; wine sold in its first or second year. (The words *sin crianza* are not seen on the label.)

Crianza   With a minimum of 12 months in wood and some further months in bottle; cannot be sold before its third year. Whites will have had a minimum of six months in cask before bottling.

Reserva   Selected wine from a good harvest with a minimum of 36 months' aging, in cask and bottle, of which 12 months minimum in cask. It cannot leave the bodega until the fifth year after the vintage. Whites have at least six months in cask, and 24 months' aging in total.

Gran Reserva   Wine from an excellent vintage (supposedly) that will stand up to aging: 24 months minimum in cask and 36 months in bottle, or vice-versa. It cannot leave the bodega until the sixth year after the vintage. White wines have six months in cask and 48 months' aging in total.

the more elegant Tempranillo, some more of the fatter, riper Garnacha, perhaps adding a little of the two minority grapes, Graciano and Mazuelo. The Rioja Alavesa region makes more delicate, scented wines; Rioja Alta is firmer, leaner, slower to show its character but slower to lose it too, and the lower, hotter Rioja Baja grows mostly Garnacha, which gets super-ripe and rather lumpish. Best are *Bodegas Riojanas, Campo Viejo, El Coto, CVNE, Faustino, López de Heredia, Marqués de Cáceres, Marqués de Murrieta, Martínez Bujanda, Montecillo, Muga, Olarra, La Rioja Alta, Palacio, Campillo, Amézola de la Mora* and *Marqués de Riscal*.

White Rioja *can* be buttery and rich, slightly Burgundian. *Marqués de Murrieta* still makes a very good example of this style, and so, with rather less oak, does *CVNE* with its *Monopole* and *Reserva*, and *Bodegas Riojanas* with its *Monte Reál*. *López de Heredia* makes an old-fashioned style, while *Navajas, Viña Soledad* from *Franco Españolas* and *Siglo Gold* from *AGE* are all oak-aged. The best new white Riojas are full of fresh, breath-catching raw fruit, with the acid attack of unsugared grapefruit.

RUEDA, DO (white) A brilliant source of light table wines, picked early and fresh and fermented cool. The local grape, the Verdejo, makes soft, full, nutty wines, sometimes padded out with the dull Palomino, or sharpened up with the more acid Viura. Most are best young, but there are oaked ones. The most interesting Ruedas are *Marqués de Griñon*, made at *Bodegas Castilla La Vieja*. Others include *Marqués de Riscal*, which is also growing Sauvignon Blanc and re-discovering the use of oak, and *Alvarez y Diez*, which makes stylish Sauvignon and Verdejo. Rueda has also introduced a Champagne-method fizz.

SHERRY (JEREZ-XÉRÈS-SHERRY, DO) (fortified) There are two basic sherry styles, *fino* and *oloroso*, each with sub-divisions. *Fino*, from Jerez or Puerto de Santa Maria, should be pale and dry, with an unnerving dry austerity. The tang comes from a layer of natural yeast, called *flor*, that forms on the surface of the wine in the barrels. The lightest wines are selected for *fino*, which is drunk cool and fresh, often as an apéritif.

Manzanilla is a form of *fino* matured by the sea at Sanlúcar de Barrameda. It can be almost savoury-dry, and you might imagine a whiff of sea salt – if you catch it fresh enough. Best: *Barbadillo, Caballero, Diez-Merito, Don Zoilo, Garvey, La Gitana, Hidalgo, La Ina, Inocente, Lustau, La Riva, Sanchez Romate, Tío Pepe*. Good Puerto *fino* comes from *Burdon* and *Osborne*.

In Britain there can be a problem with freshness: *fino* and *manzanilla* won't usually keep longer than six months in bottle.

Real *amontillado* begins life as *fino*, aged in cask until the *flor* dies and the wine deepens and darkens to a tantalizing, nutty dryness. In the natural state, as drunk in Spain, it is *completely* dry, and a proper *amontillado* will usually say *seco* ('dry'), on the label. But we've adulterated the word in English to mean a bland, downmarket drink of no interest. Look out for *almacenista* sherries, wines from small stockholders, which can be wonderful.

Look out also for *Solear* from *Barbadillo, La Goya Manzanilla Pasada* and *Amontillado Fino Zuleta* (*Delgado Zuleta*), *Amontillado del Duque* (*Gonzalez Byass*), *Hidalgo Manzanilla Pasada, Valdespino*'s *Amontillado Coliseo* and *Don Tomás.* (*Manzanilla pasada* has extra barrel age, and should be wonderful.)

Real *olorosos*, made from richer, fatter wines without any *flor*, are deep and dark, packed with violent burnt flavours – and usually dry, though you may find *oloroso dulce* (sweet). In Britain most are sweetened with Pedro Ximénez or Moscatel. They usually come as 'Milk', 'Cream' or 'Brown'. Pale Creams are sweetened (inferior) *fino*, and are some of the dullest drinks around. For the real, dry thing, once again, look for *almacenista olorosos* from *Lustau*. There are a few good, concentrated sweetened *olorosos* around,

THE COST OF A BOTTLE

	Palo Cortado Sherry	**£9.00**
VAT		1.34
Mark-up		1.87
Duty		1.40
Distribution		0.17
Shipping		0.17
Wine		4.05

like *Apostoles* and *Matusalem*, both from *González Byass, Solera 1842 (Valdespino)*. Dry: *Barbadillo, Don Zoilo, Sandeman, Valdespino Don Gonzalo, Williams & Humbert Dos Cortados*. These intense old wines are one of today's great bargains.

SOMONTANO, DO (red, white, rosado) The most exciting of Spain's newer regions. Attractive, lightly scented table wines, and some decent fizz. The *Cooperativa de Sobrarbe* under the *Camporocal* label is encouraging. *Covisa, Enate* and *Bodegas Pirineos* are good.

TARRAGONA, DO (red, white, rosado) There is some progress discernible here, in the form of *crianzas* made from Cabernet Sauvignon, Garnacha and Tempranillo.

TERRA ALTA, DO (red) Decent Tempranillo. Good producers include the *Gandesa* co-op, *Ferrer Escod*.

TIERRA DE BARROS, Vino de la Tierra (red) One major bodega (*Inviosa*) has blazed a trail with its excellent *Lar de Barros* from Cencibel and Cabernet Sauvignon. *Viniberia* leads the followers.

TORO, DO (red) This can make excellent, cheap, beefy, tannic but richly fruity reds from the Tinto de Toro – yet

another alias for the Tempranillo. The best wines still probably come from *Bodegas Fariña*, whose *Gran Colegiata* is aged French-style in small oak barrels. *Bodegas Frutos Villar* and the co-op at *Morales* offer good value at lower prices.

UTIEL-REQUENA, DO (red, rosado) The reds, from the Bobal grape, are robust, rather hot and southern. The rosados *can* be better – delicate and fragrant.

VALDEORRAS, DO (red, white) The reds are best young. The ordinary whites, fresh and fruity at their best, are made from Palomino and Doña Blanca, but there is work being done with Godello.

VALDEPEÑAS, DO (red) The best reds here are from Cencibel (Tempranillo) and turn out deep and herby with good strawberry fruit – and excellent value at very low prices, even for *gran reservas* with a decade's aging. Look for the soft wines, aged in new oak, of *Señorío de Los Llanos*, *Viña Albali* from *Bodegas Felix Solís* and fruity *Marqués de Gastañaga* and *Casa de la Viña*.

VALENCIA, DO (red, white, rosado) Large quantities of wines fine for the beach. Some low-priced reds from *Schenk* and *Gandía Pla* can be good, and sweet Moscatels can be tasty and good value. Gandía's *Castillo de Liria*, is an attractive red.

VALLE DE MONTERREI, DO (white) Another of Galicia's new 'superwhite' DOs. Good value whites from Godello, Doña Blanca and even Palomino.

VINOS DE MADRID, DO (red) Mainly young wines, plus some *crianza* from Tempranillo and Garnacha.

YECLA, DO (red, white) Fairly full-bodied reds and more dubious whites. Some decent wines from *Bodegas Castaño*, from the cheap and cheerful *Dominio de Espinal* to the better *Pozuelo Reserva*.

PRODUCERS WHO'S WHO

ANTONIO BARBADILLO ★★★★(★)
(Sanlúcar de Barrameda) Top *manzanilla*.

CAMPO VIEJO ★★★ (Rioja) Decent
Riojas, soft, traditional *reservas*, and varietals.

VINÍCOLA DE CASTILLA ★★★ (La
Mancha) Up-to-date producer of white and
oaky red Señorío de Guadianeja. Soft red
Castillo de Alhambra is good value.

JULIÁN CHIVITE ★★★ (Navarra)
Clean white from Viura, attractive *rosado*
from Garnacha, and a good Tempranillo-
based red, all under the Gran Feudo label.

CODORNÍU ★★★ (Penedés) Giant
Cava company making likeably reliable fizz.
Good soft and honeyed Anna de Codorníu,
and a very good, creamy Chardonnay Cava.

**CONTINO (SOCIEDAD VINÍCOLA
LASERNA)** ★★★★(★) (Rioja) Excellent,
single-vineyard wines. Big, plummy and
spicily complex.

CVNE ★★★(★) (Rioja) Excellent *crianza*
and *reserva* whites (Monopole and CVNE
Reserva), but its fame rests on its two
ranges of reds: Imperial and Viña Real, from
crianza to *gran reserva* level.

DOMECQ ★★★★(★) (Jerez) Leading
sherry house, with top *fino* La Ina, Botaina
amontillado and Rio Viejo *oloroso*. Also Rioja.

FAUSTINO MARTÍNEZ ★★★ (Rioja)
Good reds. Look out also for the new
Campillo bodega.

FREIXENET ★★ (Penedés) High-tech
Cava firm best known for Cordon Negro,
but also good value Carta Nevada, Vintage
Brut Nature, and upmarket Brut Barroco.

GONZÁLEZ BYASS ★★★★★ (Jerez)
Producer of the best-selling *fino* Tío Pepe.

GB also makes an impressive top range of
wines, and a Rioja, Bodegas Beronia.

CAVAS HILL ★★(★) (Penedés) Table
wines as well as fresh, clean Cava Reserva
Oro Brut Natur. Look out for Blanc Cru
and Oro Penedés Blanco Suave whites, and
Rioja-style reds, Gran Civet and Gran Toc.

JEAN LEÓN ★★★★ (Penedés) Some of
Spain's most 'Californian' wines: super-oaky,
pineapple-and-honey Chardonnay, and soft,
blackcurranty Cabernet Sauvignon.

LOS LLANOS ★★★ (Valdepeñas) The
brightest spot is wonderfully soft, oaky reds.

LÓPEZ DE HEREDIA ★★★★ (Rioja)
Rich, complex whites, Viña Tondonia and
Viña Gravonia, and delicate, ethereal reds,
Viña Cubillo and Viña Tondonia.

LUSTAU ★★★★ (Jerez) 'Reviving
Traditional Sherry Values', to use its own
phrase, with its range of *almacenista* wines.

MARQUÉS DE CÁCERES ★★★(★)
(Rioja) Whites are cool-fermented and
fresh, and reds have less wood-aging than
usual, but still keep an attractive style.

MARQUÉS DE GRIÑÓN ★★★★
(Toledo) Very good Cabernet, aided by
advice from Professor Émile Peynaud from
Bordeaux. Also a joint venture with
Berberana in Rioja which is looking good.

MARQUÉS DE MURRIETA ★★★★
(Rioja) A remarkable, ultra-traditional
winery with wines oak-aged far longer than
in any other Rioja bodega; Etiqueta Blanca
wines, the youngest, spend at least two
years in barrel, and are richly oaky, pungent
and lemony. The red is soft and fruity-oaky,
while the *reservas* are deep and complex.
Castillo Ygay wines (the best from the very
top years) may sit in barrel for 40 years.

MARTÍNEZ BUJANDA ★★★ (Rioja)
Super-fresh and lively Valdemar white and strongly oaky *reserva* and *gran reserva* Condé de Valdemar.

MONTECILLO ★★★(★) (Rioja)
Aromatic white Viña Cumbrero, a raspberry and oak red, Viña Cumbrero *crianza*, and a *reserva*, Viña Monty.

MUGA ★★★(★) (Rioja) This bodega has a sternly traditional image. For reds, this traditionalism does nothing but good, and the *crianza* is fragrant and delicate, while the Prado Enea *reserva* or *gran reserva* is more complex, but still subtle and elegant. It's not cheap, though.

VIÑA PESQUERA ★★★(★) (Ribera del Duero) Prices have shot up since American wine writer Robert Parker likened this to Château Pétrus. Made from Tinto Fino and Garnacha, it's good but not *that* good, oaky and aromatic, with rich savoury fruit.

PRÍNCIPE DE VIANA ★★★(★)
(Navarra) Innovative bodega which used to be a co-op, and became known as Bodegas Cenalsa. Agramont is its best-known UK brand, and look out for new Bodegas Guelbenzu, a Cabernet/Tempranillo estate in Cascante.

RAÏMAT ★★★ (Costers del Segre) The Raïmat Chardonnay Cava is honeyed, with grassy acidity. Abadía is an oak-enhanced blend of Cabernet, Tempranillo and Garnacha. Also Cabernet Sauvignon, Pinot Noir and Merlot.

REMELLURI ★★★★(★) (Rioja) Single-estate wine, not that common in Rioja; the bodega makes a fine, meaty *reserva*, barrel-aged for two to three years.

LA RIOJA ALTA ★★★★ (Rioja)
A traditional bodega, firm believer in long barrel-aging: over half the wines qualify as *reserva* or *gran reserva*. Even the Viña Alberdi *crianza* has a delightfully oaky flavour. It makes two styles of *reserva*, the elegant Viña Arana and the rich Viña Ardanza. In the best years, it makes exceptional *gran reservas*.

RIOJANAS ★★★(★) (Rioja) The best reds here are the *reservas*: the light, elegant, plummy Viña Albina and the richer, more concentrated Monte Reál. White Monte Reál *crianza* is soft and peachy, with just enough oak to fatten it.

MIGUEL TORRES ★★★★ (Penedés)
Viña Sol is a super-fresh modern white. Gran Viña Sol is Parellada and Chardonnay, fresh and pineappley, enriched with hints of vanilla oak. Gran Viña Sol Green Label pairs Parellada with Sauvignon Blanc, like oakier Sancerre. The superstar white is Milmanda Chardonnay. Viña Esmeralda is Gewürztraminer and Muscat d'Alsace. Mas la Plana Cabernet Sauvignon is the top red. Viña Magdala is Pinot Noir and Tempranillo, Gran Sangredetoro is mainly Garnacha, Mas Borras is Pinot Noir, Las Torres is Merlot and Coronas Tempranillo is least exciting.

VALDESPINO ★★★★★ (Jerez) Family-owned bodega making a range of top-class, dry sherries. Inocente is superb, characterful *fino*. The Pedro Ximénez Solera Superior is one of the few examples of sherry's great sweetening wine bottled by itself. *Amontillados* and *olorosos* from here are about as good as you can get.

BODEGAS VEGA SICILIA ★★★★(★)
(Ribera del Duero) Makers of Spain's most famous and expensive red wine – Vega Sicilia Unico, sometimes kept in barrel for ten years. The younger Valbuena offers a cheaper glimpse of Vega Sicilia's glories.

VICENTE GANDÍA ★★(★) (Valencia)
Perhaps this DO's most go-ahead producer. Fresh white Castillo de Liria and juicy red and rosado from Bobal.

SPAIN PRICE GUIDES

RIOJA RED

Under £3.50

1996
Campo Viejo Albor £3.85 (GRE)
1992
CVNE Viña Real ½ bottle £3.80 (GN)
1990
CVNE Viña Real ½ bottle £3.50 (VIG)

£4.50 → £4.99

1995
Berberana Tempranillo £4.99 (SAF)
Bodegas Muerza Vega £4.94 (LA)
Campo Viejo Albor £4.59 (NA)
Marqués de Griñon £4.99 (THR) £4.99
  (WR) £4.99 (BOT)
Martinez Bujanda Valdemar £4.69 (WR)
  £4.69 (BOT) £4.69 (THR)
1994
Campo Viejo £4.75 (GRE)
Marqués de Griñon £4.95 (WS) £4.99 (MAJ)
1992
Berberana Carta de Oro £4.99 (UN)

£5.00 → £5.49

1994
Viña Berceo £5.49 (NEW)
1993
Campillo £5.49 (ASD)
1992
Marqués de Cáceres £5.40 (HOG) £5.49
  (POR)
1991
Campillo £5.49 (VIC)

£5.50 → £5.99

1995
Palacio y Hermanos Cosmo £5.75 (WAI)
1994
CVNE £5.95 (STA)
El Coto Crianza £5.95 (ROB)

1993
CVNE £5.51 (PLA) £5.70 (PEN)
El Coto Crianza £5.99 (NA)
Marqués de Cáceres £5.85 (GRE) £5.95
  (HAH) £5.99 (WHI)
1992
CVNE £5.99 (JON)
La Rioja Alta Viña Alberdi £5.95 (SOM)
Marqués de Cáceres £5.99 (NA)
Viña Salceda Crianza £5.95 (AD)
1991
CVNE Viña Real £5.83 (ROS)
Marqués de Cáceres £5.90 (TAN)

£6.00 → £6.49

1994
CVNE £6.24 (LAY)
1993
CVNE £6.25 (VIG)
1991
Campo Viejo Reserva £6.49 (VIC) £6.49
  (THR) £6.49 (WR) £6.49 (BOT)
La Rioja Alta Viña Alberdi £6.49 (LA)
Muga Reserva £6.45 (SOM)
1989
Campo Viejo Reserva £6.49 (POR)
Gran Condal Reserva £6.49 (CO)
1988
Berberana Reserva £6.49 (FUL)

£6.50 → £6.99

1993
★ Viña Ijalba Múrice £6.99 (WHI)
1992
CVNE Viña Real £6.75 (ROB) £6.86 (GN)
La Rioja Alta Viña Alberdi £6.99 (POR)
Siglo Saco £6.75 (QUE)
Viña Salceda Crianza £6.50 (WS)
1991
Barón de Ley £6.79 (ASD) £6.99 (THR)
CVNE Viña Real £6.50 (VIG)
Faustino V Reserva £6.99 (SAF) £6.99 (BOT)
  £6.99 (GRE) £6.99 (POR) £6.99 (THR)

MERCHANTS SPECIALIZING IN SPAIN
see Merchant Directory (page 413) for details

Adnams (AD), Bibendum (BIB), Direct Wine
(DI), Eldridge Pope (EL), J E Hogg (HOG) –
particularly sherry, Lay & Wheeler (LAY),
Lea & Sandeman (LEA), Moreno Wines – a
mostly Spanish list, Thos. Peatling, Reid
Wines (1992) Ltd (REI) – good sherries,
Roberson (ROB), Tanners (TAN), Wine
Society (WS)

1990
Amézola de la Mora Crianza £6.99 (RAE)
Berberana Carta de Oro £6.99 (SAT)

£7.00 → £7.49

1992
La Rioja Alta Viña Alberdi £7.49 (AME)
Marqués de Riscal Reserva £7.29 (MAJ)
Muga Reserva £7.49 (WHI)
Viña Salceda Crianza £7.23 (ROS)
1991
Campo Viejo Reserva £7.25 (QUE)
Faustino V Reserva £7.15 (WHI)
La Rioja Alta Viña Alberdi £7.25 (COU)
Marqués de Murrieta £7.35 (HOG)
Viña Berceo Reserva £7.49 (NEW)
1990
CVNE Reserva £7.25 (WAT)
Viña Amezola Crianza £7.40 (BER)

£7.50 → £7.99

1993
Viña Salceda Crianza £7.50 (LEA)
1991
Amézola de la Mora Viña Amézola £7.99 (JON)
Campo Viejo Reserva £7.60 (BEN) £7.99 (NA)
CVNE Reserva £7.99 (PEN)
Faustino V Reserva £7.65 (UN)
Marqués de Murrieta Reserva £7.99 (NI)
Marqués de Riscal £7.99 (UN)
Muga Reserva £7.81 (PEN) £7.95 (DI)
1990
Baron de Oña Torre de Oña Reserva £7.57 (LA)
Marqués de Murrieta £7.99 (WHI)

£8.00 → £8.99

1993
Remelluri £8.30 (SOM)
Remelluri Reserva £8.60 (COU)
1992
CVNE Reserva £8.95 (STA)
Marqués de Murrieta Reserva £8.50 (GRE) £8.79 (MAJ)
Muga Reserva £8.55 (GN)
Viña Berceo Reserva £8.85 (AUR)
1991
Amézola de la Mora Crianza £8.00 (BIB)
CVNE Reserva £8.92 (PLA)
Marqués de Murrieta Reserva £8.40 (LA) £8.75 (WS) £8.99 (JON)
Marqués de Riscal Reserva £8.29 (NEW) £8.30 (LA)
Muga Reserva £8.00 (PIP)

1990
Baron de Oña Torre de Oña Reserva £8.85 (SAT) £8.99 (AME)
Marqués de Cáceres Reserva £8.95 (POR)
1989
Campo Viejo Gran Reserva £8.89 (VIC)
CVNE Reserva £8.07 (ROS) £8.75 (WS)
Marqués de Murrieta Reserva £8.99 (RAE)
1988
La Rioja Alta Viña Arana Reserva £8.90 (SOM)
1987
Montecillo Gran Reserva £8.99 (OD)

£9.00 → £9.99

1994
Remelluri £9.95 (AD)
1991
Marqués de Murrieta Reserva £9.15 (WRI) £9.25 (HAH) £9.27 (PLA) £9.45 (BEN)
Marqués de Riscal Reserva £9.18 (FLE)
1990
Marqués de Cáceres Reserva £9.95 (STA)
Marqués de Murrieta Reserva £9.36 (PEN) £9.49 (NI)
1989
Contino Reserva £9.95 (WAT)
CVNE Viña Real Reserva £9.65 (REI)
La Rioja Alta Viña Ardanza Reserva £9.35 (SOM) £9.61 (LA) £9.69 (HOG) £9.99 (POR)
Marqués de Cáceres Reserva £9.61 (ROS)
1987
CVNE Imperial Reserva £9.54 (NO)
CVNE Viña Real Reserva £9.79 (SAT)
Faustino I Gran Reserva £9.38 (HOG)
La Rioja Alta Viña Ardanza Reserva £9.95 (GRE)
1986
La Rioja Alta Viña Arana £9.27 (HOG)
1985
Campo Viejo Gran Reserva £9.49 (POR)

£10.00 → £11.99

1991
Contino Reserva £10.99 (VIC) £11.65 (PIP) £11.75 (PEN)
Marqués de Murrieta Reserva Especial £10.75 (GRE) £11.69 (EL) £11.98 (QUE)

In each price band wines are listed in vintage order. Within each vintage they are listed in A–Z order.

1990
Contino Reserva £11.98 (LA)
CVNE Imperial Reserva £11.95 (PIP)
Marqués de Murrieta Reserva £11.25 (UB)
Marqués de Murrieta Reserva Especial
   £10.49 (MAJ)
1989
CVNE Imperial Reserva £11.50 (WAT)
CVNE Viña Real Reserva £11.00 (WS)
   £11.95 (STA)
La Rioja Alta Viña Arana Reserva £11.75
   (LAY)
La Rioja Alta Viña Ardanza Reserva
   £10.25 (WS) £10.99 (JON) £11.24 (LAY)
   £11.49 (AME) £11.95 (BEN) £11.95 (AD)
Viña Ardanza Reserva £11.59 (SAT)
1988
Conde de la Salceda Gran Reserva £10.99
   (JON)
CVNE Imperial Reserva £10.50 (GRE)
   £10.99 (SAT) £11.95 (ROB)
CVNE Viña Real Reserva £10.75 (JON)
Faustino I Gran Reserva £10.25 (GRE)
La Rioja Alta Viña Arana Reserva £10.97
   (COU)
1987
Conde de la Salceda Gran Reserva £11.00
   (TAN) £11.80 (ROS)
Faustino I Gran Reserva £10.50 (WHI)
   £10.99 (BOT) £10.99 (WR) £11.25 (JON)
   £11.55 (QUE) £11.95 (UB)
Muga Prado Enea Gran Reserva £10.20 (PIP)
1985
Campo Viejo Gran Reserva £10.99 (NA)

Marqués de Cáceres Reserva £11.95 (VIN)
1981
Faustino I Gran Reserva £10.95 (POR)

£12.00 → £13.99

1991
Contino Reserva £12.16 (PLA) £12.95 (VIG)
   £12.95 (STA) £13.20 (LAY) £13.50 (BIB)

CVNE Imperial Reserva £12.75 (STA)
1990
CVNE Imperial Reserva £13.65 (LAY)
1989
Contino Reserva £12.75 (GRE)
La Rioja Alta Viña Ardanza Reserva
   £12.99 (GN) £13.50 (DI)
1988
CVNE Viña Real Gran Reserva £13.16
   (ROS) £13.69 (PLA)
1986
CVNE Imperial Gran Reserva £12.99 (SAT)
1985
La Rioja Alta Reserva 904 Gran Reserva
   £13.70 (SOM)
Marqués de Cáceres Gran Reserva
   £13.25 (UB)
1982
Marqués de Cáceres Gran Reserva
   £13.99 (VIN)

£14.00 → £15.99

1989
CVNE Viña Real Gran Reserva £14.50 (BER)
1988
CVNE Imperial Gran Reserva £15.35 (PIP)
   £15.86 (PEN) £15.95 (STA)
CVNE Viña Real Gran Reserva £14.80 (STA)
1987
Castillo Ygay Gran Reserva Especial
   £15.50 (WS)
Marqués de Murrieta Castillo Ygay Gran
   Reserva £14.20 (HOG) £15.94 (LAY)
Muga Prado Enea Gran Reserva £15.63 (ELL)
1986
CVNE Viña Real Gran Reserva £15.95 (VIG)
1985
La Rioja Alta Reserva 904 Gran Reserva
   £14.62 (LA) £15.27 (HOG)
Muga £15.75 (REI)

£16.00 → £19.99

1987
La Rioja Alta Reserva 904 Gran Reserva
   £18.95 (LAY) £19.95 (AD)
Marqués de Murrieta Castillo Ygay Gran
   Reserva £18.43 (PLA) £18.50 (STA)
   £18.75 (RAE) £19.95 (VIG)
1985
La Rioja Alta Reserva 904 Gran Reserva
   £16.50 (POR) £16.50 (WS) £17.89 (SAT)
Muga Prado Enea Gran Reserva £19.20
   (SOM)
1982
Paternina Gran Reserva £18.00 (BU)

1981
Lander Reserva £19.50 (UB)
Marqués de Riscal Gran Reserva £16.25 (LA)
1978
Viña Berceo Gran Reserva £17.99 (AUR)

£20.00 → £29.99

1987
La Rioja Alta Reserva 904 Gran Reserva £20.60 (GN)
1985
Marqués de Murrieta Castillo Ygay Gran Reserva £22.85 (AD) £26.00 (GRE) £27.95 (RAE)
Marqués de Murrieta Gran Reserva £25.10 (HAH)
Muga Prado Enea Gran Reserva £21.74 (PEN)
1983
La Rioja Alta Reserva 904 Gran Reserva £21.40 (UB)
1976
Marqués de Murrieta Castillo Ygay Gran Reserva £25.00 (BU)

£30.00 → £49.99

1982
La Rioja Alta Reserva 904 Gran Reserva £45.00 (LEA)
1981
CVNE Viña Real Gran Reserva £39.50 (STA)
La Rioja Alta Reserva 890 Gran Reserva £31.05 (LA) £32.10 (SOM) £32.50 (REI) £44.95 (GN)
1970
CVNE Imperial Gran Reserva £44.85 (REI) £49.50 (STA)
Muga Prado Enea Gran Reserva £31.50 (DI)
1959
Marqués de Riscal £35.00 (REI)

£50.00 → £69.99

1968
CVNE Viña Real Gran Reserva £55.85 (REI)
Marqués de Murrieta Castillo Ygay Gran Reserva £51.11 (NO) £66.00 (ROB)
Marqués de Murrieta Reserva Especial £55.00 (VIG)

c. £80.00

1964
Marqués de Murrieta Castillo Ygay Gran Reserva £80.00 (GRE)

RIOJA WHITE

Under £4.00

1996
Campo Viejo Albor £3.85 (GRE)
1995
Marqués de Cáceres £3.78 (HOG)
1994
Campo Viejo Albor £3.99 (BOT) £3.99 (THR) £3.99 (WR)

£4.00 → £4.99

1996
Marqués de Cáceres £4.49 (NEW)
1995
Marqués de Cáceres £4.15 (BO) £4.24 (ROS) £4.35 (GRE) £4.45 (HAH) £4.45 (AD)
1993
Berberana Carta de Oro £4.29 (CO)
Rivarey Blanco £4.59 (VIC)
1992
Faustino V £4.99 (TES)

£5.00 → £5.99

1995
Faustino V £5.99 (QUE)
1994
CVNE £5.75 (VIG)
El Coto £5.75 (ROB) £5.79 (UN)
Marqués de Cáceres £5.45 (UB)
1993
Marqués de Cáceres £5.25 (DI) £5.39 (VIN)

£6.00 → £7.99

1996
Muga £6.25 (EL)
1995
CVNE Monopole Barrel Fermented £6.80 (PIP) £7.85 (LAY)
Martinez Bujanda Conde de Valdemar £6.50 (NI)
Muga £6.17 (PEN)
1994
CVNE Monopole £6.35 (STA) £6.49 (MAJ) £6.80 (PLA)
CVNE Monopole Barrel Fermented £6.49 (SAF) £7.15 (JON) £7.70 (GN)
Marqués de Murrieta £7.39 (WHI)
1993
CVNE Monopole £6.32 (ROS) £6.92 (PEN) £6.95 (BIB) £7.90 (TAN)
CVNE Monopole Barrel Fermented £6.00 (REI) £6.50 (LEA) £6.65 (ROS) £6.99 (GRE) £7.50 (VIG) £7.79 (NA)

Faustino V £6.95 (UN)
Martinez Bujanda Conde de Valdemar
   £7.95 (LEA)
1992
Marqués de Murrieta Reserva £7.95 (STA)
Navajas £6.50 (WS)
1991
Faustino V £6.90 (UB)
Marqués de Murrieta Reserva £7.50 (WS)
   £7.50 (GRE) £7.69 (MAJ) £7.99 (RAE)
Marqués de Murrieta Ygay Gran Reserva
   £7.81 (NO)
1990
Marqués de Murrieta £6.80 (HOG)
Marqués de Murrieta Reserva £7.66 (LA)
1989
La Rioja Alta Viña Ardanza Reserva £7.32
   (LA)
Marqués de Murrieta Reserva £7.69 (BOT)
   £7.69 (WR) £7.69 (THR)

£8.00 → £10.99

1994
Martinez Bujanda Conde de Valdemar
   £8.80 (PLA)
1993
CVNE Monopole £9.75 (UB)
1991
Marqués de Murrieta £8.19 (EL) £8.20
   (TAN) £8.40 (BEN)
Marqués de Murrieta Reserva £8.09 (PLA)
   £8.95 (ROB) £9.85 (AD)
Marqués de Murrieta Ygay Gran Reserva
   £8.65 (QUE)
1990
Marqués de Murrieta Reserva £8.00 (WRI)
   £8.99 (UB)
1989
La Rioja Alta Viña Ardanza Reserva £8.49
   (AME) £8.60 (COU) £9.85 (ROB)
1988
Marqués de Murrieta £8.49 (NI)

£15.00 → £19.99

1986
Marqués de Murrieta Ygay Gran Reserva
   £19.99 (OD)
1985
Marqués de Murrieta Ygay Gran Reserva
   £19.95 (VIG)
1983
Marqués de Murrieta Reserva £15.28 (NO)
1976
López de Heredia Tondonia Gran
   Reserva £19.50 (WS)

£20.00 → £29.99

1986
Marqués de Murrieta Ygay Gran Reserva
   £20.00 (GRE) £21.75 (RAE)
1970
Marqués de Murrieta Ygay Gran Reserva
   £26.40 (NO) £29.50 (GRE)

RIOJA ROSÉ

Under £5.00

1995
Marqués de Cáceres Rosado £4.23 (HOG)
   £4.49 (NEW) £4.65 (GRE) £4.95 (DI)

£5.00 → £5.99

1995
Faustino V Rosado £5.99 (QUE)
1994
Faustino V Rosado £5.45 (GRE)
Marqués de Cáceres Rosado £5.39 (NA)
1993
Marqués de Cáceres Rosado £5.80 (UB)

NAVARRA RED

Under £4.00

1995
Luis Gurpegui Muga, Monte Ory Reserva
   £3.79 (NEW)
Nekeas Vega Sindoa Tempranillo £3.99
   (OD)

£4.00 → £4.99

1996
Luis Gurpegui Muga, Monte Ory £4.89
   (AUR)
1995
Agramont Tempranillo £4.95 (VIC)
Ochoa £4.81 (PLA)
1994
Luis Gurpegui Muga, Monte Ory £4.95
   (COU)
1993
Agramont Tempranillo £4.75 (WAI)
Julián Chivite Gran Feudo £4.68 (HOG)
   £4.97 (ROS) £4.99 (GRE) £4.99 (DI)
Luis Gurpegui Muga, Monte Ory £4.39
   (THR) £4.39 (WR) £4.39 (BOT)
1992
Agramont Tempranillo £4.79 (SAF) £4.99
   (THR) £4.99 (BOT) £4.99 (WR)

£5.00 → £6.99

1994
Guelbenzu Crianza £5.50 (WS) £5.99 (MAJ)
£5.99 (NI) £6.50 (GRE)
Ochoa £5.05 (PEN)
Ochoa Tempranillo £6.50 (PIP)
1993
Luis Gurpegui Muga, Monte Ory Crianza
£5.75 (BU)
Ochoa £6.82 (FLE)
Ochoa Tempranillo £6.10 (FLE) £6.15 (REI)
£6.18 (HOG) £6.33 (ROS) £6.49 (MAJ)
£6.57 (PLA) £6.59 (JON) £6.65 (WAT)
Palacio de la Vega Cabernet/Tempranillo
Crianza £5.99 (UB)
1992
Palacio de la Vega Cabernet/Tempranillo
Crianza £5.50 (GRE)
1991
Julián Chivite Gran Fuedo Reserva £5.65
(WRI) £5.99 (DI)
Ochoa Tempranillo £6.49 (BO)

£7.00 → £9.99

1994
Ochoa £7.40 (PIP)
1993
Ochoa Tempranillo £7.00 (TAN) £7.70 (GN)
1992
Ochoa £7.15 (JON)
Ochoa Tempranillo £7.25 (VIG)
Palacio de la Vega Cabernet Sauvignon
Reserva £7.99 (AME)
1991
Ochoa Reserva £8.35 (PIP)
1990
Ochoa Reserva £8.45 (WAT) £8.95 (STA)
1988
Luis Gurpegui Muga, Monte Ory Reserva
£7.99 (AUR) £8.96 (COU)
1987
Ochoa Cabernet Sauvignon £7.76 (FLE)
Ochoa Reserva £8.81 (PEN) £9.00 (TAN)

NAVARRA WHITE

Under £5.00

Non-vintage
Agramont £4.99 (BOT) £4.99 (WR)
1996
Agramont £4.75 (WAI)
1994
Agramont £4.79 (SAF)

£5.00 → £8.99

1996
Ochoa Seco £5.25 (STA)
1995
Julián Chivite Gran Feudo Blanco £6.18
(HA)
Ochoa Vino Dulce de Moscatel £8.08
(ROS) £8.59 (LA) £8.75 (STA)
1994
Ochoa Vino Dulce de Moscatel £8.55
(VIG)

OTHER SPANISH RED

Under £4.00

Non-vintage
Rancho Viejo, Vino de Mesa £3.75 (COU)
Vitorianas Don Darias, Vino de Mesa
£3.29 (TES) £3.49 (WR) £3.49 (BOT)
Vitorianas Don Hugo, Alto Ebro, Vino de
Mesa £3.35 (WAI)
1996
Rama Corta Tempranillo/Cabernet, La
Mancha £3.79 (ASD)
Vivala, Jumilla £3.50 (GRE)
1994
Bodegas Inviosa, Lar de Barros
Tempranillo £3.85 (SOM)
Bodegas Picqueras, Picqueras £3.95 (LEA)
1992
Palacio de León, Vino de Mesa £3.99
(BOT) £3.99 (THR) £3.99 (WR)
Señorio de los Llanos Reserva,
Valdepeñas £3.95 (WS) £3.99 (TES)

£4.00 → £4.99

1996
★ Baso, Rueda £4.25 (AD)
1995
Fariña Colegiata, Toro £4.85 (EL)
Torres Sangredetoro, Penedés £4.99
(BOT) £4.99 (THR) £4.99 (WR)
Vinos del Bierzo Viña Oro Tinto, Bierzo
£4.30 (LA)

> *Please remember that*
> ***Webster's*** *is a price*
> *guide and not a price list. It*
> *is not meant to replace up-*
> *to-date*
> *merchants' lists.*

1994
Bodegas Señorio Montenovo Tinto £4.99 (JON)
Fuente del Ritmo, La Mancha £4.49 (BOT) £4.49 (WR) £4.49 (THR)
Torres Coronas, Penedés £4.80 (DI)
Torres Sangredetoro, Penedés £4.79 (TES)
Covisa Viñas del Vero Pinot Noir, Somontano £4.99 (OD)
1993
Torres Sangredetoro, Penedés £4.99 (CO)
1992
Señorio de los Llanos Reserva, Valdepeñas £4.00 (GAL) £4.26 (HOG) £4.49 (POR) £4.73 (LA) £4.75 (JON)
Señorio de los Llanos, Valdepeñas £4.10 (SOM)
1991
Torres Coronas, Penedés £4.99 (FUL)
1990
Bodegas Piqueras Castillo de Almansa, Almansa £4.95 (DI)
Bodegas Piqueras Marius Tinto Reserva, Almansa £4.95 (LEA)
Señorio de los Llanos Gran Reserva, Valdepeñas £4.99 (MAJ)
1989
Felix Solis Viña Albali Reserva, Valdepeñas £4.49 (FUL)

£5.00 → £5.99

1996
Enate Crianza, Somontano £5.45 (AV)
1995
Bodegas Villar Cigales, Conde Ansurez £5.60 (LAY)
Enate Crianza, Somontano £5.99 (FUL)
Torres Coronas, Penedés £5.75 (GRE)
Torres Las Torres, Penedés £5.99 (DI)
1994
Señorio de Nava Crianza, Ribera del Duero £5.29 (LAY)
1993
Torres Coronas, Penedés £5.29 (VIC) £5.49 (UN) £5.49 (TES)
Torres Gran Sangredetoro, Penedés £5.75 (DI) £5.99 (WR) £5.99 (THR)
1992
Bodegas Inviosa, Lar de Barros Tempranillo £5.21 (TAN)
Bodegas Inviosa, Lar de Barros Tinto Reserva £5.95 (BU)
Masía Vallformosa Vall Reserva, Penedés £5.95 (GRE)
René Barbier Reserva, Penedés £5.75 (PLA)

Torres Coronas, Penedés £5.59 (JON)
Torres Gran Sangredetoro, Penedés £5.78 (HOG) £5.99 (MAJ)
Torres Las Torres Merlot, Penedés £5.99 (FUL)
1991
Condé de Caralt Reserva, Penedés £5.60 (TAN)
Raïmat Cabernet Sauvignon, Costers del Segre £5.99 (CO)
Torres Sangredetoro, Penedés £5.44 (PEN)
1990
Marqués de Monistrol Gran Reserva, Penedés £5.95 (BU)
Señorio de los Llanos Gran Reserva, Valdepeñas £5.74 (LA) £5.95 (POR)
Señorio de Nava Crianza, Ribera del Duero £5.99 (FUL)
1989
Bodegas Piqueras Marius Tinto Reserva, Almansa £5.10 (TAN)
Fariña Gran Colegiata Reserva, Toro £5.70 (TAN)
Torres Gran Sangredetoro, Penedés £5.99 (CO)
1987
Señorio de Nava Crianza, Ribera del Duero £5.89 (CO)

£6.00 → £7.99

1996
Torres Las Torres Merlot, Penedés £6.25 (GRE)
1995
Fernandez Condado de Haza, Ribera del Duero £7.99 (OD)
1994
★ Matarromera, Ribera del Duero £7.40 (NEZ)
Torres Las Torres Merlot, Penedés £6.22 (LA)
1993
Enate Crianza, Somontano £6.04 (NO) £6.75 (GRE)
Enrique Mendoza Viña Alfaz Seleccion, Alicante £6.98 (NO) £7.35 (LEA)
Masia Barril Tipico Tinto, Priorato £7.91 (LA) £7.95 (POR) £7.99 (BO)
1992
Raïmat Abadia Reserva, Costers del Segre £6.21 (LA)
Raïmat Tempranillo, Costers del Segre £7.35 (LA)
Covisa Viñas del Vero Pinot Noir, Somontano £6.99 (GRE) £7.20 (LA)

1991
Bodegas Inviosa, Lar de Lares Tinto Gran
Reserva £7.40 (TAN)
Callejo, Ribera del Duero £7.95 (STA)
Covisa Viñas del Vero Pinot Noir,
Somontano £6.80 (PLA)
Masia Barril Tipico Tinto, Priorato £7.58
(NO)
Priorato Scala Dei £9.95 (ROB)
Torres Gran Coronas, Penedés £7.49 (CO)
£7.69 (HOG) £7.99 (THR) £7.99 (BOT)
Torres Gran Sangredetoro, Penedés
£6.29 (LA)
Covisa Viñas del Vero Merlot/Cabernet
Sauvignon Reserva, Somontano £7.84
(ROS)
Covisa Viñas del Vero Pinot Noir,
Somontano £6.59 (ROS) £7.95 (BIB)
1990
Fariña Gran Colegiata, Toro £6.49 (EL)
Torres Gran Coronas, Penedés £7.25 (REI)
1989
Torres Gran Sangredetoro, Penedés
£6.15 (UB) £7.45 (ROB)
Torres Las Torres, Penedés £6.57 (PEN)
Covisa Viñas del Vero Pinot Noir,
Somontano £7.50 (VIG)
1988
Torres Gran Sangredetoro, Penedés
£6.35 (NO)
1984
Señorio de los Llanos Gran Reserva,
Valdepeñas £6.25 (JON) £6.35 (PEN)
£6.50 (GN)

£8.00 → £9.99

1993
Marqués de Griñon Cabernet Sauvignon,
Rueda £8.99 (FUL)
Torres Gran Coronas, Penedés £8.50
(PIP) £8.75 (GRE) £8.95 (STA) £9.72 (GN)
1992
Covisa Viñas del Vero Merlot/Cabernet
Sauvignon Reserva, Somontano £8.95
(LAY)
1991
Pesquera, Ribera del Duero £9.49 (NI)
Torres Gran Coronas, Penedés £8.50
(TAN) £8.52 (LA) £8.60 (PEN) £8.87 (ROS)
1990
Raïmat Merlot, Costers del Segre £8.40
(LA)
1989
Bodegas Inviosa, Lar de Lares Tinto Gran
Reserva £8.50 (BU)

£10.00 → £19.99

1995
Mauro, Vino de Mesa £10.99 (NI)
1994
Pesquera, Ribera del Duero £10.99 (DI)
£10.99 (OD)
1993
Pesquera Reserva, Ribera del Duero
£15.75 (GRE)
Pesquera, Ribera del Duero £10.80 (TAN)
1992
Pesquera, Ribera del Duero £10.25 (WS)
Torres Mas Borras Pinot Noir, Penedés
£12.50 (GRE)
1991
Pesquera, Ribera del Duero £14.95 (UB)
Torres Mas Borras Pinot Noir, Penedés
£12.09 (LA)
1990
Torres Gran Coronas Black Label (Mas La
Plana), Penedés £19.50 (GRE)
1989
Torres Gran Coronas Black Label (Mas La
Plana), Penedés £17.95 (DI) £18.69 (LA)
£19.95 (STA) £19.98 (QUE)
1988
Torres Gran Coronas Black Label (Mas La
Plana), Penedés £18.95 (DI) £19.95 (STA)
Torres Mas Borras Pinot Noir, Penedés
£11.56 (PEN)
1987
Torres Gran Coronas Black Label (Mas La
Plana), Penedés £17.29 (HOG)
1986
Masía Barril Priorato Extra, Priorato
£16.85 (REI)
1985
Pesquera, Ribera del Duero £13.42 (BER)
Torres Coronas, Penedés £14.50 (REI)
Vega Sicilia Valbuena 3rd year, Ribera del
Duero £19.61 (PEN)
1979
Jean León Cabernet Sauvignon, Penedés
£13.50 (DI) £14.69 (PEN)

£20.00 → £39.99

1992
Vega Sicilia Valbuena 5th year, Ribera del
Duero £37.00 (DI)
1990
Vega Sicilia Valbuena 5th year, Ribera del
Duero £39.95 (VIG)
Vega Sicilia Valbuena, Ribera del Duero
£37.95 (BEN) £39.36 (PLA)

1989
Torres Gran Coronas Black Label (Mas La Plana), Penedés £20.20 (TAN) £20.65 (WRI) £21.96 (GN)
1988
Torres Gran Coronas Black Label (Mas La Plana), Penedés £20.73 (NO) £21.25 (JON) £22.00 (UB) £22.75 (ROB)
Vega Sicilia Valbuena 5th year, Ribera del Duero £35.95 (GN)
1985
Vega Sicilia Valbuena 3rd year, Ribera del Duero £24.95 (DI)
Vega Sicilia Valbuena 5th year, Ribera del Duero £34.55 (PEN)
1982
Torres Gran Coronas, Penedés £29.38 (PEN)
1962
Torres Gran Coronas, Penedés £37.50 (VIG)

£40.00 → £59.99

1991
Vega Sicilia Valbuena 5th year, Ribera del Duero £43.30 (TAN)
1985
Torres Gran Coronas Black Label (Mas La Plana), Penedés £47.00 (PEN)
Vega Sicilia Unico, Ribera del Duero £55.00 (REI)
Vega Sicilia Valbuena 5th year, Ribera del Duero £43.00 (BER)
1983
Vega Sicilia Unico, Ribera del Duero £59.90 (DI)
1981
Torres Gran Coronas Black Label (Mas La Plana), Penedés £46.95 (STA)
1980
Vega Sicilia Unico, Ribera del Duero £46.45 (PEN)

£60.00 → £99.99

1985
Vega Sicilia, Ribera del Duero £71.35 (UB)
Vega Sicilia Unico, Ribera del Duero £65.75 (BEN)
1974
Vega Sicilia Unico, Ribera del Duero £69.95 (DI)
1970
Vega Sicilia, Ribera del Duero £90.00 (DI)
Vega Sicilia Unico, Ribera del Duero £99.50 (BEN)

£100.00 → £116.00

1970
Vega Sicilia, Ribera del Duero £115.84 (FA)
Vega Sicilia Unico, Ribera del Duero £104.00 (RAE) £110.61 (GN)

OTHER SPANISH WHITE

Under £4.00

Non-vintage
Castillo de Liria, Vicente Gandia, Valencia £3.19 (VIC) £3.85 (TAN)
Moscatel de Valencia Castillo de Liria, Vicente Gandia, Valencia £3.61 (VIC) £3.89 (THR) £3.89 (WR) £3.89 (BOT) £3.99 (FUL)
1996
Moscatel de Valencia Castillo de Liria, Vicente Gandia, Valencia £2.99 (KWI)
1995
Basa, Rueda Blanco £3.60 (SOM) £3.97 (FLE)
1994
Ryman Santara, Conca de Barberà £3.29 (WR) £3.29 (BOT)
1993
Hermanos Lurton Sauvignon Blanc, Rueda £3.89 (CO)

£4.00 → £4.99

Non-vintage
Bodegas Alvear Medium Dry, Montilla £4.45 (TAN)
Bodegas Alvear Pale Dry, Montilla £4.45 (TAN)
1996
★ Basa, Rueda £4.25 (AD) £4.80 (PIP)
Marqués de Alella, Alella Clasico £4.75 (WS)
Palacio de Bornos, Rueda £4.25 (SOM)
Torres San Valentin, Penedés £4.49 (DI) £4.75 (GRE)
Torres Viña Esmeralda, Penedés £4.99 (DI)
Torres Viña Sol, Penedés £4.39 (CO) £4.49 (DI) £4.75 (GRE) £4.99 (BO)
1995
Barbadillo Castillo de San Diego, Vino de Mesa £4.17 (HOG)
Enate Vinedos y Crianzas, Somontano £4.99 (GRE) £4.99 (UB)
Los Llanos Armonioso, Valdepeñas £4.30 (UB)
Marqués de Griñon Durius, Vino de Mesa £4.49 (FUL)

Marqués de Riscal, Rueda £4.99 (MAJ)
Torres Viña Sol, Penedés £4.25 (HOG)
£4.39 (TES) £4.69 (THR) £4.69 (BOT)
£4.69 (WR) £4.75 (POR)
1994
Lurton Rueda, Rueda £4.49 (BOT) £4.49
(THR) £4.49 (WR)
Torres San Valentin, Penedés £4.86 (LA)
Torres Viña Esmeralda, Penedés £4.99
(FUL)
Torres Viña Sol, Penedés £4.55 (TAN)
£4.55 (FUL)
1992
Torres Viña Sol, Penedés £4.79 (SAT)

£5.00 → £5.99

1996
Torres Gran Viña Sol, Penedés £5.99 (BOT)
£5.99 (THR) £5.99 (WR) £5.99 (GRE)
Torres Viña Esmeralda, Penedés £5.45
(GRE) £5.79 (AME) £5.85 (PIP) £5.95 (STA)
1995
Enate Vinedos y Crianzas, Somontano
£5.75 (DI)
Marqués de Riscal, Rueda £5.98 (PLA)
£5.99 (NEW)
Raïmat Chardonnay, Costers del Segre
£5.99 (UN)
Torres Gran Viña Sol, Penedés £5.75 (DI)
Torres Viña Esmeralda, Penedés £5.10
(HOG) £5.49 (POR) £5.49 (WR) £5.49
(THR) £5.49 (BOT) £5.59 (LA) £5.69 (PEN)
£5.73 (ROS)
Covisa Viñas del Vero Barrel-fermented
Chardonnay, Somontano £5.99 (OD)
Covisa Viñas del Vero Chardonnay,
Somontano £5.99 (GRE) £5.99 (VIC)
1994
Palacio de Bornos, Rueda £5.35 (BER)
Torres Viña Esmeralda, Penedés £5.35
(UB) £5.35 (WHI) £5.50 (TAN) £5.69 (JON)
£5.83 (NO)
1993
Torres Gran Viña Sol, Penedés £5.35
(WHI)
1991
Covisa Viñas del Vero Chardonnay,
Somontano £5.60 (UB)

> **Webster's** is an annual
> publication. We welcome
> your suggestions for next
> year's edition.

£6.00 → £9.99

Non-vintage
Torres Moscatel Malvasia de Oro,
Penedés £6.19 (NO) £6.65 (GRE)
1996
Alvarez y Diaz Verdejo/Sauvignon Blanc,
Rueda £6.35 (LAY)
Lagar de Fornelos Albariño Lagar de
Cervera, Rias Baixas £8.10 (PIP)
Marqués de Alella, Alella £6.90 (TAN)
Torres Gran Viña Sol, Penedés £6.83 (GN)
Covisa Viñas del Vero Chardonnay,
Somontano £7.50 (LAY)
Covisa Viñas del Vero Gewürztraminer,
Somontano £7.50 (LAY)
1995
Covisa Viñas del Vero Chardonnay,
Somontano £6.45 (PLA)
Lagar de Cervera Hermanos, Galicia
£8.70 (TAN) £8.95 (LAY)
Lagar de Fornelos Albariño Lagar de
Cervera, Rias Baixas £6.99 (VIC) £7.55
(LA) £9.53 (GN)
Marqués de Alella, Alella Clasico £6.87 (LA)
Marqués de Riscal, Rueda £6.20 (LA)
Raïmat Chardonnay, Costers del Segre
£7.35 (LA)
Torres Fransola, Penedés £9.85 (STA)
Torres Gran Viña Sol, Penedés £6.11
(ROS) £6.55 (HAH) £6.58 (BY)
Torres Viña Esmeralda, Penedés £6.00
(WRI)
Covisa Viñas del Vero Gewürztraminer,
Somontano £6.16 (ROS) £6.79 (LA)
1994
Castilla la Vieja, Rueda £6.25 (STA)
Cellers Puig & Roca, Augustus
Chardonnay, Penedés £8.99 (FUL)
Lagar de Fornelos Albariño Lagar de
Cervera, Rias Baixas £7.65 (REI) £9.40
(BER)
Marqués de Alella, Alella Clasico £6.45
(GRE)
Torres Fransola, Penedés £8.35 (DI) £8.45
(REI) £9.02 (LA)
Torres Gran Viña Sol, Penedés £6.40
(WRI)
Covisa Viñas del Vero Barrel-fermented
Chardonnay, Somontano £6.17 (ROS)
1993
Lagar de Cervera Hermanos, Galicia
£9.75 (ROB)
Covisa Viñas del Vero Chardonnay,
Somontano £6.95 (VIG)

1989
Marqués de Riscal Reserva Limousin,
Rueda £6.97 (LA)

£10.00 → £16.99

Non-vintage
Scholtz Lagrima 10 años, Málaga £10.20
(TAN)
Scholtz Solera 1885, Málaga £15.95 (ROB)
1996
Enate Vinedos y Crianzas Barrel-
Fermented Chardonnay, Somontano
£11.11 (AV)
1995
Enate Vinedos y Crianzas Barrel-
Fermented Chardonnay, Somontano
£10.75 (LAY) £10.95 (GRE)
Torres Milmanda Chardonnay, Penedés
£14.61 (LA) £14.95 (GRE)
1994
Belondrade Y Lurton, Rueda £10.95 (WAI)
£10.99 (RAE) £12.00 (BIB)
Torres Milmanda Chardonnay, Penedés
£13.75 (REI) £13.99 (DI) £16.32 (NO)
1992
Jean León Chardonnay, Penedés £13.60
(DI) £14.10 (PEN)
Lagar de Fornelos Albariño Lagar de
Cervera, Rias Baixas £12.80 (UB)

£20.00 → £20.99

1991
Torres Milmanda Chardonnay, Penedés
£20.99 (NO)
1989
Torres Milmanda Chardonnay, Penedés
£20.75 (UB)

OTHER SPANISH ROSÉ

Under £5.50

1996
Torres de Casta, Penedés £5.25 (GRE)
1995
Chivite Gran Feudo, Navarra £4.25 (GRE)
Torres de Casta, Penedés £4.50 (DI) £5.32
(LA)
1993
Torres de Casta, Penedés £5.15 (UB)

c. £7.00

1994
Enate Vinedos y Crianzas Cabernet
Sauvignon, Somontano £6.75 (GRE)

SPARKLING

Under £6.00

Non-vintage
Castellblanch Cristal Seco, Cava £5.99 (GRE)
Marqués de Monistrol Brut, Cava £5.79
(ELL)
Segura Viudas Brut, Cava £5.13 (HOG)
£5.99 (DI)
Segura Viudas Brut Reserva, Cava £5.99
(OD)
1993
Bodegas Inviosa Bonaval Brut, Cava £5.85
(FLE)

£6.00 → £6.99

Non-vintage
Codorníu Brut Première Cuvée, Cava
£6.49 (CO) £6.87 (LA)
Freixenet Brut Rosé, Cava £6.99 (WHI)
Freixenet Carta Nevada, Cava £6.39
(WHI) £6.95 (PIP)
Freixenet Cordon Negro Brut, Cava
£6.29 (WHI) £6.69 (FUL) £6.95 (POR)
£6.95 (WAT) £6.99 (MAJ) £6.99 (VIC)
£6.99 (CO)
Palau Brut, Cava £6.54 (GN)
★ Vallformosa Brut, Cava £6.90 (FOR)
1993
Freixenet Cordon Negro Brut, Cava £6.95
(PIP) £6.95 (WAI) £6.99 (JON) £6.99 (SAF)

£7.00 → £7.99

Non-vintage
Freixenet Brut Rosé, Cava £7.25 (STA)
Freixenet Cordon Negro Brut, Cava
£7.39 (SAT) £7.45 (QUE)
Torre del Gall Brut, Cava £7.79 (VIC)
1992
Freixenet Cordon Negro Brut, Cava
£7.95 (ROB)
Torre del Gall Brut, Cava £7.63 (PLA)
1991
Bodegas Inviosa Bonaval Brut, Cava £7.47
(NO)
Freixenet Cordon Negro Brut, Cava
£7.53 (NO)

£8.00 → £9.49

Non-vintage
Parxet Extra Brut Nature, Cava £9.35 (ROS)
1992
Juvé y Camps Reserva de la Familia, Cava
£8.10 (LA)

SHERRY

DRY

Under £4.50

Fino Hidalgo £4.45 (PLA)
la Gitana Manzanilla, Hidalgo ½ bottle
£2.65 (REI) £3.15 (SOM) £3.25 (TAN) £3.26
(LA) £3.49 (OD) £3.50 (GAL) £3.87 (HAL)
Inocente Fino, Valdespino ½ bottle £3.95
(LEA)
Valdespino Fino £4.35 (WAT)

£4.50 → £4.99

Amontillado de Sanlúcar, Barbadillo £4.79
(LON) £4.85 (WHI) £4.95 (NO)
Amontillado Hidalgo £4.85 (SOM)
Elegante, González Byass £4.92 (HOG)
£4.99 (WR) £4.99 (THR) £4.99 (BOT)
Fino de Sanlúcar, Barbadillo £4.85 (WHI)
Fino Hidalgo £4.85 (HAH) £4.85 (PIP) £4.99
(NI)
Lustau Fino £4.79 (MAJ)
Manzanilla de Sanlúcar, Barbadillo £4.79
(LON) £4.85 (WHI) £4.95 (GRE)
Oloroso Seco Barbadillo £4.53 (HOG)
£4.95 (GRE)
Valdespino Fino £4.95 (LEA)

£5.00 → £6.99

Amontillado de Sanlúcar, Barbadillo £5.00
(BIB) £5.35 (GN)
Amontillado Napoleon, Hidalgo £6.30 (NI)
£6.60 (PIP)
Elegante, González Byass £5.15 (FUL)
£5.25 (GRE) £5.50 (WHI) £5.59 (EL)
Fino Amontillado de Jerez, Alberto
Lorente Piaget ½ bottle £6.85 (REI)
Fino Bertola £5.99 (GRE)
Fino de Sanlúcar, Barbadillo £5.19 (AME)
Fino Superior Miraflores, Hidalgo £6.25 (NI)
la Gitana Manzanilla, Hidalgo £5.45 (HOG)
£5.65 (PIP) £5.69 (EL) £5.75 (PLA) £5.99
(WAI) £5.99 (HAH) £5.99 (GRE) £5.99
(MAJ) £6.00 (BIB) £6.30 (AD) £6.75 (COU)
Harvey's Luncheon Dry £5.17 (HOG)
£5.60 (HAH) £5.79 (BOT) £5.79 (WR)
£5.79 (THR) £5.85 (WHI) £6.88 (SAT)
la Ina, Domecq £6.24 (HA) £6.27 (HOG)
£6.70 (WRI) £6.79 (WAT) £6.99 (UN)
Inocente Fino, Valdespino £6.35 (WAT)
Manzanilla de Sanlúcar, Barbadillo £5.19
(AME) £5.19 (ROS) £5.29 (OD) £5.35 (GN)

Manzanilla Pasada Solear, Barbadillo £5.92
(HOG) £6.45 (GRE)
Oloroso Anada 1918 Solera, Emilio
Lustau ½ bottle £5.65 (REI)
Oloroso Seco Napoleon, Hidalgo £6.90 (PIP)
Ostra Manzanilla £6.70 (LAY)
Palo Cortado de Jerez Videz, Emilio
Lustau ½ bottle £6.95 (VIG)
San Patricio Fino, Garvey £5.99 (MAJ)
Tio Pepe, González Byass £6.56 (HOG)
£6.95 (STA) £6.99 (FUL) £6.99 (WAI)
Valdespino Manzanilla Deliciosa £6.49 (OD)

£7.00 → £8.99

Amontillado Napoleon, Hidalgo £7.28
(LA) £7.30 (AD) £7.49 (JON) £7.50 (COU)
Dos Cortados Old Dry Oloroso, Williams
& Humbert £7.99 (HOG) £8.75 (GRE)
la Gitana Manzanilla, Hidalgo £7.81 (TW)
la Guita Manzanilla, Hidalgo £7.99 (DI)
Harvey's Palo Cortado £8.12 (HA)
la Ina, Domecq £7.05 (HAH) £7.40 (EL)
Inocente Fino, Valdespino £7.49 (OD) £7.50
(WRI) £7.75 (REI) £7.95 (LEA) £8.30 (AD)
Lustau Fino £7.86 (PLA)
Manzanilla Pasada de Sanlúcar, Hidalgo
£8.50 (TAN) £8.50 (LA) £8.99 (JON)
Oloroso Anada 1918 Solera, Emilio Lustau
½ bottle £7.38 (ROS) £7.99 (DI) £8.10 (LAY)
Oloroso Dry, Hidalgo £8.50 (TAN) £8.95
(AD)
Oloroso Especial, Hidalgo £7.95 (NI)
Oloroso Seco Napoleon, Hidalgo £7.50
(COU)
Palo Cortado de Jerez Videz, Emilio
Lustau ½ bottle £8.29 (GN)
Palo Cortado del Carrascal, Valdespino
£8.16 (WAT)
Tio Pepe, González Byass £7.15 (WHI)
£7.25 (WRI) £7.30 (HAH) £7.49 (BOT)
£7.49 (OD) £7.49 (WR) £7.49 (THR)
£7.49 (SAF) £7.49 (UN) £7.49 (TES)

£9.00 → £9.99

Don Gonzalo Old Dry Oloroso,
Valdespino £9.95 (LEA)
Fino Especial, Hidalgo £9.65 (LAY)
Jerez Cortado, Hidalgo £9.00 (TAN) £9.60
(AD) £9.75 (JON)
Lustau Dry Oloroso £9.25 (STA)
Tio Diego Amontillado, Valdespino £9.95
(LEA)

£10.00 → £11.99

Manzanilla Pasada Almacenista, Lustau £11.99 (SAT)
Oloroso Especial, Hidalgo £10.22 (TW)

£14.00 → £19.99

Amontillado del Duque, González Byass £18.99 (HOG) £19.75 (GRE) £19.96 (VIN)

Amontillado Very Old Dry Coliseo, Valdespino £19.95 (LEA)
Amontillado Viejo, Hidalgo £19.60 (COU)
Palo Cortado Cardenal, Valdespino £14.50 (LEA)
Palo Cortado Vides £14.50 (GRE)

MEDIUM

Under £5.00

Amontillado Lustau £4.79 (MAJ)
Amontillado Martial, Valdespino £4.75 (HAH)
Amontillado Valdespino £4.35 (WAT) £4.79 (OD) £4.95 (LEA)
la Concha Amontillado, González Byass £4.92 (HOG)
Dry Sack, Williams & Humbert £4.99 (TES)

£5.00 → £6.99

Caballero Amontillado, González Byass £5.25 (GRE) £5.69 (SAF) £5.69 (TES) £5.99 (SAT)
la Concha Amontillado, González Byass £5.25 (GRE) £5.29 (WAI) £5.50 (WHI) £5.69 (SAF) £5.99 (SAT)
Croft Particular £5.79 (GRE)
Dry Sack, Williams & Humbert £5.36 (HOG) £5.89 (GRE) £6.50 (HIC) £6.65 (QUE)
Harvey's Club Amontillado £5.22 (HOG) £5.49 (WAI) £5.59 (WR) £5.59 (BOT) £5.59 (THR) £5.69 (WHI) £6.25 (HAH) £6.50 (ROB)
Tanners Medium Sherry £5.10 (TAN)

£7.00 → £10.99

Oloroso de Jerez, Viuda de Antonio Borrego ½ bottle £7.38 (ROS)
Solera 1842 Oloroso, Valdespino £9.40 (TAN) £9.95 (LEA)

c. £13.00

Sandeman Royal Corregidor Oloroso £12.95 (ROB)

£16.00 → £19.99

Apostoles Oloroso, González Byass £18.99 (HOG) £19.75 (GRE) £19.96 (VIN)
Oloroso de Jerez, Almacenista Viuda de Antonio Borrego £16.95 (VIG)

SWEET

Under £5.50

Bertola Cream £5.29 (HOG) £5.45 (GRE)
Harvey's Bristol Cream £5.49 (TES) £5.49 (BO)
Hidalgo Cream £4.85 (PIP)
Oloroso Lustau £4.79 (MAJ)
Sanlúcar Cream, Barbadillo £5.35 (GN)
Valdespino Dark Cream £4.95 (LEA)

£5.50 → £6.99

Croft Original Pale Cream £5.68 (HOG) £5.99 (WAI) £6.25 (WHI) £6.29 (TES) £6.29 (UN) £6.29 (SAF) £6.49 (OD) £6.49 (EL)
Harvey's Bristol Cream £5.99 (UN) £5.99 (GRE) £6.20 (HOG) £6.26 (HA) £6.29 (WAI) £6.29 (OD) £6.29 (SAF) £6.29 (THR) £6.29 (WR) £6.29 (BOT) £6.59 (WHI)

£7.00 → £10.50

Lustau's Old East India £9.53 (HOG) £9.99 (MAJ)
★ Matusalem Oloroso, González Byass ½ bottle £9.99 (SAF)
Pedro Ximenez, Barbadillo £8.99 (GRE)
Pedro Ximenez Solera Superior, Valdespino £8.95 (LEA)
Pedro Ximénez Viejo, Hidalgo £10.50 (BEN)

£18.00 → £22.99

Apostles Oloroso Viejo, Gonzalez Byass £21.20 (AD)
Matusalem Oloroso, González Byass £18.99 (HOG) £19.75 (GRE) £19.96 (VIN)

UNITED KINGDOM

**English wine has developed a recognisable style – but the
quirkier wines can make other countries
look positively staid**

Making wine in England and Wales is never going to be easy or cheap. There can never be the economies of scale achieved in Australia or Chile, or the weather either; and while English and Welsh growers have experimented with most styles the winners are turning out to be sparkling wines, the better dry whites and, less obviously, late-picked sweet wines. There are even a few good reds too.

The typical style is quite aromatic, with lingering grapefruity acidity which is often well suited to bottle aging. Think delicate, not blowsy; graceful, not clumping. And while you might see the name of a grape on the label, a lot of wines are blends of two or more varieties, generally to the benefit of both of them.

What you're less likely to see on a label are the words 'Cabernet' or 'Chardonnay'. Both grapes are grown in England and Wales, but so far they show no sign of taking over as they have in other countries. A good thing too: do you want all wines to taste the same? Do you want no oddities with which to surprise your friends?

GRAPE VARIETIES

BACCHUS (white) Sharp, strong flavours of gooseberry, elderflower and orange rind. Best: *Partridge Vineyard, Three Choirs, Wyken, Staverton, Sandhurst, Lamberhurst.* Also good sweet ones from *Chiltern Valley, Cane End.*

FABER (white) Fragrant wines with good acidity. Often blended.

HUXELREBE (white) In England this has a grapefruit-pith taste and a greenish bite. For this reason it is often softened up by blending. Best: *Biddenden, Bothy* (blended with Perle), *Monnow Valley* (blended with Seyval Blanc), *Staple St James, Three Choirs.*

KERNER (white) *Carr-Taylor* blends this with Reichensteiner for fizz; *Elham Valley* blends it with Seyval Blanc, likewise for fizz.

MADELEINE ANGEVINE (white) A somewhat fruit-juicy character is matched by good acidity, either in a green but refreshingly elderflower-perfumed style, or a more honeyed but appley style. *Halfpenny Green* and *Sharpham* are good.

MÜLLER-THURGAU (white) This used to be the English workhorse, but is now much less planted. *Wootton, Bruisyard, Breaky Bottom, St Nicholas, Staple St James, Elham Valley, Penshurst, Tenterden* and *St George's* are good producers. And it can make very attractive, slightly sweet wine, as at *Rowney.*

ORTEGA (white) *Hidden Spring* is concentrated, and *Biddenden,* in particular, makes a delicious, slightly sweet but tremendously fruity elderflower-and-apricot-tasting example. It is usually blended (as at *Rock Lodge*) and rarely appears on its own.

PINOT NOIR (red) Used mostly for rosé and sparkling wine; or indeed sparkling rosé. *Thames Valley's* Pinot Noir is the best red so far. *Denbies* makes a nice light,

*The Price Guides for this section
are on page 389.*

scented rosé and *Carr Taylor* makes good rosé fizz; *Chiddingstone* blends it with Pinot Meunier to make a delicious Blanc de Noirs redolent of eucalyptus; *Bodiam Castle* makes a tasty rosé, as well as a dry, honeyed Blanc de Pinot Noir white; *Biddenden* and *Tenterden* use it for rosé blends. *Three Choirs* rosé from Pinot Noir has earthy raspberry-and-Morello-cherry fruit; *Conghurst's* grapy, herbaceous rosé is also good, and *Denbies, South Ridge* and *Nyetimber* sparklers are notable.

REICHENSTEINER (white) Usually pretty dull when dry, but made slightly sweet, it can develop a pleasant, smoky, quince-and-peaches taste which ages well. *Carr Taylor* and *Rock Lodge* use it for Champagne-method fizz, *Northbrook Springs* is barrel fermented. *Nutbourne Manor* and *Three Choirs* are also good.

SCHEUREBE (white) Good grapefruity, curranty wines in good years. It needs a hot site. It goes into *Thames Valley's Clocktower Selection Botrytis,* when it's made, along with Reichensteiner.

SCHÖNBURGER (pink) A good grape that makes a fat wine by English standards, with a pear-lychee flavour and good acidity. Best: *Coxley, Saxon Valley, Nutborne Manor, Wootton, Carr Taylor, Woolding, Three Choirs.*

SEYVAL BLANC (white) *Breaky Bottom* is the most successful – dry and Sauvignon-like when young, honeyed like Burgundy after four to five years – but Seyval Blanc is generally best blended with something more exotic like Schönburger or Huxelrebe, or made sweetish. *Three Choirs* blends it with Reichensteiner and *Adgestone* with Reichensteiner and Müller, while *Tenterden* makes a very good oaked Reserve. *Thames Valley* is oaked. *Hidden Spring* blends it successfully with Ortega and gives it some oak. *Elham Valley* uses it in good fizz. Other good ones: *Headcorn, Penshurst, Shawsgate, Wootton.*

OTHER REDS *Beenleigh Manor* has a good reputation for Cabernet and Merlot grown under plastic; there is also some potential in Dunkelfelder and Dornfelder, plus plantings of Léon Millet and Maréchal Foch, both more commonly seen in Canada. Gamay is being used by *Thames Valley* for a sparkler. *Dunkery's Prometheus* (from Somerset) is delicious, as is *Chapel Down's* Epoch 1. *Wyken's* red is pretty good.

OTHER WHITES The most interesting are Gewürztraminer at *Barton Manor* on the Isle of Wight, and Ehrenfelser at *Penshurst;* *Wootton's* Auxerrois is a pungent, salty-sappy wine. *Carr Taylor* has achieved good results with Pinot Blanc for its concentrated *Kemsley Dry.* There are also some efforts with Chardonnay, at, for example, the 250-acre *Denbies Estate* at Dorking in Surrey, England's biggest vineyard project yet. *Nyetimber* and *Thames Valley* are also in the running. Denbies' Riesling is showing potential.

UNITED KINGDOM PRICE GUIDES

WHITE

Under £4.50

Non-vintage
Denbies Surrey Gold £4.49 (WAI)
Lamberhurst Sovereign £2.99 (SAI)
Wootton Trinity £4.25 (SAI)
1995
Carr Taylor Hastings Medium Dry £3.39 (SAI)
Denbies £2.99 (KWI)
1994
Saxon Valley £3.99 (BOT) £3.99 (THR) £3.99 (WR)
Three Choirs Premium, Medium Dry £3.99 (THR) £3.99 (WR) £3.99 (BOT)
1993
Three Choirs Medium Dry £3.99 (SAI)

£4.50 → £4.99

1994
Downs Edge Special Release Fumé £4.95 (LEA)
Three Choirs Premium, Medium Dry £4.95 (WS)
Wake Court £4.95 (EL)
1993
Chiltern Valley Medium Dry £4.99 (WAI)
1992
Moorlynch £4.79 (THR) £4.79 (BOT)
Pilton Manor Oak-Matured Dry Reserve £4.59 (BOT) £4.59 (WR) £4.59 (THR)

£5.00 → £5.99

1995
Three Choirs Medium Dry £5.10 (TAN)
1994
Astley Severn Vale £5.80 (TAN)
Downs Edge Special Release Fumé £5.49 (AUR)

1993
Elmham Park Medium Dry £5.74 (SAT)
1992
Mersea Island White, Essex £5.55 (THR) £5.55 (BOT)
Wootton Auxerrois £5.60 (WS)
1991
Tenterden £5.50 (HIC) £5.75 (BER)

£6.00 → £7.99

1994
Denbies £7.95 (BER)
Saxon Valley £6.26 (HA)
1993
Thames Valley Regatta £7.50 (BER)
1992
Thames Valley Fumé Blanc £6.89 (WR) £6.89 (BOT) £6.89 (THR)
Wyken Vineyards Bacchus £7.95 (AUR)
1990
Pulham Vineyards Magdalen Rivaner £6.45 (TW)

£8.00 → £8.99

1993
Sharpham Barrel-Fermented Dry £8.78 (NO) £8.99 (WR) £8.99 (BOT) £8.99 (THR)
Staple St-James Huxelrebe £8.50 (BER)
1992
Sharpham Barrel-Fermented Dry £8.17 (NO)

RED

Under £7.00

1995
Chapel Down Epoch 1 £4.99 (WAI) £6.95 (LEA)
1992
Denbies Red £4.99 (SAI)

MERCHANTS SPECIALIZING IN UNITED KINGDOM
see Merchant Directory (page 413) for details

Nobody has very long lists of English wines, but the following have a fair selection: Averys of Bristol (AV), The Nobody Inn (NO), Thos. Peatling, Terry Platt (PLA) – well, wines from Wales actually, Safeway (SAF), Tanners (TAN), Thresher (THR) – an exceptionally long list, Unwins (UN), Wine Society (WS). Otherwise the best thing is to buy direct from the vineyard itself.

UNITED STATES

World-class quality is going hand in hand with high prices. But the wines have more character than ever before, and the natives are drinking all they can get

Well, US wine isn't getting any cheaper. And nor will it: demand in the US is very healthy, thank you (partly because red wine is increasingly seen as the way to keep American hearts ticking along nicely into their dotage). But the good news is that US wine is increasingly interesting. It was always (well, since way back) well made and technically sound, provided you liked a lot of oak. Now there's less overoaking and more emphasis on personality.

More emphasis, too, on grape varieties other than Chardonnay and Cabernet. That will come as a relief to those of us who like pineapple-and-cream whites and blackcurrants-and-vanilla reds, but not all the time. The best Pinot Noirs are providing a credible challenge to Burgundy,

and the so-called Californian Rhône Rangers – made from southern French grape varieties – are getting better and better. They're still not exactly mainstream, but that's probably a relief. There are plenty of basic, tasty, inexpensive wines coming out of southern France itself: what we want from California, at these prices, is class.

We'll be seeing more wines from outside California in the next few years – providing we're prepared to pay for them. The Pacific Northwest states – Oregon, Washington and Idaho – intend to export more of their wines, and very good many of them are too. Oregon in particular is starting to live up to its early hype as Pinot Noir heaven. And with so little good Burgundy to go round, that is good news for all of us.

GRAPE VARIETIES

BARBERA (red) The Italian variety most grown in California. *Louis M Martini, Sebastiani, Il Podere dell' Olivos* and *Bonny Doon* are good, as is *Monteviña* with an intense, blackberry-and-black-cherry wine; also *Preston Vineyards* (Sonoma County).

CABERNET SAUVIGNON (red) Still the top grape for premium California reds. Napa Cabernet is the classic style, rich, tannic yet seductive at a young age. Prices for the top wines continue to climb, making me wonder if they all have the personality to justify their price tags. Washington State Cabernet continues to improve as the vines age, yielding intense fruit and concentration. For cellaring (never as long as for the equivalent quality Bordeaux), good names are: *Beaulieu Vineyards Georges de Latour Private Reserve, Beringer Reserve, Buena Vista, Burgess, Cain, Carmenet Reserve, Caymus*

Special Selection, Clos du Val, Conn Creek, Cuvaison, Diamond Creek, Dominus, Dunn, Franciscan, Grgich Hills, Groth, Heitz Bella Oaks, Kenwood Artist Series, La Jota, Laurel Glen, Louis M Martini, Robert Mondavi Reserve and *Opus One, Chateau Montelena, Newton, Niebaum Coppola, Raymond Reserve, Ridge Monte Bello, Sequoia Grove, Shafer Hillside Select, Spottswoode, Stag's Leap Cask 23, Sterling Vineyards Diamond Mountain Ranch, Stonestreet* (California); *Ste Chapelle* (Idaho); *Fall Creek Vineyards, Llano Estacado, Messina Hof, Oberhellmann, Pheasant Ridge* (Texas); *Arbor Crest, Hogue Cellars, Chateau Ste Michelle, Columbia, Staton Hills* (Washington). For light Cabernet, the list is practically endless, but includes: *Beringer, Caymus Liberty School, Chateau Souverain, Clos du Bois, Cosentino, Fetzer, Estancia, Foppiano, Kendall-Jackson* (California); *Columbia Crest* (Washington).

CHARDONNAY (white) This is less relentlessly oaky than it was, and a great deal more interesting as a result. Many of the more popular brands – such as *Kendall-Jackson* and *Sebastiani* – have a slightly sweet finish to make them more commercial. The best can age, but seldom need to, they are so attractive young. For balance and poise look for: *Acacia, Arrowood, Beringer, Buena Vista, Chalone, Chateau St Jean, Cuvaison, Dehlinger, Far Niente, Flora Springs, Franciscan, Kistler, Mondavi Reserve, Newton, Raymond Reserve, Renaissance, Signorello, Simi* and *Sonoma-Cutrer* (California); *Bridgehampton* (New York); *Prince Michel* (Virginia). For simpler wines, try *Callaway, Clos du Bois, Estancia, Matanzas Creek, Kendall-Jackson, Morgan, Mirassou, Phelps, Monterey Vineyards, Wente Bros* (California); *Fall Creek* (Texas); *Chateau Ste Michelle, Columbia Crest, Hogue Cellars* (Washington).

GEWÜRZTRAMINER (white) It's really too hot in California for this grape, although a few people are beginning to get it right, making wines with that spiciness that keeps you reaching for another glass. Look for *Adler Fels* (sometimes), *Lazy Creek, Handley Cellars, Rutherford Hill, Obester* (California); *Llano Estacado* (Texas); *Columbia, Chateau Ste Michelle* (Washington).

MERLOT (red) At its best, American Merlot shows lovely black cherry with a pleasing brambly edge. But it's frighteningly fashionable, and so quality doesn't always match price. Best are *Arrowood, Bellerose, Cuvaison, Duckhorn, Geyser Peak, Gundlach-Bundschu, Murphy-Goode, Newton, St Francis, Pine Ridge, Ridge Santa Cruz, Silverado, Sinskey, St Clement, Sterling, Vichon,* (California); *Bedell Cellars, Bridgehampton, Peconic Bay* (New York); *Chateau Ste Michelle, Columbia, Columbia Crest, Hogue Cellars, Leonetti, Staton Hills, Paul Thomas* (Washington).

PETITE SIRAH (red) This is emphatically not the same as the great red Syrah grape

of the Rhône Valley or the Shiraz of Australia. It produces big, stark, dry, almost tarry wines – impressive, but needing a good winemaker. *Ridge* is superb. Also look for *Christopher Creek, Concannon, Stag's Leap* and *Foppiano*.

PINOT NOIR (red) Oregon and California are the main Pinot Noir states, but it's always a difficult grape. Oregon, after several bad years, seems to be getting back on track, while in California good to very good Pinot Noir is turning up all over the place. And there's also Long Island, where an occasional flash of excellent Pinot can be seen. Try *Au Bon Climat, Acacia, Bouchaine, Byron, Calera, Carneros Creek, Chalone, Dehlinger, De Loach, Gary Farrel, Iron Horse, Lazy Creek, Robert Mondavi, Patz & Hall, Saintsbury, Sanford, Sinskey, Whitcraft, Wild Horse, Zaca Mesa* (California); *Bridgehampton* (New York); *Adelsheim, Amity, Drouhin, Elk Cove, Eyrie, King Estate, Knudsen Erath, Rex Hill, Scott Henry, Sokol Blosser* (Oregon).

SYRAH/RHÔNE VARIETIES (red) There has been an explosion of interest in the vines of the Rhône in California; they seem in many ways more suited to the climate than the Bordeaux or Burgundian grapes, and they add to the US range of flavours. Most eyes are on Syrah, but there is also Mourvèdre, Cinsaut, Grenache and Carignan. Whites include Viognier and Marsanne. The best so far are from California: *Bonny Doon, Duxoup, Kendall-Jackson, Jade Mountain, La Jota, McDowell Valley, Joseph Phelps Mistral* series, *Il Podere dell' Olivos, Preston Vineyards, Qupé, Santino.*

RIESLING (white) This grape likes cool spots, which means that it all too often makes dull wines in California. *Renaissance* is streets ahead; other good ones are *Alexander Valley Vineyards, Konocti, Navarro* (California); *Lamoureux Landing, Wagner Vineyards* (New York); *Amity* (Oregon); *Chateau Morrisette, Prince Michel* (Virginia);

Hogue Cellars, Columbia Cellars, Chateau Ste Michelle, Kiona (Washington).

SAUVIGNON BLANC/FUMÉ BLANC (white)
Generally riper and broader than the New Zealand prototype, and sometimes oaked. Grassy-tasting ones include *Dry Creek Vineyards Reserve*; for more restraint try *Chateau St Jean, Geyser Peak, Ferrari-Carano, Hanna, Markham, Robert Mondavi, Murphy-Goode, Renaissance, Simi, Sterling, William Wheeler* (California); *Hargrave* (New York); *Arbor Crest, Columbia* (Washington).

SEMILLON (white)
Usually added to Sauvignon Blanc for complexity (*Clos du Val, Carmenet, Vichon*, California). For stand-alone Semillon try *Alderbrook, Ahlgren* (California); *Chateau Ste Michelle* (Washington).

ZINFANDEL (red)
This comes in 'white' (usually pink and usually sweetish) as well as red, but the best ones are all red. There are big rustic styles and lighter, elegant wines; the best share ripe, red-berries fruit. Big Zins: *Cline Cellars, Deer Park, Kendall-Jackson Ciapusci Vineyard, Murrieta's Well, Preston Vineyards, La Jota, A Rafanelli, Ravenswood, Ridge Lytton Springs, Rosenblum, Shenandoah, Joseph Swan*. Lighter ones: *Buehler, Buena Vista, Burgess, Clos du Val, Fetzer, Haywood, Howell Mountain, Kendall-Jackson Mariah Vineyard, Kenwood, Louis M Martini, Nalle, Quivira, Renaissance*.

WINE REGIONS

CARNEROS (California; red, white)
This covers the southern ends of the Napa and Sonoma Valleys, where it's cool enough for Pinot Noir (many of California's best come from here) and Chardonnay. Star names include *Acacia, Domaine Carneros, Saintsbury, Buena Vista, Carneros Creek*.

CENTRAL VALLEY (California; red, white)
Huge and hot. This is where much of California's everyday jug wine comes from, and it's usually drinkable. Chardonnay, especially, is much improved.

LAKE COUNTY (California; red, white)
Good Cabernet Sauvignon and Sauvignon Blanc territory. *Louis M Martini, Konocti* and *Guenoc* have vines here.

LIVERMORE VALLEY (California; red, white)
Decent Sauvignon Blanc from *Wente Bros*, and some good Cabernet Sauvignon.

MENDOCINO COUNTY (California; red, white)
The cool Anderson Valley is becoming a sparkling wine star, led by *Roederer Estate*, the US offshoot of Champagne Roederer, and *Handley Cellars*. Elegant Riesling, Gewürztraminer, Pinot Noir and Chardonnay comes from here, too. Some Cabernet Sauvignon is good.

MISSOURI (red, white)
At the turn of the century this midwestern state was the third largest wine producer in the US. Now it's making a comeback, growing both standard vinifera grapes and a range of French hybrids like Vidal, as well as native American grapes like Cynthiana/Norton. *Stone Hill Winery's* Norton red is pretty good; there are also some pleasing Rieslings from *Mount Pleasant Vineyard*.

MONTEREY COUNTY (California; red, white)
Riesling, Chenin Blanc and Pinot Noir are the best bets here, though some Cabernet Sauvignon is grown in the cool Carmel Valley and the Arroyo Seco region. Top names: *Mirassou* and *Wente Bros*.

NAPA COUNTY (California; red, white)
There are several important sub-regions within Napa: Calistoga, Carneros, Chiles Valley, Howell Mountain, Mount Veeder, Oakville, Pope Valley, Rutherford, Spring Mountain and Stag's Leap. Some of these

are formally designated viticultural regions. This is California's classic wine country. Napa's strong suit is red – Cabernet Sauvignon and Merlot – with Pinot Noir in Carneros. Star producers are too many to list, but include *Mondavi, Phelps, Newton, Stag's Leap, Diamond Creek, Spottswoode, Beaulieu, Beringer, Clos du Val, Dominus, Heitz, Opus One.*

NEW MEXICO (red, white) Good producers here are *Anderson Valley*, especially for Chardonnay, and a fizz from *Devalmont Vineyards* under the Gruet label.

NEW YORK STATE (red, white) The big news in New York continues to be Long Island, with outstanding Chardonnay and Pinot Noir. The Chardonnays here are very different from those of California, with more austere flavours, a bit like ripe Chablis. There's also decent Chardonnay and good Riesling coming from the Finger Lakes and the Hudson River Valley areas. Try *Bedell Cellars, Bridgehampton, Brotherhood, Hargrave, Lenz, Pindar* and *Wagner.*

OREGON (red, white) We all expected too much, too soon, but Oregon Pinot Noir is at last becoming consistently good. The second best grape is Pinot Gris, which can often be charming. Riesling can also be quite good, although it is a little short on that floral intensity one looks for in a great Riesling. For Pinot Gris, try *Adelsheim, Amity, Eyrie, King Estate* or *Knudsen Erath. Oak*

Knoll has the best Riesling. For Pinot Noir, go for *Adelsheim, Amity, Drouhin, Elk Cove, Eyrie, King Estate, Knudsen Erath, Rex Hill, Scott Henry, Sokol Blosser.*

SAN LUIS OBISPO COUNTY
(California; red, white) Has some good sites for Pinot Noir and Chardonnay, and there are a few surprising old Zinfandel vineyards. Edna Valley is the chief sub-region with a deserved reputation for Chardonnay. *Maison Deutz* makes good fizz.

SANTA BARBARA COUNTY
(California; red, white) Some outstanding Pinot Noirs from the Santa Maria and Santa Ynez valleys, plus some good Sauvignon and Merlot. Best names: *Au Bon Climat, Firestone, Qupé, Sanford, Zaca Mesa.*

SANTA CRUZ MOUNTAINS
(California; red, white) Pinot Noir here is promising, but still patchy. *David Bruce* and *Santa Cruz Mountain Winery* have had various degrees of success. *Mount Eden* and *Ridge Vineyards* are good for Cabernet.

SIERRA FOOTHILLS (California; red, white) California's gold country was one its busiest wine zones until Prohibition, but only a few Zinfandel vineyards survived. These are the basis of the area's reputation, plus good Sauvignon Blanc and Barbera. Best are *Amador Foothill Winery, Boeger Winery, Monteviña, Santino, Shenandoah Vineyards* and *Renaissance* (stunning Riesling).

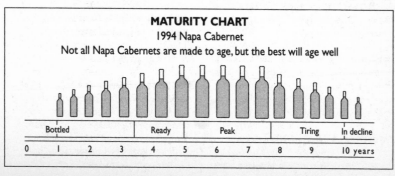

MATURITY CHART
1994 Napa Cabernet
Not all Napa Cabernets are made to age, but the best will age well

Bottled				Ready		Peak			Tiring		In decline
0	1	2	3	4	5	6	7	8	9	10 years	

SONOMA COUNTY (California; red, white) Sonoma's Chardonnay, long in the shade of Napa, need take a back seat to no-one. Sonoma Valley is the main sub-region, but there are many others, in particular Alexander Valley, Chalk Hill, Dry Creek, Knight's Valley, and the Russian River Valley itself (including its sub-region Green Valley). Cabernet Sauvignon is the other star grape, and it and Chardonnay are usually a little fruitier and softer than they are in Napa. There's also some first rate Pinot Noir emerging from the lower Russian River Valley. There are loads good producers, but *Carmenet, Chateau St Jean, Dehlinger, De Loach, Iron Horse, Jordan, Kistler, Simi, Sonoma-Cutrer, Williams-Selyem* are tops.

TEXAS (red, white) Texas wines continue to surprise. Cabernet Sauvignons from Texas have a drink-me-now rich fruitiness and the Chardonnays and Sauvignon Blancs are looking better every year. In short, it's goodbye Chateau Redneck. The best producers currently are: *Fall Creek, Llano Estacado, Messina Hof, Oberhellmann* and *Pheasant Ridge*.

VIRGINIA (red, white) Growing good wine grapes in Virginia's hot, humid climate is certainly a man-over-nature drama. Besides the heat and the humidity, there is the occasional hurricane to contend with. Nevertheless, there are some good Rieslings and Chardonnays being made. Top producers are *Chateau Morrisette, Ingleside Plantation* and *Prince Michel*.

WASHINGTON STATE (red, white) There are those – and they're increasing in number – who believe that the finest wines from North America may eventually come from here. There is an incredible intensity of fruit from Cabernet, Merlot, Sauvigon Blanc, Semillon, Riesling and Chardonnay. Good wineries include *Arbor Crest, Chateau Ste Michelle, Columbia Cellars, Columbia Crest, Hogue Cellars, Staton Hills*.

PRODUCERS WHO'S WHO

ACACIA ★★★(★) (Carneros/Napa) Attractive Pinot Noir and Chardonnay. Reserve wines heavy on oak.

ADLER FELS ★★(★) (Sonoma) A quirky winery, taking chances that sometimes miss. Top Gewürztraminer and an unusual Riesling sparkler.

ARROWOOD ★★★★ (Sonoma) Superb Cabernet Sauvignon and Merlot, providing you like oak.

AU BON CLIMAT ★★★★ (Santa Barbara) Fine Pinot Noir with intense black cherry fruit. Chardonnay can also be impressive. Podere dell' Olivos label is for quirky, characterful Italian varietals.

BEAULIEU VINEYARDS ★★★ (Napa) The top-of-the-line George de Latour Private Reserve Cabernet Sauvignon is still marvellous. Also lean, supple Carneros Chardonnay, and inexpensive Beautour Cabernet.

BERINGER ★★★★(★) (Napa) Reserve Cabernets are top of the line. Sbragia Chardonnay (he's the winemaker) is rich and loaded with buttery oak. The second label, Napa Ridge, is good value.

BETHEL HEIGHTS ★★★(★) (Oregon) Impressive, intense Pinot Noirs. The Reserves can be among Oregon's finest and most concentrated.

BONNY DOON ★★★★ (Santa Cruz) One of California's most innovative winemakers, Grenache (Le Cigare Volant) and Mourvèdre (Old Telegram, a pun on Châteauneuf's Vieux Télégraphe, if you hadn't guessed) and a new line of Italian styles called Ca' Del Solo.

BRIDGEHAMPTON ★★★(★) (New York) First-class Chardonnay from Long Island as well as a fresh, light quaffable Pinot Noir and a fruity, forward Merlot.

BUENA VISTA ★★★(★) (Sonoma/Carneros) This has made a big comeback in recent years, with balanced, understated Merlot, Pinot Noir and Cabernet Sauvignon. Reserve wines have intensity and depth. Very good Lake County Sauvignon Blanc.

CAKEBREAD CELLARS ★★★ (Napa) Always sound, and are sometimes outstanding: it makes one of California's very best Sauvignon Blancs.

CALERA ★★★★(★) (San Benito) Possibly the best Pinot Noir in California. Rich and intense; Jensen Vineyard is their best. Also fine Viognier and Chardonnay.

CAYMUS ★★★★ (Napa) Benchmark California Cabernet which shows no sign of faltering. Special Selection is the top wine. Liberty School is the second label.

CHALONE ★★★★(★) (Monterey) Individualistic, ageworthy Pinot Noir and big, buttery Chardonnay. Also some nice Pinot Blanc and Chenin Blanc.

CHATEAU POTELLE ★★★(★) (Napa) Run by two transplanted French wine buffs. Very good Sauvignon Blanc and Cabernet, outstanding Zinfandel.

CHATEAU ST JEAN ★★★(★) (Sonoma) Rich Chardonnay, outstanding Cabernet and Merlot, and justly famous botrytized Rieslings.

CHATEAU STE MICHELLE ★★★(★) (Washington) Consistently good with Cabernet Sauvignon and Merlot being the real strengths; pretty good bubbly.

CHIMNEY ROCK ★★★(★) (Napa) Powerful yet elegant Cabernet Sauvignon

and reserve-style Bordeaux blend called Elevage. Deep, rich, and complex fruit.

CLOS DU BOIS ★★★(★) (Sonoma) Consistently good Merlots, Chardonnays and a claret-style blend called Marlstone.

CLOS DU VAL ★★★(★) (Napa) Elegant, ageworthy, well-balanced reds. Best from this underrated winery are Cabernet and Zinfandel.

COLUMBIA ★★★★ (Washington) Reds are excellent: Syrah, soft, peppery Pinot Noir, seductive Merlot (Red Willow vineyard), and ripe Cabernet (Otis vineyard). Very good whites include Semillon, Gewürztraminer.

COLUMBIA CREST ★★★(★) (Washington) Highly drinkable wines, not expensive: Cabernet, Merlot, Chardonnay.

CUVAISON ★★★ (Napa) Delicious Merlot, Pinot Noir and Cabernet: elegant, and understated with unexpected complexity.

DEHLINGER ★★★★ (Sonoma) One of the best Pinots in North America; also good Cabernets including a good value Young Vine Cabernet.

DOMAINE CARNEROS ★★★(★) (Napa) This Taittinger-owned sparkling wine house makes remarkable vintage Brut and silky, powerful Blanc de Blancs.

DOMAINE CHANDON ★★★ (Napa) Owned by Champagne house Moët & Chandon, and making consistently good non-vintage bubblies, plus rich and creamy Reserve and Carneros Blanc de Blancs.

DOMAINE MUMM ★★★★ (Napa) Outstanding fizz, often better than that made by the parent company in Champagne. Look for the Brut and an impressive Blanc de Noirs.

DROUHIN ★★★★ (Oregon) This is the Pinot Noir we were all waiting for Oregon to make, from a Burgundian-owned company. There's a little Chardonnay, too.

DRY CREEK VINEYARDS ★★(★) (Sonoma) Tasty Sauvignon Blanc, plus reliable, though unremarkable, Zinfandel and Cabernet.

DUCKHORN ★★★ (Napa) Intensely flavoured, deep and rich Merlot, and a weighty Cabernet.

ELK COVE VINEYARDS ★★★(★) (Oregon) One of Oregon's best Pinot Noirs, and very good Pinot Gris.

EYRIE ★★★ (Oregon) David Lett is Oregon's Pinot pioneer, and still makes some of the best: supple and flavoursome.

FALL CREEK VINEYARDS ★★★ (Texas) Good blended Proprietor's Red, nice Semillon and first-rate Cabernet Sauvignon.

FETZER ★★★ (Mendocino County) Organic, reliable, middle of the road Cabernets and Chardonnay, with an occasional better-than-usual Zinfandel. Reserve wines are best.

FLORA SPRINGS ★★★(★) (Napa) Excellent Chardonnay and a fair Bordeaux blend called Trilogy. Soliloquy is a creamy, rich, floral white that belies its Sauvignon Blanc base.

FOPPIANO★★(★) (Sonoma) A Reserve bottling of Zinfandel and Petite Sirah are a cut or two above average. Fox Mountain Cabernet is also very good.

FRANCISCAN ★★★★ (Napa) On the way up again. The estate-bottled Chardonnays, especially the Cuvée Sauvage, are outstanding. Straight Cabernets and Bordeaux blends are usually superb.

HANDLEY CELLARS ★★★★ (Mendocino) Excellent fizz, especially Brut and rosé. Very good Chardonnay and Sauvignon, promising Pinot Noir.

HEITZ ★★★ (Napa) Martha's Vineyard Cabernet has a devoted following and fetches high prices; it's dark and uncompromising.

IRON HORSE ★★★★ (Sonoma) Terrific racy, incisive fizz, very good Pinot Noir and Chardonnay. Cabernet is also worth trying.

JORDAN ★★★★(★) (Sonoma) The rich, ripe Cabernet Sauvignon ages well, and there's a classic, biscuity fizz called J.

KENDALL-JACKSON ★★★ (Lake) Makes massive amounts of smooth, rich, off-dry Chardonnay.

KENWOOD ★★★(★) (Sonoma) Consistent quality. Jack London and Artist Series Cabernets are outstanding, as is the Zinfandel and Sauvignon Blanc.

KUNDE ESTATE WINERY ★★★ (Sonoma) The powerful, buttery Reserve Chardonnay and the Sauvignon Blanc are the best; also rich old vine Zinfandel.

LAMOREAUX LANDING ★★★ (New York) Chardonnay is rather good; the Pinot Noir improves with each vintage.

LAUREL GLEN ★★★★ (Sonoma) Intense, black cherry Cabernet Sauvignon is the only wine here, very good at its best.

LENZ VINEYARDS ★★★ (New York) Merlot is elegant and quite powerful wine, and dry Gewürztraminer is tasty – a good apéritif.

LOUIS MARTINI ★★★ (Napa) Quality is somewhat patchy these days. Highlights are Monte Rosso Cabernet, and Zinfandel, Chardonnay and Carneros Pinot Noir.

MAYACAMAS ★★★ (Napa) Firm Cabernet and rich Chardonnay are the stars here; there's some Pinot Noir as well.

ROBERT MONDAVI ★★★★(★) (Napa) Superb Straight and Reserve Cabernets; Opus One reds seem to lack the Reserve's intensity. Improving Carneros Pinot Noir, and very good Chardonnay. Newest is a line of French wines under the Vichon Mediterranean label.

NEWTON ★★★★ (Napa) Excellent, unfiltered Chardonnay; cedary, cinnamon-spiced Cabernet and succulent Merlot.

PECONIC BAY VINEYARDS ★★★ (New York) Light, unoaked Chardonnay and a barrel-fermented Reserve

PHEASANT RIDGE ★★(★) (Texas) Quite good Chardonnay and Chenin and promising Cabernet Sauvignons.

PHELPS ★★★(★) (Napa) Best here is the Insignia Bordeaux blend. Mistral label is for interesting Rhône varieties.

RAVENSWOOD ★★★★ (Sonoma) Zinfandel is the only grape here. Dickerson Vineyard, Old Hill and Old Vines have ripe, concentrated fruit, bold and stylish.

RIDGE ★★★★(★) (Santa Clara) Benchmark Zinfandel, probably California's best. The Monte Bello Cabernets are also remarkable, with great balance and long-lasting, perfumed fruit. Petite Sirah from York Creek is brilliant.

ROEDERER ESTATE ★★★★ (Mendocino County) Excellent Champagne-style sparklers from a company owned by Roederer Champagne. Brut and rosé are both very good.

SAINTSBURY ★★★★ (Napa) Stylish, supple, elegant Pinot Noir and Chardonnay. Lovely Garnet, from young Pinot Noir vines.

SANFORD WINERY ★★★(★) (Santa Barbara) At its best, Sanford Pinot Noir can be a real treat, with spicy, lush, intense fruit. Good Sauvignon and Chardonnay.

SCHRAMSBERG ★★★★ (Napa) Big, lush fizz. Reserve Brut is best, often world class. Blanc de Noirs is big and bold.

SHAFER ★★★★ (Napa) Very good, very long-lived Cabernet Sauvignon and Merlot.

SIMI ★★★(★) (Sonoma) Rich, sometimes voluptuous, always reliable Chardonnay, concentrated Cabernets. Reserves are excellent, as is Sauvignon Blanc.

SONOMA-CUTRER ★★★★ (Sonoma) Chardonnay specialist. Les Pierres is made to age. Russian River Ranches is more forward, Cutrer is rich, archetypal California.

STAG'S LEAP WINE CELLARS ★★★★ (Napa) After a few years unaccountably adrift, the estate-bottled Cabernet Sauvignon is focused and back on track, especially the Cask 23 and the SLV Vineyard. Elegant Chardonnay, too.

STATON HILLS VINEYARD ★★★(★) (Washington) Silky Bordeaux-style Merlot; Cabernet with staying power.

STEELE WINES ★★★(★) (Lake County) Expensive, vivid Chardonnays. Shooting Star is a second, budget label.

ROD STRONG VINEYARDS ★★★(★) (Sonoma) Fine single-vineyard Cabernet Sauvignon, Pinot Noir, Chardonnay.

TREFETHEN ★★★ (Napa) Good Cabernet Sauvignon, other bottlings more middle-of-the-road. Library wines, released after extra aging, have good depth.

ZD WINES ★★★ (Napa) Excellent Cabernet Sauvignon, Pinot Noir and Chardonnay with lovely intensity and depth.

UNITED STATES PRICE GUIDES

CALIFORNIA RED

Under £4.50

Non-vintage
Dry Reserve E&J Gallo £3.99 (SO) £4.39
(VIC) £4.39 (SAI) £4.39 (SAF) £4.39 (CO)
£4.39 (THR) £4.39 (WR) £4.39 (BOT)
1994
Zinfandel Sutter Home £4.25 (GRE)

£4.50 → £4.99

Non-vintage
Cabernet Sauvignon Canyon Cellars
£4.95 (WS)
Cabernet Sauvignon E&J Gallo £4.79 (SAI)
£4.79 (VIC) £4.79 (CO)
Pinot Noir South Bay Vineyards £4.99 (SAI)
Pinot Noir Thornhill £4.99 (FUL)
Zinfandel South Bay £4.99 (SAI)
1995
Pinot Noir Redwood Trail £4.99 (OD)
1994
Cabernet Sauvignon E&J Gallo £4.79 (SAF)
Cabernet Sauvignon Glen Ellen £4.99 (GRE)
Pinot Noir Redwood Trail £4.60 (HOG)
Zinfandel Sutter Home £4.69 (VIC)
1993
Cabernet Sauvignon Glen Ellen £4.52 (HOG)
Cabernet Sauvignon Sutter Home £4.99
(UN)
Merlot Glen Ellen £4.99 (CO) £4.99 (GRE)
Zinfandel Sutter Home £4.89 (JON) £4.99
(UN)
1992
Cabernet Sauvignon Sutter Home £4.89
(JON)

£5.00 → £5.99

1995
Black Muscat Quady Elysium ½ bottle £5.95
(NI) £5.98 (PEN) £5.99 (NA) £5.99 (MAJ)

1994
Cabernet Sauvignon Robert Mondavi
Woodbridge £5.90 (FOR)
Zinfandel Fetzer £5.45 (SOM) £5.99 (OD)
1993
Cabernet Sauvignon Konocti Mount
Konocti £5.75 (WS)
Cabernet Sauvignon Robert Mondavi
Woodbridge £5.25 (NI)
Zinfandel Redwood £5.78 (COU)
1992
Cabernet Sauvignon Fetzer Valley Oaks
£5.99 (CO)
Cabernet Sauvignon Robert Mondavi
Woodbridge £5.99 (JON)

£6.00 → £7.99

Non-vintage
Primo Misto Pedroncelli £6.60 (GN)
Starboard Batch 88 Quady £7.99 (NA)
1996
Black Muscat Quady Elysium ½ bottle
£7.70 (AD)
★ Grenache Bonny Doon Clos de Gilroy
£7.00 (REI) £7.65 (MV)
Zinfandel Redwood £7.70 (GN)
1995
Big House Red Ca' del Solo, Bonny Doon
£6.99 (NI) £7.00 (REI) £7.95 (GRE)
Grenache Bonny Doon Clos de Gilroy
£6.99 (NI)
Zinfandel Fetzer £6.12 (FLE)
1994
Barbera Monteviña £6.90 (PIP) £6.99 (PLA)
Big House Red Ca' del Solo, Bonny Doon
£6.75 (SOM)
Black Muscat Quady Elysium ½ bottle
£6.45 (JON) £7.50 (ROB) £7.91 (NO)
Cabernet Sauvignon Fetzer Valley Oaks
£6.49 (WAI)
Cabernet Sauvignon Robert Mondavi
Woodbridge £6.75 (GRE) £7.05 (ROS)

MERCHANTS SPECIALIZING IN UNITED STATES
see Merchant Directory (page 413) for details

Adnams (AD), Averys (AV), Bennetts (BEN),
Bibendum (BIB), Croque-en-Bouche (CRO),
Lay & Wheeler (LAY), Oddbins (OD),
Majestic (MAJ), Morris & Verdin (MV) – very

good for Rhône rangers, James Nicholson
(NI), The Nobody Inn (NO), Reid Wines
(1992) Ltd (REI), T&W Wines (TW), The
Ubiquitous Chip (UB)

Merlot Washington Hills £6.95 (SAI)
Zinfandel Beringer £6.99 (MAJ) £7.75 (PIP)
Zinfandel Kenwood £7.99 (VIC)
Zinfandel Pedroncelli £7.95 (LAY)
1993
Black Muscat Quady Elysium ½ bottle
£6.59 (UN)
Cabernet Sauvignon Fetzer Valley Oaks
£6.49 (JON)
Cabernet Sauvignon Pedroncelli £6.99 (DI)
Grenache Bonny Doon Clos de Gilroy
£6.65 (SOM)
Zinfandel Beringer £7.00 (NEZ)
1992
Cabernet Sauvignon E&J Gallo £7.99 (CO)
Cabernet Sauvignon Round Hill £7.74
(COU)
Merlot/Cabernet Newton Newtonian
£6.50 (SOM)
1989
Merlot Newton £6.99 (YOU)

£8.00 → £9.99

1996
Grenache Bonny Doon Clos de Gilroy
£8.25 (WRI)
1995
Big House Red Ca' del Solo, Bonny Doon
£8.35 (AD) £8.50 (MV) £8.52 (PLA) £8.95
(ROB)
Cardinal Zin Bonny Doon £9.95 (NI)
Grenache Bonny Doon Clos de Gilroy
£8.50 (MV)
Pinot Noir Saintsbury Garnet £9.95 (AD)
1994
Cabernet Sauvignon Hawk Crest £8.17
(DOM)
★ Nero Misto Elyse £8.75 (BIB)
Pinot Noir Rutz Cellars Quail Hill £9.99
(OD)
★ Pinot Noir Saintsbury Garnet £9.99 (AD)
★ Zinfandel Elyse £9.58 (BIB)
Zinfandel Franciscan Oakville £8.99 (OD)
Zinfandel Rutherford Ranch £8.60 (LAY)
1993
Big House Red Ca' del Solo, Bonny Doon
£8.99 (UB)
Cabernet Sauvignon Beringer £9.99 (MAJ)
Cabernet Sauvignon Firestone £9.51 (HA)
Cabernet Sauvignon Kendall-Jackson
Vintner's Reserve £9.99 (DI)
Cabernet Sauvignon Lohr £9.99 (ELL)
Pinot Noir Carneros Creek Fleur de
Carneros £8.25 (FLE)
Pinot Noir Saintsbury Garnet £8.99 (FUL)

1992
Cabernet Sauvignon Firestone £8.25 (WS)
Zinfandel Ravenswood North Coast
Vintners Blend £9.25 (UB)
1991
Zinfandel Sutter Home £8.19 (EL)
1990
Cabernet Sauvignon Firestone £8.57 (HOG)
1988
Cabernet Sauvignon Rutherford Hill £9.45
(UB) £9.85 (HOG)
Starboard Batch 88 Quady £8.12 (NO)
£8.50 (GRE)
1987
Cabernet Sauvignon Clos du Bois £8.75 (BU)
Cabernet Sauvignon Franciscan £8.45 (PEN)
1986
Merlot Stag's Leap £8.25 (REI)

£10.00 → £11.99

1995
Pinot Noir La Crema £11.95 (DI)
Syrah Qupé Bien Nacido £11.63 (PLA)
1994
Cabernet Sauvignon Beringer £10.50 (NEZ)
Cabernet Sauvignon Rutherford Hill
£10.77 (AV)
Mataro Ridge £10.35 (SOM)
Merlot Rutherford Hill £11.75 (REI)
Pinot Noir Saintsbury £10.15 (SOM)
Zinfandel Frog's Leap £11.69 (FLE)
1993
Cabernet Sauvignon Beringer £10.49 (VIC)
£11.00 (PIP)
Cabernet Sauvignon Firestone £10.90 (PIP)
Nebbiolo Il Podere dell'Olivos £11.00 (MV)
Pinot Noir Calera Central Coast £11.75
(COU)
Pinot Noir Saintsbury £11.35 (NI)
1992
Le Cigare Volant Bonny Doon £11.99 (NI)
Pinot Noir Calera Central Coast £10.45
(SOM)
Zinfandel Clos du Val £10.99 (MAJ) £11.95
(AV)
1988
Cabernet Sauvignon Rutherford Hill
£10.83 (PEN)

> *Stars (★) indicate wines
> selected by Oz Clarke in the
> Best Buys section which begins
> on page 12.*

1987
Cabernet Sauvignon Beringer £10.19 (SO)
Cabernet Sauvignon Conn Creek £11.04 (NO)
1986
Cabernet Sauvignon Renaissance £11.62 (PEN)

£12.00 → £14.99

1995
La Provençale Jade Mountain £14.98 (PLA)
Pinot Noir Acacia Carneros £12.00 (BIB)
Pinot Noir Saintsbury £12.50 (WS) £13.95 (AD)
Zinfandel Frog's Leap £14.99 (GN)
1994
Cabernet Sauvignon Laurel Glen £12.50 (NI)
Cabernet Sauvignon Ridge Monte Bello £14.80 (TAN)
Cabernet Sauvignon Ridge Santa Cruz Mountain £12.50 (SOM) £12.90 (PIP) £13.95 (NI) £14.39 (NO)
La Provençale Jade Mountain £14.40 (MV)
Pinot Noir Clos du Val £12.93 (AV) £13.25 (STA)
Pinot Noir Saintsbury £13.95 (BEN)
Syrah Duxoup £13.00 (BIB)
Zinfandel Frog's Leap £12.80 (MV)
Zinfandel Frog's Leap St Helena £12.95 (LEA)
Zinfandel Grgich Hills £14.50 (GRE)
Zinfandel Lytton Springs £13.99 (NI) £14.98 (DOM)
Zinfandel Nalle £13.51 (DOM)
Zinfandel Ridge Geyserville £12.50 (SOM) £13.58 (FLE) £13.95 (NI) £14.39 (NO) £14.93 (ELL)
1993
Cabernet Sauvignon Dry Creek £12.50 (GRE)
Cabernet Sauvignon Ridge Santa Cruz Mountain £14.69 (DOM)
Cabernet Sauvignon Stag's Leap £14.69 (DOM)
Le Cigare Volant Bonny Doon £12.75 (REI)
Merlot Clos du Bois £12.69 (JON)
Petite Sirah Ridge Vineyards York Creek £12.95 (WS) £13.51 (DOM) £14.00 (PIP) £14.95 (LEA) £14.95 (VIG)
Pinot Noir Calera Jensen £14.50 (PIP)
Pinot Noir Monticello Corley Family Vineyards £14.50 (LAY)
Zinfandel E&J Gallo £12.99 (EL)
Zinfandel Grgich Hills £13.35 (EL)

1992
Cabernet Sauvignon Clos du Val £14.99 (MAJ)
Cabernet Sauvignon Mount Eden £12.95 (RAE)
Cabernet Sauvignon Ridge Santa Cruz Mountain £12.50 (REI)
Le Cigare Volant Bonny Doon £12.95 (RAE) £14.91 (PLA)
Pinot Noir Calera Central Coast £12.16 (HA) £12.95 (VIG)
Zinfandel Topolos Rossi Ranch £13.00 (BIB)
1991
Le Mistral Joseph Phelps £14.95 (BEN)
1990
Merlot Cuvaison £14.97 (HOG)
1989
Cabernet Sauvignon Joseph Phelps £12.50 (REI)
Rubicon Niebaum-Coppola £13.50 (REI)
1988
Cabernet Sauvignon Robert Mondavi £13.80 (NI)
1983
Cabernet Sauvignon Ridge York Creek £12.95 (VIG)

£15.00 → £19.99

1996
Pinot Noir Au Bon Climat £15.26 (PLA)
1995
Mourvèdre Jade Mountain £15.25 (REI) £18.50 (MV)
1994
Cabernet Sauvignon Joseph Phelps £16.99 (YOU)
Cabernet Sauvignon Ridge Santa Cruz Mountain £15.65 (BEN) £15.75 (LAY) £15.99 (YOU) £16.50 (MV) £16.50 (LEA) £16.95 (VIG)
Cabernet Sauvignon Stag's Leap £17.50 (ROB)

Le Cigare Volant Bonny Doon £16.50 (MV) £17.34 (GN)
Merlot Clos du Val £19.58 (AV)

Merlot Cuvaison £17.20 (SOM)
Merlot Duckhorn £17.70 (FLE) £19.95 (LAY)
Merlot Frog's Leap £15.60 (MV) £15.65
(LAY)
Merlot Shafer £17.95 (AD)
Pinot Noir Robert Mondavi Reserve
£19.40 (NI)
Syrah Qupé Bien Nacido £16.99 (YOU)
£18.41 (FA) £18.50 (MV)
Zinfandel Frog's Leap £15.25 (UB)
Zinfandel Lytton Springs £15.30 (PIP)
£15.99 (EL) £16.45 (AD)
Zinfandel Ridge Geyserville £15.00 (WS)
£15.22 (DOM) £15.65 (BEN) £15.75 (LAY)
£15.99 (YOU) £16.50 (LEA) £16.50 (MV)
1993
Cabernet Sauvignon Clos du Val £16.55 (AV)
Cabernet Sauvignon Francis Coppola
Family Wines £16.50 (YOU)
Cabernet Sauvignon Ridge Santa Cruz
Mountain £15.50 (WS)
Cabernet Sauvignon Spottswoode £19.92
(DOM)
Le Cigare Volant Bonny Doon £16.45 (ROB)
Merlot Havens Reserve £16.00 (BIB)
Merlot Newton £17.35 (BEN)
Petite Sirah Ridge Vineyards York Creek
£15.40 (MV)
Pinot Noir Robert Mondavi £15.00 (TAN)
Pinot Noir Sanford £15.35 (BEN)
Pinot Noir Marimar Torres Estate Don
Miguel £16.99 (DI)
Zinfandel Lytton Springs £18.30 (BER)
Zinfandel Ridge Geyserville £15.57 (COU)
1992
Cabernet Sauvignon Clos du Val £15.95
(STA)
Cabernet Sauvignon Durney Reserve
£18.95 (LEA)
Cabernet Sauvignon Grgich Hills £18.95
(EL)
Merlot Duckhorn £19.59 (YOU)
Merlot Shafer £16.45 (ROB)
Pinot Noir Saintsbury Reserve £18.20
(SOM) £18.96 (NI)
1991
Cabernet Sauvignon Jordan £15.84 (PEN)
Le Cigare Volant Bonny Doon £15.13 (NO)
Pinot Noir Mount Eden £18.50 (RAE)
1990
Cabernet Franc Carmenet £15.50 (WS)
Cabernet Sauvignon Shafer £16.20 (BER)
Cabernet Sauvignon Simi £17.50 (ROB)
Pinot Noir Chalone £19.95 (BIB)
Syrah Joseph Phelps £16.95 (BEN)

1988
Pinot Noir Au Bon Climat £16.94 (BUT)
Rubicon Niebaum-Coppola £17.00 (TAN)
1987
Rubicon Niebaum-Coppola £19.89 (YOU)
1985
Pinot Noir Robert Mondavi Reserve
£19.50 (REI)
1984
Cabernet Sauvignon Carmenet £17.75 (NO)
Cabernet Sauvignon Renaissance £17.61
(PEN)
Rubicon Niebaum-Coppola £16.95 (REI)
1981
Pinot Noir Sanford £15.67 (FA)
1980
Cabernet Sauvignon Robert Mondavi
Reserve £15.50 (REI)

£20.00 → £29.99

1995
Mourvèdre Jade Mountain £20.34 (NO)
1994
Merlot Cuvaison £21.50 (VIG)
Pinot Noir Au Bon Climat £28.00 (MV)
Pinot Noir Robert Mondavi £23.49 (MAJ)
Pinot Noir Saintsbury Reserve £21.00 (WS)
1993
Cabernet Sauvignon Philip Togni £25.00
(REI)
Merlot Matanzas Creek £25.99 (OD)
1992
Cabernet Sauvignon Durney Reserve
£22.50 (VIG)
Cabernet Sauvignon Robert Mondavi
Oakville £21.97 (PEN)
Cabernet Sauvignon Spottswoode £23.99
(YOU)
Cabernet Sauvignon Stag's Leap £25.95
(BER)
Pinot Noir Calera Jensen £22.85 (REI)
£28.95 (BEN)
Pinot Noir Robert Mondavi Reserve
£23.95 (BEN)
Pinot Noir Saintsbury Reserve £20.99
(YOU) £22.70 (BEN)

> *Please remember that*
> **Webster's** *is a price
> guide and not a price list. It
> is not meant to replace up-
> to-date
> merchants' lists.*

1991
Cabernet Sauvignon Beringer Private
   Reserve £28.14 (NO)
Rubicon Niebaum-Coppola £24.50 (REI)
1990
Cabernet Sauvignon Shafer Hillside Select
   £25.79 (YOU)
1989
Rubicon Niebaum-Coppola £29.70 (UB)
1988
Cabernet Sauvignon Spottswoode £25.75
   (BUT)
1986
Dominus Christian Moueix £25.50 (HAH)
1981
Rubicon Niebaum-Coppola £22.99 (YOU)
1975
Cabernet Sauvignon Firestone £25.00 (BU)

£30.00 → £39.99

1994
Cabernet Sauvignon Diamond Creek
   Volcanic Hill £38.50 (LAY)
Gravelly Meadow Diamond Creek £36.75
   (LAY)
Red Rock Terrace Diamond Creek
   £37.50 (LAY)
1992
Cabernet Sauvignon Ridge Monte Bello
   £36.00 (AD)
Dominus Christian Moueix £32.95 (LAY)
1991
Cabernet Sauvignon Gallo-Sonoma Estate
   £32.00 (EL)
Cabernet Sauvignon Ridge Monte Bello
   £32.75 (REI)
1989
Cabernet Sauvignon Robert Mondavi
   Reserve £32.50 (NI)
Cabernet Sauvignon Ridge Monte Bello
   £39.50 (BEN)
1985
Cabernet Sauvignon Heitz £35.54 (BUT)
Cabernet Sauvignon Robert Mondavi
   Reserve £33.72 (NO)
1982
Cabernet Sauvignon Heitz Martha's
   Vineyard £35.00 (GRE)

£40.00 → £49.99

1994
Cabernet Sauvignon Ridge Monte Bello
   £45.50 (NI)
1993
Opus One Mondavi/Rothschild £48.96 (WY)

1992
Cabernet Sauvignon Ridge Monte Bello
   £42.50 (REI) £45.00 (WS) £48.47 (ELL)
   £49.93 (NO) £49.95 (BEN)
Dominus Christian Moueix £49.25 (FA)
Opus One Mondavi/Rothschild £48.00 (NI)
1991
Cabernet Sauvignon Ridge Monte Bello
   £41.99 (YOU)
Opus One Mondavi/Rothschild £45.00 (UN)
1988
Dominus Christian Moueix £40.44 (FA)
Opus One Mondavi/Rothschild £43.93 (NO)
1986
Cabernet Sauvignon Beringer Private
   Reserve £40.00 (VIG)
Opus One Mondavi/Rothschild £42.85
   (JON) £49.90 (NO)
1984
Dominus Christian Moueix £40.44 (FA)

£50.00 → £59.99

1993
Opus One Mondavi/Rothschild £56.20 (TAN)
   £57.00 (STA) £59.50 (BEN) £59.95 (VIG)
1985
Dominus Christian Moueix £52.19 (BUT)

£60.00 → £75.00

1991
Dominus Christian Moueix £67.00 (UB)
1972
Cabernet Sauvignon Heitz Martha's
   Vineyard £75.00 (REI)

c. £89.00

1981
Opus One Mondavi/Rothschild £88.13 (WY)

CALIFORNIA WHITE

Under £4.00

Non-vintage
Chenin Blanc E&J Gallo £3.79 (SAI) £3.99
   (WR) £3.99 (BOT) £3.99 (THR) £3.99 (UN)
French Colombard E&J Gallo £3.79 (SO)
   £3.99 (UN) £3.99 (CO) £3.99 (BOT) £3.99
   (THR) £3.99 (SAF) £3.99 (WR) £3.99 (VIC)

£4.00 → £5.99

Non-vintage
Chardonnay E&J Gallo £4.49 (SAI)
   £4.79 (BOT) £4.79 (WR) £4.79 (CO)
   £4.79 (THR) £4.79 (VIC)

Chardonnay South Bay £4.99 (SAI)
Orange Muscat Quady Essensia ½ bottle
£5.95 (WS)
Sauvignon Blanc E&J Gallo £4.39 (BO)
£4.39 (VIC) £4.39 (BOT) £4.39 (THR)
£4.39 (CO) £4.39 (WR)

1995
Chardonnay Fetzer Sundial £5.99 (WAI)
£5.99 (UN)
Chardonnay E&J Gallo £4.79 (SAF)
Chardonnay Glen Ellen £4.99 (CO)
Chardonnay Sutter Home £4.50 (GRE)
Fumé Blanc Fetzer £5.76 (FLE)
Orange Muscat Quady Essensia ½ bottle
£5.95 (NI) £5.98 (PEN) £5.99 (MAJ)
Sauvignon Blanc E&J Gallo £4.39 (SAF)
Sauvignon Blanc Robert Mondavi
Woodbridge £5.85 (GRE)
Zinfandel Robert Mondavi Woodbridge
£5.97 (FOR)

1994
Chardonnay Clos du Bois £5.75 (REI)
Chardonnay Fetzer Sundial £5.95 (SOM)
Chardonnay Glen Ellen £4.99 (GRE)
Chardonnay Sutter Home £4.89 (JON)
£4.99 (UN)
Fumé Blanc Beringer £5.99 (MAJ)
Orange Muscat Quady Essensia ½ bottle
£5.75 (GRE)
Primavera Mista Pedroncelli £4.99 (DI)
Sauvignon Blanc Robert Mondavi
Woodbridge £5.60 (FOR)

1993
Sauvignon Blanc Robert Mondavi
Woodbridge £4.99 (NI)

1992
Sauvignon Blanc Robert Mondavi
Woodbridge £5.99 (JON)

£6.00 → £7.99

Non-vintage
Chardonnay Mount Aston £6.50 (WS)
Primavera Mista Pedroncelli £6.60 (GN)
1996
Chardonnay Redwood £7.70 (GN)
Fumé Blanc Beringer £7.40 (PIP)
Malvasia Ca' del Solo Bianca £7.25 (REI)
Orange Muscat Quady Essensia ½ bottle
£6.06 (AV)
1995
Chardonnay Edna Valley ½ bottle £6.50
(LEA)
Chardonnay Fetzer Bonterra £7.49
(WAI)
Chardonnay Round Hill £7.20 (LAY)

Chardonnay Sterling £6.99 (OD)
Chardonnay Washington Hills £6.45 (SAI)
Chenin Blanc Dry Creek £7.50 (GRE)
Fumé Blanc Beringer £6.80 (NEZ)
Fumé Blanc Murphy-Goode £7.95 (AD)
Malvasia Ca' del Solo Bianca £6.99 (NI)
£7.95 (POR)
Orange Muscat Quady Essensia ½ bottle
£6.25 (WRI) £6.50 (STA) £6.92 (GN)

Riesling Bonny Doon Pacific Rim £6.99 (NI)
Sauvignon Blanc Robert Mondavi
Woodbridge £6.20 (ROS) £6.99 (NA)
Zinfandel Robert Mondavi Woodbridge
£6.20 (ROS)
1994
Chardonnay Clos du Val £7.75 (GRE)
Chardonnay Villa Mt Eden £7.99 (UN)
Fumé Blanc Beringer £6.71 (ELL)
Riesling Firestone Selected Harvest
Johannisberg £7.50 (PIP)
Riesling Renaissance £7.95 (AD)
1993
Chardonnay Beaulieu Vineyard £7.20
(HOG)
Fumé Blanc Robert Mondavi £7.69 (MAJ)
Riesling Bonny Doon Pacific Rim £7.85
(RAE)
1992
Chardonnay Fetzer Sundial £6.99 (JON)
Chardonnay Pedroncelli £7.50 (FLE)
Malvasia Ca' del Solo Bianca £7.99 (RAE)
1990
Orange Muscat Quady Essensia ½ bottle
£7.28 (NO)

> Stars (★) indicate wines
> selected by Oz Clarke in the
> Best Buys section which begins
> on page 12.

1989
Chardonnay Wente Bros £7.15 (SO)
Fumé Blanc Robert Mondavi £7.50 (REI)

£8.00 → £9.99

1996
Malvasia Ca' del Solo Bianca £8.95 (ROB)
1995
Chardonnay Acacia Caviste £8.75 (BIB)
Chardonnay Beaulieu Vineyard £9.75 (NA)
Chardonnay Firestone £8.95 (SAI)
Chardonnay Hawk Crest £8.17 (DOM)
Chardonnay Kendall-Jackson Vintner's
   Reserve £9.99 (DI)
Chardonnay Robert Mondavi £9.95 (ROS)
Chenin Blanc Dry Creek £8.44 (GN)
Fumé Blanc Dry Creek £8.21 (HOG) £8.95
   (GRE) £9.90 (GN)
Il Pescatore Ca' del Solo £8.95 (NI)
Malvasia Ca' del Solo Bianca £8.10 (TAN)
   £8.15 (WRI) £8.50 (MV) £8.52 (PLA)
Riesling Bonny Doon Pacific Rim £8.50 (MV)
Sauvignon Blanc Simi £9.85 (STA)
1994
Chardonnay Beringer £9.95 (NEZ)
Chardonnay Firestone £8.50 (WS)
Sauvignon Blanc Frog's Leap £9.19 (FLE)
1993
Chardonnay Acacia Caviste £8.95 (WS)
Chardonnay Durney Cachagua £8.50 (VIG)
Chardonnay Edna Valley £9.95 (BIB)
Chardonnay Firestone £8.49 (WR)
Chardonnay Pedroncelli £8.95 (LAY)
Chardonnay Saintsbury £9.65 (SOM)
Il Pescatore Ca' del Solo £9.85 (RAE)
Riesling Renaissance Select Late Harvest
   ½ bottle £9.95 (BU)
1992
Chardonnay Beringer £9.49 (MAJ)
Riesling Bonny Doon Pacific Rim £8.99 (UB)
Sauvignon Blanc Simi £9.86 (PLA)
1991
Chardonnay Rutherford Hill Jaeger £9.99
   (PEN)
1990
Chardonnay Carneros Creek £9.90 (WS)
Chardonnay St-Supéry £9.95 (TAN)
1988
Chardonnay Swanson £9.95 (PEN)
Sauvignon Blanc Renaissance £8.31 (PEN)

£10.00 → £11.99

1995
Chardonnay Beringer £10.70 (PIP)
Chardonnay Clos du Val £11.34 (AV)

Chardonnay Landmark Overlook £11.99
   (OD)
Chardonnay Robert Mondavi £11.99 (NI)
Chardonnay Saintsbury £11.95 (WS)
Sauvignon Blanc Duckhorn £11.75 (LAY)
Sauvignon Blanc Frog's Leap £10.80 (MV)
1994
Chardonnay Clos du Val £11.60 (PIP)
Chardonnay Cuvaison £11.15 (SOM)
Chardonnay Rutherford Hill £10.57 (AV)
Fumé Blanc Grgich Hills £11.75 (EL)
Fumé Blanc Robert Mondavi £11.71 (PLA)
Sauvignon Blanc Frog's Leap £10.20 (LAY)
Sauvignon Blanc Philip Togni £10.65 (REI)
1993
Chardonnay Clos du Val £11.75 (DOM)
Chardonnay Dry Creek £10.15 (JON)
Chardonnay Saintsbury £10.69 (NI) £11.89
   (NO)
Chardonnay Simi £11.39 (PEN)
1992
Chardonnay Saintsbury £11.55 (HAH)
Fumé Blanc Robert Mondavi £11.00 (TAN)
1983
Botrytis Sauvignon ½ bottle Renaissance
   £10.76 (NO)

£12.00 → £14.99

1995
Chardonnay Edna Valley £12.65 (LEA)
Chardonnay Frog's Leap £14.50 (LAY)
   £14.80 (MV)
Chardonnay Sonoma-Cutrer £12.65 (AV)
   £14.95 (LEA)
Chardonnay Stag's Leap £14.69 (DOM)
1994
Chardonnay Robert Mondavi £14.20 (TAN)
Chardonnay Newton £13.99 (AME)
Chardonnay Qupé £14.65 (BER)
Chardonnay Ridge £13.95 (NI) £14.93 (ELL)
Chardonnay Saintsbury £13.20 (BEN)
Chardonnay Marimar Torres Estate Don
   Miguel Vineyard £14.99 (DI)
Sauvignon Blanc Matanzas Creek £13.20
   (BEN)
1993
Chardonnay Morgan £12.99 (WR) £12.99
   (BOT)
Chardonnay Stag's Leap £13.45 (AD)
Pinot Blanc Chalone £13.95 (BIB)
1991
Chardonnay Simi £12.33 (PLA)
Chardonnay Swanson £14.98 (HOG)
Chardonnay Marimar Torres Estate Don
   Miguel Vineyard £13.51 (PEN)

1990
Chardonnay Marimar Torres Estate Don Miguel Vineyard £12.74 (NO)
1988
Chardonnay Chalone £12.50 (REI)
Chardonnay Edna Valley £13.83 (NO)
1986
Chardonnay Robert Mondavi Reserve £13.60 (GAU)
1985
Chardonnay Acacia £12.50 (BU)

£15.00 → £19.99

1995
Chardonnay Au Bon Climat £15.00 (MV)
1994
Chardonnay Matanzas Creek £19.60 (BEN)
Chardonnay Ridge £15.65 (BEN)
Chardonnay Saintsbury Reserve £19.95 (AD)
Chardonnay Shafer £16.52 (NO)
Chardonnay Stag's Leap £18.75 (ROB)
Chardonnay Swanson £18.95 (LEA)
1993
Chardonnay Chalone £19.95 (BIB)
Chardonnay Robert Mondavi Reserve £18.20 (FOR)
Chardonnay Saintsbury Reserve £18.95 (BEN)
Chardonnay Sonoma-Cutrer les Pierres £17.00 (REI)
Fumé Blanc Grgich Hills £15.37 (GN)
Le Sophiste Bonny Doon £16.99 (OD)
1992
Chardonnay Au Bon Climat £15.22 (PLA)
Chardonnay Iron Horse £16.58 (BER)
Chardonnay Saintsbury Reserve £15.75 (NI)
Chardonnay Simi Reserve £17.99 (YOU)
Le Sophiste Bonny Doon £18.99 (RAE)
1991
Chardonnay Clos du Bois Calcaire £16.50 (DI)
Chardonnay Sonoma-Cutrer les Pierres £18.45 (UB)
1990
Chardonnay Sonoma-Cutrer les Pierres £17.16 (HOG) £18.50 (PEN)
1988
Chardonnay Far Niente £18.71 (NO)

> In each price band wines
> are listed in vintage order.
> Within each vintage they
> are listed in A–Z order.

1983
Riesling Joseph Phelps Johannisberg Selected Late Harvest ½ bottle £18.37 (HAL)

£20.00 → £24.99

1995
Chardonnay Far Niente £24.08 (AV)
1994
Chardonnay Far Niente £22.91 (PEN)
Chardonnay Grgich Hills £20.55 (EL)
Chardonnay Sonoma-Cutrer les Pierres £22.50 (LEA)'
Le Sophiste Bonny Doon £20.00 (MV) £20.65 (UB)
1993
Chardonnay Gallo-Sonoma Estate £20.55 (EL)
1991
Chardonnay Gallo-Sonoma Estate £21.00 (VIG)
1977
Chardonnay Trefethen £20.00 (VIG)

£30.00 → £35.00

1983
Sauvignon Blanc Robert Mondavi Botrytis £30.00 (REI)
1982
Riesling Joseph Phelps Johannisberg Selected Late Harvest ½ bottle £35.00 (VIG)

CALIFORNIA ROSÉ

Under £4.00

1995
White Zinfandel Sebastiani £3.99 (CO)
White Zinfandel Sutter Home £3.99 (GRE)

£4.00 → £4.99

Non-vintage
White Grenache E&J Gallo £4.39 (WR) £4.39 (VIC) £4.39 (BOT) £4.39 (THR) £4.39 (CO)
1995
White Grenache E&J Gallo £4.39 (SAF)
1994
White Grenache E&J Gallo £4.39 (UN)
White Zinfandel Robert Mondavi £4.85 (NI)
White Zinfandel Sutter Home £4.89 (JON)

£5.00 → £7.50

1996
White Zinfandel Robert Mondavi £6.60 (STA) £7.26 (GN)

1995
White Zinfandel Robert Mondavi £7.49 (NA)
1991
White Zinfandel Robert Mondavi £5.89
(WHI)

CALIFORNIA SPARKLING

Under £5.50

Non-vintage
Gallo Brut £5.49 (SAF) £5.49 (CO)

£8.50 → £9.99

Non-vintage
Gloria Ferrer Brut £8.80 (GN) £9.80 (AD)
Mumm Cuvée Napa Brut £8.99 (GRE)
£8.99 (WAI) £8.99 (CO) £8.99 (SAF)
£8.99 (FUL) £9.49 (SAI) £9.49 (POR) £9.49
(THR) £9.49 (MAJ) £9.49 (WR) £9.49 (BOT)
Mumm Cuvée Napa Rosé £9.99 (SAT)
★ Scharffenberger Brut £9.49 (ASD)

£10.00 → £15.50

Non-vintage
Mumm Cuvée Napa Brut Blanc de Blancs
£11.99 (OD)
Roederer Estate Quartet £11.50 (REI)
£11.50 (REI) £13.50 (GRE) £13.95 (STA)
£13.95 (WS) £13.95 (POR) £13.99 (JON)
£14.90 (AD) £14.95 (BEN) £14.95 (WAI)
1990
Schramsberg Blanc de Blancs £15.50 (ROB)
1988
Schramsberg Blanc de Noirs £12.95 (LAY)

OREGON/WASHINGTON RED

Under £8.00

1995
Pinot Noir Columbia £7.38 (FOR)
1993
Merlot Columbia Crest £7.97 (ROS)
Merlot Covey Run £7.39 (PLA)
1992
Cabernet Sauvignon Columbia Crest
£6.39 (ROS)

£8.00 → £12.00

1996
Lemberger Covey Run £8.40 (PIP)
1994
Pinot Noir Elk Cove Estate £10.25 (PIP)
£11.54 (GN)

1993
Pinot Noir Elk Cove Estate £8.75 (GRE)
£10.22 (PEN) £10.57 (PLA)
Pinot Noir Sokol Blosser Yamhill £12.00
(WRI)
1988
Cabernet Sauvignon Chateau Ste Michelle
£10.80 (WRI)

£18.00 → £22.99

1994
Pinot Noir Domaine Drouhin £18.95 (REI)
£21.49 (PLA) £21.50 (STA) £21.95 (VIG)

1993
Pinot Noir Domaine Drouhin £18.20 (SOM)
£22.21 (PEN) £22.70 (BEN) £22.95 (VIG)

OREGON/WASH. WHITE

Under £6.00

1995
Gewürztraminer Columbia £5.70 (FOR)

£7.00 → £9.99

1995
Chardonnay Columbia £7.37 (FOR)
1993
Chardonnay Covey Run £8.80 (GN)
Riesling Argyle Dry Reserve £7.40 (SOM)
1991
Chardonnay Salishan £8.70 (COU)
1988
Chardonnay Columbia £7.09 (PEN)

c. £10.50

1994
Chardonnay Elk Cove Estate £10.50 (PIP)

OTHER USA RED

c. £8.50

1995
Pinot Noir Firesteed £8.49 (HOG)

OTHER REGIONS

Argentina could one day produce the finest reds in South America; Austria already has world-class whites, but we still don't drink many of them here. These countries could be the fashions of the future

ARGENTINA

Argentinian wines have made huge strides forward here in the last year. Suddenly you can hardly go into a supermarket or off-licence without falling over one – and frankly, there are few things I'd be happier to fall over. I love all that concentrated smoky, minty fruit you find in the reds, and I'm delighted, too, that the wines we're seeing here are not Australian or even Chilean me-toos.

Argentina makes Cabernet Sauvignon, yes, and very good much of it is, too. But the grape with which it's increasingly making its name is Malbec, powerful, tannic and reeking of damsons. The same dear old Malbec, in fact, that plays a very minor role in red Bordeaux, and that until now had reached its apogee in Cahors.

Whites are (inevitably) mostly from Chardonnay, but there are a few other grapes like Chenin Blanc around as well.

The best wines aren't dirt cheap, but that's all right, because they're worth it. And there's plenty of stuff around at under a fiver for those who want an inexpensive taste of what Argentina is doing. Try *Catena* (and second label *Alamos Ridge*), *Trapiche*, *San Telmo*, *Navarro Correa*, *Cavas de Weinart*, *Etchart*, *Bodegas Norton*, *Santa Julia*, *Lurton*, *La Rural*, *Esmeralda*.

AUSTRIA

At last we're starting to see Austrian wines make the sort of impact they deserve. It's been building up for a couple of years, with more and more merchants thinking – yes, perhaps it's time we had something from Austria. Now lots of the best producers are represented here, and it's my bet there'll be a slow but steady increase in the popularity of these wines. Why? Because they've got

structure and acidity and a sort of rich dryness, allied to good fruit flavours and an ability to age in bottle. There's one part of the country, the Neusiedlersee in Burgenland, which can make botrytized sweet wines with greater ease than just about anywhere else in the world, and they have higher alcohol than their German equivalents, so they go better with food. There are light, bay-leaf scented dry Grüner Veltliners from Lower Austria and classy Rieslings from the Wachau, and increasingly good reds from many parts, too. The grape varieties to look for, apart from the national speciality Grüner Veltliner, include Welschriesling (perfectly respectable here), Rhine Riesling, Traminer, Pinot Banc, Pinot Gris, Sauvignon, Bouvier, Blaufrankisch, Blauer Zweigelt and Sankt Laurent.

Best producers include *Bründlmayer, Alois Kracher, Franz Hirtzberger, Josef Pöckl, Krutzler, Willi Opitz, Paul Achs, Robert Wenzel, Georg Stiegelmar, Feiler-Artinger, Lenz Moser, Prager, Erich Salomon, Umathum, Fritz Wieninger, Prieler, Heinrich, Erwin Tinhof* and *Nekowitsch*.

CANADA

Because of a quirk of EU law Canada's best wines, her Icewines, have only recently started to be imported – and while the other wines are promising, they're pleasant rather than thrilling. Cool Ontario's best bets are Riesling and Chardonnay; British Columbia, which is tiny in comparison, does well with Pinot Blanc, Pinot Gris, Riesling, Gewürztraminer and sometimes Merlot. Best names include *Inniskillin, Henry of Pelham, Mission Hill, Cedar Creek, Calona Vineyards, Chateau des Charmes, Hillbrand, Gray Monk, Hainle, Sumac Ridge* and *Summerhill*.

CYPRUS

Still generally dreadful. Commandaria can be a decent sweet, raisiny fortified. As for the table wines – well, there are so many other good, well-made wines in the world that Cyprus is going to have to try a lot harder if she wants us to drink her wine.

GREECE

Greece, on the other hand, has started to send an awful lot of clean, fresh, fruity wines our way. The supermarkets are in the forefront, often with wines that taste more international than recognizably Greek – but given the sort of stuff that tended to be on offer before, perhaps that's no bad thing.

Greece has a vast array of native grapes possessed by no other country: for reds, Agiortítiko (principally from the Nemea region), Mavrodaphne (especially from Patras), Xynomavro and Limnió; for whites, Assyrtiko, Moscophilero, Savatiano and others – but only a few of these names are liable to appear on labels. Partly this is because a lot of wines are blends of more than one variety; partly it's because we wouldn't understand them anyway.

So what are the ones to go for? Established names like *Chateau Carras, Kourtakis, Achaia-Clauss, Tsantalis* and *Boutari* are still in the lead, but look also for *Domaine Mercouri, Chateau Harlaftis, Semeli* and sweet Muscat from Samos.

INDIA

Omar Khayyam is the most famous wine from a country that has neither the climate for wine nor, usually, the inclination. It's a reasonable sparkler, but I suspect it's drunk here more as a curiosity than for its quality.

ISRAEL

Kosher wine is the speciality here – which means that vineyards and winery are under the strict eye of a rabbi. Vineyards must usually be left fallow every seventh year, and only practising Jews may do so much as touch any of the equipment used to make the wines.

Until fairly recently the main concern of Israeli producers was to meet these requirements; making modern, tasty wine was neither here nor there. And, they probably reasoned, since practising Jews bought the wines, they must like them.

Then the *Golan Heights* winery threw a spanner in the works by producing kosher wines to modern standards. The largest producer, *Carmel*, started battling to catch up. The only fly in the ointment is that the Golan Heights, which has long been acknowledged as the best vineyard area in the country, could one day be given to Syria as part of a peace agreement.

LEBANON

Lebanese wine is, to all intents and purposes for us in Britain, *Chateau Musar*. There are other vineyards, like *Chateau Kefraya*, but none is a patch on Musar.

Musar's style is, typically, big and powerful. For a time in the late 1960s owner Gaston Hochar turned to making lighter wines more reminiscent of Médoc, but now the wines are huge again, and age superbly – Hochar in fact reckons they should be drunk at 15 years, and will be even better at 30. The trouble is, they're often so wonderful at seven, when they are released, that keeping them that long requires an awful lot of will-power.

LUXEMBOURG

Luxembourg's wines, from the banks of the Mosel, are of little other than local appeal. They lack the body, the interest and the aging potential of the best of their neighbours further down the river in Germany, but are perfectly acceptable, with light, delicate fruit. Most are made from Müller-Thurgau, here called Rivaner.

MEXICO

Mostly too hot for wine, although *LA Cetto* makes exceedingly nice red from Petite Sirah, Cabernet, Zinfandel and others. *Santo Tomas* and *Monte Xanic* are also good, and foreign investment bodes well.

NORTH AFRICA

This is another of those places that have been left so far behind in the race to make good wine that you would only drink it if you were there, if you were extremely curious (and persistent enough to track the stuff down) or if you were determined to make a house blend of the sort of red that passed for Burgundy until a few decades ago. (If you want to have a bash at the last option, you'll need a bottle of North African red – it doesn't much matter which sort. Dilute to taste with cheap red Burgundy. There you are: old-style Corton or Pommard.)

If you feel inspired to taste the wines for their own sake, look for Algeria's Coteaux de Mascara (can sometimes taste not unlike the make-up of the same name, I'm told), Tunisian Muscat or *Domaine Cigogne, Domaine Mellil* and *Prestige du Menara* from Morocco.

SWITZERLAND

There are some lovely wines here, but you need to be Swiss to afford them. Last time I went to a Swiss tasting I was told that a road sweeper in Switzerland earns, I think, the equivalent of £18,000 a year, and everything else is in keeping. If you happen to be there, save up for wines made from characterful white grapes like Petite Arvine and Amigne, and rather less characterful Chasselas; reds are mostly on the light side and come from Gamay, Pinot Noir and Merlot.

Most of the wine comes from French-speaking Switzerland, and the main regions are the Valais, the Vaud and Neuchatel; German-speaking Switzerland makes a fair bit of Müller-Thurgau, which it insists on calling Riesling-Sylvaner, and the Italian Swiss make mostly Merlot.

TURKEY

There are, so I am told, 1172 different grape varieties here, and hardly any drinkable wine. Hardly any wine at all, come to that: only two or three per cent of the crop is vinified.

It's hard positively to recommend Turkish wines or even any individual grape varieties, but *Buzbag* (red), *Villa Doluca* and *Doluca* (red and whites), *Hosbag* (red), *Villa Dona* (red and white) are brands to consider.

URUGUAY

This is everybody's latest discovery: and the grape variety we've all been discovering is Tannat. Tannat is otherwise found in the South-West of France, where it's a component of many different AC wines; but in Uruguay it's being turned into juicy reds that have found favour in many a supermarket. The whites are decent, too, when they're made in a modern style.

ZIMBABWE

There is some wine made here, and some is even exported to Britain, under the name of *Marondera*. You could try it, just to prove to your friends that it exists.

MERCHANTS SPECIALIZING IN THESE COUNTRIES
see Merchant Directory (page 413) for details

Good merchants often stock a scattering of wines from these countries. The following merchants have a slightly better choice: **Argentina** Sommelier Wine Co (SOM); **Austria** Adnams (AD), Lay & Wheeler (LAY), Christopher Piper Wines (PIP), T&W Wines (TW), Noel Young Wines (YOU); **Canada** Averys of Bristol

(AV), Corney & Barrow (CB), Grape Ideas (GRAP), The Nadder Wine Co (NA), Terry Platt (PLA); **Greece** Tanners (TAN); **Israel** no actual specialists but Averys of Bristol (AV), Corney & Barrow (CB), Safeway (SAF) have some; **Lebanon** Chateau Musar is widely available. For older vintages try Roberson (ROB)

OTHER REGIONS PRICE GUIDES

ARGENTINA

Under £4.00

1996
★ Balbi Vineyard Malbec £3.99 (SAF)
  Balbi Vineyard Syrah Rosé £3.99 (SAF)
★ La Bamba Tempranillo £3.85 (WAI)
★ Bright Bros. Argentine Dry Red £2.99 (FUL)
  Etchart Cafayate Torrentes £3.99 (THR)
    £3.99 (WR) £3.99 (BOT)
★ Lurton Malbec £3.85 (FUL)
  Santa Julia Torrontes £3.75 (WAI)
1995
  Balbi Vineyard Malbec Syrah £3.29 (KWI)

£4.00 → £6.99

1997
La Rural Malbec £4.50 (BIB)
La Rural Pinot Chardonnay £4.50 (BIB)
1996
Etchart Torrontés £4.29 (EL)
La Rural Malbec £4.49 (ASD)
La Rural Pinot Chardonnay £4.49 (ASD)
★ Norton Cabernet Sauvignon £4.99 (OD)
Norton Torrentes £4.95 (NEZ)
1995
Alamos Ridge Cabernet Sauvignon £4.99
  (SAF) £5.50 (BIB)
Etchart Torrontés £4.29 (JON) £4.45 (GRE)
Norton Torrentes £5.96 (NO) £5.99 (EL)
Trapiche Chardonnay Oak Cask Reserve
  £5.39 (COU) £6.35 (STA)
Trapiche Pinot Noir £4.69 (PLA)
Trapiche Pinot Noir Reserve £4.99 (NA)
1994
Alamos Ridge Cabernet Sauvignon £4.25
  (WS)
Etchart Torrontés £4.35 (UB)
Norton Malbec £6.49 (EL)
Norton Sangiovese £5.25 (GRE)
Trapiche Cabernet Sauvignon Reserve
  £4.69 (PLA) £6.99 (QUE)
1993
Etchart Cabernet Sauvignon £5.19 (JON)
Norton Malbec £5.39 (NI)
★ Trapiche Malbec £4.99 (GRAP)
1992
Cavas de Weinert Cabernet Sauvignon
  £5.19 (EL)
Etchart Cabernet Sauvignon £4.99 (BOT)
  £4.99 (THR) £4.99 (WR)

1990
Caves de Weinert Carrascal £6.78 (ROS)
  £6.99 (JON)

£7.00 → £9.99

1995
Catena Agrelo Cabernet Sauvignon £9.00
  (BIB)
Catena Agrelo Chardonnay £8.75 (WS)
1994
Catena Agrelo Cabernet Sauvignon £8.95
  (WS)
Norton Malbec £7.12 (NO)
Norton Sangiovese £9.18 (NO)
1993
Norton Privada £7.45 (NO) £7.95 (NEZ)
1992
Caves de Weinert Carrascal £7.75 (LEA)
  £7.99 (NA) £8.29 (DI)
Caves de Weinert Merlot £8.25 (NO)
  £8.99 (NA)

£10.00 → £11.99

1992
Caves de Weinert £11.50 (LEA)
1991
Cavas de Weinert Cabernet Sauvignon
  £10.29 (JON) £10.95 (LEA) £10.99 (NA)
1985
Caves de Weinert Carrascal £10.57 (BUT)

c. £63.50

1996
Trapiche Chardonnay Oak Cask Reserve
  £63.48 (WHI)

AUSTRIA

c. £10.50

1995
Langenloiser Steinhaus Grüner Veltliner
  Kabinett, Bründlmayer £10.50 (BER)

CANADA

Under £6.00

1995
Inniskillin Maréchal Foch Red £5.30 (AV)
1994
Inniskillin Maréchal Foch Red £5.75 (GRE)

£6.00 → £7.99

1995
★ Chateau des Charmes Late Harvest
  Riesling £6.95 (GRAP) £7.59 (NA)

CYPRUS

Under £5.00

Non-vintage
Aphrodite Keo White £3.79 (TES) £4.69
  (UN) £4.99 (DI)
Othello Keo Red £4.69 (UN)

c. £7.50

Non-vintage
Commandaria St-John £7.50 (GRE)

GREECE RED

Under £4.00

Non-vintage
Mavrodaphne Patras £3.69 (KWI)
Mavrodaphne Patras, Kourtaki £3.99 (WAI)
1994
Naoussa Boutari £3.99 (GRE)

£4.00 → £5.99

Non-vintage
Demestica Achaia Clauss £4.89 (DI)
1993
Nemea Kouros £4.49 (UN)
1992
Nemea Boutari £4.39 (JON) £4.79 (OD)

£6.00 → £7.99

1993
Château Carras £6.95 (POR) £7.70 (GN)
Château Carras Côtes de Meliton £7.50
  (TAN)

GREECE WHITE

Under £3.50

Non-vintage
Retsina Achaia Clauss £3.49 (ASD)
Retsina Kourtaki £2.89 (KWI) £3.49 (VIC)

£3.50 → £4.99

Non-vintage
Retsina Metaxas £4.20 (AD)
Retsina Tsantali £4.00 (TAN)

1995
Santorini Boutari £4.60 (GRE)
1994
Patras Kouros £3.79 (WAI)

£5.00 → £7.99

Non-vintage
Samos Nectar, Vinicoles de Samos £7.66
  (NO)
1995
Domaine Carras £5.69 (JON)

ISRAEL

Under £5.00

Non-vintage
Palwin No. 10 £4.59 (SAF)
1996
Carmel Petite Sirah Shomron Israel £3.49
  (MAR)

£5.00 → £5.99

Non-vintage
Palwin No. 4 £5.39 (SAF)
1995
Yarden Mount Herman Dry White £5.95
  (GRE)

£6.00 → £7.99

1995
Carmel Cabernet Sauvignon £6.19 (SAF)
Yarden Chardonnay £7.95 (GRE)

LEBANON RED

Under £8.00

1988
Château Musar £7.99 (WAI) £7.99 (FUL)

£8.00 → £9.99

1990
Château Musar £8.00 (REI) £9.24 (CHA)
£9.75 (WRI) £9.95 (LEA) £9.99 (EL)
1989
Château Musar £8.23 (PEN) £8.63 (CHA)
£8.75 (GRE) £8.85 (BO) £8.95 (POR) £8.99
(MAJ) £8.99 (NA) £8.99 (NI) £8.99 (UB)
£9.20 (FLE) £9.20 (TAN) £9.39 (PLA) £9.44
(ROS) £9.59 (JON) £9.60 (GAU) £9.65
(BEN) £9.71 (BY) £9.95 (ROB) £9.95 (AD)
1988
Château Musar £8.95 (POR) £8.99 (GRE)
£8.99 (CHA) £8.99 (SO) £8.99 (CO) £8.99
(WHI) £9.95 (VIG) £9.95 (BEN)
1987
Château Musar £9.49 (GRE) £9.98 (CHA)

£10.00 → £19.99

1986
Château Musar £11.60 (BEN) £11.95 (VIG)
£12.50 (WRI) £12.95 (ROB)
1983
Château Musar £12.00 (CHA)
1982
Château Musar £11.75 (QUE) £13.49 (POR)
£14.75 (GRE) £16.25 (BEN) £17.50 (WRI)
1981
Château Musar £14.50 (ROB) £14.80 (CHA)
£16.95 (POR) £18.90 (BEN) £18.95 (QUE)
1980
Château Musar £15.95 (POR) £16.60 (GRE)
1979
Château Musar £18.50 (GRE) £19.62 (CHA)

£20.00 → £29.99

1978
Château Musar £22.75 (CHA) £23.50 (GRE)
1977
Château Musar £23.80 (NI) £27.50 (ROB)
1975
Château Musar £29.95 (POR)

c. £57.00

1969
Château Musar £57.09 (FA)
1966
Château Musar £57.09 (FA)

£66.00 → £85.00

1972
Château Musar £66.88 (FA) £70.00 (CHA)
1970
Château Musar £80.00 (VIG) £85.00 (CHA)

LEBANON WHITE

Under £7.00

1993
Château Musar Blanc £6.85 (GRE)
1992
Château Musar Blanc £6.45 (UB)

£7.00 → £7.99

1994
Château Musar Blanc £7.07 (ROS) £7.95
(ROB)
1992
Château Musar Blanc £7.85 (WRI)
1990
Château Musar Blanc £7.95 (VIG)
1987
Château Musar Blanc £7.55 (QUE)

LUXEMBOURG

Under £8.00

Non-vintage
Cuvée de l'Ecusson Brut £7.50 (EL)

MEXICO

Under £5.50

1994
L A Cetto Cabernet Sauvignon £5.22 (GN)
L A Cetto Petit Sirah £4.92 (PLA)
1993
L A Cetto Cabernet Sauvignon £4.92 (PLA)
L A Cetto Petit Sirah £4.49 (CO) £4.49
(GRE) £4.95 (TAN)

c. £8.60

1993
L A Cetto Nebbiolo £8.60 (TAN)

MERCHANT DIRECTORY

All these merchants have been chosen on the basis of the quality and interest of their lists. We feature wines from the majority of them in our Price Guides. Unfortunately, a few were unable to get their stock details and prices to us in time for inclusion in the Price Guides, but I have picked out highlights from all the lists to add to the Best Buy, Supermarket Selection and Ideal Cellar recommendations at the front of the book.

If you want to find local suppliers, merchants are listed by region in the Who's Where directory on page 448; if you're looking for a specialist in a particular country's wines, you'll find a list at the start of each country's Price Guides.

The following services are available where indicated: **C** = cellarage, **EP** = en primeur offers, **G** = glass hire/loan, **M** = mail order, **T** = tastings and talks. There is a key to name abbreviations on page 10.

ADNAMS (AD)
(Head office & mail order) The Crown, High St, Southwold, Suffolk IP18 6DP, (01502) 727220, fax (01502) 727223; Mail order: (01502) 727222
The Cellar & Kitchen Store, Victoria St, Southwold, Suffolk IP18 6JW;
The Wine Shop, South Green, Southwold, Suffolk IP18 6EW;
The Grapevine, 109 Unthank Rd, Norwich NR2 2PE, (01603) 613998
Hours Mail order: Mon–Fri 9–6.30, Sat 9–12; Cellar & Kitchen Store: Mon–Sat 10–6.30; Wine Shop: Mon–Sat 10–7.15;
The Grapevine: Mon–Sat 9–9.
Cards MasterCard, Switch, Visa.
Discounts £3 per case off mail order price if collected.
Delivery £5 1 case, free 2 or more cases or over £100 mainland UK.
Minimum order 1 mixed case.
C EP G M T
Well, I've been saying it for years and I'll say it again: Adnams is brilliant. You want an incredible range of wines you've never thought of, as well as an incredible range of great names? Adnams is your

company. *The South African range has been cut, which is a fair reflection of the available quality, but the rest of the New World is there in force, with names like Charles Melton and St Hallett (Australia), Martinborough (New Zealand), Crasto (Portugal), Remelluri (Spain) and Saintsbury and Ridge (California).*
1995 Carignanissime, P&D Domergue, £5.95 Wonderful scented, supple Minervois.
1996 Château Lacroix, Merlot Rosé, £5.95 A pink Merlot from Bordeaux? Sounds good.

AMEY'S WINES (AME)
83 Melford Road, Sudbury, Suffolk CO10 6JT, (01787) 377144
Hours Tue–Sat 9.30–6.
Cards MasterCard, Visa.
Discounts 5% off 12 or more bottles.
Delivery Free within 20 miles of Sudbury, min order £50. **G**
Supposing you were bored, and wanted something you'd never tried before? You could do worse than go to Amey's, where you'll find Pinot Gris from Gisborne, New Zealand, for £9.49, or Pinot Noir from Navarra for £4.99. Equally, you could find familiar but good names like Dashwood from New Zealand, Cape Mentelle or Wynns from Australia, and Thelema from South Africa. The prices here look good.
1993 Rutherglen Durif, Mick Morris, £9.95 Huge, beefy Aussie red from a rare French grape.
1996 Gros Manseng, Domaine de Maubet £5.49 Honeyed, late-harvest white from one of France's good but lesser known grapes.
1997 Etchart Torrontes, £3.99 Lovely aromatic dry white from Argentina.

ASDA (ASD)
(Head office) Asda House, Southbank, Great Wilson Street, Leeds LS11 5AD, (01532) 435435, fax (01532) 418666
Hours Mon–Fri 9–8, Sat 8.30–8; open most bank hols; selected stores open Sunday.
Cards MasterCard, Switch, Visa.
Discounts £1 off any 6 bottles. **G T**

A reasonably adventurous range, and the Chablis here is pretty good. Overall it's sound rather than hugely exciting, and in common with so many supermarket chains these days, many of the wines are commercial but without great individuality.
1995 Chablis Fourchaume, Domaine de Colombier, £10.99 Decent Chablis that needs a year or two's aging yet.

ASHLEY SCOTT (AS)
PO Box 28, The Highway, Hawarden, Deeside, Flintshire CH5 3RY, tel & fax (01244) 520655
Hours 24-hr answerphone.
Discounts 5% unmixed case.
Delivery Free in North Wales, Cheshire, Merseyside.
Minimum order 1 mixed case.
G M T
A short but quite interesting list of well-priced lesser clarets, Loires and Australians. The rest of France, Germany, Italy and much of the New World, too.
1990 Château Beau-Site Blanc, Premières Côtes de Bordeaux, £6.00 Inexpensive nobly rotten sweet white from a good year.

STÉPHANE AURIOL WINES (AUR)
High St, Hartley Wintney, Hampshire RG27 8NY, (01252) 843190, fax (01252) 844373
Hours Mon–Sat 9–9, Sun 11.30–2.
Cards Amex, MasterCard, Switch, Visa.
Discounts On half cases.
Delivery Free locally and for over £150 central UK. Otherwise at cost.
G M T
A sound selection that efficiently covers the world. France and the New World (Wirra Wirra and

Collards stand out) are the main focuses, but there are also interesting diversions like Chapel Down Epoch Brut fizz from England.
1994 Trentino Marzemino, Cavit, £5.39 The favourite wine of Mozart's Don Giovanni, and therefore essential drinking for wannabe Don Juans.

AUSTRALIAN WINE CENTRE (AUS)
Australian Wine Club, Freepost WC5500, Slough, Berks SL3 9BH, Freefone orderline (0800) 856 2004; 24-hr answerphone, fax (01753) 591369
Hours Mon–Fri 9–6, Sat 9–2.
Cards Amex, MasterCard, Visa.
Delivery Free anywhere in UK 1 case or over.
M T
Well, guess what this one sells. Yes, Australia all the way. It's not the definitive range of Aussie wines, and you won't find everything here, but you will find a very good list. There's Tim Adams, St Hallett, Henschke, Penley Estate, De Bortoli, Chapel Hill and Bowen Estate and lots more. The range of wines submitted for our Best Buys tasting was superb and scooped the two top slots.
1994 Heritage Cabernet Franc, Clare Valley, £7.99 An Australian rarity.

AVERYS OF BRISTOL (AV)
Orchard House, Southfield Road, Nailsea, Bristol BS19 1JD (01275) 811100, fax (01275) 811101
Hours Shop: 8 Park St, Bristol: Mon–Sat 10–6; Wine Cellar: Culver St: Mon–Sat 9–7.
Cards MasterCard, Visa.
Discounts Monthly mail order offers, Bin Club 10% off most list prices.
Delivery Free local area or 2 or more cases, otherwise £5.50 per consignment.
C EP G M T
One of the few merchants still to have a strong list of fine German wines, Averys was also a pioneer of the New World, and was crying the virtues of Australia and California when others were still saying 'What? Who?' So this is a merchant that manages to be both traditional and go-ahead, and do both very well. France, particularly Bordeaux, is good, and there is Inniskillin from Canada, Enate from Spain and Hamilton Russell from South Africa.

1993 Pinot Noir, Knudsen-Erath, £10.48 One of the best Pinot Noirs in Oregon.

1994 Tyrrells Vat 1 Semillon, £14.18 Classic unoaked Semillon from Australia that really should be put away for a decade.

1990 Ockfener Bockstein Riesling Spätlese, Dr Fischer, £8.95 And I'd put this wonderful Mosel Riesling away for a few years yet, too.

ADAM BANCROFT (BAN)

57 South Lambeth Road, London SW8 1RJ, 0171-793 1902, fax 0171-793 1897
Hours Mon–Fri 9–6.
Cards MasterCard, Visa.
Discounts Negotiable.
Delivery Outside London, 3 cases or over free; 2 cases £8.50, 1 case £6.50
Minimum order 1 mixed case.

France is at the heart of this mail-order-only list, with good stuff from the Loire, Rhône and South in particular. From Burgundy there is an encouraging number of basic Bourgognes at affordable prices from good names like Chopin-Groffier and Maréchal Jacquet, and from south-west France there are good summer wines like Corbières Gris de Gris, and serious reds like Jean-Luc Colombo's Côtes du Roussillon. Italy is good, too, and the Australia and New Zealand sections are short but include top wines like Howard Park's Cabernet.

1995 Jurançon Sec, Domaine Castera, £6.99 Quirky flavours from south-west France.

BENEDICT'S

28 Holyrood St, Newport, Isle of Wight PO30 5AU, (01983) 529596
Hours Mon–Sat 9–5.30.
Cards Amex, MasterCard, Visa.
Discounts 5% on a case.
Delivery Free on Island.
G

An attractive list that doesn't reveal any particular passion for a single region but which can produce something pretty interesting from most places. Burgundies are largely from Drouhin and Bouchard Père, and from Italy there are more whites than reds, which is unusual. There's a good selection of wines from the Isle of Wight, too, including one from Barton Manor called Lillie Langtry's Loving Cup. I dread to think.

Crémant d'Alsace Cuvée Julien, Dopff au Moulin, £9.45 A chance to taste Alsace's sparkling wine, not often seen here these days.

Henriques & Henriques 10 year old Verdelho, £16.55 Excellent, characterful off-dry Madeira from a leading producer.

BENNETTS (BEN)

High Street, Chipping Campden, Glos GL55 6AG, 24-hr tel & fax (01386) 840392
Hours Mon–Fri 10–1 & 2–6, Sat 9–6.
Cards MasterCard, Switch, Visa.
Discounts On collected orders only.
Delivery Free 3 cases or more, England and Wales.
Minimum order 1 case.
EP G M T

A wide-ranging list that dares to be honest: 'As a general rule we are steering clear of '93, '92 and '91 clarets' says Bennetts: 'there's better stuff from outside Bordeaux.' Quite right. Palmer 1983 is 'probably not worth the price it is commanding now' it says, before going on to list it at £106.50. How refreshing. The emphasis here is on fine wine, and

prices are not the lowest, though the list ranges so widely and so thoroughly (and so carefully) that if you popped in for a quick bottle to go with supper you could be sure it would be good. For example: Domaine Drouhin from Oregon or Chapoutier from the Rhône don't count as particularly adventurous any more – though they are super – but Zinfandel from Arizona? Now that's new.

1993 Buena Suerte Zinfandel, Callaghan Vineyards, Arizona, £16.60 Well, Zinfandel likes heat…

1994 Duas Quintas Tinto, £6.40 Wonderful quality Portuguese red.

BERRY BROS. & RUDD (BER)

3 St James's St, London SW1A 1EG, 0171-396 9600, fax 0171-396 9611;
Berry's Wine Warehouse, Hamilton Close, Houndmills, Basingstoke, Hants RG21 2YB, (01256) 323566, fax (01256) 340106;
Terminal 3 Departures, Heathrow Airport, TW6 1JH, 0181-564 8361/3, fax 0181-564 8379
Hours St James's St: Mon–Fri 9–5.30; Berry's Wine Warehouse: Mon–Thurs 10–5.30, Fri 10–8, Sat 10–4; Terminal 3 Duty Free: Daily 6am–10pm.
Cards Amex, Diners, MasterCard, Switch, Visa.
Discounts 3–7.5% according to quantity.
Delivery Free for orders of £100 or more
C EP G M T
Coming this year is another duty-free shop at Heathrow's Terminal 4, but don't rely on either duty-free shop having what you want: ring in advance and order your wines for collection. And what should you order? Well, there's a classically good range of Bordeaux, Burgundy and Rhônes (names like Etienne Sauzet and Ch. de Beaucastel), and an increasingly good list of French country wines, with lots of new names appearing. Germany, Italy and the New World all look excellent: Berry Bros has been remarkably successful in updating its list in recent years. And of course for anyone travelling from Heathrow there's a far, far better range of spirits than you'll see in the standard duty-free shop: vintage malt whiskies and Cognacs make far better presents for one's hosts than a teddy bear wearing a policeman's helmet, I find.

1995 Quinta de Pedralvites, Bairrada, £6.45 Good aromatic Portuguese white.

1995 Vom Stein Federspiel, Nicolaihof, £16.50 Yes, it's expensive, but Nicolaihof makes wonderfully complex wines in Austria's Wachau.

BIBENDUM (BIB)

113 Regents Park Rd, London NW1 8UR, 0171-916 7706, fax 0171-916 7705
Hours Mon–Thur 10–6.30, Fri 10–8, Sat 9.30–5.
Cards Amex, MasterCard, Switch, Visa.
Delivery Free mainland England and Wales, £10 per consignment Scotland.
Minimum order 1 mixed case.
C EP G M T
Bibendum manages to cover both ends of the spectrum: there's a fine wine list (and a broking business) for those with serious bank balances, and the normal list for the rest of us. The fine wine list is – well, fine; the normal list explores nooks and crannies of the wine world, finding exciting growers in Béarn, Côtes de Castillon and Baja California (Mexico to you and me), as well as New World superstars like Chalone. And if you want to cheer yourself up on a rainy Monday, visit the shop.

Chardonnay Brut, Méthode Traditionelle, Charnay, £7.85 Excellent value Champagne lookalike from Mâcon.

1996 Pinot Noir, Bouchard Finlayson, £9.95 South African Pinot Noir of world-class quality.

BOOTHS (BO)

4 Fishergate, Preston PR1 3LJ, (01772) 251701, fax (01772) 204316
Hours Office: Mon–Fri 9–5; shop hours vary.
Cards MasterCard, Switch, Visa.
Discounts 5% any 6 bottles; 15% on wine orders of £150 or more. **G T**
The standard range here is exactly that, but there are also plenty of extremely good wines. If you don't want to lash out on Joseph Drouhin's Corton-Charlemagne 1989 at £40.95 you might think about Alquier's Faugères at £6.99 or Lustau's Manzanilla Pasada sherry at £8.29 per half. But yes, you have to pick your branch.

> *Recommended wines are a selection from the merchants' lists; for Oz's Best Buys see page 12.*

1994 Chablis Vieilles Vignes, Defaix, £10.99
This Chablis is never cheap, but it's worth it.
1993 Warwick Estate Cabernet Franc, £7.69
Classy red from a South African red specialist.

BORDEAUX DIRECT (BOD)

New Aquitaine House, Paddock Rd, Reading,
Berks RG4 5JY, 0118-948 1718, fax 0118-946
1493
Hours Mon–Fri 9–5.30 (Thur until 8), Sat 9–6;
24-hr answerphone;
Mail order: Mon–Fri 9–7, Sat–Sun 10–4.
Cards Amex, Diners, MasterCard, Switch, Visa.
Discounts Special offers.
Delivery £3.99 per order.
G C EP M T
*If you always wish you could trundle round wine
regions yourself making your own discoveries rather
than going by the recommendations in the papers,
then this is the company for you. The idea is that
Bordeaux Direct has done the trundling for you,
found the unknown producers with (sometimes)
brilliant wines and will now deliver them to you.
Quality and value are generally good, and the
emphasis is increasingly on fine wines. This is the
sister company to the Sunday Times Wine Club.*
Crémant de Loire Rosé, Cave des Vignerons
de Saumur, £9.70 Good dry summer fizz.

BOTTOMS UP (BOT)

(Head office) Sefton House, 42 Church Rd,
Welwyn Garden City, Herts AL8 6PJ, (01707)
328244, fax (01707) 371398
Hours Mon–Sat 9–10, Sun 12–3 & 7–10.
Cards Amex, MasterCard, Switch, Visa.
Discounts 10% mixed cases wine, 17.5%
mixed cases Champagne.
Delivery Free locally (all shops). National
delivery via Drinks Direct. **G T**
See Thresher.

BUTE WINES (BUT)

2 Cottesmore Gardens, London W8 5PR, 0171-
937 1629, fax 0171-361 0061
Delivery £9 for 1 case, £13 for 2, £15.60 for 3,
£18 for 4, £20 for 5.
Minimum order 1 case. **EP M**
*The Bute list is almost entirely of fine wines, with just
enough everyday ones to give its customers*

*something to drink in front of the telly. Interestingly,
it seems to have cornered the market in the
Massandra wines: there was a big sale at Sotheby's
some years ago of old wines from the Massandra
cellars in the Crimea. Most were sweet and fortified,
and many were pre-Revolutionary. Bute Wines is
now one of the few places where you can buy a
1914 'Malaga' from Massandra, for £235.*
1988 Carruades de Lafite, £13.70 This claret
looks like rather a good buy.

BUTLERS WINE CELLAR (BU)

247 Queens Park Rd, Brighton BN2 2XJ,
(01273) 698724, fax (01273) 622761
Hours Tue–Wed 10–6, Thu–Fri 10–7, Sat 10–7.
Cards Amex, MasterCard, Switch, Visa.
Delivery Free locally 1 case or more, free
mainland England and Wales, some parts of
Scotland 3 or more cases; ring for further details.
G M T
*Okay, get this. Snow Wine from Varna, Bulgaria. It's
made from Ugni Blanc 'picked during the first
winter snows'. Bulgarian Eiswein, I suppose, and a
mere £3.75 a bottle. Wierd or what? That's what I
like about Butlers: this list comes in, and it starts off
with nice standard reds and whites, and then
suddenly it throws something at you that you've
never heard of. There are old vintages, too, if you're
searching for a particular year as a present: a bottle
of Château Trotanoy 1977 at £32.50 for a
deserving 21-year-old-to-be, perhaps? There are
lots of bin-ends, so it pays to be on the mailing list.*
1992 Arneis Passito, Bric Tupin, Deltetto,
£7.75 half bottle Sweet white from Piedmont.

ANTHONY BYRNE (BY)

Ramsey Business Park, Stocking Fen Rd, Ramsey,
Cambs PE17 1UR, (01487) 814555, fax (01487)
814962
Hours Mon–Fri 9–5.30.
Cards MasterCard, Visa.
Discounts available on cases.
Delivery Free 5 cases or more, or orders of
£250 or more; otherwise £6.
C M T
*There are 12 pages of Alsace wines from Zind-
Humbrecht in this A4 list. Yes, that's right, 12
pages. Then we go on to other producers. That
gives you an idea of the depth of the range here.*

Admittedly, Anthony Byrne has been shipping Zind-Humbrecht since before the Flood, but it's still an awful lot of different wines. Every other country and region is well represented with good names – such as Alain Bromont in Madiran – and that adds up to a first-class list.

1994 Admiral's Red, Palliser Bay, New Zealand, £7.98 I do love wacky New World blends – this one's Pinot Noir and Cabernet.

1994 Côtes du Rhône Blanc, Guigal, £6.10 You often see the excellent red, but this white is a much rarer bird.

CAPE PROVINCE WINES (CAP)

77 Laleham Rd, Staines, Middx TW18 2EA, (01784) 451860/455244, fax (01784) 469267
Hours Mon–Sat 9–5.30.
Cards MasterCard, Switch, Visa.
Delivery £6.50 locally and London, UK mainland varies with quantity.
Minimum order 6 bottles.
M T
If you want South African wines, this is your place. The list is not comprehensive – some of the best names, like Warwick Farm or Hamilton Russell, aren't here. But it does have a wide range of Shiraz, for example, that it can be hard to find elsewhere.
Simonsig Chenin Blanc, £4.80 Good straightforward everyday drinking.

CHÂTEAUX WINES (CHA)

Paddock House, Upper Tockington Rd, Tockington, Bristol BS12 4LQ, tel & fax (01454) 613959
Hours Mon–Fri 9–5.30, Sat 9–12.30.
Cards MasterCard, Switch, Visa.
Discounts Negotiable.
Delivery Free UK mainland 2 cases or £120 (inc vat) in value.
Minimum order 1 case (unmixed).
C EP M T
Small mail order French specialist with a nice list of clarets at quite attractive prices. New this year are a

> **Webster's** *is an annual publication. We welcome your suggestions for next year – see page 463.*

couple of vins de pays. Champagne is from Laurent-Perrier, and from outside France there are several vintages of Chateau Musar.

1990 Château Cheret-Pitres, Graves, £10.00 A good price for a claret of a good year.

CONNOLLY'S WINE MERCHANTS

Arch 13, 220 Livery Street, Birmingham B3 1EU, 0121-236 9269/3837, fax 0121-233 2339
Hours Mon–Fri 9–5.30, Sat 9.30–variable closing times; ring to check.
Cards Amex, MasterCard, Switch, Visa.
Delivery Surcharge outside Birmingham area.
Discounts By agreement.
G EP M T
It's worth being a cash and carry customer here: you buy by the case, pay by cash, cheque or debit card, load up the car and take a good discount home with you. Bought that way, Domaine des Baumard's Savennières, Clos du Papillon 1993, comes down to £8.96 from £9.95, and Grant Burge's Shiraz comes down to £8.50 from £9.45. This is also the sort of list from which one would be happy to buy all sorts of cases: Burgundy (René Engel), the Loire, the Rhône and California (Frog's Leap) look particularly interesting. I especially like Connolly's explanation of biodynamism, as practised by Rhône estate Chapoutier: 'following the phases of the moon and not taking aspirin if you have a headache appear to be the principal tenets of their philosphy'.
1992 Cabernet Sauvignon, Rutherford, Beaulieu Vineyards, £8.49 Classy Napa Cabernet. Californians pronounce Beaulieu 'Bolio.' Yes, I know it's wrong, but there's no telling them.

CORNEY & BARROW (CB)

(Head office)12 Helmet Row, London EC1V 3QJ, 0171-251 4051;
194 Kensington Park Rd, London W11, 0171-221 5122;
31 Rutland Sq, Edinburgh EH1 2BW, 0131-228 2233;
Belvoir House, High St, Newmarket CB8 8OH, (01638) 662068;
Corney & Barrow (Scotland) with Whighams of Ayr, 8 Academy Street, Ayr KA7 1HT, (01292) 267000

Hours Mon–Fri 9–6 (24-hr answerphone); Kensington Pk Rd: Mon–Sat 10.30–8; Newmarket: Mon–Sat 9–6; Ayr: Mon–Sat 9.30–5.30.
Cards Amex, MasterCard, Visa.
Delivery Free 2 or more cases within M25 boundary, elsewhere free 3 or more cases. Otherwise £8 + VAT per delivery.
C EP M T
Okay, we're in cult country here. Corney & Barrow may have royal warrant upon royal warrant, but it can bandy marketingspeak with the best of them, and it has a very sharp eye indeed for the Next Big Thing. This was the company, don't forget, that signed up Pétrus when nobody else had heard of it. So: look out for a Ribero del Duero called Dominio de Pingus. C&B showed it to American wine critic Robert Parker over dinner, and Parker acclaimed it as the most exciting young wine he'd ever tasted. Result: it's already sold out in the Far East and in the UK. The standard wine from the same producer, Hacienda Monasterio, costs £11.95, and is described by C&B as 'desperately drinkable'. So there you go. There are plenty of other wonderful wines here too, from Pétrus down, including Dom.

Joseph Roty from Burgundy and Castello di Rampolla from Tuscany, but, encouragingly, there are plenty of well-priced everyday wines too – lots of temptation, in fact. Corney & Barrow's stock details and prices were not available in time to be included in our Price Guides this year, but have a look at these:
1993 Notre Dame de Landiras, £7.29 Excellent value white Bordeaux from a producer, Peter Vinding-Diers, who has been at the forefront of the improvements in the region.
1994 Roccolo di Mizzole Valpolicella Classico Superiore, Cecilia Beretta, £7.76 A lot of money for Válpolicella? Not a bit of it: this is proper Valpol.
1990 Château la Grave, Fronsac, £11.99 Look outside the classic regions of Bordeaux and you can find gems like this.

COUNTRY WINE MERCHANT LTD (COU)

The Ox House, Market Place, Northleach, Cheltenham, Glos GL54 3EG, (01451) 860680, fax (01451) 861166;
Hours Shop: Mon 10–5; shop & wine bar: Tues–Sat 10am–11pm.
Cards Amex, MasterCard, Switch, Visa.
Discounts In bond and ex-cellar terms available.
Delivery Free locally 1 case, elsewhere on UK mainland free 3 cases, otherwise £8.81 per consignment.
C EP G M T
Good news – Mark Savage is back. That, for those who remember his previous company Windrush Wines, means a knowledgeable, considered list of wines you might never have heard of – but if you haven't, it's time you did. Start with his offerings from the Côtes du Frontonnais, or the Languedoc, or Austria, or Soave, or Jerez.
1979 Tokaji Aszú 4 Puttonyos, Slovenske Nove Mesto, £7.70 50cl Tokaji from Slovakia, not Hungary – which means it's from the bit of the Tokaj vineyard that just slips across the border. The Slovaks used to lease it back to Hungary, so this wine is a real novelty.
1995 Eyrie Vineyards Pinot Noir, £13.61 Good to see this top Oregon Pinot being shipped to the UK again.

CROQUE-EN-BOUCHE (CRO)

221 Wells Road, Malvern Wells, Worcestershire WR14 4HF, (01684) 565612

Hours No fixed hours; open by telephone appointment 7 days a week.

Cards MasterCard, Visa.

Discounts 4% on 48 or more bottles, if cash and collected; 2.5% if paid by credit card.

Delivery Free locally or for orders over £280; otherwise £8.50.

Minimum order 1 case.

M T

Croque-en-Bouche sells more wine from the Rhône than from any other single region, and that's true of both the restaurant and the retail side. And it is indeed a tremendous list. There's Chave, Rayas and, if you happen to have £120 to spare, Châteauneuf-du-Pape from Beaucastel back to 1967; or you can have Coudoulet de Beaucastel 1990 for £8.90. This, pricewise, is roughly the range of the list. There's not a great deal under £8 and quite a lot at considerably more; but then there is a high proportion of wines from mature vintages here, even from Australia, and these are pretty rare. £11.50 for Cape Mentelle Cabernet 1988 isn't overpricing; nor is £36 for Lindemans Limestone Ridge 1978. The list is stuffed with oddities you won't find elsewhere.

1974 Colares, Comp. Réal Vinicola, £12.00 Real old-style Portuguese red from ungrafted vines, and not a flying winemaker in sight.

1973 Vouvray Clos Naudin, Foreau, £19.00 Off-dry Vouvray lasts and lasts and lasts. This should be superb.

1986 Recioto della Valpolicella Classico Amarone, Zenato, £14.50 Wonderful smoky cherry flavours.

CWS (CO)

(Head office) New Century House, Manchester M60 4ES, 0161-834 1212, fax 0161-827 5117

Hours Variable.

Cards Variable.

For CWS read the Co-op. And lucky you if you have a big one near you: you can treat yourself to Weinert Malbec and Etchart Cafayate Torrontes from Argentina, Bouvier Trockenbeerenauslese from Austria and Château Cissac 1986 from Bordeaux. No, these wines don't apply to the run-of-the-mill Co-ops, but the list in its full glory is remarkably innovative.

Gaierhof Teroldego Rotaliano, £4.49; Cortese Alto Monferrato, Araldica, £3.99 The first is in 69 stores, the second in only 27 – but well done to the Co-op for listing unusual Italians.

DIRECT WINE (DI)

5–7 Corporation Square, Belfast, Northern Ireland BT1 3AJ, (01232) 243906, fax (01232) 240202

Hours Mon–Fri 9–6.30 (Thurs till 8), Sat 9.30–5.

Cards MasterCard, Switch, Visa.

Discounts 10% in the form of complimentary wine with each mixed or unmixed case.

Delivery Free Northern Ireland 1 case or more.

C EP G M T

An ever-improving list that is now so good it's difficult to see where it will go next. The New World has been jazzed up a lot and the range is strong just about everywhere else, too. California looks particularly good, with names like Caymus and Sonoma Cutrer, but look too at the Loire (Nicolas Joly, Charles Joguet), Burgundy (Faiveley, Dujac) and the Rhône (Chapoutier, Château Rayas).

1995 Henschke Julius Riesling, £10.99 One of the best Rieslings in Australia; put it away for a few years.

DOMAINE DIRECT (DOM)

29 Wilmington Square, London WC1X 0EG, 0171-837 1142, fax 0171-837 8605

Hours 8.30–5.30; or answering machine.

Cards Mastercard, Visa.

Delivery Free London; elsewhere in UK mainland 1 case £8.81, 2–3 cases £11.75, 4 free.

Minimum order 1 mixed case.

EP M

Now, don't confuse Domaine Direct with Bordeaux Direct, or indeed with Direct Wine. This is a mail-order-only outfit offering very serious Burgundies (Etienne Sauzet, Tollot-Beaut, Alain Michelot, Denis Mortet, Domaine G Roumier, R Dauvissat...) at prices that look as fair as anything else in this hugely expensive region. But if you haven't got your spending boots on don't worry: the Domaine Direct world extends far beyond Burgundy.

1994 Fay McKenzie Noble Late Harvest Riesling, South Australia, £5.82 half bottle
Luscious, well-balanced pudding wine.

1990 Château Rondillon, Loupiac, £11.69 No, I don't know this château either – but 1990 was a year in which the lesser sweet wine regions of Bordeaux had to be very incompetent indeed to make poor wine.

ELDRIDGE, POPE & CO (EL)

(Head office) Weymouth Ave, Dorchester, Dorset DT1 1QT, (01305) 251251; Mail order: (01305) 258347, fax (01305) 258155
Hours Mon–Sat 9–5.30.
Cards Amex, MasterCard, Visa.
Discounts On application.
Delivery Free to one address for 5 cases or more, or orders exceeding £225 in value; otherwise £6 per case UK mainland except Scottish Highlands.
C G M T
Eldridge Pope seems to be making enormous efforts to find good and interesting wines at reasonable prices – not an easy combination at the moment. There are a lot from the New World, including some gems like Grgich Hills Zinfandel, but also well-chosen numbers from Spain, Germany, Alsace, the Rhône... Without doing an actual count, I'd guess that the bulk of the list is under £10, with some quite serious stuff between £10 and £20. Oh, and in case you'd been searching high and low for wines from Luxembourg, here they are: sparkling wines from Bernard Massard, who is apparently 'supplier to the Royal Court of Luxembourg'. Now there's posh.

1996 Neethlingshof Gewürztraminer, £7.49
This unusual South African wine is off-dry stuff.
1994 Lar de Barros Tempranillo, Bodegas Inviosa, £4.75 Good value, juicy red from Extremadura in Spain.

BEN ELLIS WINES (ELL)

Brockham Wine Cellars, Wheelers Lane, Brockham, Surrey RH3 7HJ, (01737) 842160, fax (01737) 843210
Hours Mon–Fri 9–6, Sat 9.30–1.
Cards MasterCard, Visa.
Delivery Free 1 case Surrey and Surrey borders and Central London, elsewhere free 5 cases or orders over £350, other orders £10 most of UK, otherwise at cost.
Minimum order 1 mixed case.
C G M T
'The long-awaited return of interest in fine German wines is flickering into life,' says Ben Ellis. Well, steady on there, chaps. Let's not get too excited here. What happens when wines get popular? The prices go up, that's what happens. And then I can't afford them. So why don't I point you towards, um, Ben Ellis's splendid clarets? Or his splendid Italians, such as Aldo Conterno's Gran Bussia Barolo? Or, perhaps, his splendid Australians? Knappstein Riesling, for example. Now, there's a wine. Cheap, too: a mere £6.76. It's a terrific list, honest. Just leave those German wines to me, all right?

BY APPOINTMENT TO
HER MAJESTY QUEEN ELIZABETH
THE QUEEN MOTHER
WINE MERCHANTS
ELDRIDGE POPE & CO p.l.c.

ELDRIDGE POPE
FINE WINE SHIPPERS SINCE 1833

Please ask for a copy of our wine list,
featuring over 900 wines,
&
"En-Primeur" offers;

BORDEAUX
Pétrus, Valandraud, Lafite, Margaux...

RHONE
Beaucastel, La Chapelle, Chapoutier...

BURGUNDY
de Vogüé, Rousseau, Girardin...

also
Domaine de la Romanée Conti

for regular special offers and wine list
please contact our Mail Order office;

Tel: 01305 258347   Fax: 01305 258155
Eldridge Pope & Co.,
Weymouth Avenue, Dorchester, Dorset DT1 1QT

1995 Château de Castelneau Sémillon Vieilles Vignes, Entre-Deux-Mers, £8.91 Mind you, I don't want Semillon getting too fashionable, either…

FARR VINTNERS (FA)
19 Sussex St, London SW1V 4RR, 0171-821 2000, fax 0171-821 2020
Hours Mon–Fri 10–6.
Cards MasterCard, Switch, Visa.
Discounts Orders over £2000.
Delivery £8.50 London; (per case) £3.75 Home Counties, minimum £11.25; £3.85 rest of England and Wales, minimum £11.55; £5.80 Scotland, minimum £17.40 or give 48 hours notice of collection.
Minimum order £500 plus vat.
C EP M T
Serious wines for serious spenders. Farr Vintners is Mecca for investors and collectors – and when you're in that sort of market, a £500 minimum order is neither here nor there. The range is excellent, and since Farr is a broker it changes rapidly. Prices are actually remarkably good, and the wines range from Bordeaux and Burgundy through the Rhône, Champagne and port to the best of Alsace, New Zealand, Australia and South Africa. Don't be nervous of trying them: they're very informal.
1991 Chassagne Caillerets, Domaine Jean-Noël Gagnard, £23.50 Benchmark white Burgundy.

FINE WINES OF NEW ZEALAND (FIZ)
PO Box 476, London NW5 2NZ, 0171-482 0093, fax 0171-267 8400
Hours Mon–Sat 9–5.
Cards MasterCard, Visa.
Discounts 2 or more cases.
Delivery £9 mixed case except special offers.
Minimum order 1 mixed case.
M T
New Zealander Margaret Harvey MW was importing the wines of her homeland long before most people got in on the act – and it was she who introduced many of its top names. These days she even has her own label, Aotea, and you'll find Vidal, Rippon, Mark Rattray, Te Motu and Hunter's.
1995 Mark Rattray Pinot Noir £10.00 Top NZ Pinot, bursting with fruit.

LE FLEMING WINES (FLE)

9 Longcroft Avenue, Harpenden, Hertfordshire
AL5 2RB, (01582) 760125
Hours 24-hour answering machine.
Discounts 5% on large orders.
Delivery Free locally.
Minimum order 1 case.
EP G M T

An attractive list in which France gets most of the attention, followed by names like Cullen and Rockford from Australia. Europe outside France gets pretty short shrift, although there's a sprinkling of excellent names like Ascheri and Villa di Capezzana from Italy, and Ochoa from Spain.
1993 Pikes Riesling, Clare Valley, £6.34;
1995 Rockford Eden Valley Riesling, Barossa
Valley, £7.70 Compare and contrast these two top Aussie Rieslings.

FORTH WINES LTD (FOR)

Crawford Place, Milnathort, Kinross-shire
KY13 7XF, (01577) 862513, fax (01577)
865296
Hours Mon–Fri 9–5.30.
Cards MasterCard, Switch, Visa.
Delivery Free 3 or more cases.
Minimum order 1 case.
M T

Clarets are very good here, at both ends of the range; French country wines are also excellent. Forth ships the Austrian wines of Lenz Moser, so has the full range: the Blaufränkisch, for example, or a 1976 Trockenbeerenauslese, or, at the cheaper end, a 1996 Grüner Veltliner.
1996 Lenz Moser Prestige Grüner Veltliner,
£2.40 Classic light, bayleaf-scented wine for immediate drinking.
1991 Terra Franca, Bairrada, £4.80 Seductive new wave Portuguese red.

FULLER'S (FUL)

Head office: Griffin Brewery, Chiswick Lane
South, Chiswick W4 2QB, 0181-996 2000, fax
0181-996 2087
Hours Mon–Sat 10–10, Sun 11–10.
Cards MasterCard, Switch, Visa.
Discounts 1 bottle free with every case and 10% on selected unmixed cases.
Delivery Free locally. **G T**

We haven't yet got to the point where house prices rise if there's a good wine merchant round the corner, but if that ever happens people near a branch of Fuller's will be quids in. It's a remarkably adventurous chain that focuses on good value and good quality – which is not at all the same thing as merely selling cheap wine. Clarets and Burgundies look good, but what I'd come here for is the Rhône and Australia, both of which are bursting with my sort of flavours.
1994 Grant Burge Old Vine (Black Monster)
Shiraz, £8.99 How can I resist a wine called Black Monster? Especially when it comes from the Barossa Valley, and from a grower like Grant Burge.
1992 St-Joseph, Jean-Luc Colombo, £8.99 Rich, spicy Syrah from the northern Rhône.

GALLERY WINES (GAL)

Gomshall Cellars, The Gallery, Gomshall, Surrey
GU5 9LB, (01483) 203795, fax (01483) 203282
Hours Mon–Sat 10–5.30.
Cards MasterCard, Switch, Visa.
Discounts Wine Club members get 5% on all purchases and 10% on monthly offers.
Delivery Free 2 or more cases within local area, otherwise £7.50 for 1 case, £3.00 each additional case.
Minimum order 1 bottle.
C G M T

An entirely French list, with a handful of ports, sherries and Spanish table wines tacked on to the end. The main focus is the classic areas of France: there are a few country wines, but the list's heart is in Bordeaux and Burgundy. The latter is now from Domaines Parent and AF Gros, which is a huge improvement.
Bourgogne Pinot Noir, Domaine Parent, £7.50
Good price, good wine.
Château Cissac 1989, £13.90 A pretty good price for this classic claret.

C = *cellarage,* ***EP*** = *en primeur offers,* ***G*** = *glass hire/loan,* ***M*** = *mail order,* ***T*** = *tastings and talks.*

A LITTLE INSIDE INFORMATION...

Not so many years ago, the subject of wine was an area which many people avoided. Having little or no knowledge of wine, they mistakenly believed it to be far too complex. Of course, the situation has changed considerably since then, partly thanks to guides such as this one.

But, to many people, Scotch whisky is equally as daunting and as complicated as wine used to be. Faced with a shelf full of unfamiliar names, many will opt for a well-advertised brand simply because of the reassurance that advertising provides. However, as readers of this book well know, the exploration of an unknown field can be intensely rewarding. And as far as Scotch whisky goes, a little rudimentary knowledge goes a long way.

Malt whisky is a subject which has been dissected in hundreds of books and there are always a few tomes in any bookshop. Most are good quality and easy to understand. However, blended whisky is considerably more popular than malt whisky but has yet to receive the same amount of attention.

Although there are considerably more varieties of blended whisky than there are malts, choosing a quality blend is not quite as complicated as it looks.

The art of blending whisky originated in about 1865, when it was discovered that blending malt whisky with its lighter counterpart, grain whisky, resulted in a much lighter spirit. It had all the benefits of its constituent parts but none of the heaviness that some people found off-putting. It was this development that launched what is now the world's number one spirit.

However, as with any boom industry, unscrupulous traders sought to exploit it. Without any legal standardisation, 'blended whiskies' were appearing which were no more than ethyl alcohol with colour added. A famous one in particular was known as N.S.S., popularly translated as 'Never Seen Scotland'!

Thankfully, the definition of Scotch whisky is now legally enshrined. Leaving aside the technical jargon, it is spirit that has been distilled in Scotland from a mash of cereals (either malted barley or grain), and matured in Scotland in oak casks for a minimum of three years. Once bottled for consumption, its strength can be no less than 40% alc./vol.

If you have ever visited a distillery and seen freshly distilled spirit coming off the still, you will have noted that it is the same colour as vodka. It is only after the mandatory three years mellowing in oak casks that it loses some of the harshness of new spirit and takes on the colour of whisky as we know it. However, few malt distillers would consider their product ready for drinking at three years of age, even though it is legally Scotch whisky. A quick look at any supermarket shelf will show that most will wait up to eight, ten or sixteen years, or even longer; the maturation period will vary from malt to malt. What you can be certain of is that the distiller will have matured his malt for as long as it takes to reach perfection.

The question of age for blend drinkers is a little more complex. In addition to the grain which lightens it, a blend can contain anything from ten to thirty different malts. But what is not divulged is the age of these malts. Theoretically, they could all be the legal minimum of three years old. The question is, how do you know? The simple answer is you don't – unless there is an age statement on the label, e.g. 8 years old, etc.

Yet, with up to thirty or more whiskies in the blend, what does the age statement on the label actually mean? Quite simply, it is the age of the *youngest* whisky in the blend. The number of malts doesn't matter, nor does the average age. It is only the youngest whisky that is relevant, as this tells you the *minimum* maturity the blender considered suitable for his blend.

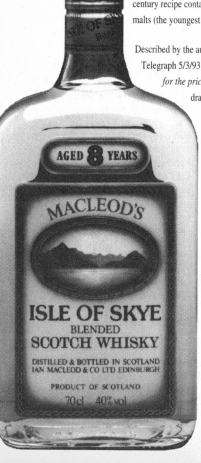

Now that we've established a few relevant whisky facts, here's the advert. We'd like to introduce you to Isle of Skye 8-Year-Old Blend, a 19th century recipe containing a high proportion of mature Island and Speyside malts (the youngest of which you will now realise is 8 years old).

Described by the author of the book as "...extremely good..." (Daily Telegraph 5/3/93), Isle of Skye is available in the stockists listed below *for the price of an ordinary blend*. So if your preference is a dram with the elegance and harmony that only maturity can bestow – you know now what to ask for. Unless, of course, you prefer something a little younger. In which case, you have plenty of choice.

...FOR THOSE IN THE KNOW!

———— STOCKISTS ————

UK	SCOTLAND
Savacentre	Asda
Major Sainsbury's	Tesco
Major Budgen's	Victoria Wine
Stewarts Wine Barrel	Haddows
	Scotmid
	Selected Threshers
	Selected Co-ops

and independent stockists
throughout the country

**Ian Macleod & Co 01506 852205
e-mail Ian.Macleod@btinternet.com.**

GAUNTLEYS (GAU)

4 High St, Exchange Arcade, Nottingham NG1 2ET, (01159) 417973, fax (01159) 509519
Hours Mon–Sat 9–5.30.
Cards MasterCard, Switch, Visa.
Delivery Free within Nottingham area, otherwise £6.50 per case + VAT.
Minimum order 1 case.
C EP (not Bordeaux) **G M T**

If I were filling my cellar from Gauntleys, what sort of cellar would it be? Well, for a start it would be mainly French: short on Bordeaux but longer on Burgundy, with names like Michel Lafarge, Patrice Rion and Domaine Rousseau. Daniel Defaix Chablis, too: I'd have some of that. Lots of Rhônes – ten red Hermitages – and oodles of wonderful French country wines, kicking off with Trévallon and Tempier. Then, outside France: Grant Burge and Rockford from Australia, Angelo's Old Vine White from Joseph Swan of California and Warwick from South Africa. I think I'd better move to Nottingham.
1994 Faugères Domaine Alquier, £7.35 The best Faugères there is, full of complexity and spice.
1993 VHSR Zinfandel, Joseph Swan, £14.70 Big, bold Zin – I love it.

GELSTON CASTLE FINE WINES

Castle Douglas, Scotland DG7 1QE, (01556) 503012, fax (01556) 504183; James King, 45 Warwick Square, London SW1V 2AJ, 0171-821 6841, fax 0171-821 6350
Hours Mon–Fri 9–6.
Cards Visa.
Delivery Free within 25 miles of Castle Douglas 1 case or more, £7 rest of mainland UK, free for orders over £150.
Minimum order None, but mixed cases carry a surcharge of £3 per case.
C EP G M T

Parts of this list read like the weather forecast ('Off-dry, turning dry later', of a Rheingau Spätlese) but that's just an indication of how seriously Gelston

Castle takes its wine. The focuses are France and Germany (look for Loosen and Richter here), which are represented in depth; there is just a sprinkling of wine from Italy, Spain, Portugal, California, Argentina and South Africa, and nothing at all from Australia. So expect subtlety, a taste of terroir, all that sort of thing, rather than upfront fruit. Quality is exceedingly high, and while you don't have to spend more than a tenner if you don't want to, there's nothing under a fiver. Best buys at lower prices include a good range of French country wines. Stock details and prices were not available in time to be included in our Price Guides, but try...
1995 Ségura Carte Noire, La Clape, Domaine Rivière-le-Haut, £5.95 'gets wackier with age', says Gelston Castle. I can't wait.
1995 Sancerre Vieilles Vignes, Bailly-Reverdy, £11.25 My God, the price of Sancerre nowadays. But this promises well.

GOEDHUIS & CO (GOE)

6 Rudolf Place, Miles Street, London SW8 1RP, 0171-793 7900, fax 0171-793 7170
Hours Mon–Fri 9–6.30.
Cards MasterCard, Visa.
Delivery Free 3 or more cases in London, 5 or more cases UK mainland, otherwise £10.
Minimum order 1 case.
C EP G M T

Classic wines from classic regions are the preoccupation here. There were a handful of California wines listed at the last count, and a single Australian. That, plus Cloudy Bay from New Zealand, was the extent of wines from outside Europe. But if you want Bordeaux or Burgundy, including Carillon and Jadot, then you're in clover.
1990 Chambertin Clos-de-Bèze, Domaine Armand Rousseau, £83.23 If I start saving now...

GRAPE IDEAS (GRAP)

47 West Way, Botley, Oxford OX2 0JF, (01865) 263303, fax (01865) 791594
Hours Mon–Fri 10–7, Sat 10–6.
Cards MasterCard, Switch, Visa.
Discounts 5% on an unmixed case.
Delivery Usually free locally; 'competitive rates' elsewhere. **G**
A pretty good list, this, from the retail wing of wholesalers Stevens Garnier. Not outstanding, but

Explore the world of wine further with Oz Clarke's multimedia Wine Guide – see page 462 for details.

good. There are some appealing French country wines for around a fiver and some interesting Loires; Burgundies range from the not-too-expensive to the hugely expensive; Rhône looks better value. There are some nice Portuguese wines from Sogrape; Australia is a little unimaginative. Stock details and prices were not available in time to be included in our Price Guides, but this is one of my Best Buys:

1995 Chateau des Charmes Late Havest Riesling £6.95 half bottle Sweet wine from Canada.

THE GREAT NORTHERN WINE COMPANY (GN)

Granary Wharf, The Canal Basin, Leeds, Yorkshire LS1 4BR (01132) 461200, fax (01132) 461209;
The Warehouse, Blossomgate, Ripon, North Yorkshire HG4 2AJ tel & fax (01765) 606767
Hours Mon–Fri 9–6, Sat 9.30–5, Sun 11–4.30.
Cards Diners, MasterCard, Switch, Visa.
Discounts Wholesale price available for purchases of mixed or unmixed cases.
Delivery Free within van delivery area, elsewhere £3.53 per case, 5 cases or over free.
A chatty, exclamation-mark-strewn list! Do try this! says Great Northern. Or 'It is a revelation!' But luckily Great Northern is better at choosing wine than it is at writing, and just about every country is marked by some exciting wines. From Australia comes Mitchelton III, a delectable blend of Marsanne, Roussanne and Viognier; from California, Frog's Leap Zinfandel.

1993 Petite Sirah, LA Cetto, £5.39 Yes, I know it's not new, but I love this Mexican red.
1995 Primitivo del Tarantino, Perulli, £5.20 Primitivo is the grape periodically said to be the same as Zinfandel. Try it for yourself and see what you think.

GREAT WESTERN WINE

The Wine Warehouse, Wells Road, Bath (01225) 446009, fax (01225) 442139
Hours Mon–Fri 9–7, Sat 10–7.
Cards Amex, MasterCard, Switch, Visa.
Discounts Negotiable.
Delivery Free 3 or more cases, otherwise £6.50.
Minimum order 1 mixed case.
C EP G M T

No relation to the above company, but another list full of well-chosen wines that are often not available elsewhere. Bordeaux has a good range of lesser (i.e. affordable) clarets as well as some mature finer ones. The bulk of the list is generally under a tenner, in fact, which is encouraging in these days of ever-rising wine prices. Stock details and prices were not available in time to be included in our Price Guides this year, but make a start with these:

Crémant de Bourgogne Rosé, Domaine Denizot, £8.23 A good value substitute for pink Champagne, made from the same grapes.
1996 David Wynn Unoaked Shiraz, £6.99 Lovely smoky, berried fruit from Australia.
1996 Soave Classico, Pra, £6.99 Proper Soave, with some depth and some nice nutty fruit.

PETER GREEN & CO (GRE)

37a/b Warrender Park Road, Edinburgh EH9 1HJ, tel & fax 0131-229 5925
Hours Mon–Fri 9.30–6.30, Sat 9.30–7.
Cards MasterCard, Switch, Visa.
Discounts 5% on a case or two unmixed half-dozens.
Delivery 1 case £6; extra cases £4 each.
G M T
Now here's a novel way of helping customers distinguish between German wines from Grosslagen and German wines from Einzellagen. It's quite simple: you put a little 'e' in your list against Einzellagen wines and a 'g' against Grosslagen ones. Any other wine merchants want to pinch the idea? And indeed the list is good in other ways, too, not least for its brilliant wines. Classic regions are strong, and there are plenty of affordable clarets and even some affordable Burgundies. Italy is

excellent, with names like Isole e Olena, as is Spain, with Pesquera. Australia and New Zealand look classy, too.

1995 Morbisch Prestige Blaufränkisch, Lenz Moser, £7.99 Good rich, typical Austrian red.

Enate Cabernet Merlot, £5.99 Exciting red from Somontano, made by one of Spain's most go-ahead producers.

HALVES (HAL)

5 Long Lane Industrial Estate, Craven Arms, Shropshire SY7 8DU, (01588) 673040, fax (01588) 673020

Hours Mail order only: Mon–Fri 9–6.
Cards MasterCard, Switch, Visa.
Discounts Frequent mixed case offers.
Delivery Free to mainland UK 24 halves, otherwise £4.70; N Ireland £9.99.

C EP M T

There's something irresistible about half bottles; and Tim Jackson would no doubt prefer us not to try to resist them. He sells only half bottles (as you might have guessed), and an extraordinary list it is too: Alsace, Australia, Burgundy, vintage port, Chile, Champagne (of course), New Zealand... There are half bottle wine racks, too, if you're wondering what to do with these baby bottles once you've got them.

1993 St-Joseph, Alain Graillot £6.21 Top wine from a top maker.

1994 Errázuriz Cabernet Sauvignon, Chile £3.89 Soft and ripe and just enough for me.

ROGER HARRIS WINES (HAW)

Loke Farm, Weston Longville, Norfolk NR9 5LG, (01603) 880171, fax (01603) 880291
Hours Mon–Fri 9–5.

Cards Amex, MasterCard, Visa.
Delivery Free UK mainland, orders over £150.
Minimum order 1 mixed case.

M T

Beaujolais is Roger Harris's passion, and he has a marvellous list of wines from hand-picked growers in every appellation. If you've only ever tried the Beaujolais Nouveau from your local corner shop this list may well make you feel you've been missing out – as indeed you have. More recent additions to the Harris list are wines from Mâcon – mostly, he says, to have some whites – and some vins de pays, in order to be able to offer something cheaper than Beaujolais.

1995 Moulin-à-Vent, Domaine Lapierre, £7.95 1995 was a tremendous year in Beaujolais, and I'd tuck this away for a few years.

1995 Chiroubles, Alain Passot, £7.75 Lovely light and aromatic, perfect for drinking now.

JOHN HARVEY & SONS (HA)

12 Denmark St, Bristol BS1 5DQ, (01179) 275009, fax (01179) 275001
Hours Mon–Fri 10–6, Sat 10–1.
Cards Amex, Diners, MasterCard, Switch, Visa.
Delivery Free 4 cases or more UK mainland, no mixed cases.

C EP G M T

Is it my imagination, or has this list shrunk? Once we're through the Bordeaux (a pretty strong range) the regions and countries seem to flash past rather quickly. Just 11 French country wines; six from Germany; four from Spain; two from Portugal, excluding fortifieds; ten wines from the whole of Australia. I don't know. Doesn't seem all that many, does it? But Bordeaux looks good.

1990 Château Tourteau Chollet, Graves, £7.70
A good price for a mature lesser Graves from a
good year. It's drinking now.
1989 Château de la Chartreuse, Sauternes,
£16.75 It'll be a while before another run of good
years; buy Sauternes with some maturity now.

HAYNES HANSON & CLARK (HAH)

Sheep St, Stow-on-the-Wold, Glos GL54 1AA,
(01451) 870808, fax (01451) 870508;
25 Eccleston St, London SW1W 9NP, 0171-259
0102, fax 0171-259 0103
Hours Sheep St: Mon–Fri 9–6, Sat 9–5.30.
Eccleston St: Mon–Fri 9–7, Sat 10–6;
Cards MasterCard, Switch, Visa.
Discounts 10% unsplit case.
Delivery Free central London and Glos,
elsewhere free for 5 or more cases.
EP G M T
*This is Burgundy heaven, and a place where you will
get sound advice on this trickiest of all wines.
Lafarge and Roumier are just two of many great
names. But it's also very good for Bordeaux, the
Loire and most of France. Other countries are
covered with care and knowledge but in less depth.*
Champagne Pierre Vaudon Brut, £13.70 This is
HH&C's own label, and is astonishingly good. I'd
rather have this than many Grandes Marques.
1992 Volnay Premier Cru, Domaine Hubert de
Montille, £16.20 I'd drink Burgundy all the time,
if only I could afford it...

DOUGLAS HENN-MACRAE

81 Mackenders Lane, Eccles, Aylesford, Kent
ME20 7JA, (01622) 710952, fax (01622) 791203
Hours Mail order & tel only, Mon–Sat to 10pm.

Delivery Free UK mainland 10 cases, otherwise
£8 plus vat per order.
Minimum order 1 case. **M T**
*A German specialist with a few wines from the
USA's Pacific Northwest and Texas. The latter
includes 1987 Cabernet Sauvignon from Llano
Estacado and a 1988 Emerald Riesling from Fall
Creek. Henn-Macrae describes the latter as
'medium-bodied and medium-dry – a wine for
almost anyone, whether they ask for dry or sweet.'
Um. Well, maybe. The German wines are equally
esoteric, and include red Auslesen. Very much a list
for those who enjoy the wilder shores of German
wine-making. Details didn't arrive in time to be
included in our Price Guides, but have a look at:*
1988 Trittenheimer Altärchen Riesling
Spätlese, Weingut Hubertushof, £6.40 Classic
German wine from a good year, at a good price.
1993 Ahrweiler Daubhaus Spätburgunder
Auslese, Ahrwinzer, £10.52 I'm not saying I like
sweet reds from the Ahr, I'm just saying that if
you want one, here's where to buy it.

HICKS & DON (HIC)

Park House, Elmham, Dereham, Norfolk NR20
5JY, (01362) 668571, fax (01362) 668573;
The Old Bakehouse, Alfred St, Westbury,
Wiltshire BA13 3DY, (01373) 864723, fax
(01373) 858250
Hours Mon–Fri 9–5.
Cards Amex, MasterCard, Switch, Visa.
Discounts Negotiable.
Delivery Free for orders over £90, otherwise
£4.50.
Minimum order 1 mixed case.
C EP G M T
*A careful, well-chosen list that clearly has a lot of
hard work behind it. France is the main focus, with
good names including Ch. de Fuissé and Robert
Michel in Cornas; but Austria, Italy, Germany and
Spain can all offer interesting bottles. There's even a
red from Kent, Epoch 1 from Chapel Down Wines,
made from something called Rondo. Very intriguing.*
1995 Mantinia Dry White, A Cambas, Greece,
£5.25 Get your friends to guess the grape. It's
the Moschofilero.
1994 Sämling Beerenauslese, Neusiedlersee,
Helmut Lang, £11.80 Very good value for a
wine of this richness; what Austria is so good at.

HIGH BRECK VINTNERS (HIG)

Bentworth House, Bentworth, Nr Alton, Hants GU34 5RB, (01420) 562218, fax (01420) 563827

Hours Mon–Fri 9.30–5.30, or by arrangement.

Delivery (South-east) £6 for 1 case, £4 for 2, 3 free; (rest of England) £9 for 1, £6 for 2, £4 for 3, 4 or more free.

Minimum order 1 mixed case.

EP G M T

New wines here this year include the lovely Champagne of Billecart-Salmon, and some nice clarets, some of which look good buys at under a tenner – la Tour-de-By 1995, for example, at £9.99. Elsewhere in this list you'll find lots of wines only imported by High Breck. Hervé Olivier of the Côte de Beaune is one such; Daniel Wiederhirm of Alsace another; Charles Martin of Bergerac another. As you might have guessed, it's a mostly French list, though the smattering of wines from elsewhere is good: Petaluma from Australia, Royal Tokaji Wine Company from Hungary, Berberana from Spain.

Coliseo Very Old Dry Amontillado, Valdespino, £19.58 Simply one of the very best sherries there is.

**J. Straker,
Chadwick & Sons**

—— Established 1872 ——

conduct regular sales of
**FINE, RARE AND
INTERESTING WINES**
throughout the year.

We offer a personal,
helpful and professional
service to buyers and
sellers alike from single
bottles to complete
cellars.

Further imformation from
The Wine Department,
Market Street Chambers,
Abergavenny, Gwent
Tel: 01873 852624 / Fax: 01873 857311

1993 Côtes de Gien, Vigne de Taureau, Gitton Père et Fils, £6.99 Tastes like Sancerre, comes from a terrific producer, costs less. What more could one ask?

J E HOGG (HOG)

61 Cumberland St, Edinburgh EH3 6RA, 0131-556 4025

Hours Mon–Tue, Thu–Fri 9–1 & 2.30–6; Wed, Sat 9–1.

Cards Switch.

Delivery Free 12 or more bottles within Edinburgh. **G T**

The standard list here contains the everyday wines, but don't be fooled into thinking that's all there is. Either pop into the shop or ring and ask for the more comprehensive lists of specific regions, which will detail all those wines likely to go out of stock quickly. Even the standard list of everyday stuff is pretty interesting, and there's a superb list of German wines, plus good South Africans from Saxenburg and Meerlust.

1990 Wegeler Deinhard Estate Rheinpfalz Riesling Kabinett, £6.95 Wegeler Deinhard no longer uses vineyard names on most of their German wines, which makes life simpler for us. This is ripe, petrolly and ready.

S H JONES (JON)

27 High Street, Banbury, Oxfordshire OX16 8EW, (01295) 251179, fax (01295) 272352

9 Market Square, Bicester, Oxfordshire OX6 7AA (01869) 322448

Hours Mon–Sat 8.30–6.

Cards Amex, MasterCard, Switch, Visa.

Delivery Free within van delivery area for 2 cases or more; 'small delivery charge' otherwise. Elsewhere, rates available on application.

C EP G M T

Interesting to see a wide range of village and premier cru wines from really good Burgundy growers such as Etienne Grivot. No, they're still not cheap, but they're not so expensive as to be inconceivable for a special occasion. It rather sums up the approach of the company (of which Philip Eyres, previously a separate merchant, is now part): serious, subtle, beautifully made wines for people who want to drink well but are not millionaires. Bordeaux is as good as Burgundy, and the Rhône, the Loire and Alsace all look thoughtful and affordable, with producers including Dom. du Vieux Télégraphe and Gaston Huet. Germany is wonderful, Italy very good and the New World well put together.

1990 Pernand-Vergelesses 1er Cru, Île des Vergelesses, Rollin Père et Fils, £12.99 This is the sort of thing I mean: not a high price at all for a well-chosen Burgundy.

1991 Vacqueyras Maître de Chai, Domaine la Fourmone, Roger Combe, £8.99 Roger Combe does not filter his wines, so they keep all their considerable character.

1990 Schlossböckelheimer Kupfergrube Riesling QbA, Staatliche Weinbaudomäne, £7.59 That simply means that the local branch of the state wine domain has made a lovely Riesling from the Kupfergrube site in Schlossböckelheim in a very good year, and it's ready now.

JUSTERINI & BROOKS

61 St James's Street, London SW1A 1LZ, 0171-493 8721, fax 0171-499 4653
45 George Street, Edinburgh EH2 2HT, 0131-226 4202, fax 0131-225 2351
Hours London, Mon–Fri 9–5.30; Edinburgh, Mon–Sat 9–6.
Cards Amex, MasterCard, Switch, Visa.
Discounts £1 per case 2–4 cases, £2 per case 5–7 cases, £3 per case 8 cases and over.
Delivery Up to 2 cases, £9 per consignment UK mainland and N Ireland; free 2 cases and over; offshore UK £15 per case. **C M**
A long, long list, classic in conception but innovative as well. So Bordeaux, Burgundy and the Rhône are first class, and the Loire boasts such names as Lucien Crochet and Charles Joguet. The German range is tremendous, and includes the superb red Rheingaus of JB Becker. The New World looks well chosen, too, including Saintsbury (California) and Cape Mentelle (Australia). Stock information and prices were not available in time to be included in our Price Guides, but try:
1993 Late Picked Gewürztraminer, Husch £10.95 half bottle Unusual rich sweet white from the cool Anderson Valley in California.
1989 Deidesheimer Leinhöhle Riesling Kabinett, Bassermann-Jordan, £7.95 A mature Pfalz Riesling from a good producer.

1986 Château Canon-Moueix, Canon-Fronsac, £12.50 A lesser Bordeaux region but a good estate and a good year – good value at this price. It's drinking now, too.

KWIKSAVE (KWI)

Head office: Warren Drive, Prestatyn, Denbighshire LL19 7HU, (01745) 887111
Hours Variable.
Cards Switch, MasterCard, Visa some stores.
Everything's at the lowest end of the price scale here, as you might expect, but for the last few years KwikSave has been busy proving that wines can still be cheap and cheerful. No, you won't find huge individuality here, but you will find good flavours, well-made, clean wine and extraordinary value.
Skylark Hill Vin de Pays d'Oc Very Special White, £2.99 Flying winemaker-style white, all greengage and peach fruit; very attractive.

LAY & WHEELER (LAY)

(Head office & shop) The Wine Centre, Gosbecks Park, Colchester CO2 9JT, (01206) 764446, fax (01206) 560002
Hours Mon–Sat 9–7, Sun 10–4.
Cards Amex, MasterCard, Switch, Visa.
Discounts 5% 5 or more mixed cases.
Delivery Free over £150.
C EP G M T
It's worth getting on the Lay & Wheeler mailing list just for their bin end sales – though unless you have very fast fingers on the telephone when the sale opens you may find yourself at the back of a very long queue. The bargains are known to be good. And if you're not successful you could even buy from the regular list, which includes such established names as Henschke (Australia), Rust-en-Vrede (South Africa) and Schramsberg and Peter Michael (California). This is undoubtedly one of Britain's best merchants, with high quality across the board.
1992 Château la Prade, Côtes de Francs £5.99 A lesser known part of Bordeaux, and an off-vintage – but very nice wine.

> **C** = cellarage, **EP** = en primeur offers, **G** = glass hire/loan, **M** = mail order, **T** = tastings and talks.

1994 Sparkling Merlot, Hollick, Coonawarra £13.95 A fizzy Aussie red that's as wacky as they come.

LAYMONT & SHAW

The Old Chapel, Millpool, Truro, Cornwall TR1 1EX (01872) 270545, fax (01872) 223005
Hours Mon–Fri 9–5
Discounts £2.50 per case on all wines collected from premises at Truro.
Delivery UK mainland delivery included in wine price.
Minimum order 1 mixed case.
G M T
A Spanish specialist offering good value across the range. Excellent sherry (Cornwall is obviously a thoroughly civilized place), plus Priorato, Rias Baixas, Navarra… Oddity of the list? Aguardiente de Orujo de Albariño – like grappa, but made from the skins of the Albariño grape. We didn't receive details in time to feature them in our Price Guides, but have a look at…
1995 Marqués de Alella Clásico, Bodegas Parxet, £6.87 Off-dry, totally distinctive white. I've always loved it.

LAYTONS (LAYT)

20 Midland Road, London NW1 2AD, 0171-388 4567, fax 0171-383 7419;
50–52 Elizabeth Street, London SW1W 9PB, 0171-730 8108, fax 0171-730 9284;
21 Motcomb Street, London SW1X 8LB, 0171-235 3723, fax 0171-235 2062
23 Elystan Street, London SW3 3NT, 0171-581 2660, fax 0171-581 1203
Hours Mon–Sat 9–7.
Cards Amex, MasterCard, Switch, Visa.

LAYTONS

INDEPENDENT SHIPPERS OF FINE WINES

The World's finest wines, London's finest service

ESTABLISHED 1934

CORPORATE AND PRIVATE SALES
20 Midland Road, London NW1 2AD
Telephone: 0171-388 4567

Delivery Free for orders of £130 ex-VAT, otherwise £8.50 + VAT. Scotland and Cornwall: free for orders of £250 ex-VAT, otherwise £20 + VAT. **C EP G M T**
Now, how's this for a tasting note? 'Remarkable array of complexities that one day will explode. Drink from 1997' – before it explodes, presumably. This is one of the reasons I love the Layton's list: these wonderful tasting notes that look as though they were written with the aid of a phrase book. Fancy another one? 'Here is a Chevalier-Montrachet likely to be enormous in proportion BUT all the depth and weight will be contained in an overcoat of the finest materials'. But of course the other reason I like this list is the wines. Bordeaux and Burgundy are the focus, including the excellent Domaine Dujac at Morey-St-Denis, and there's a sprinkling of stuff from the New World.
1994 La Dame de Montrose, St Estèphe, £16.65 The second wine of Château Montrose, and always one of the best second wines.

LEA & SANDEMAN (LEA)

301 Fulham Road, London SW10 9QH, 0171-376 4767, fax 0171-351 0275;
211 Kensington Church Street, London W8 7LX, 0171-221 1982, fax 0171-221 1985
51 Barnes High Street, London SW13 9LN, 0181-878 8643, fax 0181-878 6522
Hours Mon–Fri 9–8.30, Sat 10–8.30.
Cards Amex, MasterCard, Switch, Visa.
Discounts 5–15% min 1 case.
Delivery Free to UK mainland south of Perth on orders over £150.
C EP G M T
A wide-ranging list put together by people who take the trouble to find interesting wines for themselves, rather than buying from other shippers. France is the driving force, and Italy is excellent, including Terriccio and Manzano; outside these countries the wines are good (often first class, in fact), but there are not so many of them. But if you want Bordeaux and Burgundy at all levels, lovely Rhônes and Loires from Clusel-Roch and Ch. Pierre-Bise, characterful country wines and the sublime Alsace wines of Marcel Deiss, this is your place.
1996 Bolgheri Bianco Vermentino, Vigneto Le Contessine Le Macchiole, £7.95 Intense, unusual flavours from Tuscany.

1995 Château Renard Mondesir, Fronsac, £9.95
Rich and concentrated claret from a good vintage.
Put it away for three or four years.

LONGFORD WINES (LON)

Longford Farmhouse, Barcombe, Lewes, East
Sussex BN8 5ED, tel & fax (01273) 480761
(London office) Freddy Price, 48 Castlebar Rd,
London W5 2DD, 0181-997 7889, fax 0181-
991 5178
Hours Mon-Fri 9–5; answerphone out of hours
Cards MasterCard, Visa.
Delivery Free England & Wales 1 case,
Scotland £5 per consignment.
Minimum order 1 case
C EP G M T
*Summerlee Wines has closed, but Freddy Price has
gone to mail-order specialist Longford Wines, to
whom Summerlee used to supply some wines.
Longford has also taken over the rest of
Summerlee's stocks, so the Longford list isn't hugely
dissimilar to Summerlee's old list. Claret is a
strength, as before – not because there are yards of
famous names but because there is a short list of
very well chosen wines at affordable prices. The rest
of France is handled in the same way and includes
Bott-Geyl from Alsace and Masson-Blondelet from
the Loire. Germany is another strength, and the
Australians are interesting.*
**1993 Cape Charlotte Dry Muscat à Petits
Grains, £5.95** I adore fresh, grapy, dry Muscat –
but it's got to be really fresh and aromatic. This
one from Australia is.
**1989 Serriger Schloss Saarsteiner Riesling
Kabinett, £6.47** A very good price for a classic
Saar Riesling that will last and last.
**1995 Bourgogne Pinot Noir, William Fèvre,
£5.68** Yes, I know Fèvre is a Chablis producer –
but for the first time he has made a red wine
from vineyards in Chablis. It's not the weightiest
of Pinots, but it's a great wine for summer
drinking.

MAJESTIC (MAJ)

(Head office) Odhams Trading Estate, St Albans
Road, Watford, Herts WD2 5RE, (01923)
816999, fax (01923) 819105
Hours Mon–Sat 10–8, Sun 10–6 (may vary).
Cards Amex, Diners, MasterCard, Switch, Visa.

Delivery Free locally.
Minimum order 1 mixed case.
G M T
*Majestic and Oddbins seem to vie with each other
for the best Champagne offers, which is very nice
for the rest of us. Champagne aside, the list is
enormous and sparky, without that feeling of
deadness that usually afflicts wine warehouses.
Majestic is confident enough to have plenty of fine
Germans, but there's curiously little from Argentina
or Portugal. But I'm not quibbling. France is brilliant,
including Chapoutier in the Rhône and Drouhin in
Burgundy. Italy and Spain (look out for Marqués de
Murrieta) are very good; more New Zealanders are
promised. Look out for special offers.*
**1992 Eitelsbacher Kartäuserhofberg Riesling,
£4.99** There may not be any of this left by the
time you read this. I might have bought it all.
1995 Domaine de la Janasse, £5.99 A Merlot
and Syrah vin de pays from the Principauté
d'Orange, stuffed with fruit (I don't mean oranges).

MARKS & SPENCER (MAR)

(Head office) Michael House, 47–67 Baker
Street, London W1A 1DN, 0171-935 4422; 290
licensed stores all over the country
Hours Variable.
Discounts 12 bottles for the price of 11.
M
*At the last count the M&S list included no fewer
than 29 varietal Chardonnays; and if you include
Chardonnay blends you arrive at almost half the
white list. Give us a break, guys, there are other
flavours in the world. On the other hand, if that's
what we're all buying… The truth is, you won't go
far wrong with an M&S wine. It'll be tasty, well
made and decent value. It won't frighten the horses,
but then we don't go there for that. Names to rely
on include Dom. Virginie from France's Midi and
Geyser Peak from California.*
Jeunes Vignes, la Chablisienne, £5.99 Young,
fresh Chardonnay made from vines too young to
make Chablis.

> *Explore the world of wine
> further with Oz Clarke's
> multimedia Wine Guide –
> see page 462 for details.*

1995 Counoise, Paul Jeune £4.49 This is more like it: earthy, raspberryish, with a touch of spice.

MORENO WINES

11 Marylands Road, London W9 2DU, 0171-286 0678, fax 0171-286 0513; 2 Norfolk Place, London W2 1QN, 0171-706 3055, fax 0171-724 3813

Hours Marylands Road: Mon–Wed 2–10, Thurs–Fri 12–10.30, Sat 10-10.30, Sun 12–8; Norfolk Place: Mon–Sat 10–7.

Cards MasterCard, Switch, Visa.

Discounts 5% mixed case.

Delivery Free locally. **G M T**

Everything the expatriate Spaniard could want is here, including octopus in garlic, Eureka tuna (probably leaps from the tin) and bottles of malt whisky. There are also wines from all over Spain, so whether you hail from Chacoli in the Basque country or Zamora or Toro or good old Rioja, you'll be able to find your local hooch. The list of Riojas is as long as your arm, from 1928 (Paternina Gran Reserva) to infants of two months' aging (San Isidro Torrealdea Tinto). There's also a fair bit from Chile, France, Italy, New Zealand, Portugal and, for some reason, postcards of Leeds. Baffling. Stock information and prices were not available in time to be included in our Price Guides, but what about…

Farina Blanco Botrytis, Zamora, £5.55 No, I haven't tasted it – but it's got to be interesting.

1989 Gran Colegiata Tinto Reserva, Toro, £5.85 An old friend, and it's brilliant.

1991 Pazo San Mauro Albariño, £5.99 The Lord be praised, an affordable Albariño.

MORRIS & VERDIN (MV)

10 The Leathermarket, Weston Street, London SE1 3ER, 0171-357 8866, fax 0171-357 8877

Hours Mon–Fri 8–6; closed bank hols.

Discounts 10 or more cases.

Delivery Free central London, elsewhere free 6 or more cases.

Minimum order 1 mixed case.

C EP G M T

There was a time when Morris & Verdin specialized in French wines – and indeed it still does have a stunning range from France, particularly Burgundy from makers like Daniel Rion and Compte Lafon, though everywhere else in that country is good too.

Each year has seen more wines from elsewhere added, too, so that if you want California wines from southern French varieties made by the likes of Bonny Doon and Jade Mountain, this is one of the places you look first. This year Ridge Vineyards has been added, plus New Zealand estate Isabel.

1993 Qupé Syrah/Mourvèdre, Los Olivos Vineyard, £13.80 Wonderful stuff from California, ripe and spicy.

1994 Bourgogne Rouge les Bons Bâtons, Patrice Rion, £9.80 Good basic red Burgundy.

NADDER WINES LTD (NA)

Hussars House, 2 Netherhampton Road, Harnham, Salisbury, Wiltshire SP2 8HE, (01722) 325418, fax (01722) 421617

Hours Mon–Fri 9–6, Sat 9–1.

Cards Amex, MasterCard, Switch, Visa.

Discounts 5% on orders £100–£249, 7.5% on £250–£499, 10% on £500 plus. 7.5% discount card for regular customers.

Delivery Free Salisbury area & Central London on orders over £75; rest of UK mainland at carrier's cost. Ten cases or over free.

Minimum order 1 case. **G M T**

France is your best bet from the newly revamped Nadder Wines, in particular the country wines and the Bordeaux. There's quite a range of decent, inexpensive claret, and the Loires and Rhônes look interesting, too. From Italy there are the excellent wines of Avignonesi, and from Portugal, the wines of Sogrape, always favourites of this Guide. Down Under? De Bortoli (love it), Selaks (ditto) and Seifried Estate (ditto again).

1995 Chateau des Charmes Late Harvest Riesling, Canada £7.59 half bottle Delicious, elegant and serious.

1994 Château Loudenne Blanc, £7.49 Well-made white Bordeaux.

NEW LONDON WINE (NEW)

1E Broughton Street, London SW8 3QJ, 0171-622 3000, Freefone order line (0800) 581266

Hours Mon–Fri 9–6.

Cards Amex, MasterCard, Switch, Visa.

Delivery Free in central London, quotes available for national delivery.

Minimum order 1 case.

EP G M T

A functional list offering little to make the heart race. If you had 20 people arriving in half an hour's time and nothing to give them you could do worse: you'd find sound drinking here. If you had more time to consider you might want to look elsewhere.

1994 Orvieto Classico Secco, Antinori Good everyday drinking

1995 Marqués de Riscal Blanco, Rueda, £5.99 Good, reliable stuff.

LE NEZ ROUGE (NEZ)

12 Brewery Rd, London N7 9NH,
0171-609 4711, fax 0171-607 0018;
Unit 456, St 7, Thorpe Arch Trading Estate,
Wetherby, Yorkshire LS23 7BT, (01937) 844711
Hours Mon–Fri 9–5.30, (Sat 10–2 for occasional tasting); closed bank holiday weekends.
Cards MasterCard, Switch, Visa.
Discounts £3.50 per case collected.
Other quantity discounts as well.
Delivery Included in price for mainland UK.
Minimum order 1 mixed case.
C EP M T
This started life as a French specialist and has gradually expanded into other areas. Burgundy and Bordeaux are still at the heart of the list, but there are some interesting Austrians from Malat-Bründlmayer and good New World wines from Morton Estate (NZ), Coldstream Hills (Australia) and Beringer (California). It's worth noting that the raison d'être of the list is that wine is made to go with food; so expect subtlety.

1995 Durius Tinto, Marqués de Griñón, £4.40 Good value and rich fruit from this maverick Spanish producer.

1993 Chardonnay Auslese, Weingut Nigl, £6.80 50cl Medium-sweet Chardonnay from a top Austrian producer – now there's a novelty.

1994 Savigny-lès-Beaune les Gollardes, Domaine Vincent Girardin, £11.17 I love Savigny, and this single-vineyard one is brilliant.

JAMES NICHOLSON (NI)

27A Killyeagh St, Crossgar, Co. Down, Northern Ireland BT30 9DG, (01396) 830091, fax (01396) 830028
Hours Mon–Sat 10–7.
Cards MasterCard, Switch, Visa.

Discounts 7–10% mixed case.
Delivery Free Northern Ireland for orders of £50 or 1 case, otherwise at cost.
C EP G M T
A serious list of fine wines with plenty at the affordable level, as well. I'd be happy just in the Rhône section, tasting my way through René Rostaing, Colombo and Beaucastel; although I might then move on to Italy, Bordeaux, Burgundy...

1993 Ser Gioveto, Rocca delle Macìe, £7.95 Lovely cherry and violet red from Tuscany.

THE NOBODY INN (NO)

Doddiscombsleigh, Nr Exeter, Devon EX6 7PS,
(01647) 252394, fax (01647) 252978
Hours Mon–Sat 12–2.30 & 6–11 (summer),
7–11 (winter), Sun 12–3 & 7–10.30; or by appointment.
Credit Cards Amex, MasterCard, Switch, Visa.
Discounts 5% per case.
Delivery Up to 2 cases £7.90; each additional case £3.90.
G M T
There's a huge variety of wine here: name a country and the odds are that the Nobody Inn will say, 'Oh, yes, we've got a Riesling from there somewhere.' Excellent well-known names include Cloudy Bay, J-L Chave and Dr Loosen.

1994 Seghesio Old Vine Zinfandel, £11.55 Wonderful rich red from California.

ODDBINS (OD)

(Head office) 31–33 Weir Road, London SW19 8UG, 0181-944 4400; 225 shops.
Hours Generally Mon–Sat 10–10, Sun 10–8 in England & Wales, 12.30–8 Scotland.
Cards Amex, MasterCard, Switch, Visa.
Discounts 5% split case wine; 10% split case tasting wines on day of tasting. 7 bottles of Champagne and sparkling wine for the price of 6.
Delivery Free locally from most shops.
Still the most adventurous of the high street chains, and the one where you're most likely to pick up something quirky, original or just plain good value. They rightly make a great brouhaha about their New World wines from names like Coldstream Hills and Villa Maria, but there are some sensational European ones here, too.

1995 Saumur-Champigny Vieilles Vignes, La Vigne, £6.99 Good raspberryish Loire red from the best red vintage for years.

THOS. PEATLING

(Head office) Westgate House, Bury St Edmunds, Suffolk IP33 1QS, (01284) 714466, fax (01284) 705795
Hours Variable.
Cards Amex, MasterCard, Switch, Visa.
Discounts 5% mixed case.
Delivery Free UK mainland 2 or more cases.
C EP G M T

A nice list with some interesting wines. Bordeaux is its strongest suit: some other regions can look a little routine, although enlivened by some more unusual numbers and good names like Chapoutier. Peatlings says it has changed many of the wines it has listed in the past 'to improve product reliability and continuity of supply'. If those are topics close to your heart, this is the list for you. Stock information and prices were not available in time for inclusion in our Price Guides, but here's my pick from the new list:

1990 le Domaine de Fourgas, Ste-Croix-du-Mont, £9.99 A year in which even the lesser sweet wine regions of Bordeaux had to work hard to make poor wine.

1989 McWilliams Elizabeth Semillon, £8.99 One of the few unoaked Hunter Valley Semillons available: full marks to Peatlings for stocking it.

PENISTONE COURT WINE CELLARS (PEN)

The Railway Station, Penistone, Sheffield, South Yorkshire S30 6HG, (01226) 766037, fax (01226) 767310
Hours Mon–Fri 9–6, Sat 10–3.
Delivery Free locally, rest of UK mainland charged at cost 1 case or more.
G M

A curious list, this: in much of Europe there's a slightly depressing reliance on a handful of not necessarily exciting names – Louis Latour and Bichot in Burgundy, for example – but the New World is a little more adventurous. Lindemans is another big name, to be sure, but there's Pyrus, St George and Limestone Ridge: excellent wines all. There is also an interesting selection of sweet wines,

including sweet Champagnes – must be those cold Yorkshire nights.

Barbadillo Palo Cortado, £9.99 Wonderful, elegant dry sherry.

1985 Renaissance Late Picked Riesling, £8.92 half bottle Classic stuff from a most unusual California winery.

PHILGLAS & SWIGGOT

21 Northcote Road, London SW11, 0171-924 4494, fax 0171-978 5881
Hours Mon 5–8.30, Tues–Sat 11–8.30, Sun 12–2 & 6.30–8.30.
Cards Amex, MasterCard, Switch, Visa.
Discounts 5% per case.
Delivery Free 1 case West End, Wandsworth and other South London boroughs, elsewhere £20 per case, or free if you subscribe to the Door to Door Home Delivery Club.
G

An adventurous merchant with a strong local following and an eye for an interesting wine, particularly if it comes from Australia. But there's very good stuff from France, as well, plus excellent Italians, Germans, sherries… Look out for Howard Park and Mt Langhi-Ghiran from Australia and Pieropan and Aldo Contino from Italy. This is just the sort of unusual list that a small merchant can do so well. Stock information and prices weren't available in time to be included in our Price Guides, but I have to let you know about these:

1996 Montara M, £6.95 What's in this one? I'll tell you. Pinot Noir and Shiraz. It comes from Victoria, and it's got bags of spicy, berried fruit.

1993 Aramon, Terrasses de Languedoc, Vin de Pays de l'Herault, £4.59 Aramon is a much-maligned red grape variety; this just shows what the South of France can do.

1990 Château de Prade, Côtes de Castillon, £8.99 Mature claret from an outlying area: just the sort of wine we're all looking for.

CHRISTOPHER PIPER WINES (PIP)

1 Silver St, Ottery St Mary, Devon EX11 1DB, (01404) 814139, fax (01404) 812100
Hours Mon–Sat 9–6.
Cards MasterCard, Visa.
Discounts 5% mixed case, 10% 3 or more cases.

Delivery Free in south-west England for 4 cases, elsewhere free for 6 cases.
Minimum order 1 mixed case.
C E P G M T
A real enthusiasts' list, written for people who love wine, by people who've taken the trouble to go out and hunt for the good stuff. There's nothing predictable, except that I predict you'll find a lot of wines you want to try. While there's a pretty good range of wines under a fiver, the strength is in the £5 to £15 area – which means wonderful wines from France (1995 Savigny-lès-Beaune les Liards, Rossignol-Trapet), Germany (1995 Erdener Treppchen Riesling Kabinett, Dr Loosen), Italy (1993 Amarone della Valpolicella, Masi), Spain, Australia (1995 Verdelho, Pendarves Estate) and more.
1993 Domaine de St Georges, Côtes du Rhône, £5.50; 1992 Cuvée Spéciale Syrah, Domaine de St Georges, Côtes du Rhône, £9.70 Christopher Piper reckons these are among the best wines on his list.

TERRY PLATT (PLA)

Ferndale Road, Llandudno Junction LL31 9NT, (01492) 592971, fax (01492) 592196;
World of Wine, 29 Mostyn Ave, Craig Y Don, (01492) 872997
Hours Ferndale Rd: Mon–Fri 8.30–5.30; Mostyn Ave: Mon–Sat 10–8, Sun 12–5.
Cards MasterCard, Switch, Visa.
Delivery Free locally, or in mainland UK with minimum order of 3 cases.
Minimum order 1 mixed case. **G M T**
A thorough, well-thought-out list. Australia and California both look excellent – the latter boasts Bonny Doon, Au Bon Climat and Domaine

TERRY PLATT
WINE MERCHANT

FERNDALE ROAD,
LLANDUDNO JUNCTION,
CONWAY LL31 9NT
Tel: 01492 592971 Fax: 01492 592196

Carneros, among others – and from France there's red and white Côteaux Champenois, if you feel so inclined. The claret list is varied and there are plenty of good inexpensive French country wines, as well as good Alsace. Burgundy and Spain are both carefully selected and include Joseph Drouhin and Marqués de Riscal.
1994 Bourgogne Aligoté, Domaine Maurice Rollin, £8.21 Too good to use for kir.
NV Pinot Noir, Au Bon Climat, £15.22 Good Pinot Noir is never cheap.

PLAYFORD ROS

1 Middle Park House, Sowerby, Thirsk, Yorkshire YO7 3AH, (01845) 526777, fax (01845) 526888
Hours Mon–Fri 9–5.
Cards MasterCard, Visa.
Discounts 2.5 per cent on orders over 6 cases.
Delivery Free Yorkshire, Derbyshire, Durham, Newcastle, elsewhere on UK mainland, £9 1 case, £6 2 cases, £5 3 cases, £4.50 4 cases, free 5 cases.
Minimum order 1 mixed case.
E P G M T
The information about climate and soil conditions in China in this list is written in Chinese, exactly as received from the producers of Dragon Seal – or perhaps it just says 'fax not readable, please re-send'. Who knows? More to the point, there's good stuff from just about every country and region here, and an encouragingly long list of good everyday wines. You can drink some thoroughly fine wines from Playford Ros (Sassicaia, Château Ausone 1985) but there's plenty for normal people, as well, including good unusual wines from Cline Cellars (California) and Moss Wood (Australia)
1995 Thesis, del Cerro, £5.81 Italian blend of Pinot Bianco, Trebbiano and Sauvignon.

PORTLAND WINE CO (POR)

16 North Parade, off Norris Road, Sale, Cheshire M33 3JS, 0161-962 8752, fax 0161-905 1291;
152a Ashley Road, Hale WA15 9SA, 0161-928 0357; 82 Chester Road, Macclesfield SK11 8DL, (01625) 616147
Hours Mon–Sat 10–10, Sun 12–3 & 7–9.30.
Cards Amex, MasterCard, Switch, Visa.
Discounts 10% off 1 mixed case, 5% off half a mixed case.

Delivery Free locally.
G M T
*There's good wine from pretty well everywhere in
the world here, from Uruguay to Hungary.
Everything's carefully chosen, but South Africa with
Meerlust, South America with Concha y Toro and
Australia with Mitchell look particularly good. Spain
and Italy are interesting, too.*
**1988 Tokaji 5 Puttonyos, Domain Disznókö,
£10.75** New-style Tokaji, sweet, rich and fresh.
1989 Guelbenzu Evo Gran Reserva, £12.95
Good spicy, cigar-box and fruit red from
Navarra, rich and intense.

QUELLYN ROBERTS (QUE)

15 Watergate Street, Chester CH1 2LB,
(01244) 310455, fax (01244) 346704
Hours Mon–Sat 8.45–5.45.
Cards Amex, MasterCard, Switch, Visa.
Discounts 5% on a mixed case.
Delivery Free 2 cases or more, Chester and
surrounding districts.
C G M T
*A thorough list, not enormously long, but with some
nice surprises. Spain looks good, as does South
Africa and the Loire. There's Chateau Musar, too.*
1995 Faustino V Rosado, Rioja, £5.99 Pink
Rioja: now there's a temptation.

RAEBURN FINE WINES (RAE)

23 Comely Bank Rd, Edinburgh EH4 1DS, tel &
fax 0131-332 5166
Hours Mon–Sat 9–6, Sun 12.30–5.
Cards MasterCard, Switch, Visa.
Discounts 5% unsplit case, 2.5% mixed.
Delivery Price negotiable, all areas.
EP G M T
*A top-class list, reflecting Raeburn's knowledge of
and love for claret, Burgundy, French country wines,
plus Alsace, Rhône, Loire, Germany, Italy, Spain:
shall I go on? You've probably taken the point.
Claret and Burgundy are the focus, but there's
some excellent stuff from California, South Africa,
Australia and New Zealand, as well, including La
Jota, Warwick Estate, Brokenwood and Cloudy Bay.
Yes, the emphasis is on fine wines, but the prices
here look fair to me.*
1991 Côte-Rôtie, Niero-Pinchon, £15.95 Quite
a good year – and a good producer.

1987 Pinot Noir, Joseph Swan, £11.95 Ten-
year-old California Pinot Noir? Well, from
Joseph Swan it's probably worth a try.

REID WINES (1992) LTD (REI)

The Mill, Marsh Lane, Hallatrow, Nr Bristol
BS18 5EB, (01761) 452645, fax (01761) 453642
Hours Mon–Fri 10.30–5.30.
Cards MasterCard, Visa (3% charge).
Delivery Free within 25 miles of Hallatrow
(Bristol), and in central London.
C G M T
*I have my favourite quotes from this list every year.
This year's award for honesty goes to Reid's note on
Meursault Charmes 1961, Prosper Maufoux:
'Probably awful – most Prosper Maufoux wines are,
after all.' Runner up: 'Near dross' for 1975 Puligny-
Montrachet, Berry Bros. But of course Reid does like
most of the wines on its list – and with good reason,
because it's an outstanding list. Fine and rare wines
take up a large part of it but there's lots of good
everyday drinking as well, from France, Italy,
California, Australia and most other places, too.
Look out for Deiss (Alsace), Isole e Olena (Tuscany)
and Niebaum-Coppola (California).*
**1992 Hautes-Côtes de Nuits, Jean Gros,
£11.60** Excellent basic red Burgundy.
1993 Pinot Blanc de Bergheim, Deiss, £8.81
Alsace from a most meticulous winemaker.
1969 Château de Pez, £8.50 Quoted for Reid's
tasting note: 'Grim.'

LA RÉSERVE (RES)

56 Walton St, London SW3 1RB, 0171-589
2020, fax 0171-581 0250
Hours Mon–Fri 9.30–9, Sat 9.30–6.
Credit Cards Amex, MasterCard, Switch, Visa.
Discounts 5% per case except accounts.
Delivery Free 1 case or more Central London
and orders over £200 UK mainland. Otherwise
£7.50. **C EP G T**
*A list – and a merchant – for those who take their
wine buying seriously and want a merchant they
can trust. The main focus of the list is France, and
within France, Burgundy and Bordeaux, but there
are good ranges from most other places, including
Petaluma from Australia and the excellent Thelema
Mountain wines from Stellenbosch. La Réserve isn't
keen on hype, and prefers to treat its customers as*

intelligent beings able to understand why one wine is better than another and therefore more expensive. And is it an expensive list? Well, it's not cheap, but then these are very good wines, chosen with great expertise.

1993 Hautes-Côtes de Nuits Pinot Beurot, Thévenot-Le-Brun, £11.50 There's not much (white) Pinot Beurot in the Côte d'Or, so this is a real curiosity. There's a Chardonnay at the same price, if you insist on being conventional.

1993 Beaumes-de-Venise, Château Redortier, £6.95 No, not Muscat; this is rich and spicy red from the same village in the southern Rhône.

HOWARD RIPLEY (RIP)

35 Eversley Crescent, London N21 1EL, 0181-360 8904, fax 0181-351 6564
Hours Mon–Fri 9–10, Sat 9–1.
Delivery London free 5 cases or more, otherwise £8.50 plus vat, elsewhere at cost.
Minimum Order 1 mixed case.
E P G M T
Burgundy heaven. There are six new domaines added to what was already an astonishing list: they are Henri Gouges, Géantet-Pansiot, Fourrier, Paul Pernot, Pierre Boillot and Château de Puligny-Montrachet. Howard Ripley knows his Burgundy

INTRODUCING THE COMPLETE GUIDE TO WINE STORAGE

A new range of wine storage equipment to suit all situations, volume requirements and pockets

1). The Spiral Cellar
The French designed, prefabricated wine cellar which goes under any home or garage. It is 2.00m wide and comes in various depth up to 3.00m. It will hold up to 1600 bottles of wine.

2). Wine Hives
This is a new concept in wine storage from France. Wine Hives come in two sizes, 12 bottle and 24 bottle. They are made of a special concrete designed to absorb humidity and vibration and keep wine in the dark. They are very strong ochre coloured units which stack on top of each other, need no fixing and are ideal for the garage, existing cellar or space under the stairs.

3). Made to Measure Racking
The racks blend the strength of steel with the subtlety of wood. They can be made to any size or shape furnished in pine, oak or mahogany with galvanised steel or brass.

4).Wine Storage Cabinets
We offer a range of wine storage cabinets from a variety of manufacturers.

For a full brochure contact:

Spiral Cellars Limited
Court House, 23 Woodfield Lane, Ashtead,
Surrey KT21 2BB Tel: 01372 279166 Fax: 01372 273482
Name _____
Address _____
_____
Telephone _____

well enough to be honest about it: 'Too expensive, so do not buy it,' he says of Domaine Leflaive's Chevalier-Montrachet at £82.25 per bottle. So when he describes a Mâcon Verze at £5.82 as 'an absolute bargain at this price' you're inclined to believe him. The list majors on serious Burgundy, and that means serious money. £30 a bottle, that sort of money, though there's also plenty at under £20. If you're in that market, what's keeping you?

1995 Volnay Vendange Sélectionné, Domaine Michel Lafarge, £20.56 Wine made from old vines from the greatest name in Volnay.

ROBERSON (ROB)

348 Kensington High St, London W14 8NS, 0171-371 2121, fax 0171-371 4010
Hours Mon–Sat 10–8.
Cards Amex, Diners, MasterCard, Switch, Visa.
Delivery Free locally 1 case or more.
C EP G M T
When Roberson was founded in 1991 it declared its intention of being the finest wine shop in London. Personally my vote for that title would go to Bibendum, but there's no doubt that Roberson is very good. Look here for top Bordeaux and Burgundy, excellent Italians and a very good choice from just about everywhere else. Star names include J-L Chave, Mas de Daumas Gassac, Giuseppe Mascarello and Au Bon Climat. Prices are not low.

1990 Côtes du Jura Savagnin, Luc et Sylvie Boilley, £10.50 A rarity which won't be to everyone's taste – but what's wrong with that?

1990 Château Lyonnat, Lussac-St-Émilion, £9.95 One of the cheaper clarets on the list, and it's drinking now.

Pedro Ximenez, Valdespino, £7.95 Rich, sweet, dark sherry for pouring over ice cream – or even drinking with it.

ROSE TREE WINE COMPANY (ROS)

15 Suffolk Parade, Cheltenham, Gloucestershire GL50 2AE, (01242) 583732, fax (01242) 222159
Hours Mon–Fri 9–7, Sat 9–6.
Cards MasterCard, Switch, Visa.
Delivery Free locally, elsewhere by arrangement.
Minimum Order 1 mixed case.
C EP G M T
'One of the most interesting areas of France is the Rhône, the Luberon and surrounding areas', says

Rose Tree, which features the wines of Dard & Ribo and Ch. Fortia – now there's a company after my own heart. In truth the selection isn't enormous, but it looks interesting. Portugal could do with an upgrade, but Italy looks good.

1993 Barbera d'Asti, Cepi Storici, £6.00 Good tasty Barbera.

THE RSJ WINE COMPANY (RSJ)

13A Coin Street, London SE1 8YQ, 0171-633 0489

Hours Mon–Fri 9–5, answering machine at other times.

Cards Amex, Diners, MasterCard, Switch, Visa.

Delivery Free central London, minimum 1 case. Rates elsewhere on request.

T

This is a spin-off from the restaurant of the same name, which has made its wine name with its excellent list of Loires. For this mail-order-only list a couple of Beaujolais have been added, and other regions might join it, too: 'We hear that other regions of France and, indeed, other countries also make wine,' says the list. There are most kinds of Loire here, from Muscadet through Anjou to single-vineyard Bourgueil; and if you want to know how they go with food, try the restaurant.

1995 Anjou-Villages, Domaine Ogereau £6.30 An inexpensive introduction to red Loires – though it'll keep for the best part of a decade.

1995 Vouvray Demi-sec le Bouchet, Domaine des Aubuisières £7.20 So unfashionable it's due for cult status.

SAFEWAY (SAF)

(Head office) 6 Millington Road, Hayes, Middlesex UB3 4AY, 0181-848 8744, fax 0181-573 1865

Hours Mon–Sat 8–8 (Fri till 9), Sun 10–4 (selected stores).

Cards MasterCard, Switch, Visa.

Discounts 5–10% on mixed cases.

G

It's a curious list, this, and difficult to summarize. On the one hand whenever I go into a branch of Safeway I never see anything I want to buy. Okay, maybe I just keep going into small branches. On the other hand the list has some real high points: Gevrey-Chambertin from Rossignol-Trapet, Volnay from Michel Lafarge, Côtes du Rhône from Gabriel

Meffre, Sancerre from Henri Bourgeois. There are some good South Americans, Australians and Italians tucked in among the standard names, too.

1991 Tedeschi Capitel San Rocco Rosso, £6.99 Now, if my local branch had this Italian…

1995 Safeway Stanlake, Thames Valley Vineyards, £3.99 New wave English white, and very good value.

J SAINSBURY (SAI)

(Head office) Stamford House, Stamford St, London SE1 9LL, 0171-921 6000

Hours Variable, many open late.

Cards Amex, MasterCard, Switch, Visa.

G

At last Sainsbury's is starting to look more interesting. It's got a little way to go yet – North America is sadly dependent upon Gallo – but there are some interesting Australians entering the fray, including Baileys 1920s Block Shiraz.

Rosato del Salento 1995, £3.49 I like good rosé.

Clos St-Georges 1990, Graves Supérieures £7.45 Excellent value sweet white Graves, from a great year.

SATCHELLS (SAT)

North St, Burnham Market, Norfolk PE31 8HG, tel & fax (01328) 738272

Hours Mon, Tues, Thurs, Fri 9.30–1 & 2–6; Wed 9.30–1; Sat 9.30–7.

Credit Cards MasterCard, Switch, Visa.

Discounts 5% cases, larger orders negotiable.

Delivery Free locally, at cost nationally.

G M T

An independent merchant with a nice list at affordable prices. Portugal looks good, as does the range of pudding wines. There's a good list of affordable clarets, as well.

1986 Domaine Bouscassé, Pacherenc du Vic-Bilh, £8.42 Luscious exotica from south-west France, and a good price, too.

SHERSTON WINE COMPANY

97 Victoria Street, St Albans AL1 3TJ, (01727) 858841

Hours Tues–Fri 9.30–7, Sat 9.30–6

Cards MasterCard, Switch, Visa.

Delivery Free locally; elsewhere by arrangement. **G T**

Gosh, what a lot of goodies: densely packed and full of flavour, as one of Sherston's own tasting notes might say. Among the highlights are some very well priced and mature lesser clarets – and I mean 1989s and 1990s, not just the lighter, more recent years. There are some Beaujolais from old vines, which bode well, and Alsace is superb: inexpensive from the Turckheim co-op, expensive from Schlumberger. California is notable by its absence. Stock information and prices weren't available in time to be include in our Price Guides, but try:

1990 Château des Annereaux, Lalande-de-Pomerol, £9.99 Decent claret at this price seems destined to become a thing of the past.

1994 Quinta da Murta Branco, Bucelas, £6.50 When do you ever see Bucelas on a list? Buy some, if only to encourage them.

SOMERFIELD/GATEWAY (SO)

(Head office) Somerfield House, Hawkfield Business Park, Whitchurch Lane, Bristol BS14 0TJ, 0117-935 9359
Hours Mon–Sat 9–8, variable late opening Friday all stores.
Cards MasterCard, Switch, Visa.
T

There are some tasty everyday wines here if you're prepared to pay more than the very lowest prices. Alsace wines from the Turckheim co-op, for example, or Portuguese red from Caves Aliança. A promising-looking list.

Rheingau Riesling, Schloss Reinhartshausen, £3.65 Non-vintage and bargain-priced, with that authentic Riesling taste.

1993 Châteauneuf-du-Pape, Domaine de la Solitude, £9.49 Classy Rhône at a fair price.

SOMMELIER WINE CO (SOM)

23 St George's Esplanade, St Peter Port, Guernsey, Channel Islands, GY1 2BG (01481) 721677, fax (01481) 716818
Hours Mon–Thu 10–5.30, Fri 10–6, Sat 9–5.30; answerphone out of hours.
Cards MasterCard, Switch, Visa.
Discounts 5% 12 or more bottles.
Delivery Free 1 unmixed case.
G M (locally) **T**
A well-thought-out list put together by people with an original turn of mind. You'll find plenty of big-

name wines here (Chapoutier and Jean-Luc Colombo from the Rhône, Comte Armand and Hudelot-Noëllat in Burgundy, Henschke and Charlie Melton from Australia) but plenty you haven't come across before, as well – what about Madfish Bay Unwooded Chardonnay from Western Australia? The note on Evian water puzzles me, though: 'Neutral tasting and therefore ideal with a meal'. Tell that to Charlie Melton.

1995 Ribolla, Paolo Rodaro, Friuli, £7.30 A rarely seen white variety of high quality.

1990 Plantagenet Riesling, Mount Barker, £5.95 Mature Australian Riesling. Good price, too.

FRANK STAINTON WINES (STA)

3 Berry's Yard, Finkle Street, Kendal, Cumbria LA9 4AB, (01539) 731886, fax (01539) 730396
Hours Mon–Sat 9–5.30.
Cards MasterCard, Visa.
Discounts 5% mixed case.
Delivery Free Cumbria and North Lancashire; elsewhere £7.25 1 case, £5 2–4 cases, £3.25 5–9 cases, 10 cases free.
G C EP T

There's a very good range of clarets here. Most are over a tenner, but that's the nature of the beast these days. Burgundy looks thorough and Germany quite interesting: Wehlener Sonnenuhr Riesling Auslese Halbtrocken 1988 from SA Prüm, for example. The New World looks pretty good, too, with names like Clos du Val and Taltarni.

1995 Oakland Full Bodied Red, Grant Burge, £6.25 Lovely Cabernet, Mourvèdre and Grenache blend from Australia.

1994 Bairrada Reserva, Caves Aliança, £4.74 Aliança has long been at the forefront of new-wave wine-making in Portugal.

SUNDAY TIMES WINE CLUB (SUN)

New Aquitaine House, Paddock Road, Reading, Berks RG4 5JY, 0118-948 1713, fax 0118-946 1953
Hours Mail order, 24-hr answerphone.

C = cellarage, **EP** = en primeur offers, **G** = glass hire/loan, **M** = mail order, **T** = tastings and talks.

Cards Amex, Diners, MasterCard, Switch, Visa.
Discounts On special offers.
Delivery £3.99 per order.
C EP M T

The associate mail order company of Bordeaux Direct. The membership fee is £10 per annum. The club also runs tours and tastings and an annual festival in London, and does monthly promotions to its members. See Bordeaux Direct for more details.

T & W WINES (TW)

51 King St, Thetford, Norfolk IP24 2AU, (01842) 765646
Hours Mon–Fri 9.30–5.30, Sat 9.30–1.00.
Cards Amex, Diners, MasterCard, Visa.
Delivery Free UK mainland 2 or more cases.
C EP G M

This has always been a top-class list, but it's adventurous, too. T&W got into Austria while most merchants were still dismissing it, with the result that you can get the wines of Willi Opitz and Umathum here. From Burgundy there is botrytized white Mâcon as well as more conventional wine from the Domaine de la Romanée Conti, Domaine de la Pousse d'Or and Domaine Rossignol-Trapet, and Sauternes majors on Château Gilette, the extraordinary wine kept for decades in cement tanks before release. The latest vintage at T&W is 1962. But although a lot of the wine here is expensive there are well-chosen inexpensive wines too: the excellent Château la Borderie from Monbazillac for under a tenner, for example. Rhône is a strength, well-represented by Colombo, Guigal and Rayas; French country wines are good but few in number. There's lots of Alsace, all from Trimbach and Hugel; Italy includes the hugely expensive Gaja wines. Australia is sound, with no great discoveries; Spain could do with something apart from Rioja and Torres. What else to go for here? Good German wines, old vintages and anniversary years, for the 21-year-old who has everything.

Jerez Cortado, Hidalgo, £11.65 Why don't more people drink sherry like this? It's rich yet dry, and incredibly pungent. Wonderful stuff.
1993 Château la Borderie, Bergerac, £7.30 Lovely well-made white Bergerac from a château that also makes a nifty Monbazillac.
1994 Rasteau, Vin Doux Naturel, £14.05 Sweet red – sticky, spicy stuff to drink with chocolate.

TANNERS (TAN)

26 Wyle Cop, Shrewsbury, Shropshire SY1 1XD, (01743) 232400, fax (01743) 344401;
4 St Peter's Square, Hereford HR1 2PJ, (01432) 272044, fax (01432) 263316;
36 High Street, Bridgnorth WC16 4DB, (01746) 763148;
The Old Brewery, Brook St, Welshpool SY21 7LF, (01938) 552542, fax (01938) 556565
Hours Mon–Sat 9–6.
Cards Amex, MasterCard, Switch, Visa.
Discounts 5% 1 mixed case (cash & collection); 2.5% mixed case, 5% for 5, 7.5% for 10 cases (mail order).
Delivery Free 1 mixed case or more locally, or nationally over £75, otherwise £6.
EP G M T

If you want reasons why one might go to an independent wine merchant rather than a supermarket, take a look at this list. No, there's not a lot at £2.99, but if paying as little as possible is your sole aim you may be reading the wrong book. At Tanners you'll find good value, which can be entirely different. The range is enormous, as is Tanners' depth of knowledge. And that applies whether you're talking about trendy New World wines like Jim Barry's monumental Armagh Shiraz from the Clare Valley, or untrendy parts of the Old World like Germany.

1994 Oberemmeler Hütte Riesling Kabinett, von Hövel, £7.95 I'd put this German away until the Millennium, and then bless my good fortune.

TESCO (TES)

(Head office) Delamare Road, Cheshunt, Herts EN8 9SL, (01992) 632222, fax (01992) 630794; 544 licensed branches;
Mail order: Via Tesco Direct, (0800) 403403
Hours Variable (open Sunday).
Cards MasterCard, Switch, Visa.
G M T

I'm not sure about this idea of selling wine called Great With Fish or Great With Chicken – a wine that works with grilled trout will not necessarily be a wow with bouillabaisse, and chicken salad is a very different kettle of, er, fish to coq au vin. But while Tesco plays safe on one hand (California consists almost entirely of Gallo), it takes chances with the other. Excellent Australians include Chapel Hill

Shiraz and Tim Adams Semillon. There are some nice red Loires, for example, and even some wines from Odessa in the Crimea. You can buy Moroccan red and Peruvian white here; perhaps more interestingly, you can get a half bottle of botrytis Gewürztraminer for under a fiver.

Old Penola Botrytis Gewürztraminer, £4.99 half bottle Well made and not over-sweet stuff from Australia. Try it chilled as an apéritif.

THRESHER (THR)

(Head office) Sefton House, 42 Church Street, Welwyn Garden City, Herts AL8 6PJ, (01707) 328244, fax (01707) 371398
Hours Mon–Sat 9–10 (some 10.30), Sun 12–3, 7–10; Scotland 12.30–10.30.
Cards MasterCard, Switch, Visa.
Discounts Available on quantity.
Delivery Free locally, some branches. National delivery via Drinks Direct, 0800 232221.
G T
The Thresher group incorporates Wine Rack and Bottoms Up, and the lists appear to be pretty much the same. Gaps in the range are usually in Thresher rather than in the other two. For example, if Roederer Cristal Champagne (£79.95) is your usual weekend tipple you'll find it in Wine Rack and Bottoms Up but not in Thresher. There's a fair sprinkling of seriously expensive wines in this list, but the bulk of it is under a tenner, and very adventurous it is too. Alsace looks especially good (go to Wine Rack for these) and there's a splendid range of English and Welsh wine in all three chains. If you want something a little more mainstream, try South Africa (Wine Rack is best here, too), South America (all three chains) or Australia (all three).

THE VINTNERS SELECTION LTD

*SPECIALISTS IN
GOOD QUALITY WINES
AT SENSIBLE PRICES
BY MAIL ORDER*

The Barn, Corby Glen, Grantham,
Lincolnshire NG33 4NJ
Tel: 01476 550 476   Fax: 01476 550 777

1992 Etchart Cafayate Cabernet Sauvignon, £4.99 Good, juicy Argentine stuff at a good price.
1993 Vin Sec de Château Coutet, £8.99 I asked for this white Graves in Bottoms Up, who are supposed to stock it, and they couldn't find it. I shall persevere. Wine Rack ought to have it, too.

THE UBIQUITOUS CHIP (UB)

8 Ashton Lane, Glasgow G12 8SJ, 0141-334 5007, fax 0141-337 1302
Hours Mon–Fri 12–10, Sat 11–10.
Cards Amex, Diners, MasterCard, Switch, Visa.
Discounts 5% cash or cheque purchases of cases.
Delivery Free Glasgow 3 cases or more, otherwise negotiable.
C G M T
A terrific list, with no expense spared. Am I quibbling, or is it reasonable to ask for a little more at around the £5 mark? Certainly there are wonderful wines at £10, £15 or more. Top names, top quality. Mitchelton is good value, but Cloudy Bay Sauvignon at £25.60 a bottle? Come on.
1994 Etchart Torrontes, Argentina £4.35 Well, it's good. And it's affordable.

UNWINS (UN)

(Head office) Birchwood House, Victoria Road, Dartford, Kent DA1 5AJ, (01322) 272711/7; 386 specialist off-licences in south-east England
Hours Variable, usually Mon–Sat 9–10.30, Sun 12–10.
Cards Amex, MasterCard, Switch, Visa.
Discounts 10% mixed case, 5% on six bottles.
G M T
I can't help noticing that there are an awful lot of clarets from off-vintages here. Admittedly, there are Bordeaux off-vintages on most lists at the moment, but the 'growth claret' section here jumps straight from 1984 (the year the Merlot failed) to 1992 (the wettest summer in Bordeaux for 50 years). It goes on to 1993 (when it rained some more), and there it stops. Never mind. If you look outside Bordeaux and Burgundy you can find some treats at Unwins. Bourgueil and Chinon from Couly-Dutheil (1995 – good vintage) and nice country wines like Cahors and Buzet. The New World is headed by Opus One (California) and Rosemount Balmoral Syrah.

1993 Château de Crouseilles 1993, les Vignerons Réunis, Madiran, £7.99 Superior Madiran for, admittedly, a superior price.
1996 Etchart Torrontes, Argentina, £4.49 Good tangy white for instant pleasure.

VALVONA & CROLLA (VA)

19 Elm Row, Edinburgh EH7 4AA, 0131-556 6066
Hours Mon–Wed 8.30–6, Thu–Fri 8.30–7.30, Sat 8.30–6.
Cards Amex, MasterCard, Switch, Visa.
Discounts 5% mixed case, 10% unmixed case.
Delivery Free locally for orders over £30. Mail order £9.50 per case, £5.30 4 cases or more, free 10 or more. **G M T**

In case you hadn't guessed from the name, this is where Italian freaks (and probably a few Italians) gather north of the border. And it's a terrific list: there are Passiti and Vin Santi and Baroli (yards of those, with great names such as Aldo Conterno, Mascarello, Scavino and Voerzio) and – well, everything, really. Philip Contini, who runs the show, says that top Italian wines are currently being panic-bought by the Far East. Typical. No sooner have we discovered them than they're pushing the prices up. More importantly, now that Enotria Winecellars is wholesale only, this is probably the best Italian list in the country. So get a copy.
1995 Soave Classica Superiore La Rocca, Pieropan, £9.89 Nearly a tenner for Soave? Yes, and it's worth it.
1995 Bardolino Classico Cortegiara, Allegrini, £4.99 Perfect light red.

VICTORIA WINE (VIC)

(Head office) Dukes Court, Duke St, Woking, Surrey GU21 5XL, (01483) 715066; over 1550 branches (including Haddows, Victoria Wine Cellars and Firkin off-licences)
Hours Variable, usually Mon–Sat 9–6 (high street), 10–10 (local shops), Sun 12–3 & 7–10.
Cards MasterCard, Switch, Visa.
Discounts 5% on any 6 bottles, 10% on 12 or more bottles, 7 bottles for the price of 6 on all Champagnes and fizz over £5.99.
Delivery Free locally (by arrangement only in shops). **G T**

The proliferation of different sorts of Victoria Wine continues, with Firkin off-licences now added to the empire. Victoria Wine Cellars have the best list, and frankly if you go into your local beer 'n' fags VW corner shop you're not likely to see too much to inspire you. But you can order anything from the list, and the list in its full glory is pretty impressive. VW have persevered with good German estate wines while almost everybody else has given up, and there are equally unfashionable and hugely underrated wines like Vouvray demi-sec. More fashion-conscious items include Albariño from Rias Baixas and Libertad Sangiovese/Malbec from Argentina. Australians worth a special order include Katnook Botrytised Chardonnay and Penfolds Old Vine Barossa Valley red. There are special parcels of good Burgundy and the odd top claret, but these are not the main focus of the list, which is strongest in the up-to-£15 range.
1995 Château la Tuque, Bordeaux Blanc, £3.99 Nice light, softish basic white Bordeaux with some character.
1994 Costera, Cannonau di Sardegna, Argiolas, £5.95 Nice cherry toffee fruit at a good price.
1995 Basedow Semillon, Barossa Valley, £6.49 Classic toasty Semillon.

LA VIGNERONNE (VIG)

105 Old Brompton Rd, London SW7 3LE, 0171-589 6113, fax 0171-581 2983
Hours Mon–Fri 10–8, Sat 10–6.
Cards Amex, Diners, MasterCard, Switch, Visa.
Discounts 5% mixed case (collected).
Delivery Free locally, £7.50 mainland England and Wales for orders under £250; mainland Scotland at cost. **EP M T**

A treasure-trove of wines you won't see elsewhere: mature Lindemans Classic Release wines from

Australia, for example (1985 Padthaway Botrytis Riesling for £16.95 a bottle), or wines from France's Midi that they've discovered themselves, including Mas Jullien and Dom. la Grange des Pères. At the time of writing there was no actual list: stock changes all the time, so it's worth popping in if you can.

1994 Syrah/Cabernet Sauvignon, Domaine de Baruel, £8.95 Marvellous vin de pays from low-yielding vines in the Cevennes.

VINTAGE WINES LTD (VIN)

116/118 Derby Rd, Nottingham NG1 5FB, 0115-947 6565/941 9614

Hours Mon–Fri 9–5.15, Sat 9–1.
Cards MasterCard, Visa, Switch.
Discounts 10% mixed case.
Delivery Free within 60 miles.
G M T

An efficient list that covers most of the appellations and regions one is likely to want, and yet a list that doesn't ooze the enthusiasm that the best ones do. There's a feeling that it's all just a bit routine, and that while one could drink very well here, one's not going to get carried away with new discoveries.

1995 Pouilly-Fumé les Logères, Domaine Guy Saget, £9.99 Good stuff from a good producer.

WAITROSE (WAI)

(Head office) Doncastle Rd, Southern Industrial Area, Bracknell, Berks RG12 8YA (01344) 424680; 118 licensed shops. (Mail order) freephone 0800 188881, freefax 0800 188888

Hours Mon–Tue 8.30–6, Wed–Thurs 8.30–8, Fri 8.30–9, Sat 8.30–6.
Cards MasterCard, Visa.
Discounts 5% 6 bottles or more.

WATERLOO WINE CO

61 Lant Street, London SE1 1QN
Tel: 0171-403 7967

agents for

Waipara West
Waipara Springs
Mark Rattray Vineyard

premium North Canterbury producers

Delivery (From Waitrose Direct/Findlater Mackie Todd) Free for orders of £75 or more throughout mainland UK or Isle of Wight, otherwise £3.95.
G M

Still the most interesting and most adventurous of the supermarkets. It perseveres with good German wines and even sells Canadian framboise. An even better range is available through Waitrose Direct, its mail-order arm. Top names are J-L Chave (Rhône), Browns of Padthaway (South Australia) and Mondavi (Napa Valley).

1995 Cigala, Vin de Pays d'Oc, Chapoutier, £3.95 'Ideal with meat pies' says Waitrose. Ideal price, too.

1994 Warwick Estate Cabernet Franc, Stellenbosch, £7.95 Wonderful red from one of South Africa's best winemakers. It's only available from the biggest Waitroses, but you can order it.

WATERLOO WINE CO (WAT)

6 Vine Yard, Borough, London SE1 1QL, 0171-403 7967, fax 0171-357 6976; shop at 61 Lant Street, London SE1 1QN

Hours Mon–Fri 10–6.30, Sat 10–5.
Cards MasterCard, Switch, Visa.
Delivery Free 5 cases or more.
G T

An idiosyncratic list that is very strong on the Loire and pretty strong on Germany, with mature wines bought at auction and sold on at reasonable prices. Bordeaux is interesting, too, as is Alsace, and there are some exceptionally good New Zealand wines: Waipara Springs, Waipara West and Mark Rattray. Also Stonier's Merricks from Australia.

1976 Wehlener Sonnenuhr Auslese, Justerini & Brooks, £11.95 This German is the sort of thing you'll find at Waterloo – and cheap at the price.

1995 Pinot Noir, Mark Rattray Vineyard, £9.99 One of New Zealand's best Pinots.

DAVID J WATT (WATT)

1–3 Mill Lane Mews, Ashby-de-la-Zouch, Leicester LE65 1HP, (01530) 413953, fax (01530) 413960

Hours Mon–Sat 9–5.
Cards Amex, MasterCard, Visa (2.5% surcharge).
Delivery Free 4 cases or over; otherwise £8 a case. **C EP T**

You wouldn't go here unless you were after seriously fine wines – and yet, curiously, Watt also lists Taylor's First Estate port, which, though perfectly nice, hardly fits the pattern of the rest of the list. But never mind. Almost everything else is fine to very fine indeed, from 1961 Château Palmer to 1963 Quinta do Noval Nacional. Most of the wines are much younger than this, and the focus is on claret. Champagne, Rhône, Alsace, Australia and others get a small look-in. There's a shop, called Davids of Ashby, at the same address.

1995 Château le Pin, £594.75 I can dream.

1994 Côtes du Rhône, Guigal, £6.22 This is more my level.

WHITESIDES OF CLITHEROE (WHI)

Shawbridge St, Clitheroe, Lancs BB7 1NA, (01200) 422281, fax (01200) 427129

Hours Mon–Fri 10–8, Sat 9–5.30.

Cards MasterCard, Switch, Visa.

Discounts 5% per case.

G M T

I really wish Whitesides would redesign its list. It gives me a headache every time I look at it. Which is a pity, because it does have some goodies. Guigal Côte-Rôtie, for example, or Antinori Orvieto, or Bethany Shiraz from the Barossa Valley.

1993 Lindemans Pyrus, Coonawarra, £12.99 Buy it for a treat.

WINE RACK (WR)

(Head office) Sefton House, 42 Church Street, Welwyn Garden City, Herts AL8 6PJ, (01707) 328244, fax (01707) 371398

Hours Mon–Sat 9–10 (some 10.30), Sun 12–3 & 7–10.

Cards Amex, MasterCard, Switch, Visa.

Discounts 5% mixed cases wine, 12.5% mixed cases Champagne.

Delivery Free locally, all shops, and nationally via Drinks Direct, 0800 232221. **G T**

See Thresher.

WINE SOCIETY (WS)

Gunnels Wood Rd, Stevenage, Herts SG1 2BG, (01438) 741177, fax (01438) 741392

Hours Mon–Fri 8.30–9, Sat 9–2; showroom: Mon–Fri 9–5.30, Sat 9–4.

Cards MasterCard, Switch, Visa.

Discounts (per case) £1 for 5–9, £2 for 10 or more, £3 for collection.

Delivery Free 1 case or more UK mainland and Northern Ireland. Collection facility at Hesdin, France at French rates of duty and VAT.

C E P G M T

Why doesn't everybody belong to The Wine Society? You have to be a member, but it's only £20 and you're in for life. Delivery is usually included in the (reasonable) price. The list itself is huge, wide-ranging, and stuffed with top-class wines. Some are from famous producers like Armand Rousseau (Burgundy) and Clos des Papes (Châteauneuf-du-Pape); others you might never have heard of. It's as adventurous as any list in the country, with lots around £5, but also Huet's 1947 Vouvray Le Haut Lieu Moelleux at £125 a bottle.

1995 Sancerre les Cailleries, Vacheron, £7.95 Dry rosé that the Society recommends with poached salmon. I won't argue with that.

1995 Arneis delle Langhe, Alasia, £6.50 Lovely aromatic white from Piedmont that can be higher on price than on flavour. Not here.

WINES OF WESTHORPE LTD (WIW)

Marchington, Staffs ST14 8NX, (01283) 820285, fax (01283) 820631

Hours Mon–Sat 8.30–6.00.

Cards MasterCard, Switch, Visa.

Discounts (per case) £2.60 for 6–15, £3.60 for 16–25, 50p for Switch/debit cards.

Delivery Free UK mainland 2 or more cases.

Minimum order 1 mixed case.

M T

This is the place for those who want a different Bulgarian wine for every day of the month (at least – I haven't counted). There are loads of Hungarians, as well, plus some Chileans and Australians, including d'Arenberg. There are curiosities like barrel-fermented Muscat. Is this a good thing? Hmm.

1995 Liubimetz Merlot, £2.75 I like young reds like this as well as anything else from Bulgaria.

WRIGHT WINE CO (WRI)

The Old Smithy, Raikes Rd, Skipton, N. Yorks BD23 1NP, (01756) 700886

Hours Mon–Sat 9–6.

Cards MasterCard, Switch, Visa.

Discounts Wholesale price unsplit case, 5% mixed case.

Delivery Free within 30 miles. **G**

If you suddenly remember you need a nebuchadnezzar of Pol Roger Champagne, this is the place for you. At £655, it'll work out slightly more expensive than buying the equivalent 20 individual bottles, but what the hell, a party's a party. Actually, this whole list is an array of splendid wines. Burgundy includes some well-chosen wines under a tenner (including Faiveley's St-Véran), which isn't that easy these days, and the Rhône likewise is selected with an eye for value as well as good names. There's a lovely selection of French country wines, and the Australian list alone would keep me happy for quite a long time, with Charles Melton, Yarra Yering and rare Morris Rutherglen Durif.

1996 Old Vine Semillon, Barossa Valley, Grant Burge, £8.25 Classic stuff from 60-year-old vines.

1993 Quintet, William Wheeler, Sonoma County, £7.00 This is a blend of Pinot Meunier, Pinot Noir, Syrah, Grenache and Malbec. Worth trying for that reason alone.

PETER WYLIE FINE WINES (WY)

Plymtree Manor, Plymtree, Cullompton, Devon EX15 2LE, (01884) 277555, fax (01884) 277557

Hours Mon–Fri 9–6.

Discounts Unsplit cases.

Delivery Free London 3 or more cases, UK mainland 1 case £12 2 cases £6.50 per case, 3 or more cases £4 per case.

C EP M

We're in collector's country here: there's 1906 Haut-Brion ('on last legs like most 90-year-olds') and indeed clarets from most years up to the present. To describe such wines as odds and ends seems a touch disrespectful, but never mind: there are odds and ends of old Burgundies, too, and Champagnes, and ports and Madeiras and Sauternes. But it's not all museum stuff: there's an excellent list of contemporary vintages of fine wines.

1948 Château Lafite, £85 half bottle Anybody looking for a 50th birthday present?

YAPP BROTHERS (YAP)

The Old Brewery, Mere, Wilts BA12 6DY, (01747) 860423, fax (01747) 860929

Hours Mon–Fri 9–5, Sat 9–1.

Cards MasterCard, Visa.

Discounts £3 per case on collection, quantity discount on 6 or more cases.

Delivery £5 single case or less.

C EP G M T

Rhône and Loire freaks will find their hearts' desire here: too many growers to enumerate, but everything wonderful. And if you feel like a change there are lovely wines from Provence – including Dom. de Trévallon and the rare Ch. Simone from Palette – from Alsace (Charles Schléret) and from Champagne, including Yapp's own label. Now, given the fact that unripe Champagne can do some pretty awful things to your teeth, and given the fact that Robin Yapp is a dentist, one might think twice about buying Champagne from him. But have no fear. It's quite safe.

1994 Domaine Ilarria Cuvé Bixintxo, Irouléguy, £10.75 Fierce, tannic red. Pronounced 'Bishintsho', and it's Basquais for St Vincent, patron saint of winegrowers. Well, you knew that.

NOEL YOUNG WINES (YOU)

56 High Street, Trumpington, Cambridge CB2 2LS, (01223) 844744, fax (01223) 844736

Hours Mon–Sat 10–9, Sun 12–2.

Cards MasterCard, Switch, Visa (2% surcharge).

Discounts 5% 5–10 cases, 10% 10 cases or more.

Delivery £7.50 on orders up to £50, £6 on orders up to £100, £5 on orders up to £500, free over £500.

Minimum order 1 mixed case.

G M T

What do I think makes a good wine merchant? Two things: a passion for wine, and a deep knowledge of it. I reckon Noel Young has both. I don't think I've ever tasted anything of his that hasn't at least been interesting and unusual – which means that he's buying with his heart and his palate, not with his accountant. If I had to pick any goodies in particular, I'd choose his Austrian range from Kracher and Bründlmayer, which creams off much of the best of that country, and Ridge Vineyards from California. There's a fine wine list, too.

1994 Cabernet Sauvignon, Santa Cruz Mountains, Ridge Vineyards, £14.99 No, it's not cheap – but just taste it.

WHO'S WHERE

Name abbreviation codes are shown for merchants whose wines appear in the Price Guides

LONDON

Adam Bancroft	BAN
Berry Bros. & Rudd	BER
Bibendum	BIB
Bottoms Up	BOT
Bute Wines	BUT
Corney & Barrow	CB
Domaine Direct	DOM
Farr Vintners	FA
Fine Wines of New Zealand	FIZ
Fuller's	FUL
Gelston Castle Fine Wines	
Goedhuis & Co	GOE
Haynes Hanson & Clark	HAH
Justerini & Brooks	
Laytons	LAYT
Lea & Sandeman	LEA
Longford Wines	LON
Moreno Wines	
Morris & Verdin	MV
New London Wine	NEW
Le Nez Rouge	NEZ
Philglas & Swiggot	
La Réserve	RES
Howard Ripley	RIP
Roberson	ROB
RSJ Wine Company	RSJ
Unwins	UN
La Vigneronne	VIG
Waterloo Wine Co	WAT

SOUTH-EAST AND HOME COUNTIES

Stéphane Auriol Wines	AUR
Australian Wine Centre	AUS
Benedict's	
Berry Bros. & Rudd	BER
Bottoms Up	BOT
Butlers Wine Cellar	BU
Cape Province Wines	CAP
Ben Ellis Wines	ELL
Le Fleming Wines	FLE
Fuller's	FUL
Gallery Wines	GAL
Douglas Henn-Macrae	
High Breck Vintners	HIG

Longford Wines	LON
Sherston Wine Company	
Unwins	UN

WEST AND SOUTH-WEST

Averys of Bristol	AV
Bennetts	BEN
Bottoms Up	BOT
Châteaux Wines	CHA
Country Wine Merchant	COU
Croque-en-Bouche	CRO
Eldridge, Pope & Co	EL
Great Western Wine	
John Harvey & Sons	HA
Haynes Hanson & Clark	HAH
Hicks & Don	HIC
Laymont & Shaw	
Nadder Wines Ltd	NA
The Nobody Inn	NO
Christopher Piper Wines	PIP
Reid Wines (1992) Ltd	REI
Rose Tree Wine Co	ROS
Peter Wylie Fine Wines	WY
Yapp Brothers	YAP

EAST ANGLIA

Adnams	AD
Amey's Wines	AME
Anthony Byrne	BY
Corney & Barrow	CB
Roger Harris Wines	HAW
Hicks & Don	HIC
Lay & Wheeler	LAY
Thos. Peatling	
Satchells	SAT
T & W Wines	TW
Noel Young Wines	YOU

MIDLANDS

Connolly's Wine Merchants	
Gauntleys	GAU
Grape Ideas	GRAP
Halves	HAL
SH Jones	JON
Portland Wine Co	POR
Quellyn Roberts	QUE
Tanners	TAN
Vintage Wines Ltd	VIN
David J Watt	WATT
Wines of Westhorpe	WIW

NORTH

Booths	BO
Great Northern Wine Co	GN
Le Nez Rouge	NEZ
Penistone Court	PEN
Playford Ros	
Frank Stainton Wines	STA
Whitesides of Clitheroe	WHI
Wright Wine Co	WRI

WALES

Ashley Scott	AS
Tanners	TAN
Terry Platt	PLA

SCOTLAND

Corney & Barrow	CB
Forth Wines	FOR
Gelston Castle Fine Wines	
Peter Green & Co	GRE
J E Hogg	HOG
Justerini & Brooks	
Raeburn Fine Wines	RAE
The Ubiquitous Chip	UB
Valvona & Crolla	VA

CHANNEL ISLANDS

Sommelier Wine Co	SOM

NORTHERN IRELAND

Direct Wine	DI
James Nicholson	NI

COUNTRYWIDE

ASDA	ASD
Bordeaux Direct	BOD
CWS (Co-op)	CO
KwikSave	KWI
Majestic	MAJ
Marks & Spencer	MAR
Oddbins	OD
Safeway	SAF
J Sainsbury	SAI
Somerfield/Gateway	SO
Sunday Times Wine Club	SUN
Tesco	TES
Thresher	THR
Victoria Wine	VIC
Waitrose	WAI
Wine Rack	WR
Wine Society	WS

INDEX

Explore the world of wine further with

Oz Clarke's Wine Guide

The complete interactive CD-ROM

The essential guide to getting the most out of your wine drinking

'One of the best CD-ROMs you can buy' – PC World

- 'How-to' Wine Tasting videos
- Food and Wine matching database
- 3,000-entry Encyclopedia
- 7,100-entry Wine Selector database
- Scrolling maps

Available on CD-ROM for Windows ® and Mac from September 1997

PRIZE DRAW QUESTIONNAIRE

Every year we update and try to improve Oz Clarke's Wine Guide and this year, for the first time, you can have your say in this process. Let us know what you like and what you don't like about the guide so that we can make the next edition even more useful. All replies will automatically be entered in our prize draw and the winner will receive a mixed case of wine, chosen by Oz, from a leading wine merchant. In order to be eligible for the draw, please return your questionnaire by 2nd January 1998 to The Editor, Oz Clarke's Wine Guide, Websters International Publishers, FREEPOST LON7896, London SE1 1BT.

None of the information you disclose will be sold on or used for mailing purposes.

Name: Title .... First name .... Surname ....

Address: ....

....

Postcode .... Daytime telephone number: ....

Occupation: ....

Age: *(Please mark the box that applies to you)*

❑ 18-25, ❑ 26-35, ❑ 36-45, ❑ 46- 55, ❑ 56-65, ❑ 66+

1 Which other annual wine guides do you own?

(Please mark as many boxes as apply)

❑ Grapevine
❑ Superplonk
❑ Gluck on High
❑ The Which? Wine Guide
❑ The Sunday Telegraph Good Wine Guide
❑ Wine Magazine Pocket Wine Buyer's Guide
❑ Hugh Johnson's Pocket Wine Guide
❑ Oz Clarke's Pocket Wine Book

2 Where do you usually buy your wine?

(Please mark as many boxes as apply)

❑ From an independent wine merchant
❑ From a high street wine merchant
❑ From a supermarket
❑ From a wine society/wine club
❑ By mail order

3 On average, how much do you spend on a bottle of wine when buying from a shop or a merchant?

❑ up to £2.99   ❑ £7.00–£10.00
❑ £3.00–£4.99   ❑ over £10.00
❑ £5.00–£6.99

4 What was the most you spent on a bottle of wine last year?

a) from a shop/merchant ....

b) in a restaurant ....

5 For what purpose do you use Oz Clarke's Wine Guide?

(Please mark as many boxes as apply)

❑ To choose all my wine
❑ To choose wines for special occasions
❑ To choose wines from independent merchants
❑ To choose wines from high street merchants
❑ To choose wines from supermarkets
❑ To look up wine prices
❑ To compare wine prices between different merchants
❑ To look up Oz Clarke's 'Best Buy' recommended wines
❑ To look up information about a wine region
❑ To look up information about a wine producer
❑ To find local wine merchants

Other, please state ....

....

....

6 Do you find the regional wine information in Oz Clarke's Wine Guide
- ❑ Not detailed enough
- ❑ Just the right amount of detail
- ❑ Too detailed

What would you like to see added or taken away? ....
....
....
....

7 Do you find the Price Guides in Oz Clarke's Wine Guide
- ❑ Not comprehensive enough
- ❑ Just right
- ❑ Too comprehensive

What would you like to see added or taken away? ....
....
....
....

8 Are there any new features or changes you would like to see in future editions of the guide? If so, what are they? ....
....
....
....
....

9 If Oz Clarke's Wine Guide had its own website on the internet would you use it?
- ❑ Never
- ❑ Once
- ❑ Occasionally
- ❑ Frequently
- ❑ I don't have access to the internet

10 Will you buy next year's guide?
- ❑ Yes
- ❑ No

If no, please state why not ....
....
....
....

For questions 11 to 13, please enter the relevant figure in each box

11 How often do you use the following sections of Oz Clarke's Wine Guide?
| **1** Never | **2** Once |
| **3** Occasionally | **4** Frequently |

- ❑ Best Buys
- ❑ Supermarket Selection
- ❑ Ideal Cellars
- ❑ Wine region information sections
- ❑ Price Guides
- ❑ Merchant Directory

12 How useful do you find the following sections of Oz Clarke's Wine Guide?
1 Not very useful
| **2** Useful | **3** Very useful |

- ❑ Best Buys
- ❑ Supermarket Selection
- ❑ Ideal Cellars
- ❑ Wine region information sections
- ❑ Price Guides
- ❑ Merchant Directory

If there are any sections which you don't find useful, please state why ....
....
....
....

13 How easy to use do you find the following sections?
1 Not very easy to use
| **2** Easy to use | **3** Very easy to use |

- ❑ Best Buys
- ❑ Supermarket Selection
- ❑ Ideal Cellars
- ❑ Wine region information sections
- ❑ Price Guides
- ❑ Merchant Directory

If there are any sections which you don't find easy to use, please state why ....
....
....
....